Clinical Coding Workout

Practice Exercises for Skill Development

Without Answers

2007 Edition

Prepared by the Coding Products and Services Team
of the American Health Information Management Association

Contributing Authors

June Bronnert, RHIA, CCS, CCS-P
Melanie Endicott, MBA/HCM, RHIA, CCS
Karen Kostick, RHIT, CCS, CCS-P
Susan Hull, MPH, RHIA, CCS, CCS-P
Rita Scichilone, MHSA, RHIA, CCS, CCS-P
Mary Stanfill, RHIA, CCS, CCS-P
Ann Zeisset, RHIT, CCS, CCS-P

AHIMA

American Health Information
Management Association®

The Web sites listed in this book were current and valid as of the date of publication. However, Web page addresses and the information on them may change or disappear at any time and for any number of reasons. The user is encouraged to perform his or her own general Web searches to locate any URLs listed here that are no longer valid. Web sites listed in this book are assumed to be preceded by *http://www*.

AHIMA certifications are administered by the AHIMA Council on Certification (COC). The COC does not endorse any publications or exam preparatory activities.

Use of this product for AHIMA certification exam preparation in no way guarantees an exam candidate passage of the exam.

ISBN 1-58426-171-4
Product No. AC201607 (without answers)

Ken Zielske, Director of Publications
Claire Blondeau, MBA, Project Editor
Melissa Ulbricht, Editorial/Production Coordinator

AHIMA strives to recognize the value of people from every racial and ethnic background as well as all genders, age groups, and sexual orientations by building its membership and leadership resources to reflect the rich diversity of the American population. AHIMA encourages the celebration and promotion of human diversity through education, mentoring, recognition, leadership, and other programs.

American Health Information Management Association
233 North Michigan Avenue, Suite 2150
Chicago, Illinois 60601-5800

http://www.ahima.org

Contents

Preface

The *Clinical Coding Workout* is designed to challenge coding professionals and students alike to develop expert skills in the assignment of clinical codes required for administrative use.

The coding process requires a range of skills that combines knowledge and practice. Someone new to this discipline must conquer the basic principles of using the required code sets. A student at the intermediate level learns to apply code set conventions, guidelines and principles in various combinations, settings, and scenarios. A person with advanced coding skills analyzes complex health data and determines what needs to be reported to accurately reflect each patient's condition and treatment. Like a violinist or a gymnast, the coding professional develops virtuosity step-by-step through systematic exercise. At each level of skill development, practice enhances performance.

The AHIMA Practice Resources team has gathered coding scenarios and case studies together to create a resource for skill development and review of guidelines and conventions applied in code selection. Practice exercises take the user from beginning concepts and selection of codes, through intermediate applications using short code assignment scenarios, to advanced case studies that are based on excerpts from health records and that require complex clinical analysis skills and multiple code assignments. Coding challenges in the final chapter include exercises for ICD-10-CM and ICD-10-PCS, CPT modifier use, HCPCS Level II modifiers, home health, LTAC coding, and rehabilitation and SNF cases. Appendix A contains tables that link each exercise to the AHIMA certifications and competencies to which it pertains. Lastly, the annotated answer key serves as a unique instructional guide not only providing the correct answer to each question, but also explaining why the answer is correct and why the incorrect answers are not appropriate.

Ways in which this valuable resource can be used include the following:

- Health information management (HIM) educators and coding program trainers can use the exercises to supplement basic- and intermediate-level course materials for students seeking extra credit or advanced preparation.

- HIM students can use the exercises for self-directed learning.

- Coding professionals can use the exercises to gain additional coding experience in a variety of specialties and settings that may not be available to them in their current workplace.

- Employers can use this resource to challenge new coding professionals who are ready to sharpen their skills to the intermediate and advanced levels of coding performance.

- Coding managers can use this material as a tool to assess the competency of coding staff for complex coding practice.

- Employers seeking high-level competency in the more difficult coding practice areas can use the case studies as a means of screening for advanced coding skills.

Clinical Coding Workout is also an excellent tool for:

- Preparing to sit for the mastery-level coding exams offered by AHIMA (CCS and CCS-P) to gain additional insight into a variety of specialty coding topics

- Evaluating or instructing coding professionals as part of ongoing compliance initiatives

How to Use This Book

Unlike coding instructional books that are based on one coding classification system, *Clinical Coding Workout* uses the full range of administrative code sets applicable in today's healthcare environment for reporting diagnoses, procedures, and services in various settings and specialty practice areas.

The actual codes used in the exercises and answer key for this book are those that were confirmed or already in effect at the time of publication, as follows:

- *International Classification of Diseases, 9th Revision, Clinical Modification (ICD-9-CM)*, 2007 edition, codes effective October 1, 2006

- *Current Procedural Terminology (CPT)*, 2006 edition, codes effective January 1, 2006

- *Healthcare Common Procedural Coding System Level II (HCPCS)*, 2006 edition, codes effective January 1, 2006

Use of different versions of coding books with this resource will require attention to the code changes after the effective date. Revised answer keys will be created that are consistent with coding changes for the upcoming year soon after the effective date of the new codes. All answer keys are available to instructors in online format from the individual book page in the AHIMA Bookstore (http://imis.ahima.org/orders), and also are posted on the AHIMA Assembly on Education Community of Practice (AOE CoP) Web site. Instructors who are AHIMA members can sign up for this private community by clicking on the help icon within the CoP home page and requesting additional information on becoming an AOE CoP member. An instructor who is not an AHIMA member or a member who is not an instructor may contact the publisher at publications@ahima.org.

As in actual practice, ICD-9-CM codes are used for diagnoses and inpatient procedures for hospital reporting in this book; whereas for ambulatory facility and physician service reporting, ICD-9-CM codes are used for diagnoses, and HCPCS/CPT codes are used for procedures and services.

Federal Register notices and other regulatory updates are available from the Centers for Medicare and Medicaid Systems at www.cms.hhs.gov/. HCPCS Level II codes are updated each quarter and are available by download from www.cms.hhs.gov/HCPCSReleaseCodeSets/. CPT code sets are generally released in mid-September for implementation by January 1 of the following year.

Please refer to the instructions in each chapter for additional information.

Part I
Beginning Coding Exercises

Chapter 1

Basic Principles of ICD-9-CM Coding

Note: The exercises in this chapter are based on the 2007 edition of the ICD-9-CM Classification System but are suitable for other editions in most cases. Annual updates are made to the ICD-9-CM coding system with changes effective October 1 of each year.

The Centers for Medicare and Medicaid Services (CMS) and the National Center for Health Statistics (NCHS) provide the *ICD-9-CM Official Guidelines for Coding and Reporting*, which should be used as a companion document to the official version. The guidelines have been approved by the four organizations that make up the Cooperating Parties for the ICD-9-CM: the American Hospital Association (AHA), the American Health Information Management Association (AHIMA), CMS, and NCHS.

The guidelines are a set of rules that has been developed to accompany and complement the official conventions and instructions provided within ICD-9-CM. The guidelines are based upon the coding and sequencing instructions found in ICD-9-CM, and they provide additional instruction. Adherence to the guidelines is required under the Health Insurance Portability and Accountability Act (HIPAA). The guidelines are organized into sections. Section I includes the structure and conventions of the classification, general guidelines that apply to the entire classification, and chapter-specific guidelines that correspond to the chapters as they are arranged in the classification. This section is applicable to all healthcare settings unless otherwise indicated. Section II includes guidelines for selecting principal diagnoses for nonoutpatient settings. Section III includes guidelines for reporting additional diagnoses in nonoutpatient settings. Section IV is for outpatient coding (including physician) and reporting.

These guidelines are regularly updated and are available at: www.cdc.gov/nchs/datawh/ ftpserv/ftpicd9/ftpicd9.htm#guide

Instructions: Circle the correct answer, fill in the blank, or assign the correct code(s) for each of the following exercise items.

Characteristics and Conventions of the ICD-9-CM Classification System

1.1. Nonessential modifiers are enclosed in:

a. Brackets
b. Parentheses
c. Slanted brackets
d. Boxes

1.2. A diagnostic descriptor that is listed in italics is a(n):

a. Manifestation code
b. Inappropriate principal diagnosis
c. CC exclusion
d. Code that must be reported first

1.3. The abbreviation UHDDS refers to the _____.

1.4. Diagnoses described as "possible," "probable," "likely," and "rule out" are reported if present for _____ records.

1.5. For patients seen in the outpatient setting for chemotherapy, radiation therapy, or rehabilitation, the first reported diagnosis is:

a. The diagnosis toward which the treatment is directed
b. The appropriate V code
c. Either a or b
d. The diagnosis that the physician lists first on the order

1.6. When multiple burns are present, the first sequenced diagnosis is the:

a. Burn that is treated surgically
b. Burn that is closest to the head
c. Highest-degree burn
d. Any of the above

1.7. A coding professional may assume a cause-and-effect relationship between hypertension and which of the following complications?

a. Hypertension and heart disease
b. Hypertension and chronic kidney disease
c. Hypertension and heart and chronic kidney disease
d. None of the above

1.8. ICD-9-CM codes that describe the behavior of cells in neoplasms are called _____.

1.9. New ICD-9-CM codes go into effect on _____ of each year.

1.10. Supplementary classifications include:

    a. V codes
    b. V codes and E codes
    c. V codes, E codes, and M codes
    d. None of the above

1.11. The neoplasm table includes:

    a. The nature and status (primary, secondary, in situ) for malignancies
    b. A listing of the morphology codes
    c. The stage of benign neoplasms
    d. E codes for reactions to chemotherapy

1.12. V codes can be used as:

    a. Principal diagnosis only
    b. Secondary diagnosis only
    c. Either principal diagnosis or secondary diagnosis, depending upon the code and the circumstances of the admission
    d. Secondary diagnosis only on inpatient stays and principal diagnosis only on outpatient visits

1.13. Terms listed in the Alphabetic Index in boldface type are known as

_____.

1.14. Manifestation codes:

    a. Can never be reported first
    b. Are printed in italics in the Tabular List
    c. Describe a condition that results from another, underlying condition
    d. All of the above

1.15. Codes that contain the descriptive abbreviation NOS are to be used:

    a. When the record itself is not available for review
    b. When the coder lacks sufficient information to assign a more specific code
    c. When only outpatient diagnostic records are being coded
    d. All the time

Infectious and Parasitic Diseases

1.16. Meningitis due to ECHO virus

    Code(s): _____

1.17. Chickenpox

    Code(s): _____

1.18.   Cutaneous anthrax

Code(s): _____

1.19.   Aerobacter aerogenes is an example of a gram-_____ bacterial organism.

1.20.   Genital herpes

Code(s): _____

1.21.   Patients with any known prior diagnosis of an HIV-related illness should be reported with this ICD-9-CM code: _____.

1.22.   Acute salpingitis due to gonococcal infection

Code(s): _____

1.23.   A patient with known AIDS is admitted to the hospital for treatment of Pneumocystis carinii pneumonia. Assign the principal diagnosis.

   a. 042
   b. 486
   c. 136.3
   d. Any of the above

1.24.   A patient with known chronic hepatitis C is seen in the outpatient department for interferon treatment. Assign the primary diagnosis.

   a. 070.51
   b. 070.44
   c. 070.54
   d. 070.32

1.25.   Typhoid fever

Code(s): _____

1.26.   Food poisoning due to Staphylococcus organism

Code(s): _____

1.27.   Infectious diarrhea

Code(s): _____

1.28.   Pulmonary tuberculosis, bacilli identified with microscopy

Code(s): _____

1.29.   Scarlatina

Code(s): _____

1.30. Streptococcal septicemia

Code(s): _____

1.31. Dermatophytosis of scalp

Code(s): _____

1.32. Pneumonia as a complication of measles

Code(s): _____

1.33. Mumps

Code(s): _____

1.34. Condylomata acuminata

Code(s): _____

1.35. Infectious mononucleosis

Code(s): _____

Neoplasms

1.36. Hodgkin's disease of thoracic lymph nodes

Code(s): _____

1.37. Benign neoplasm of bronchus

Code(s): _____

1.38. When a patient is admitted to the hospital for radiation therapy for a primary malignancy that is still present, what code is reported as the principal diagnosis? _____

1.39. A patient is admitted as an inpatient to receive radiation and chemotherapy for distal esophageal carcinoma. What is the appropriate principal diagnosis?

a. V58.0
b. V58.11
c. 150.5
d. Either a or b

1.40. Carcinoma of the broad ligament (confined to this location)

Code(s): _____

1.41. Adenoma of the islet cells of the pancreas

Code(s): _____

1.42.   Neoplasms at the cellular level that are incapable of spreading to distant sites are called _____ neoplasms.

1.43.   Malignant melanoma of the skin of the chest wall

Code(s): _____

1.44.   Adenocarcinoma of the lesser curvature of the stomach

Code(s): _____

1.45.   Secondary carcinoma of the submandibular salivary gland

Code(s): _____

1.46.   Carcinoma of the bladder trigone

Code(s): _____

1.47.   Carcinoma in situ of breast

Code(s): _____

1.48.   Rhabdomyosarcoma is an example of which of the following kinds of neoplasms?

   a. Benign
   b. Malignant
   c. Uncertain behavior
   d. Unspecified

1.49.   Myxofibrosarcoma is a malignant neoplasm that affects what type of tissue?

_____

1.50.   The site at which a malignant neoplasm originated is known as the _____ site.

1.51.   Bronchogenic carcinoma

Code(s): _____

1.52.   Carcinoma in situ of the uterine cervix

Code(s): _____

1.53.   In coding for neoplasms of the lymphatic and hematopoietic systems (200–202), a fifth digit of 4 refers to which organs?

   a. Lymph nodes of inguinal region and lower limb
   b. Lymph nodes of head, face, and neck
   c. Lymph nodes of axilla and upper limb
   d. Intrapelvic lymph nodes

1.54. Multiple myeloma in remission

Code(s): _____

1.55. Acute myelogenous leukemia

Code(s): _____

Endocrine, Nutritional and Metabolic Diseases, and Immunity Disorders

1.56. Agammaglobulinemia

Code(s): _____

1.57. Hyponatremia

Code(s): _____

1.58. Primary hypercholesterolemia

Code(s): _____

1.59. Bartter's syndrome is a form of which of the following?

a. Diabetic neuropathy
b. Hyperaldosteronism
c. Hypertriglyceridemia
d. Polycystic ovarian disease

1.60. Type I diabetes mellitus with diabetic renal nephrosis, out of control

Code(s): _____

1.61. Diabetes mellitus

Code(s): _____

1.62. Type I diabetes mellitus with proliferative retinopathy

Code(s): _____

1.63. Type I diabetes mellitus with ketoacidosis

Code(s): _____

1.64. Type I diabetes mellitus with ophthalmic manifestations

Code(s): _____

1.65. Hypoinsulinemia following total pancreatectomy

Code(s): _____

1.66. Code 255.2 (adrenogenital disorders) includes which of the following?

  a. Achard-Thiers syndrome
  b. Macrogenitosomia praecox in the male
  c. Congenital adrenal hyperplasia
  d. All of the above

1.67. Hypophyseal dwarfism

  Code(s): _____

1.68. Hypopotassemia

  Code(s): _____

1.69. Cystic fibrosis with pulmonary manifestations

  Code(s): _____

1.70. Hurler's syndrome, gargoyle syndrome, and Sanfilippo's syndrome are all forms of _____.

1.71. Morbid obesity

  Code(s): _____

1.72. Polycystic ovaries

  Code(s): _____

1.73. Renal glycosuria

  Code(s): _____

1.74. Nodular goiter with hyperthyroidism

  Code(s): _____

1.75. Congenital hypothyroidism

  Code(s): _____

Disorders of the Blood and Blood-Forming Organs

1.76. Iron deficiency anemia secondary to chronic blood loss

  Code(s): _____

1.77. Sickle-cell anemia and thalassemia are both types of:

  a. Iron deficiency anemias
  b. Hereditary hemolytic anemias
  c. Aplastic anemia
  d. Coagulation defects

1.78.   Sickle-cell trait

Code(s): _____

1.79.   Anemia due to acute blood loss

Code(s): _____

1.80.   Anemia in end-stage renal disease

Code(s): _____

1.81.   Which of the following is (are) not an example(s) of constitutional red blood cell aplasia (284.01)?

    a. Fanconi's anemia
    b. Familial hypoplastic anemia
    c. Blackfan-Diamond syndrome
    d. All of the above

1.82.   Von Willebrand's disease

Code(s): _____

1.83.   Agranulocytosis is a disease of the _____ blood cells.

1.84.   Fe deficiency anemia

Code(s): _____

1.85.   Folate deficiency anemia due to drugs

Code(s): _____

1.86.   Refractory megaloblastic anemia

Code(s): _____

1.87.   Osteosclerotic anemia

Code(s): _____

1.88.   Purpura fulminans

Code(s): _____

1.89.   Thrombocytopenic purpura

Code(s): _____

1.90.   Thrombocytopenia following massive blood transfusions

Code(s): _____

1.91. Anemia

Code(s): _____

1.92. Congenital aplastic anemia

Code(s): _____

1.93. Acute hemolytic anemia

Code(s): _____

1.94. Anemia secondary to vitamin B_{12} deficiency

Code(s): _____

1.95. Hemophilia

Code(s): _____

Mental Disorders

Because the code assignment for mental disorders can have significant impact on the patient, coding professionals must take special care to ensure that codes are based on diagnostic statements clearly provided in physician documentation.

1.96. To report Jakob-Creutzfeldt disease with dementia, you would need:

a. One code
b. Two codes
c. Either one or two codes
d. More than two codes

1.97. Chronic alcoholic brain syndrome

Code(s): _____

1.98. Chronic paranoid schizophrenia with acute exacerbation

Code(s): _____

1.99. Hypomanic personality disorder

Code(s): _____

1.100. Panic attack

Code(s): _____

1.101. Which of the following is a synonym for multiple personality disorder?

    a. Dissociative identity disorder
    b. Factitious illness
    c. Adjustment reaction
    d. Multiple psychoses

1.102. Hospital addiction syndrome

    Code(s): _____

1.103. Which of the following is a sexual deviation or disorder per ICD-9-CM?

    a. Bestiality
    b. Pedophilia
    c. Voyeurism
    d. All of the above

1.104. Alcoholism with acute intoxication

    Code(s): _____

1.105. Morphine addiction, in remission

    Code(s): _____

1.106. Heroin and diazepam addiction

    Code(s): _____

1.107. Psychogenic torticollis

    Code(s): _____

1.108. Gilles de la Tourette's syndrome

    Code(s): _____

1.109. Depression

    Code(s): _____

1.110. Separation anxiety disorder

    Code(s): _____

1.111. Mental retardation, measured IQ of 42

    Code(s): _____

1.112. Attention deficit/hyperactivity disorder

    Code(s): _____

1.113. Alcoholic paranoia

Code(s): _____

1.114. DTs due to alcohol withdrawal

Code(s): _____

1.115. Multi-infarct dementia with depression

Code(s): _____

Nervous System and Sense Organs

1.116. Endophthalmitis

Code(s): _____

1.117. Duchenne's muscular dystrophy

Code(s): _____

1.118. Which of the following are the correct codes for proliferative diabetic retinopathy?

   a. 250.53, 362.01
   b. 362.02, 250.50
   c. 250.50, 362.02
   d. 362.02, 250.00

1.119. Central retinal artery occlusion

Code(s): _____

1.120. Nuclear cataract

Code(s): _____

1.121. Retinal detachment, traction type

Code(s): _____

1.122. Senile cataract, posterior subcapsular

Code(s): _____

1.123. Angle closure glaucoma, acute

Code(s): _____

1.124. According to the notes in the Tabular List of ICD-9-CM, tritan defect color blindness causes difficulty distinguishing between:

    a. Green and red
    b. All colors
    c. Blue and yellow
    d. Red and blue

1.125. Bullous keratopathy

    Code(s): _____

1.126. Dacryocystitis

    Code(s): _____

1.127. All but one of the following conditions are examples of strabismus (category 378). Identify the condition that is not a form of strabismus.

    a. Esotropia
    b. Exotropia
    c. Presbyopia
    d. Heterotropia

1.128. Chronic serous otitis media

    Code(s): _____

1.129. Acute suppurative otitis media with eardrum rupture due to pressure

    Code(s): _____

1.130. Cholesteatoma involving middle ear and mastoid

    Code(s): _____

1.131. Hyperactive labyrinth, right side

    Code(s): _____

1.132. Anisocoria

    Code(s): _____

1.133. Malignant otitis externa

    Code(s): _____

1.134. Otitis media

    Code(s): _____

1.135. Reflex sympathetic dystrophy, both arms

    Code(s): _____

Circulatory System

1.136. Left ventricular aneurysm

Code(s): _____

1.137. Malignant hypertension with hypertensive heart disease and congestive heart failure is coded:

    a. 402.01
    b. 402.01, 428.9
    c. 428.0, 402.11
    d. 402.01, 428.0

1.138. Mitral valve stenosis and aortic valve insufficiency

Code(s): _____

1.139. Hospital discharge diagnosis: Acute inferolateral myocardial infarction

Code(s): _____

1.140. A myocardial infarction is considered to be acute when it is less than _____ weeks old.

1.141. Hypertension

Code(s): _____

1.142. Identify the main term in the diagnostic statement "idiopathic hypertrophic subaortic stenosis (IHSS)": _____

1.143. Atrial flutter

Code(s): _____

1.144. Ventricular fibrillation

Code(s): _____

1.145. Chronic diastolic heart failure

Code(s): _____

1.146. Preinfarction angina

Code(s): _____

1.147. Pulmonary infarction

Code(s): _____

1.148. ASHD of transplanted heart

Code(s): _____

1.149. Atherosclerosis of left internal mammary artery bypass graft

Code(s): _____

1.150. Dysphasia secondary to old stroke (cerebrovascular disease)

Code(s): _____

1.151. Cerebral infarct due to stenosis of the vertebral artery

Code(s): _____

1.152. TIA

Code(s): _____

1.153. Orthostatic hypotension

Code(s): _____

1.154. Varicose veins of the legs with ulceration

Code(s): _____

1.155. Abdominal aortic aneurysm, ruptured

Code(s): _____

Respiratory System

1.156. Acute bronchitis

Code(s): _____

1.157. Acute laryngitis with airway obstruction

Code(s): _____

1.158. Hypertrophy of tonsils and adenoids

Code(s): _____

1.159. Maxillary sinus polyp(s)

Code(s): _____

1.160. The correct code assignment(s) for pneumonia due to the RSV organism is (are):

a. 486 and 079.6
b. 480.1
c. 466.11
d. 079.6

1.161. Pneumonia due to Gram-negative anaerobic organisms

Code(s): _____

1.162. Acute exacerbation of chronic obstructive pulmonary disease

Code(s): _____

1.163. Emphysema

Code(s): _____

1.164. Bilateral granulomatous hemorrhagic septic pneumonia

Code(s): _____

1.165. Aspiration pneumonia

Code(s): _____

1.166. Chronic obstructive asthma with status asthmaticus

Code(s): _____

1.167. Postoperative pneumothorax

Code(s): _____

1.168. Chronic respiratory failure

Code(s): _____

1.169. Tracheostomy stenosis

Code(s): _____

1.170. Postinfective bronchiectasis

Code(s): _____

1.171. What is the correct code assignment for childhood asthma with acute exacerbation?

a. 493.92
b. 493.90
c. 493.02
d. 493.00

1.172. Spontaneous pneumothorax

Code(s): _____

1.173. COPD

Code(s): _____

1.174. Radiation pneumonitis

Code(s): _____

1.175. Common cold

Code(s): _____

Digestive System

1.176. Dental caries

Code(s): _____

1.177. Acute duodenal ulcer with bleeding

Code(s): _____

1.178. Gastric ulcer

Code(s): _____

1.179. Leukoplakia of tongue

Code(s): _____

1.180. Identify the appropriate code for reflux esophagitis

    a. 530.81
    b. 530.11
    c. 530.10
    d. 530.89

1.181. Select the correct code for acute peptic ulcer of stomach with perforation

    a. 533.10
    b. 531.50
    c. 533.60
    d. 531.10

1.182. Angiodysplasia of the stomach

Code(s): _____

1.183. Alcoholic gastritis with hemorrhage

Code(s): _____

1.184. Acute obstructive appendicitis

Code(s): _____

1.185. Incisional hernia

Code(s): _____

1.186. Bilateral inguinal hernia, recurrent

Code(s): _____

1.187. Incarcerated right femoral hernia

Code(s): _____

1.188. Crohn's disease of the small bowel

Code(s): _____

1.189. Ulcerative colitis

Code(s): _____

1.190. Ileus due to gallstones impacting the intestine

Code(s): _____

1.191. Select the correct code for diverticulosis of the colon

a. 562.11
b. 562.00
c. 562.10
d. 562.12

1.192. Postoperative peritoneal adhesions

Code(s): _____

1.193. Cholelithiasis with acute cholecystitis

Code(s): _____

1.194. Acute pancreatitis

Code(s): _____

1.195. Melena

Code(s): _____

Genitourinary System

1.196. Acute renal failure

Code(s): _____

1.197. Ureterolithiasis

Code(s): _____

1.198. Acute pyelonephritis

Code(s): _____

1.199. Urethrolithiasis

Code(s): _____

1.200. Hydronephrosis

Code(s): _____

1.201. UTI

Code(s): _____

1.202. Overactive bladder

Code(s): _____

1.203. Hematuria

Code(s): _____

1.204. Select the appropriate code for urethral stricture.

    a. 598
    b. 598.9
    c. 598.00
    d. 598.8

1.205. In the diagnostic statement "urinary tract infection due to Escherichia coli," which condition is coded as the principal diagnosis?

    a. The E. coli
    b. The urinary tract infection
    c. Either may be coded as the principal diagnosis.
    d. The circumstances of the admission determine which condition is coded as the principal diagnosis.

1.206. Select the appropriate code for benign prostatic hypertrophy

    a. 222.2
    b. 600.20
    c. 600.00
    d. 600.90

1.207. PIN II

Code(s): _____

1.208. In the diagnostic statement "tuberculous prostatitis," which condition is coded as the principal diagnosis?

    a. The tuberculosis
    b. The prostatitis
    c. Either may be coded as the principal diagnosis.
    d. The circumstances of the admission determine which condition is coded as the principal diagnosis.

1.209. Mastodynia

Code(s): _____

1.210. PID

Code(s): _____

1.211. Endometriosis of the broad ligament

Code(s): _____

1.212. Corpus luteum cyst of ovary

Code(s): _____

1.213. Dysmenorrhea

Code(s): _____

1.214. Postmenopausal atrophic vaginitis

Code(s): _____

1.215. CIN II

Code(s): _____

Pregnancy, Childbirth, and the Puerperium

1.216. Contracted pelvis, infant delivered vaginally

Code(s): _____

1.217. Gestational diabetes, admitted for control, not delivered

Code(s): _____

1.218. Maternal hypotension syndrome, onset ten minutes after delivery

Code(s): _____

1.219. The postpartum period begins immediately following delivery and lasts for _____ weeks following delivery.

1.220. By ICD-9-CM definition, an "elderly primigravida" is a woman who is _____ years or older at the time of her first delivery.

1.221. Large-for-dates baby, delivered this admission (maternal record)

Code(s): _____

1.222. Primary uterine inertia, delivered this admission

Code(s): _____

1.223. Vaginal delivery with fourth-degree perineal laceration

Code(s): _____

1.224. Postpartum breast abscess, patient readmitted two weeks after delivery

Code(s): _____

1.225. Hyperemesis gravidarum at 16 weeks, with dehydration, not delivered

Code(s): _____

1.226. False labor, 39 weeks, not delivered

Code(s): _____

1.227. Pregnancy in bicornuate uterus, 20 weeks, undelivered this admission

Code(s): _____

1.228. Dehiscence of cesarean section wound requiring readmission a week after delivery

Code(s): _____

1.229. Postpartum amniotic fluid embolism occurring while patient is still in the hospital

Code(s): _____

1.230. The fifth digit to describe a delivery that was accompanied by a postpartum complication while the patient was still in the hospital is _____.

1.231. If a patient is admitted for treatment of an antepartum condition and does not deliver during the stay, the appropriate fifth digit is

_____.

1.232. Oligohydramnios, reported with code 658.0X, is:

  a. Infection of the amniotic fluid
  b. Excessive amount of amniotic fluid
  c. Deficient amount of amniotic fluid
  d. Embolism of amniotic fluid

1.233. Hydatidiform mole

Code(s): _____

1.234. When an abortion is complicated by septic shock, the appropriate fourth digit is _____.

1.235. Ectopic pregnancies include which of the following types?

  a. Tubal
  b. Abdominal
  c. Septic
  d. a and b

Skin and Subcutaneous Tissue

1.236. Carbuncle of the hand

Code(s): _____

1.237. Paronychia of finger

Code(s): _____

1.238. Sunburn

Code(s): _____

1.239. Cellulitis of face

Code(s): _____

1.240. Pilonidal cyst

Code(s): _____

1.241. Poison ivy

Code(s): _____

1.242. Dermatitis due to base metals in jewelry

Code(s): _____

1.243. Lupus erythematosus

Code(s): _____

1.244. Keloid scar

Code(s): _____

1.245. Actinic keratosis

Code(s): _____

1.246. Alopecia areata

Code(s): _____

1.247. Hidradenitis suppurativa

Code(s): _____

1.248. Select the correct code for decubitus ulcer of heel

    a. 707.15
    b. 707.14
    c. 707.07
    d. 707.10

1.249. In the diagnostic statement "diabetic foot ulcer," what condition should be assigned as the principal diagnosis?

    a. The ulcer
    b. The diabetes mellitus
    c. Either condition
    d. The circumstances of the admission will determine which condition is classified as the principal diagnosis.

1.250. Lichen planus, generalized

Code(s): _____

1.251. Contact dermatitis due to new detergent

Code(s): _____

1.252. Abscess of axilla

Code(s): _____

1.253. Ammonia dermatitis from soiled diapers

Code(s): _____

1.254. Erythema multiforme

Code(s): _____

1.255. Second-degree sunburn

Code(s): _____

Musculoskeletal System and Connective Tissue

1.256. Pyogenic arthritis of the hip

Code(s): _____

1.257. Rheumatoid arthritis involving the hands

Code(s): _____

1.258. Aseptic necrosis of femoral head

Code(s): _____

1.259. Osteoarthritis of the knees

Code(s): _____

1.260. DJD, generalized

Code(s): _____

1.261. Chronic bucket handle tear of the lateral meniscus of the knee

Code(s): _____

1.262. Chondromalacia patellae

Code(s): _____

1.263. Hemarthrosis of the elbow, chronic

Code(s): _____

1.264. Ankylosing spondylitis

Code(s): _____

1.265. Osteoarthritis of the cervical spine with cord compression documented at surgery

Code(s): _____

1.266. HNP, L4–5, with left lower extremity sciatica

Code(s): _____

1.267. Degenerative disc disease of lumbar spine

Code(s): _____

1.268. Low back pain

Code(s): _____

1.269. Synovial cyst of wrist

Code(s): _____

1.270. SLE

Code(s): _____

1.271. Osteomyelitis, acute, of first and second metatarsi

Code(s): _____

1.272. Postmenopausal osteoporosis

Code(s): _____

1.273. Pathologic fracture of neck of femur

Code(s): _____

1.274. Hallux valgus

Code(s): _____

1.275. Genu varum

Code(s): _____

Newborn/Congenital Disorders

1.276. Spina bifida of lumbar region

Code(s): _____

1.277. Branchial cleft cyst

Code(s): _____

1.278. VSD

Code(s): _____

1.279. Coarctation of the aorta

Code(s): _____

1.280. Bilateral complete cleft palate

Code(s): _____

1.281. Hypospadias

Code(s): _____

1.282. Polycystic kidney disease

Code(s): _____

1.283. Congenital dislocation of left hip, with subluxation of right hip

Code(s): _____

1.284. Syndactyly of fingers involving soft tissues only

Code(s): _____

1.285. Spondylolisthesis, L5–S1

Code(s): _____

1.286. Gastroschisis

Code(s): _____

1.287. Klinefelter's syndrome

Code(s): _____

1.288. Osteogenesis imperfecta

Code(s): _____

1.289. Congenital CMV infection

Code(s): _____

1.290. Meconium aspiration syndrome

Code(s): _____

1.291. Hemolytic disease of newborn due to Rh maternal/fetal incompatibility

Code(s): _____

1.292. DIC of the newborn

Code(s): _____

1.293. Drug withdrawal syndrome in newborn

Code(s): _____

1.294. In the diagnostic statement "newborn male with meconium aspiration syndrome, subarachnoid hemorrhage, and neonatal jaundice due to prematurity," what is the principal diagnosis?

    a. 772.2
    b. V30.00
    c. 770.1
    d. 774.2

1.295. Necrotizing enterocolitis of the newborn

Code(s): _____

Symptoms, Signs, and Ill-defined Conditions

1.296. Anorexia

Code(s): _____

1.297. Failure to thrive, 35-year-old patient

Code(s): _____

1.298. Fussy infant

Code(s): _____

1.299. Fever

Code(s): _____

1.300. Syncope

Code(s): _____

1.301. Chronic fatigue syndrome

Code(s): _____

1.302. Chest pain

Code(s): _____

1.303. Headache

Code(s): _____

1.304. Polydipsia

Code(s): _____

1.305. Abnormal GTT

Code(s): _____

1.306. Nausea and vomiting

Code(s): _____

1.307. Change in bowel habits

Code(s): _____

1.308. Urinary frequency

Code(s): _____

1.309. RUQ abdominal pain

Code(s): _____

1.310. Abnormal EEG

Code(s): _____

1.311. Nonvisualization of gallbladder on x-ray examination

Code(s): _____

1.312. Abnormal mammogram

Code(s): _____

1.313. SIDS

Code(s): _____

1.314. Cachexia

Code(s): _____

1.315. Hyperventilation

Code(s): _____

Trauma/Poisoning

1.316. Open skull fracture with subarachnoid and subdural hemorrhage, expired without regaining consciousness

Code(s): _____

1.317. Fracture of C3 with complete transection of spinal cord at that level

Code(s): _____

1.318. Fracture ribs 2–4 right and 2–5 left

Code(s): _____

1.319. Multiple fractures of pelvis with loss of continuity of pelvic circle

Code(s): _____

1.320. Comminuted, impacted fracture of surgical neck of right humerus

Code(s): _____

1.321. Compound fracture, shaft of radius and ulna

Code(s): _____

1.322. Fracture, base of thumb

Code(s): _____

1.323. Missile fracture of patella due to bullet

Code(s): _____

1.324. Dislocation of jaw

Code(s): _____

1.325. Sprained wrist

Code(s): _____

1.326. Pneumothorax with knife wound of chest wall

Code(s): _____

1.327. Mosquito bite, buttocks, with secondary infection

Code(s): _____

1.328. Third-degree burns of palm of hand

Code(s): _____

1.329. Poisoning by salicylate ingestion

Code(s): _____

1.330. Anaphylactic shock due to ingestion of pecans

Code(s): _____

1.331. Frostbite of face

Code(s): _____

1.332. Leakage of prosthetic heart valve

Code(s): _____

1.333. Rejection of transplanted liver

Code(s): _____

1.334. Accidental laceration of aorta during laminectomy procedure

Code(s): _____

1.335. Battered spouse

Code(s): _____

E Codes

There is a separate Alphabetic Index to External Causes of Injury and Poisoning. Depending upon the publisher, this index may be found in different locations within the book. E codes are not indexed in the main Alphabetic Index to Diseases.

1.336. Assign the appropriate E code for injury due to tackle in a football game.

Code(s): _____

1.337. Assign the appropriate E code for fall from ladder.

Code(s): _____

1.338. Assign the appropriate E code for burns due to ignition of clothing from fireplace in restaurant.

Code(s): _____

1.339. Assign the appropriate E code for injury from rattlesnake bite.

Code(s): _____

1.340. Assign the appropriate E code for injury in an avalanche.

Code(s): _____

1.341. Assign the appropriate E code for injury to the toe due to bumping into table.

Code(s): _____

1.342. Assign the appropriate E code for drowning in the bathtub.

Code(s): _____

1.343. Assign the appropriate E code for injury from fireworks.

Code(s): _____

1.344. Assign the appropriate E code for injury in a fight.

Code(s): _____

1.345. Laceration of hand from assault with knife. Assign both the diagnosis code and the E code.

Code(s): _____

1.346. Cervical strain due to MVA, secondary to loss of control and collision with tree. Patient was the restrained driver. Assign both the diagnosis code and the E code.

Code(s): _____

1.347. Fracture of ulna due to fall from motorcycle. Patient was passenger on the back of the motorcycle. Assign both the diagnosis code and the E code.

Code(s): _____

1.348. Assign the appropriate E code for injury due to fall from horse.

Code(s): _____

1.349. Assign the appropriate E code for injury from dog bite.

Code(s): _____

1.350. What is the appropriate place of occurrence code for an accident occurring on a street or highway?

Code(s): _____

1.351. Assign the appropriate E code for foreign body left inside a patient during a surgical procedure.

Code(s): _____

1.352. Assign the appropriate E code for injury during earthquake.

Code(s): _____

1.353. Assign the appropriate E code for injury from a lathe.

Code(s): _____

1.354. Assign the appropriate E code for burn from boiling water.

Code(s): _____

1.355. Laceration of pinna of the ear from accidental human bite, with secondary infection. Assign both the diagnosis code and the E code.

Code(s): _____

V Codes

1.356. Encounter for artificial insemination

Code(s): _____

1.357. Hepatitis B carrier

Code(s): _____

1.358. History of carcinoma of the breast

Code(s): _____

1.359. History of colonic polyps

Code(s): _____

1.360. Family history of ovarian cancer

Code(s): _____

1.361. Well-baby visit

Code(s): _____

1.362. Incidental pregnancy

Code(s): _____

1.363. Liveborn male twin, delivered by cesarean section

Code(s): _____

1.364. Encounter for amniocentesis for screening for chromosomal anomalies

Code(s): _____

1.365. Visit to lactation clinic

Code(s): _____

1.366. Kidney transplant status without complications

Code(s): _____

1.367. Cardiac pacemaker status, without complications

Code(s): _____

1.368. Encounter for reprogramming of AICD

Code(s): _____

1.369. Aftercare for pathological fracture of L4 vertebra

Code(s): _____

1.370. Admission for change of tracheostomy tube and stoma revision

Code(s): _____

1.371. Admission for planned colostomy closure

Code(s): _____

1.372. Admission for chemotherapy

Code(s): _____

1.373. Admission to donate kidney

Code(s): _____

1.374. Observation of child post MVA with no apparent injury and no complaints

Code(s): _____

1.375. Encounter for screening mammogram

Code(s): _____

ICD-9-CM Procedure Coding

1.376. Vasectomy

Code(s): _____

1.377. Ventriculoperitoneostomy

Code(s): _____

1.378. Right thyroid lobectomy

Code(s): _____

1.379. Lamellar keratoplasty with donor corneal tissue

Code(s): _____

1.380. Myringotomy with placement of pressure equalization tube

Code(s): _____

1.381. Cleft palate repair

Code(s): _____

1.382. Lung volume reduction surgery

Code(s): _____

1.383. Open-heart surgery for repair of atrial septal defect with mesh

Code(s): _____

1.384. Right coronary artery PTCA

Code(s): _____

1.385. Coronary artery bypass grafting using left and right internal mammary arteries

Code(s): _____

1.386. Bilateral radical neck dissection

Code(s): _____

1.387. Transverse colectomy

Code(s): _____

1.388. Whipple procedure

Code(s): _____

1.389. Right direct inguinal herniorrhaphy with mesh

Code(s): _____

1.390. Transplant nephrectomy

Code(s): _____

1.391. Paraurethral suspension utilizing Pereyra suture

Code(s): _____

1.392. Pelvic exenteration for ovarian cancer

Code(s): _____

1.393. Repair of fourth-degree laceration of rectum during delivery

Code(s): _____

1.394. Right total hip replacement

Code(s): _____

1.395. Reattachment of arm amputated through humerus

Code(s): _____

1.396. Mid-forceps extraction with episiotomy

Code(s): _____

1.397. Retropubic prostatectomy

Code(s): _____

1.398. Subtotal jejunectomy with end-to-end anastomosis

Code(s): _____

1.399. Percutaneous transmyocardial revascularization

Code(s): _____

1.400. Insertion of drug-eluting coronary artery stent

Code(s): _____

Review Questions

1.401. A patient with known AIDS is admitted to the hospital as an inpatient with acute appendicitis and undergoes an open appendectomy. His AIDS is under treatment and is asymptomatic at the present time. The appropriate principal diagnosis in this case would be:

    a. 042
    b. 540.9
    c. V08
    d. Any of the above

1.402. When the diagnosis is stated as "septic shock," _____ is coded as the principal diagnosis.

1.403. The four types of neoplasms are benign, malignant, uncertain behavior, and _____.

1.404. When a patient is admitted to the hospital for treatment of a secondary malignancy, and the primary is still present, the principal diagnosis is the _____ malignancy.

1.405. A patient is admitted for treatment of dehydration secondary to chemotherapy for primary liver cancer. Which condition should be sequenced as the principal diagnosis?

    a. Liver carcinoma
    b. Complication of chemotherapy
    c. Dehydration
    d. Any of the above

1.406. What code(s) are assigned for a patient with acute bronchitis and chronic obstructive bronchitis?

    a. 466.0
    b. 491.22
    c. 491.21
    d. 466.0, 491.21

1.407. Coding professionals may assume a cause-and-effect relationship between hypertension and which of the following conditions?

    a. Chronic kidney disease
    b. Heart failure
    c. Both heart and chronic kidney disease
    d. Neither condition

1.408. When a patient is admitted in respiratory failure due to/associated with a chronic nonrespiratory condition, the respiratory failure is the _____ diagnosis.

1.409. When a patient is admitted with respiratory failure due to/associated with an acute nonrespiratory condition, the _____ is sequenced as the principal diagnosis.

1.410. Code 484.5 and its descriptor "Pneumonia in anthrax" are printed in italics. This convention identifies this code as a _____ code that must not be coded first.

1.411. Per *ICD-9-CM Official Guidelines for Coding and Reporting*, chapter 11 codes have sequencing priority over:

    a. Codes from all other chapters
    b. V codes only
    c. No other codes
    d. All codes except V codes

1.412. Chapter 11 codes are reported on:

    a. The mother's and the baby's record
    b. The mother's record
    c. The baby's record
    d. Either mother's record only or mother's and baby's records, depending upon departmental coding policies

1.413. Which of the following criteria must be met to assign a diagnosis code of 650?

    a. Full-term normal delivery
    b. Single, healthy infant
    c. No maternal complications during the delivery, antepartum, or postpartum episode
    d. All of the above

1.414. According to official coding guidelines, which of the following statements is true about the assignment of code 650?

    a. It can never be assigned with any other code from chapter 11.
    b. V27.0 is the only appropriate outcome of delivery code with 650.
    c. It can be assigned if a patient had a complication at some time during her pregnancy, but it is no longer present at the time of delivery.
    d. All of the above

1.415. In the diagnostic statement "arthritis of bilateral knee joints secondary to primary hyperparathyroidism," which condition is sequenced as the principal diagnosis?

    a. The arthritis
    b. The primary hyperparathyroidism
    c. Either condition
    d. The circumstances of the admission will determine the appropriate sequencing.

1.416. Codes from categories 764 and 765 are assigned based upon review of:

    a. Documented weights and dates per office and hospital records
    b. Nursing assessment of fetal maturity
    c. Attending physician's documented clinical assessment of the maturity of the infant
    d. Any of the above

1.417. The diagnostic statement "cholelithiasis with acute cholecystitis without obstruction" is reported with one code, 574.00. This is referred to as a _____ code.

1.418. In order for a condition to be considered a late effect, how much time must elapse between the acute event and the late effect?

    a. No more than 24 hours
    b. Six weeks
    c. There is no set time.
    d. One year

1.419. Per coding guidelines, a "significant procedure" must meet which of the following conditions:

    a. It is surgical in nature.
    b. It carries an anesthetic and/or surgical risk.
    c. It requires specialized training.
    d. All of the above

1.420. When two procedures meet the criteria for principal procedure, the one coded first is:

    a. The one performed first
    b. The one most closely related to the principal diagnosis
    c. The one that was performed by the attending physician
    d. The one with the highest reimbursement

1.421. A patient was admitted for a total hip replacement for arthritis of the hip. Just prior to the surgery, he developed a fever and pneumonia was seen on the chest x-ray. The patient was discharged and the surgery was rescheduled. What is the principal diagnosis for this admission?

    a. 486, Pneumonia
    b. 715.95, Osteoarthritis of the hip
    c. 780.6, Fever
    d. V64.1, Surgical or other procedure not carried out because of contraindication

1.422. A patient was admitted for evaluation of abdominal pain. In the evening after eating dinner, she fell out of bed and sustained a fracture of the femur. The next day she underwent hip replacement surgery and was eventually discharged to a skilled nursing facility for follow-up care. What is the principal diagnosis of this admission?

    a. Fracture of hip
    b. Abdominal pain
    c. Either abdominal pain or fracture of hip per the attending physician's final diagnosis statement
    d. Either abdominal pain or fracture of hip, whichever has the higher reimbursement

1.423. A patient was admitted with nausea and vomiting, and acute gastroenteritis was diagnosed. What are the diagnoses reported?

    a. Nausea with vomiting is reported as the principal diagnosis, and acute gastroenteritis is reported as a secondary diagnosis.
    b. Acute gastroenteritis is reported as the principal diagnosis, and nausea with vomiting is reported as a secondary diagnosis.
    c. Only the nausea and vomiting are reported.
    d. Only the acute gastroenteritis is reported.

1.424. Diabetic foot ulcers may result from:

    a. Diabetic peripheral vascular complications
    b. Diabetic neurological complications
    c. Diabetic ketoacidosis
    d. Either a or b

1.425. Which of the following statements is true of gestational diabetes?

    a. It involves abnormal glucose tolerance test findings/results in pregnant women without previous history of diabetes.
    b. It is a form of true diabetes mellitus.
    c. It usually does not resolve after the patient delivers.
    d. It only occurs in patients with juvenile-onset-type diabetes.

1.426. What is meant by a provider?

    a. Physician
    b. Physician, nurse-practitioner, or physician assistant
    c. Physician or any qualified healthcare practitioner who is legally accountable for establishing the patient's diagnosis
    d. Anyone documenting in the patient record.

Chapter 2

Basic Principles of CPT Coding

The following exercises are designed to review CPT coding guidelines and to provide practice in assigning CPT codes. Because CPT indexes procedures in many different ways, the rationale for the selection of a particular code may be different from the approach that you use. The information included in the rationale is not meant to describe the only way to obtain an appropriate code but to represent one possible way. Unless the coder is specifically instructed to assign modifiers, no modifiers will appear in the rationale.

Note: These exercises were developed to be used with the 2006 edition of CPT but are suitable for other editions in most cases.

Instructions: Circle the correct answer, fill in the blank, or assign the correct code(s) for each of the following exercise items.

CPT Organization, Structure, and Guidelines

2.1.   Category II codes cover all but one of the following topics. Which is not addressed by category II codes?

   a. Patient management
   b. New technology
   c. Therapeutic, preventive, or other interventions
   d. Patient safety

2.2.   In CPT, the symbols ▶ ◀ are used to indicate:

   a. Changes in verbiage within code descriptions
   b. A new code
   c. Changes in verbiage other than that in code descriptions, for example, changes in coding guidelines or parenthetical notes
   d. A code for which there is a corresponding HCPCS Level II code

2.3.   During the performance of a femoral angioplasty, a patient develops additional areas of occlusion. A diagnostic angiogram of the affected artery is performed. Is it appropriate to code this diagnostic study in addition to the therapeutic procedure?

    a. No. All diagnostic procedures are included in therapeutic interventional procedures.

    b. Yes. Per revised coding guidelines, if there is a clinical change during an interventional procedure that requires further diagnostic study, the diagnostic angiogram may be reported in addition to the therapeutic procedure.

2.4.   Per CPT coding guidelines, a "complete" diagnostic ultrasound of the retroperitoneum includes at least the following organs:

    a. Kidneys, abdominal aorta, common iliac artery origins, inferior vena cava

    b. Kidneys, abdominal aorta, common iliac artery origins, inferior vena cava, and urinary bladder

    c. Liver, gallbladder, common bile duct, pancreas, spleen, kidneys, upper aorta, inferior vena cava

    d. Kidneys, abdominal aorta, common iliac artery origins

2.5.   A list of codes describing procedures that include conscious sedation, if administered by the same surgeon as performs the procedure, can be found in:

    a. Appendix E

    b. Appendix F

    c. Appendix G

    d. Appendix H

2.6.   True or false? Category II codes may be used as the first-listed CPT code when the patient is seen only for counseling.

    a. True

    b. False

2.7.   Which of the newly added appendices would a neurologist's practice consult to determine the nerve conduction code to assign for a study of the suprascapular motor nerve to the infraspinatus?

    a. Appendix J

    b. Appendix K

    c. Appendix I

    d. Appendix L

2.8.   In order to be included in the CPT manual, a procedure must meet which of the following criteria?

    a. It must be commonly performed by many physicians across the country.

    b. It must be consistent with contemporary medical practice.

    c. It must be covered by Medicare.

    d. Both a and b

2.9.   Which of the following statements about CPT category III codes is false?

    a. They are updated only once every two years.
    b. They were developed to reflect emerging technologies and procedures.
    c. They are archived after five years if the code has not been accepted for inclusion in the main body of CPT.
    d. Reimbursement for these services is dependent upon individual payer policy.

2.10.   Per CPT guidelines, a separate procedure:

    a. Is coded when it is performed as a part of another, larger procedure
    b. Is considered to be an integral part of another, larger service
    c. Is never coded under any circumstances
    d. Both a and b above

2.11.   Which of the following statements is (are) true of CPT codes?

    a. They are numeric.
    b. They describe nonphysician services.
    c. They are updated annually by CMS.
    d. All of the above

2.12.   What does the symbol ▲ before a code in the CPT manual signify?

    a. The code is new for this year.
    b. The code is exempt from bundling requirements.
    c. The code can only be used as an add-on code, never reported alone or first.
    d. The code has been revised in some way this year.

2.13.   What does the symbol ● before a code in the CPT manual signify?

    a. The code is new for this year.
    b. The code is exempt from bundling requirements.
    c. The code can only be used as an add-on code, never reported alone or first.
    d. The code has been revised in some way this year.

2.14.   CPT was developed and is maintained by:

    a. CMS
    b. AMA
    c. The Cooperating Parties
    d. WHO

2.15.   CPT is updated:

    a. Annually for the main body of codes and every 6 months for category III codes
    b. Annually
    c. Every 6 months
    d. As often as required by new technology

2.16. The Alphabetic Index to CPT includes listings for:

    a. Procedures/services
    b. Examinations/tests
    c. Anatomic sites
    d. All of the above

2.17. The use of the term "for" followed by a diagnosis in CPT means that:

    a. The procedure must be reported for that diagnosis.
    b. The procedure can only be reported for that diagnosis.
    c. The diagnosis is an example of the types of diagnoses for which this procedure could be done.
    d. None of the above

2.18. If a surgeon performs a procedure for which there is no CPT code and no HCPCS level II or III code, what code should be reported on the CMS 1500 form?

    a. CPT code 99999
    b. An unlisted procedure code from the appropriate chapter of CPT
    c. An ICD-9-CM procedure code
    d. A procedure that does not have a valid CPT code should not be reported.

2.19. There are six sections to CPT: evaluation and management, anesthesia, surgery, radiology, laboratory/pathology, and
_____medicine_____.

2.20. The symbol + before a code in CPT means that:

    a. This code can never be reported alone.
    b. This code can never be reported first.
    c. This is an add-on code.
    d. All of the above

2.21. A listing of all current modifiers is found in which appendix of CPT?

    a. Appendix A
    b. Appendix B
    c. Appendix C
    d. Appendix D

2.22. The codes in the musculoskeletal section of CPT may be used by:

    a. Orthopedic surgeons only
    b. Orthopedic surgeons and emergency department physicians
    c. Any physician
    d. Orthopedic surgeons and neurosurgeons

Evaluation and Management (E/M) Services

2.23. A nursing facility patient develops an acute illness and is seen by her attending physician. He performs a detailed interval history, detailed examination and performs medical decision making of moderate complexity. What code should the physician use to report these services?

    a. 99304
    b. 99305
    c. 99309
    d. 99310
    e. 99318

2.24. For reporting of physician services, evaluation and management codes are usually based upon:

    a. Documentation of history, examination, and medical decision making
    b. The final diagnosis for the visit
    c. The amount of time spent with the patient
    d. Documentation of medical decision making

2.25. Select the appropriate evaluation and management code for a new patient office visit in which a comprehensive history and comprehensive physical examination were performed and medical decision making was of high complexity. _____99205_____

2.26. Select the appropriate evaluation and management code for a new patient office visit in which a comprehensive history and comprehensive physical examination were performed and medical decision making was of straightforward complexity. _____99202_____

2.27. Select the appropriate evaluation and management code for an established patient visit in which a comprehensive history and expanded problem-focused examination was performed and medical decision making was of low complexity. _____99213_____

2.28. When counseling consumes more than half the total visit time, _____time_____ may be used as the criterion for assigning the evaluation and management code.

2.29. Observation evaluation and management codes (99218–99220) are used when:

    a. A patient is admitted and discharged on the same date.
    b. A patient is admitted for routine nursing care following surgery.
    c. A patient does not meet admission criteria.
    d. A patient is placed in designated observation status.

2.30. A physician sees a patient in his office in the morning; then again in the early afternoon, at which time he sends the patient to the hospital in observation status. Later that day he visits the patient in the hospital and admits him as a full inpatient. What evaluation and management codes should be assigned for this day of care?

    a. Two evaluation and management codes for the office visits, one for the observation care, and one for the inpatient admission

    b. One code combining the two office visits, one for the observation care, and one for the inpatient admission

    c. One code for the observation care and one for the inpatient admission

    d. One code for the inpatient admission only

2.31. History, physical examination, and medical decision making are the _____Key_____ components considered in assigning an evaluation and management code.

2.32. Which of the following are considered components of the social history?

    a. Occupational history

    b. Marital history

    c. Allergic history

    d. a and b above

2.33. Documentation in history of use of drugs, alcohol, and/or tobacco is considered part of the_____.

    a. Past medical history

    b. Social history

    c. Systems review

    d. History of present illness

2.34. Per CPT guidelines, a presenting problem of moderate severity is one that:

    a. May not require the presence of a physician, but for which care is provided under the supervision of a physician

    b. Runs a definite and prescribed course, is transient in nature and is not likely to permanently alter health status, or has a good prognosis with management and compliance

    c. Has a low risk of morbidity without treatment, little or no risk of mortality without treatment, with full recovery expected without functional impairment

    d. Has a moderate risk of morbidity without treatment, a moderate risk of mortality without treatment, uncertain prognosis, or increased probability of functional impairment

2.35. Pediatric inpatient critical care, patient six months of age, first day

    Code(s):_____99293_____

2.36. Dr. Smith sees a patient in consultation in the hospital at the request of Dr. Jones. He renders an opinion. He then takes over the management of a portion of the patient's care. What codes should Dr. Smith use to bill for his subsequent hospital visits?

    a. Subsequent inpatient consultation codes
    b. Initial inpatient hospital care codes
    c. Subsequent hospital care codes
    d. No codes; the initial consultation includes all subsequent visits.

2.37. Assign the appropriate evaluation and management code for an outpatient office consultation in which the physician performed a detailed history, a comprehensive physical examination, and medical decision making of moderate complexity. _____99243_____

2.38. Per CPT guidelines, a concise statement describing the symptom, problem, condition, diagnosis, or other factor that is the reason for the encounter, usually stated in the patient's words, is the definition of the:

    a. History of present illness
    b. Chief complaint
    c. Admission diagnosis
    d. Past history

2.39. Which of the following are parts of medical decision making?

    a. Number of possible diagnoses or management options that must be considered
    b. Amount or complexity of medical record, diagnostic tests, or other information that must be obtained, reviewed, and analyzed
    c. Risk of significant complications, morbidity, and/or mortality associated with the patient's presenting problem, the diagnostic procedures, and/or the management options
    d. All of the above

2.40. Which evaluation and management codes are used to report services to patients in a facility that provides room, board, and other personal assistance services, generally on a long-term basis?

    a. Outpatient services
    b. Nursing facility care
    c. Domiciliary, rest home, or custodial care services
    d. Care plan oversight services

2.41. Preventive medicine services are based upon which of the following criteria?

    a. Documentation of history, physical examination, and medical decision making
    b. Age of the patient
    c. Amount of time spent with the patient
    d. The final diagnosis for the visit

2.42.   AHIMA Hospital has a "fast-track" department attached to the emergency department. This area is staffed by ED physicians on a rotating basis, treats minor problems, and is open from 5:00 a.m. until 8:00 p.m. What codes should be used to report services rendered in this department?

   a. Emergency department services codes
   b. Office or other outpatient services codes
   c. These are not codable services because the department is not open 24 hours per day.
   d. Either office or emergency department codes may be used.

2.43.   In order to report a critical care code, a physician must spend at least _____ 30 _____ minutes with a critically ill patient.

Anesthesia Services

2.44.   Per CPT guidelines, anesthesia time begins when the anesthesiologist begins to prepare the patient for induction, and ends:

   a. When the patient leaves the operating room
   b. When the anesthesiologist is no longer in personal attendance on the patient
   c. When the patient has fulfilled postanesthesia care unit criteria for recovery
   d. When the patient leaves the postanesthesia care unit

2.45.   A physical status anesthesia modifier of P4 means that a patient:

   a. Has a mild systemic disease
   b. Has a severe systemic disease
   c. Has a severe systemic disease that is a constant threat to life
   d. Is moribund

2.46.   Qualifying circumstances anesthesia codes are used:

   a. In addition to the anesthesia codes
   b. To describe provision of anesthesia under particularly difficult circumstances
   c. To describe circumstances that impact the character of the anesthesia
   d. All of the above

2.47.   The qualifying circumstance code to assign when anesthesia services are provided under emergency circumstances is

   _____.

2.48.   Anesthesia for total repair of cleft palate, patient four years of age

   Code(s):_____

2.49.   Anesthesia for tracheal reconstruction, patient six months of age

   Code(s):_____

2.50. Anesthesia for permanent transvenous pacemaker insertion

Code(s):_____

2.51. Anesthesia for lumbar laminectomy with fusion and insertion of rods and hooks

Code(s):_____

2.52. Anesthesia for ventral hernia repair, patient a 76-year-old female

Code(s):_____

2.53. Anesthesia for donor nephrectomy

Code(s):_____

2.54. Anesthesia for left knee arthroscopy with medial meniscectomy

Code(s):_____

2.55. Anesthesia for total hip replacement

Code(s):_____

2.56. Anesthesia for vasectomy

Code(s):_____

2.57. Anesthesia for cesarean section following failed attempt at vaginal delivery under spinal anesthesia

Code(s):_____

2.58. Anesthesia for emergency completion of near-total amputation through the midthigh with laceration of femoral artery with imminent exsanguination

Code(s):_____

2.59. Anesthesia for ORIF of fracture of the distal tibia and fibula

Code(s):_____

2.60. Anesthesia for left ventricular reduction surgery with heart-lung bypass and systemic hypothermia

Code(s):_____

2.61. Anesthesia for Whipple procedure

Code(s):_____

2.62. Anesthesia for burn excision with skin grafting, left lower extremity, TBSA involved approximately 7 percent

Code(s):_____

2.63. Anesthesia for laparoscopically assisted, vaginal hysterectomy

Code(s):_____

Integumentary System

2.64. A patient undergoes placement of brachytherapy afterloading catheters into her right breast under conscious sedation. The physician who performs the procedure administers the Versed® himself, and a nurse is present throughout the procedure to monitor the patient. Is it appropriate for the surgeon to report the conscious sedation for this procedure?

   a. Yes
   b. No

2.65. Tissue transplanted from one individual to another of the same species but different genotype is called a(n):

   a. Autograft
   b. Xenograft
   c. Allograft or allogenic graft
   d. Heterograft

2.66. True or false? Per coding guidelines, skin grafting codes cannot be used unless there is surgical fixation of the graft to the recipient tissue.

   a. True
   b. False

2.67. When a lesion is excised and the resultant skin defect is closed with a Z-plasty, what code(s) should be reported?

   a. A code for the Z-plasty only
   b. A code for the excision, one for the Z-plasty, and code 15000
   c. A code for the lesion excision only
   d. A code for the excision and one for the Z-plasty

2.68. When lesions are excised from multiple sites, which of the following is the correct coding protocol?

   a. Add all the dimensions and assign one code based upon the total area.
   b. Code each lesion separately.
   c. Code only the largest lesion.
   d. Add all the dimensions for each body part, such as arms, legs, etc., and assign as many codes as there are body parts treated.

2.69. A patient presents with a palpable lump in the left breast. The surgeon dissects down to the mass and removes it entirely. The procedure is described as "Biopsy of mass of left breast." Assign the appropriate CPT code (omitting modifiers).

    a. 19120
    b. 19101
    c. 19125
    d. 19160

2.70. When calculating dimensions for assigning a lesion excision code, which of the following is the appropriate method?

    a. Measurement of the lesion documented by the surgeon preexcision
    b. Measurement of the lesion plus circumferential margins documented by the surgeon preexcision
    c. Measurement of the lesion documented by the pathologist postexcision
    d. Measurement of the lesion plus circumferential margins documented by the pathologist postexcision

2.71. "The sharp removal by transverse incision or horizontal slicing to remove epidermal and dermal lesions without a full-thickness dermal excision" is the CPT definition of_____.

2.72. Debridement of skin, subcutaneous tissue, and muscle

Code(s):_____

2.73. Excision of solar keratosis, face, .5 cm in diameter, with no significant margins

Code(s):_____

2.74. Excision of basal cell carcinoma, abdominal wall, 1.2 cm in diameter, with 1 cm skin margin all around

Code(s):_____

2.75. Excision of skin and subcutaneous tissue from the right groin for hidradenitis, with layered closure

Code(s):_____

2.76. Insertion and injection of tissue expander, scalp

Code(s):_____

2.77. Repair of 5.2 cm laceration of the left hand, dorsum, with layered closure

Code(s):_____

2.78.   Repair of 3.4 cm laceration of the left forearm, single-layer closure with 4-0 Dexon; repair of 2.0 cm laceration of the left upper arm, single-layer closure

Code(s):_____

2.79.   Repair of 3.0 cm laceration of the scalp, 2.5 cm laceration of the left foot, and 6.0 cm laceration of the left lower leg

Code(s):_____

2.80.   Repair of 5.0 m laceration of the left cheek, 3.2 cm laceration of the forehead, and 16.0 cm complex laceration of the left chest wall, utilizing multilayered closure

Code(s):_____

2.81.   Simple repair of 2 inch laceration of the right neck area

Code(s):_____

2.82.   A wound repair that involves layered closure of one or more of the deeper layers of subcutaneous tissue and superficial (nonmuscle) fascia or extensive cleaning of heavily contaminated wounds is a (an) _____ repair.

2.83.   Biopsy of the left breast using Mammotome® rotational biopsy device

Code(s):_____

2.84.   Moh's micrographic surgery involves the surgeon acting as:

a. Both plastic surgeon and general surgeon
b. Both surgeon and pathologist
c. Both plastic surgeon and dermatologist
d. Both dermatologist and pathologist

2.85.   Excision of nonpalpable suspicious area of possible microcalcification identified on mammogram (needle identifying the site placed at an outside radiologist's suite)

Code(s):_____

2.86.   Excision of 2 cm squamous cell carcinoma from left chest with repair of resultant 8 sq cm defect using V-Y plasty

Code(s):_____

Musculoskeletal System

2.87. True or false? Per coding guidelines, the type of fracture does not have a coding correlation to the type of treatment provided.

    a. True
    b. False

2.88. True or false? If a bone biopsy is performed in conjunction with a kyphoplasty procedure, it is separately coded.

    a. True
    b. False

2.89. Per the description of code 22523, fracture reduction and bone biopsy, if performed, are included in the procedure and are not separately coded. 3D reconstruction is not to be reported with which of the following base modalities?

    a. CT angiography
    b. MR angiography
    c. PET scans
    d. All of the above

2.90. Which of the following terms does not describe an open fracture?

    a. Missile
    b. Comminuted
    c. Infected
    d. Compound

2.91. Open-fracture treatment includes which of the following scenarios?

    a. The fractured bone is exposed to the environment.
    b. The bone ends are visualized and internal fixation inserted.
    c. The fractured bone is opened remote from the fracture site and an intramedullary nail is inserted across the fracture site.
    d. All of the above

2.92. If an orthopedic surgeon attempted to reduce a fracture but was unsuccessful in obtaining acceptable alignment, what type of code should be assigned for the procedure?

    a. A "with manipulation" code
    b. A "without manipulation" code
    c. An unlisted procedure code
    d. An evaluation and management code only

2.93.   Keller bunionectomy

Code(s):_____

2.94.   Diagnostic arthroscopy, left knee, with medial meniscectomy

Code(s):_____

2.95.   Open reduction of knee dislocation with repair of the anterior cruciate ligament by Anchor suture

Code(s):_____

2.96.   Percutaneous vertebroplasty, L5 (Do not assign radiological supervision and interpretation code.)

Code(s):_____

2.97.   Incision and drainage of infected shoulder bursa

Code(s):_____

2.98.   Putti-Platt procedure, left shoulder

Code(s):_____

2.99.   ORIF humerus shaft fracture with cast application

Code(s):_____

2.100.   Wrist fusion with bone graft from iliac crest

Code(s):_____

2.101.   Closed reduction of distal radial wrist fracture

Code(s):_____

2.102.   Total hip arthroplasty

Code(s):_____

2.103.   Casting is separately reported:

a. When applied to stabilize or for comfort, by a separate physician
b. For initial application by a physician who does not perform the fracture care
c. When recasting is done during fracture follow-up
d. All of the above

2.104.   Removal of biplane external fixator under general anesthesia

Code(s):_____

2.105. Bone biopsy obtained from iliac crest

Code(s):_____

2.106. Application of short-leg walking cast for severe sprain of ankle

Code(s):_____

2.107. Arthroscopy of shoulder with complete rotator cuff repair

Code(s):_____

2.108. Midthigh amputation of leg

Code(s):_____

2.109. Closed reduction, temporomandibular joint dislocation

Code(s):_____

Respiratory System

2.110. A pulmonologist performed a diagnostic bronchoscopy with biopsy. The endoscope was introduced into the bronchus, and attachments were used to perforate the bronchial wall. Tissue was obtained and submitted to the pathologist, who identified it as "lung parenchyma." What type of biopsy was performed?

    a. Transbronchial lung biopsy
    b. Bronchial biopsy
    c. Bronchoalveolar lavage
    d. Protected specimen brush biopsy

2.111. SMR of nasal turbinates

Code(s):_____

2.112. Control of epistaxis, anterior, by packing and silver nitrate cautery

Code(s):_____

2.113. Nasal sinus endoscopy with anterior ethmoidectomy

Code(s):_____

2.114. Total laryngectomy with left radical neck dissection

Code(s):_____

2.115. Direct laryngoscopy with vocal cord stripping using the operating microscope

Code(s):_____

2.116. Bronchoscopy with tracheal dilation and stenting

Code(s):_____

2.117. Thoracentesis with placement of tube

Code(s):_____

2.118. Thoracoscopy of the mediastinal space with biopsy

Code(s):_____

2.119. Open Caldwell-Luc procedure of maxillary sinuses

Code(s):_____

2.120. Emergency endotracheal intubation

Code(s):_____

2.121. Flexible bronchoscopy with placement of catheters for after loading of radiotherapeutic agents

Code(s):_____

2.122. Right lung middle lobectomy

Code(s):_____

2.123. Double-lung transplant with cardiopulmonary bypass

Code(s):_____

2.124. Functional endoscopic sinus surgery (FESS) with frontal sinus polyp removal

Code(s):_____

2.125. Endoscopic control of nasal hemorrhage

Code(s):_____

2.126. When a bronchoscopy is performed under fluoroscopic guidance, how are the codes assigned per CPT coding guidelines?

a. The fluoroscopy guidance code is assigned as a secondary procedure code with the bronchoscopy code.
b. The fluoroscopy guidance code is assigned as the first procedure code.
c. The fluoroscopy is included in the bronchoscopy and no code is assigned for it.
d. Individual hospital coding guidelines determine whether the fluoroscopy is separately coded.

2.127. Talc pleurodesis for pneumothorax

Code(s):_____

2.128. Laryngoplasty for reconstruction following third-degree chemical burns of the larynx

Code(s):_____

2.129. Anterovertical hemilaryngectomy

Code(s):_____

Cardiovascular System

2.130. Codes describing endovascular repair of the descending thoracic aorta include all of the following procedures except one. Which procedure is not included in the repair code?

   a. Intravascular ultrasound
   b. Angiography of the thoracic aorta
   c. Fluoroscopic guidance in delivery of the endovascular components
   d. Preprocedure diagnostic imaging

2.131. True or false? Separate codes now exist for ligation and stripping of the long saphenous vein and ligation and stripping of the short saphenous vein.

   a. True
   b. False

2.132. In coding arterial catheterizations, when the tip of the catheter is manipulated from the insertion into the aorta and then out into another artery, this is called:

   a. Selective catheterization
   b. Nonselective catheterization
   c. Manipulative catheterization
   d. Radical catheterization

2.133. Subtotal pericardiectomy

Code(s):_____

2.134. Insertion of permanent pacemaker with atrial and ventricular transvenous leads

Code(s):_____

2.135. When coding a selective catheterization, how are codes assigned?

   a. One code for each vessel entered
   b. One code for the point of entry vessel
   c. One code for the final vessel entered
   d. One code for the vessel of entry and one for the final vessel, with intervening vessels not coded

2.136. Replacement of the mitral valve with cardiopulmonary bypass

Code(s):_____

2.137. CABG using saphenous vein to the LAD

Code(s):_____

2.138. LIMA graft to the circumflex coronary artery and sequentially to the right coronary artery

Code(s):_____

2.139. Insertion of intra-aortic balloon pump, percutaneous

Code(s):_____

2.140. Introduction of catheter into the aorta

Code(s):_____

2.141. Venipuncture by cutdown, patient 32 years of age

Code(s):_____

2.142. A 35-year-old patient required implantation of a tunneled central venous catheter with insertion of a Life-Port® vascular access device (VAD).

Code(s):_____

2.143. Creation of Brescia-Cimino fistula for chronic hemodialysis

Code(s):_____

2.144. Ligation and stripping of long and short saphenous veins

Code(s):_____

2.145. Laparoscopic splenectomy

Code(s):_____

2.146. Injection for identification of sentinel node

Code(s):_____

2.147. Temporal artery biopsy

Code(s):_____

2.148. A tunneled centrally inserted central venous catheter is placed on a 57-year-old patient.

Code(s):_____

2.149. Blood transfusion

Code(s):_____

2.150. Aortobifemoral bypass graft

Code(s):_____

2.151. Percutaneous transluminal iliac angioplasty

Code(s):_____

Digestive System

2.152. Primary repair of bilateral cleft lip, one-stage procedure

Code(s):_____

2.153. Biopsy of floor of mouth

Code(s):_____

2.154. Uvulopalatopharyngoplasty for sleep apnea

Code(s):_____

2.155. T&A, six-year-old patient

Code(s):_____

2.156. Upper gastrointestinal endoscopy with biopsy of lesion of esophagus

Code(s):_____

2.157. Per CPT coding guidelines, if a lesion is biopsied and then the remainder of the lesion is removed, what code(s) is (are) assigned:

a. A code for the biopsy and one for the lesion excision
b. A code for the lesion excision only
c. A code for the biopsy only
d. Hospital-specific coding procedures determine what is coded.

2.158. Rigid esophagoscopy with removal of impacted food

Code(s):_____

2.159. EGD with esophageal dilation over guidewire

Code(s):_____

2.160. When the physician does not specify the method used to remove a lesion during an endoscopy, what is the appropriate procedure?

    a. Assign the removal by snare technique code.
    b. Assign the removal by hot biopsy forceps code.
    c. Assign the ablation code.
    d. Query the physician as to the method used.

2.161. ERCP with sphincterotomy

Code(s):_____

2.162. Laparoscopic Nissen fundoplication

Code(s):_____

2.163. Esophageal dilation with bougies

Code(s):_____

2.164. Percutaneous gastrostomy tube placement

Code(s):_____

2.165. Left partial colectomy with end-to-end anastomosis

Code(s):_____

2.166. Laparoscopic partial colectomy with end colostomy (Hartmann procedure)

Code(s):_____

2.167. Revision of colostomy with repair of paracolostomy herniation

Code(s):_____

2.168. Small bowel endoscopy with control of hemorrhagic site in ileum using bipolar cautery

Code(s):_____

2.169. Colonoscopy with removal of five colonic polyps using hot biopsy forceps

Code(s):_____

2.170. Flexible sigmoidoscopy with decompression of volvulus

Code(s):_____

2.171. Laparoscopic cholecystectomy with exploration of common duct

Code(s):_____

Urinary System

2.172. Percutaneous needle biopsy of kidney

Code(s):_____

2.173. Donor nephrectomy, live donor

Code(s):_____

2.174. Surgical laparoscopy with ablation of renal cysts

Code(s):_____

2.175. Extracorporeal sound wave lithotripsy of large kidney stone

Code(s):_____

2.176. Change of ureterostomy tube

Code(s):_____

2.177. Total cystectomy with continent diversion using large intestine

Code(s):_____

2.178. Placement of indwelling bladder catheter

Code(s):_____

2.179. Cystourethroscopy with fulguration of three bladder tumors ranging in size from 0.4 to 1.6 cm

Code(s):_____

2.180. Cystourethroscopy with insertion of urethral stent

Code(s):_____

2.181. Cystourethroscopy with insertion of double-J ureteral stent

Code(s):_____

2.182. Cystourethroscopy with balloon dilation of UPJ stenosis

Code(s):_____

2.183. Transurethral resection of prostate

Code(s):_____

2.184. Insertion of inflatable urethra–bladder neck sphincter

Code(s):_____

2.185. Repeat dilation of urethral stricture with filiforms and followers, male patient

Code(s):_____

2.186. Laparoscopic ureterolithotomy

Code(s):_____

2.187. Urethral pressure profile

Code(s):_____

2.188. Anterior vesicourethropexy by Marshall-Marchetti-Krantz procedure

Code(s):_____

2.189. Cystourethroscopy with biopsy of bladder wall

Code(s):_____

2.190. Cystourethroscopy with ureteral catheterization and removal of ureteral stones

Code(s):_____

2.191. Repeat transurethral resection of prostate tissue four years post original procedure

Code(s):_____

Male/Female Genital System and Laparoscopy

2.192. Laser destruction of condylomata of penis

Code(s):_____

2.193. Insertion of semirigid penile prosthesis

Code(s):_____

2.194. Removal and replacement of semirigid penile prosthesis from infected site, with irrigation and debridement of infected and necrotic tissue

Code(s):_____

2.195. Laparoscopic orchiopexy for undescended (intra-abdominal) testicle

Code(s):_____

2.196. Vasectomy

Code(s):_____

2.197. Needle biopsy of prostate

Code(s):_____

2.198. Radical retropubic prostatectomy

Code(s):_____

2.199. I&D of Bartholin's abscess

Code(s):_____

2.200. Colposcopy of cervix with cervical curettage

Code(s):_____

2.201. Total abdominal hysterectomy with concurrent Marshall-Marchetti-Krantz urethropexy

Code(s):_____

2.202. Vaginal hysterectomy (weight of uterus 283 grams) with bilateral salpingo-oophorectomy

Code(s):_____

2.203. Vaginal hysterectomy (weight of uterus 230 grams) with enterocele repair

Code(s):_____

2.204. Laparoscopic myomectomy with removal of eight intramural myomas

Code(s):_____

2.205. Ligation of fallopian tubes for elective sterilization

Code(s):_____

2.206. Laparoscopic sterilization procedure with Falope-Rings®, bilateral

Code(s):_____

2.207. Ovarian cystectomy

Code(s):_____

2.208. Catheterization with dye injection for hysterosalpingogram

Code(s):_____

2.209. Penile plethysmography

Code(s):_____

2.210. Third-state hypospadias repair

Code(s):_____

2.211. Laparoscopic fulguration of endometrial implants on the peritoneum and broad ligament

Code(s):_____

Endocrine System

2.212. I&D of infected thyroglossal duct cyst

Code(s):_____

2.213. Percutaneous needle biopsy of thyroid gland

Code(s):_____

2.214. Excision of adenoma of thyroid

Code(s):_____

2.215. Partial right-sided thyroidectomy

Code(s):_____

2.216. Partial right-sided thyroid lobectomy with isthmusectomy and subtotal resection of left thyroid

Code(s):_____

2.217. Left total thyroid lobectomy

Code(s):_____

2.218. Total right-sided thyroid lobectomy with isthmusectomy and subtotal resection of left thyroid

Code(s):_____

2.219. Total thyroidectomy

Code(s):_____

2.220. Total thyroidectomy for thyroid carcinoma with partial neck dissection

Code(s):_____

2.221. Thyroidectomy for thyroid carcinoma with radical neck dissection

Code(s):_____

2.222. Parathyroidectomy

Code(s):_____

2.223. Thyroidectomy (with sternal portion of thyroid) via cervical approach

Code(s):_____

2.224. Excision of recurrent thyroglossal duct cyst

Code(s):_____

2.225. Parathyroidectomy with mediastinal exploration

Code(s):_____

2.226. Transthoracic thymectomy

Code(s):_____

2.227. Exploration and biopsy of adrenal glands, transabdominal

Code(s):_____

2.228. Laparoscopic adrenalectomy

Code(s):_____

2.229. Excision of carotid body tumor and carotid artery

Code(s):_____

2.230. Thymectomy with radical mediastinal dissection

Code(s):_____

2.231. Aspiration of thyroid gland cyst

Code(s):_____

Nervous System

2.232. Cranial burr holes for drainage of subdural hematoma

Code(s):_____

2.233. Decompression craniectomy for treatment of intracranial hypertension

Code(s):_____

2.234. Excision of cerebellopontine angle tumor via craniectomy

Code(s):_____

2.235. Percutaneous transcatheter embolization, brachiocephalic artery

Code(s):_____

2.236. Stereotactic biopsy for suspected intracranial malignancy, with CT guidance

Code(s):_____

2.237. Ventriculoperitoneal shunt procedure

Code(s):_____

2.238. Diagnostic lumbar spinal tap

Code(s):_____

2.239. Implantation of cranial neurostimulator pulse generator

Code(s):_____

2.240. Injection of bupivacaine and Depo-Medrol®, L4 facet

Code(s):_____

2.241. Transforaminal epidural injection of Depo-Medrol, C4–5 interspace

Code(s):_____

2.242. Excision neuroma, digital nerve, right fourth finger. Assign the CPT code and appropriate modifier.

Code(s):_____

2.243. Subtemporal decompression procedure for pseudotumor cerebri

Code(s):_____

2.244. Repair of 20 mm aneurysm, vertebrobasilar circulation

Code(s):_____

2.245. Stereotactic biopsy of intracranial lesion with MR guidance. (Do not assign the radiological supervision and interpretation code.)

Code(s):_____

2.246. Intracranial neuroendoscopy with excision of pituitary tumor

Code(s):_____

2.247. Reprogramming of programmable cerebrospinal fluid shunt

Code(s):_____

2.248. Anterior diskectomy, T2–3 interspace

Code(s):_____

2.249. Injection of lidocaine, brachial plexus

Code(s):_____

2.250. Suture of digital nerves to the left third and fourth fingers. Assign the appropriate modifier(s) in addition to the CPT code.

Code(s):_____

2.251. Phenol injection for destruction of the infraorbital branch of the trigeminal nerve

Code(s):_____

Eye/Ocular Adnexa

2.252. Removal of corneal foreign body using slit lamp

Code(s):_____

2.253. Penetrating keratoplasty, aphakic eye

Code(s):_____

2.254. Radial keratotomy

Code(s):_____

2.255. Extracapsular cataract extraction by phacoemulsification with placement of posterior chamber IOL

Code(s):_____

2.256. Scleral buckle for retinal detachment

Code(s):_____

2.257. YAG laser photocoagulation of diabetic retinopathy

Code(s):_____

2.258. Strabismus surgery with recession of lateral rectus muscle

Code(s):_____

2.259. Strabismus surgery, recession of superior oblique muscle

Code(s):_____

2.260. Strabismus surgery with 6 mm recession of superior rectus muscle and 3 mm recession of inferior rectus muscle, with placement of adjustable suture at inferior rectus

Code(s):_____

2.261. Repair of blepharoptosis by frontalis muscle fascial sling

Code(s):_____

2.262. Repair of entropion by tarsal wedge resection

Code(s):_____

2.263. Dacryocystorhinostomy

Code(s):_____

2.264. Probing of nasolacrimal duct with stent placement

Code(s):_____

2.265. Excision of chalazions (three) from left upper and left lower eyelids

Code(s):_____

2.266. Laser photocoagulation of retina for prophylaxis of retinal detachment

Code(s):_____

2.267. Trabeculectomy ab externo

Code(s):_____

2.268. Enucleation of eyeball with implant, muscle controlled

Code(s):_____

2.269. Removal of foreign body from posterior chamber using magnet

Code(s):_____

2.270. Excision of pterygium with normal conjunctival tissue graft

Code(s):_____

2.271. Pars plana vitrectomy with epiretinal membrane stripping

Code(s):_____

Auditory System

2.272. Removal of exostosis, external ear canal

Code(s):_____

2.273. Myringotomy with aspiration under general anesthesia

Code(s):_____

2.274. Myringotomy with PE tube insertion

Code(s):_____

2.275. Tympanoplasty with mastoidectomy with ossicular chain reconstruction

Code(s):_____

2.276. Decompression of internal auditory canal

Code(s):_____

2.277. Drainage of abscess of external ear canal

Code(s):_____

2.278. Removal of bug from external ear canal using conscious sedation

Code(s):_____

2.279. Pin-back procedure for protruding ear

Code(s):_____

2.280. Removal of impacted cerumen, bilateral

Code(s):_____

2.281. Tympanoplasty without mastoidectomy, with placement of PORP

Code(s):_____

2.282. Tympanostomy with ventilation tube insertion under general anesthesia

Code(s):_____

2.283. Transmastoid excision of glomus tumor of ear

Code(s):_____

2.284. Repair of tympanic membrane perforation using synthetic patch

Code(s):_____

2.285. Stapedotomy with footplate drillout

Code(s):_____

2.286. Implantation of cochlear device

Code(s):_____

2.287. Mastoid obliteration

Code(s):_____

2.288. Transcanal labyrinthectomy with mastoidectomy

Code(s):_____

2.289. Removal and replacement of electromagnetic hearing aid in temporal bone

Code(s):_____

2.290. Debridement of mastoid cavity under general anesthesia

Code(s):_____

2.291. Removal of ventilation tubes under general anesthesia

Code(s):_____

Radiology Services

2.292. True or false? Code 76856 Ultrasound, pelvic (nonobstetrical), B scan and/ or real time with image documentation, complete, can be used to describe examinations of either the male or female pelvis.

a. True
b. False

2.293. X-ray of mandible, five views

Code(s):_____

2.294. X-ray of soft tissues of the neck for foreign body

Code(s):_____

2.295. CT brain scan, with and without contrast

Code(s):_____

2.296. Chest x-ray, AP and lateral

Code(s):_____

2.297. MRI of chest with contrast

Code(s):_____

2.298. X-ray, neck, six views, including oblique and flexion

Code(s):_____

2.299. Cervical myelogram, radiological supervision and interpretation

Code(s):_____

2.300. Shoulder arthrogram, radiological supervision and interpretation

Code(s):_____

2.301. X-ray of fractured hip in the operating room to confirm reduction

Code(s):_____

2.302. Barium enema with KUB

Code(s):_____

2.303. Percutaneous transhepatic cholangiography, radiological supervision and interpretation

Code(s):_____

2.304. Intravenous pyelogram with KUB and tomograms

Code(s):_____

2.305. Left external carotid angiography, selective, radiological supervision and interpretation

Code(s):_____

2.306. Ultrasound, pregnant uterus, first trimester

Code(s):_____

2.307. Nonselective pulmonary angiography, radiological supervision and interpretation

Code(s):_____

2.308. SPECT bone scan

Code(s):_____

2.309. Percutaneous transcatheter introduction of vascular stent, external iliac artery, radiological supervision and interpretation

Code(s):_____

2.310. Mammographic guidance for preoperative needle placement in breast, radiological supervision and interpretation

Code(s):_____

2.311. Retroperitoneal ultrasound

Code(s):_____

2.312. Acute GI blood loss imaging scan

Code(s):_____

Pathology/Laboratory Services

2.313. The symbol, ~, added to the Laboratory and Pathology section, means:

    a. This is an add-on laboratory code.
    b. The code is sex specific.
    c. This code should only be reported for Medicare patients.
    d. FDA approval of the vaccine is pending.

2.314. Mr. Smith is seen in his PCP's office for his annual physical examination. He has a digital rectal examination and is given three small cards to take home and return with fecal samples. Assign the appropriate CPT code to report this occult blood sampling.

    a. 82270
    b. 82271
    c. 82272
    d. 82274

2.315. True or false? The nuclear magnetic resonance test, reported with new code 83704, is used to manage the cardiovascular disease risk of patients with elevated triglycerides and diabetes.

    a. True
    b. False

2.316. Code 87900 Infectious agent drug susceptibility phenotype prediction using regularly updated genotypic bioinformatics is used in the management of patients with what disease?

    a. Cancer patients on toxic chemotherapy agents
    b. HIV patients on antiretroviral therapy
    c. Tuberculosis patients on rifampin therapy
    d. Organ transplant patients on immunosuppressive therapy

2.317. CPK isoenzymes

    Code(s):_____

2.318. Iron-binding capacity

    Code(s):_____

2.319. Screen for mercury

    Code(s):_____

2.320. Spinal fluid pH

    Code(s):_____

2.321. Protein, by refractometry

Code(s):_____

2.322. Urine sodium

Code(s):_____

2.323. Automated CBC with automated differential

Code(s):_____

2.324. Lee-White clotting time

Code(s):_____

2.325. Protime

Code(s):_____

2.326. ANA titer

Code(s):_____

2.327. VDRL

Code(s):_____

2.328. HBsAb

Code(s):_____

2.329. Chlamydia antibody, IgM

Code(s):_____

2.330. Erythrocyte sedimentation rate, automated

Code(s):_____

2.331. Surgical pathology, examination (gross and microscopic) of arterial biopsy

Code(s):_____

2.332. Surgical pathology, examination (gross and microscopic) of breast and regional lymph nodes

Code(s):_____

2.333. Lyme disease antibody

Code(s):_____

2.334. Protoporphyrin screen

Code(s):_____

2.335. Infrared spectroscopy of renal calculus

Code(s):_____

2.336. Blood culture

Code(s):_____

Medicine

2.337. An infusion that lasts less than 15 minutes would be reported with a(n) _____ code.

   a. Intravenous infusion
   b. Intravenous piggyback
   c. Intravenous or intra-arterial push
   d. Intravenous hydration

2.338. Codes 90760 and 90761 are used to report infusion of:

   a. Chemotherapeutic agents
   b. Sequential drugs of the same drug family
   c. Hormonal antineoplastics
   d. Prepackaged fluids and/or electrolytes

2.339. The code for moderate conscious sedation is determined by:

   a. Who administers the sedation
   b. The age of the patient
   c. The duration of the sedation
   d. All of the above

2.340. A prostate cancer patient is seen in the office for infusion of luteinizing hormone-releasing hormone agonist therapy, given subcutaneously. Assign the appropriate CPT code.

   a. 96401
   b. 96402
   c. 96413
   d. 96405

2.341. True or false? The "initial service" code under Hydration, Infusions and Chemotherapy is chosen based upon the first substance infused.

   a. True
   b. False

2.342. Select the appropriate code(s) to report an injection of rabies immune globulin performed under direct physician supervision.

    a. 90772
    b. 90471
    c. 90375, 90772
    d. 90375, 90473

2.343. Psychotherapy that involves the use of physical aids and nonverbal communication to overcome barriers to therapeutic intervention is called _____ psychotherapy.

2.344. Individual psychotherapy, inpatient hospital, 50 minutes

    Code(s):_____

2.345. Esophageal motility study with acid perfusion testing

    Code(s):_____

2.346. Fluorescein angiography

    Code(s):_____

2.347. Reprogramming of cochlear implant device, patient three years of age

    Code(s):_____

2.348. Transcatheter placement of coronary artery stent, right coronary artery

    Code(s):_____

2.349. EKG, physician interpretation and report, using hospital equipment

    Code(s):_____

2.350. Combined right heart catheterization and retrograde left heart catheterization via femoral artery approach

    Code(s):_____

2.351. Electronic analysis of pacing cardioverter-defibrillator, dual chamber, with reprogramming

    Code(s):_____

2.352. Duplex scan of bilateral lower extremity arteries

    Code(s):_____

2.353. Pulmonary stress testing

    Code(s):_____

2.354. EEG, awake and asleep

Code(s):_____

2.355. Therapeutic exercises, 23 minutes

Code(s):_____

2.356. Chiropractic manipulation of the spine, cervical, thoracic, lumbar, and sacral regions

Code(s):_____

2.357. EMG testing of both upper extremities and related paraspinal musculature

Code(s):_____

2.358. Bronchospasm evaluation

Code(s):_____

2.359. Lymphatic drainage (15 minutes of manual traction)

Code(s):_____

2.360. Chemotherapy administration via IV push

Code(s):_____

2.361. Comprehensive electrophysiologic testing with induction of arrhythmia

Code(s):_____

Modifiers

2.362. In physician professional fee coding, when multiple procedures other than evaluation and management services are provided on the same date by the same provider, modifier _____ should be appended to the second and all subsequent procedures.

2.363. The modifier used to report therapeutic interventional procedures on the right coronary artery is_____.

2.364. Which of the following circumstances can be described by the use of a HCPCS modifier?

    a. A service has been increased or reduced.
    b. Only part of a service was performed.
    c. A service was provided more than once.
    d. All of the above

2.365. A radiologist interprets x-rays for a community hospital. The equipment belongs to the hospital. What modifier should the radiologist append to his CPT codes? _____

2.366. A patient underwent repair of an ectropion of the left upper eyelid by tarsal wedge technique. Assign the appropriate CPT code and modifier(s).
_____

2.367. A pediatric thoracic and cardiovascular surgeon performs a curative procedure on an infant but does not see the child again. Instead, a pediatric cardiologist does all follow-up. What modifier should the surgeon append to his CPT procedure code? _____

2.368. A surgeon performs a palmar fasciotomy for Dupuytren's contracture of the right hand by open technique. Assign the appropriate CPT code(s) and modifier(s)._____

2.369. A patient is scheduled for a colonoscopy, but due to sudden drop in blood pressure, the procedure is canceled just as the scope is introduced into the rectum. Because of moderately severe mental retardation, the patient is given a general anesthetic prior to the procedure. How should this procedure be coded by the hospital?

   a. Assign the code for a colonoscopy with modifier -74.
   b. Assign the code for a colonoscopy with modifier -52.
   c. Assign no code because no procedure was performed.
   d. Assign an anesthesia code only.

2.370. When clinical laboratory tests are repeated on the same day, what modifier should be assigned? _____

2.371. When a surgeon performs a procedure and a separately identifiable evaluation and management service on the same date, how should codes and modifiers be assigned?

   a. Assign a code for the procedure only.
   b. Assign a code for the procedure and one for the evaluation and management service without any modifiers.
   c. Assign a code for the procedure and one for the evaluation and management service, with modifier -25 appended to the evaluation and management code.
   d. Assign a code for the procedure and one for the evaluation and management service, with modifier -25 appended to both the evaluation and management code and the procedure code.

2.372. When absolutely identical procedures are performed on both members of a set of paired organs, such as kidneys, what modifier is assigned?
_____

2.373. Planned rigid proctosigmoidoscopy with removal of foreign body under conscious sedation, procedure not completed due to hypotension. How would the physician report this?

Code(s):_____

2.374. When a surgeon sees a patient during the postoperative period from one surgery for an unrelated condition and performs evaluation and management services, what modifier should be reported with the evaluation and management code? _____

2.375. When a physician performs a consultation as a required second opinion for an HMO, what modifier should be appended to the consultation code?

_____

2.376. When a patient is seen in two hospital outpatient departments in one day, what modifier should be appended to the second evaluation and management code to ensure appropriate reimbursement? _____

2.377. When a hospital provides ambulance services by arrangement with a transport company, what modifier should be appended to the codes for ambulance services? _____

2.378. Because of language barriers and patient agitation, the performance of a consultation takes approximately twice as long as the "usual" time for a level 5 service. What modifier should be attached to the consultation code to reflect this situation? _____

2.379. In addition to the claim submitted by the surgeon, the assistant surgeon also bills for his or her services. What modifier does the assistant surgeon attach to the procedure code? _____

2.380. Sex reassignment surgery (55980 or 55970) is a complex procedure that requires a team of surgeons. What modifier should each participating surgeon attach to the surgery code? _____

2.381. Some reconstructive plastic surgical procedures are performed in multiple stages. What modifier should the surgeon report when the patient is returned to surgery for a planned-staged procedure?

_____

Category III Codes

2.382. Which of the following statements about category III CPT codes is true?

   a. They are temporary.
   b. They are updated more frequently than the rest of CPT.
   c. They are intended to allow for the coding of new technologies, services, and procedures.
   d. All of the above

2.383. Both a regular CPT unlisted procedure code and a category III code may exist to report the same procedure. Which code(s) should be reported?

    a. Report the CPT unlisted procedure code.
    b. Report the category III code.
    c. Report both the CPT unlisted procedure code and the category III code.
    d. Report the category III code with modifier -59.

2.384. After five years, all category III codes:

    a. Will be archived unless there is evidence that a temporary code is still needed
    b. Will be automatically renewed for another five years
    c. Will be automatically retired
    d. Will be replaced with a regular CPT code

2.385. Upper GI endoscopy with suturing of the esophagogastric junction

    Code(s):_____

2.386. Holotranscobalamin, quantitative

    Code(s):_____

2.387. Whole-body photography for monitoring of patients at high risk for familial melanoma or dysplastic nevus syndrome

    Code(s):_____

2.388. Speculoscopy

    Code(s):_____

2.389. How frequently are category III codes updated?

    a. Annually
    b. Semiannually
    c. Every two years
    d. Every four months

2.390. Antiprothrombin antibody

    Code(s):_____

2.391. DEXA body composition study

    Code(s):_____

2.392. Transvaginal insertion of fetal oximetry sensor

    Code(s):_____

2.393. Carbon monoxide expired gas analysis

    Code(s):_____

2.394. Anterior diskectomy and total arthroplasty, utilizing artificial disk, of C-3 and C-4.

Code(s):_____

2.395. Category III codes can be used by what groups of providers?

    a. Hospital outpatient providers only
    b. Physicians only
    c. Hospitals, physicians, insurers, health services researchers
    d. Medicare-approved providers only

2.396. Electrical impedance breast scan

Code(s):_____

2.397. Photocoagulation of macular drusen

Code(s):_____

2.398. Endoscopic lysis of epidural adhesions

Code(s):_____

2.399. Unilateral percutaneous renal tumor ablation using cryotherapy

Code(s): _____

2.400. Direct measurement of intermediate density lipoproteins

Code(s):_____

2.401. Cerebral perfusion study using CT with contrast

Code(s):_____

Review Questions

2.402. Surgical knee arthroscopy with medial meniscectomy and lateral retinacular release

Code(s):_____

2.403. Functional endoscopic sinus surgery with bilateral anterior ethmoidectomy and bilateral maxillary antrostomy with curettage of maxillary polyps

Code(s):_____

2.404. Excision of 2.3 cm (including margins) squamous cell skin cancer from the right arm with closure of the resultant defect with rotational flap advancement

Code(s):_____

2.405. Repair of multiple lacerations of the right upper extremity, including 7.6 cm laceration of the upper arm, closed with single layer of 3-0 Dexon; 5.4 cm laceration of the upper arm requiring layered closure; 3.5 cm laceration of the dorsum of the right hand, closed in layers; and 16 cm laceration of the forearm, closed in a single layer of 3-0 Dexon

Code(s):_____

2.406. Spinal fusion, L2–3 and L3–4, with laminectomy and placement of bone graft harvested from sacral spinous processes

Code(s):_____

2.407. Decompression fasciotomy of the forearm, flexor and extensor compartments, with debridement of necrotic muscle and nerve tissue

Code(s):_____

2.408. Banding of the pulmonary artery in a four-week-old infant weighing 3,650 grams. Assign modifier(s) as appropriate.

Code(s):_____

2.409. CABG using vein grafts to the left anterior descending coronary artery and internal mammary artery graft to the lateral circumflex coronary artery. Due to severe lower extremity vascular disease, vein was harvested from the right basilic vein.

Code(s):_____

2.410. Transcatheter placement of stent, abdominal aorta, using intravascular ultrasound monitoring. Assign both surgical and radiological supervision and interpretation codes.

Code(s):_____

2.411. Diagnostic upper GI endoscopy to the jejunum, with injection of esophageal varices, and biopsy of gastrojejunal junction and body of stomach

Code(s):_____

2.412. Proctosigmoidoscopy with removal of one polyp by hot biopsy forceps and biopsy of hemorrhagic area

Code(s):_____

2.413. Bronchoscopy with tracheal biopsy, and dilation and placement of tracheal stent

Code(s):_____

2.414. Needle biopsy of inguinal lymph nodes

Code(s):_____

2.415. ERCP with manipulation and removal of stone from the common bile duct

Code(s):_____

2.416. Cystourethroscopy with resection of bladder tumor, 2.3 cm in diameter, and ureteral catheterization with manipulation of ureteric stone

Code(s):_____

2.417. Radical perineal prostatectomy with complete bilateral pelvic lymph node dissection

Code(s):_____

2.418. Colposcopy of cervix with endocervical curettage

Code(s):_____

2.419. VBAC, including routine prenatal and postpartum care

Code(s):_____

2.420. Transnasal hypophysectomy

Code(s):_____

2.421. Repair of laceration of cornea, penetrating, with excision of devitalized uveal tissue

Code(s):_____

2.422. Right shoulder arthrogram. Assign surgical and radiological supervision and interpretation codes, as well as any appropriate modifiers for hospital reporting.

Code(s):_____

2.423. Liver SPECT with flow

Code(s):_____

2.424. High-sensitivity C-reactive protein

Code(s):_____

2.425. TEE, placement of probe

Code(s):_____

2.426. IM injection of HepB-Hib vaccine

Code(s):_____

Chapter 3

HCPCS Level II Coding

> **Note:** These exercises are intended for use with the 2006 version of the Healthcare Common Procedure Coding System (HCPCS) Level II codes. HCPCS codes are revised annually by the Centers for Medicare and Medicaid Services (CMS) and become effective January 1 each calendar year. Books are available from a variety of publishers. An electronic file is available for downloading from the Internet at www.cms.gov/providers/pufdownload/#alphanu
>
> **Instructions:** Circle the correct answer, fill in the blank, or assign the correct code(s) for each of the following exercise items.

Drugs

3.1. HCPCS level II contains codes for drugs that are administered:

    a. Subcutaneously
    b. Intramuscularly
    c. Intravenously
    d. All of the above

3.2. Injection Unasyn®, 1.5 grams

    Code(s):_____

3.3. Injection baclofen, 50 mcg intrathecal

    Code(s):_____

3.4. Injection Botox®, 3 units

    Code(s):_____

3.5. Injection Anzemet®, 10 mg

    Code(s):_____

3.6. Injection RhoGam®, 300 mcg

Code(s):_____

3.7. Injection Cytosar-U®, 100 mg

Code(s):_____

3.8. Injection Mitomycin, 40 mg

Code(s):_____

3.9. Injection Herceptin®, 10 mg

Code(s):_____

3.10. Intra-articular injection of Synvisc®, 16 mg, left knee

Code(s):_____

Supplies

3.11. Low osmolar contrast medium, 200 mg of iodine

Code(s):_____

3.12. Blood tubing, venous, for hemodialysis

Code(s):_____

3.13. Urinary ostomy pouch with barrier attached

Code(s):_____

3.14. Alginate dressing, 36 sq in pad

Code(s):_____

3.15. Radiopharmaceutical agent Technetium-99 medronate (^{99m}Tc), 16 mCurie

Code(s):_____

3.16. Therapeutic radiopharmaceutical agent Strontium 89 chloride, 1 mCurie

Code(s):_____

3.17. Tracheal suction, closed system, for 72 or more hours' use

Code(s):_____

3.18. Blood glucose reagent strips for home glucose monitor, bottle of 50 strips

Code(s):_____

3.19. Distilled water used with nebulizer, 1,000 ml

Code(s):_____

3.20. Surgical trays used in physician office surgery

Code(s):_____

Ambulance

3.21. The single-digit ambulance modifier designating place of pickup/drop-off of the patient's house is:

Code(s):_____

3.22. The two-digit modifier to indicate that a patient was taken from the acute hospital to a skilled nursing facility by ambulance is:

Code(s):_____

3.23. Basic life support ambulance services

Code(s):_____

3.24. Ground ambulance transport services are reported:

a. Per trip
b. Per mile
c. Per minute of travel time
d. Per hour of travel time

3.25. Helicopter transport, per mile

Code(s):_____

3.26. Because of the patient's condition, an additional EMT is required for the transport. What is the code for the presence of the extra attendant?

_____

3.27. Ambulance waiting time is measured in:

a. Minutes
b. Hours
c. Half hours
d. 10-minute increments

3.28. Routine disposable supplies used during a basic life support transport

Code(s):_____

3.29. Neonatal transport

Code(s):_____

3.30. Oxygen administered during advanced life support transport

Code(s):_____

Durable Medical Equipment

3.31. Rental of portable liquid oxygen system

Code(s):_____

3.32. Totally electric hospital bed, without mattress, and alternating pressure mattress for hospital bed

Code(s):_____

3.33. Cycler dialysis machine for peritoneal dialysis

Code(s):_____

3.34. Portable whirlpool

Code(s):_____

3.35. Wheelchair, amputee, with detachable arms and detachable, swing-away footrests

Code(s):_____

3.36. Adult transport chair

Code(s):_____

3.37. Wheelchair accessories tray

Code(s):_____

3.38. Traction frame for lower extremity, attached to footboard

Code(s):_____

3.39. Four-lead TENS unit

Code(s):_____

3.40. Recording apnea monitor

Code(s):_____

Procedures/Services

3.41. Glaucoma screening for high-risk patients

Code(s):_____

3.42. Colorectal cancer screening by barium enema

Code(s):_____

3.43. Diagnostic mammography, unilateral

Code(s):_____

3.44. PET scanning, whole body, for diagnosis of esophageal carcinoma, for restaging

Code(s):_____

3.45. Direct hospital observation admission for patient with diagnosis of CHF, chest pain, or asthma

Code(s):_____

3.46. Transcatheter placement of drug-eluting stent, coronary artery, percutaneous

Code(s):_____

3.47. Services of clinical social worker in home health setting per 15 minutes

Code(s):_____

3.48. Diabetes self-management training, group session, per 30 minutes

Code(s):_____

3.49. Trimming of dystrophic nails

Code(s):_____

3.50. SEXA bone density study, appendicular skeleton

Code(s):_____

Part II
Intermediate Coding Exercises

Chapter 4

Case Studies from Inpatient Health Records

> **Note:** Even though the specific cases are divided by setting, most of the information pertaining to the diagnosis is applicable to most settings. If you practice or apply codes in a particular type of setting, you may find additional information in other sections of this publication that may be pertinent to you.
>
> Every effort has been made to follow current recognized coding guidelines and principles, as well as nationally recognized reporting guidelines. The material presented may differ from some health plan requirements for reporting. The ICD-9-CM codes used are effective through September 30, 2007, and the HCPCS (CPT and HCPCS Level II) codes are in effect through December 31, 2006. The current standard transactions and code sets named in HIPAA have been utilized, which require ICD-9-CM Volume III procedure codes for inpatients.
>
> **Instructions:**
>
> Assign all applicable ICD-9-CM codes, including E codes, appropriate for the setting for the case studies presented. Some of the cases provide multiple-choice answers, and the reader must select the appropriate code set. In other instances, the reader is expected to assign codes without any prompts.
>
> The scenarios are based on selected excerpts from health records without reproducing the entire health record. However, in practice, the coding professional should have access to the entire health record. Health records are analyzed and codes are selected only with the physician's complete and appropriate documentation available. According to coding guidelines, codes are not assigned without physician documentation.
>
> The objective of the cases and scenarios reproduced in this publication is to provide practice in assigning correct codes, not necessarily to emulate full-record analysis. For example, the reader may be asked to assign codes based only on an operative report, when in real practice a coder has access to documentation in the entire medical record.

Disorders of the Blood and Blood-Forming Organs

4.1.   This 45-year-old male underwent colon resection for carcinoma of the transverse colon. The physician progress note on postop day 2 states anemia. How is the anemia coded?

a. 285.1
b. 998.11
c. 998.11, 285.1
d. Unable to code; the physician must be queried.

4.2.   The discharge diagnoses included for this 82-year-old female patient admitted for acute exacerbation of COPD are: neutropenia, anemia, pancytopenia, and thrombocytopenia. A blood transfusion was given. What codes are assigned for this case?

a. 491.21, 284.1, 99.03
b. 491.21, 284.1, 285.9, 288.00, 287.5, 99.03
c. 496, 284.1, 99.03
d. 491.21, 285.9, 288.00, 287.5, 99.02

4.3.   This 35-year-old female patient has carcinoma of the upper-outer left breast. She had a lumpectomy performed and a sentinel lymph node biopsy of the axillary lymph node. The pathology report for the lymph node states no pathological change. What codes are assigned in this case?

Code(s):_____

4.4.   An eight-year-old male hemophiliac is admitted with severe blood loss anemia due to uncontrolled bleeding. He is given clotting factor and six units of whole blood. Which of the following answers would be correct?

a. 286.0, 99.06, 99.03
b. 285.1, 286.0, 99.06, 99.03
c. 286.0, 285.1, 99.06, 99.03
d. 285.1, 99.06, 99.03

4.5.   What code(s) is/are assigned for a patient admitted for chemotherapy for drug induced aplastic anemia?

a. V58.11, 284.8
b. V58.12, 284.8
c. 284.8, V58.11
d. 284.8

Disorders of the Cardiovascular System

4.6. When a diagnostic statement lists hypertension and chronic kidney disease, which of the following coding guidelines applies?

   a. The conditions are reported with two separate codes unless the physician specifically states that there is a cause-and-effect relationship.
   b. Code 403.9X is assigned, with an additional code to identify the stage of chronic kidney disease.
   c. A cause-and-effect relationship is never assumed.
   d. Code 403.9X is assigned, with an additional code to specify the type of hypertension.

4.7. This 52-year-old male was admitted to City Hospital with chest pain that was determined to be due to an acute inferior wall myocardial infarction. He was subsequently transferred to Anytown Medical Center for cardiac catheterization. A right and left heart catheterization with Judkins coronary angiography and right and left angiocardiography were performed. He was also treated for atrial fibrillation and discharged on the fourth day in stable condition. What codes are reported at Anytown Medical Center?

   Code(s):_____

4.8. A patient is readmitted to the acute care hospital from a long-term care facility for treatment of heart failure. She had an acute anterior wall MI four weeks ago. She was placed in the intensive care unit and monitored on telemetry. She was also found to have UTI due to E. coli. After intense drug therapy, she continued to improve and was transferred back to the long-term care facility. The acute systolic and diastolic heart failure was improved, but she will be monitored. What codes are assigned in this case?

   a. 428.21, 428.31, 410.12, 599.0, 041.4, 89.54
   b. 428.41, 410.12, 599.0, 041.4, 89.54
   c. 428.0, 412, 599.0, 041.4, 89.54
   d. 428.41, 410.11, 599.0, 041.4, 89.54

4.9. A patient with severe ASHD of native arteries and severe COPD was admitted for CABG × 4 with cardiopulmonary bypass. Postoperatively, the patient developed pulmonary emboli that required treatment and extended the inpatient stay.

   Which of the following is the correct code assignment?

   a. 414.01, 997.3, 496, 36.14, 39.61
   b. 414.01, 415.11, 496, 36.14, 39.61
   c. 415.11, 414.01, 496, 36.14, 39.61
   d. 414.01, 997.3, 415.11, 496, 36.14, 39.61

4.10. The following was documented in the history and physical:

This patient was admitted with a diagnosis of acute myocardial infarction. He was hospitalized for pneumonia last year and two years ago had surgery for a bleeding gastric ulcer. Additional history is that he was diagnosed five years ago with Parkinson's disease, which is getting progressively worse. He is being treated with levodopa. History also notes emphysema being treated with bronchodilators and corticosteroids.

Discharge Summary: The discharge summary repeats the information in the H&P, plus adds the following information. During the hospital stay, the patient developed congestive heart failure confirmed by x-ray.

Discharge Diagnoses: Acute myocardial infarction, Parkinson's disease, congestive heart failure, emphysema, history of pneumonia, and bleeding gastric ulcer.

What conditions are coded in this example?

a. Acute myocardial infarction, congestive heart failure, Parkinson's disease, emphysema
b. Acute myocardial infarction, congestive heart failure
c. Acute myocardial infarction, congestive heart failure, Parkinson's disease, emphysema, pneumonia, bleeding ulcer
d. Acute myocardial infarction, pneumonia, congestive heart failure, emphysema

4.11. From the health record of a cardiac service patient:

Discharge Summary

Admit Date: 1/9/XX

Discharge Date: 1/12/XX

Final Diagnoses: 1. Coronary artery disease
                       2. Sick sinus syndrome

Procedures: 1. Permanent AV sequential pacemaker insertion
                       2. Percutaneous transluminal coronary angioplasty

History of Present Illness: The patient is a 60-year-old female who was admitted to another hospital on 1/8/XX, after experiencing tachycardia. There she underwent a cardiac catheterization, showing the presence of severe single-vessel coronary artery disease. The patient has a history of sick sinus syndrome. She was transferred to our hospital to undergo a percutaneous transluminal angioplasty.

Physical Examination: No physical abnormalities were found on the cardiovascular examination. Pulse 50, blood pressure 100/66. HEENT: PERRLA, faint carotid bruits. Lungs: Clear to percussion and auscultation. Heart: Normal sinus rhythm with a 2.6 systolic ejection murmur. Extremities and abdomen were negative.

Laboratory Data: Unremarkable

Hospital Course: To manage the patient's sick sinus syndrome, a permanent AV sequential pacemaker was implanted on 1/9. On 1/10, the patient underwent a PTCA without complications, and good results were obtained. Postoperatively, the patient was stable and was subsequently discharged. Patient was discharged on the following medications: Cardizem®, 30 mg p.o. q 6 hours; ASA, 5 grains q. a.m.; Metamucil® and Colace® p.r.n.; Nitro paste ½ inch q. 6 hours.

Which of the following answers is the correct code assignment?

a. 427.0, 414.01, 00.66, 37.83, 37.72
b. 414.01, 427.81, 00.66, 37.73
c. 427.81, 414.01, 00.66, 37.83, 37.72
d. 414.01, 427.81, 00.66, 37.83, 37.72

4.12. This 62-year-old male patient was admitted to the hospital with progressive episodes of chest pain determined to be crescendo angina. He had myocardial infarction 5 years ago and progressively has been having more frequent episodes of chest pain. During the hospital stay, he was given IV nitroglycerin and was subsequently placed on Cardizem for further treatment of his angina. He is scheduled for cardiac cath next week because he refused to have it performed during this admission. No other complications arose during the hospitalization. What is the code assignment?

a. 411.0, 412
b. 413.9, 412
c. 411.1, 412
d. 413.0, 412

4.13. This 55-year-old female patient is admitted with occlusion of the cerebral arteries resulting in an infarction. The patient suffered a stroke two years ago with residual hemiplegia affecting her dominant side. What would be the correct code assignment for this case?

Code(s):_____

4.14. What code is assigned to show the long-term use of aspirin in a patient with osteoarthritis and heart disease?

a. V58.64
b. V58.61
c. V58.69
d. V58.66

4.15. What code(s) is/are assigned for PTCA of two arteries using three stents and infusion of thrombolytic?

a. 00.66
b. 00.66, 00.47, 00.41, 99.10
c. 00.66, 36.06, 00.47, 00.41, 99.10
d. 36.02, 36.06

Disorders of the Digestive System

4.16.   This 44-year-old male patient is known to have diverticulitis of the colon. He has noticed melena occasionally for the past week. The initial impression was that this is bleeding from diverticulitis. Patient was scheduled for colonoscopy. Colonoscopy identified the cause of the bleeding to be angiodysplasia of the ascending colon. What are the codes assigned for this case?

Code(s):_____

4.17.   The patient was admitted because of severe abdominal pain. There has been a history of abdominal pain and some bleeding, but never this severe. Because of the symptoms, the patient underwent emergency surgery to repair the perforation in the antrum of the stomach by suturing. The physician states: acute peptic ulcer with perforation and bleeding. What codes are assigned for this case?

Code(s):_____

4.18.   This patient with chronic systolic congestive heart failure was admitted because of melena. Patient had EGD with biopsy. No other findings were found to determine the source of the melena. What codes are assigned in this case?

Code(s):_____

4.19.   A patient was seen in the ER with severe abdominal cramping, nausea and vomiting, and diarrhea. She states that she ate turkey salad several hours before these symptoms developed. The patient has had the symptoms for about 20 hours. Lab tests show severe dehydration. She is admitted for IV therapy. Diagnosis: Dehydration, Salmonella gastroenteritis, abdominal cramping, nausea, vomiting, and diarrhea. What codes are assigned in this case?

Code(s):_____

4.20.   A patient with hypertension, COPD, and end stage renal disease is admitted for bilateral inguinal hernia repair. The H&P states that the left side is recurrent. The operative report states that the surgeon repaired left direct and right indirect inguinal hernias with mesh. What is the correct code assignment?

Code(s):_____

4.21.   An 80-year-old hypertensive patient was admitted to the hospital for cholecystectomy. The patient underwent an open cholecystectomy with exploration of the common duct and choledocholithotomy. Final diagnostic statement: Acute and chronic cholecystitis with choledocholithiasis and cholelithiasis. Correct code assignment would be:

Code(s):_____

4.22. This 58-year-old patient recently had biopsy done showing adenocarcinoma of the sigmoid colon. He is admitted now for resection of the sigmoid colon. An end-to-end anastomosis was performed. CT scan shows metastasis to the liver. What codes are assigned in this case?

Code(s):_____

Endocrine, Nutritional and Metabolic Diseases, and Immunity Disorders

4.23. The patient is a 78-year-old male with severe congestive heart failure who was admitted because of nocturnal dyspnea, orthopnea. He also has type II diabetes mellitus, which is maintained on Diabinese®. During this stay he was given insulin to control his blood sugars. He also has hypertension, treated with Accupril®.

Discharge diagnosis: Congestive heart failure; type II diabetes, uncontrolled; hypertension

What are the correct codes?

a. 250.00, 428.0, 401.9
b. 428.0, 250.02, 401.9
c. 428.0, 250.03, 401.9
d. 428.0, 250.82, 401.9

4.24. This patient, who has type II diabetes, is admitted because of diabetic coma. He has nephrotic syndrome due to the diabetes and gangrene of several toes. What codes would be assigned?

a. 250.30, 250.40, 581.81, 250.70, 785.4
b. 250.30, 581.81, 785.4
c. 250.30, 250.41, 581.81, 785.4
d. 250.31, 250.41, 250.71

4.25. The following information is contained in the health record.

Chief Complaint: History of nausea with severe vomiting for the past two to three days. Type I diabetes mellitus because patient was 12 years old at time of onset.

Hospital Course: This 31-year-old male patient has a history of type I diabetes mellitus and is on 15 units of NPH and 10 of Regular in the morning, and 10 units of NPH and 5 of Regular in the evening. The patient started having symptoms of nausea. The patient at the same time had increased frequency of urination and polydipsia. The patient was severely dehydrated on admission. There was no evidence of thrombophlebitis, varicosities, or edema on examination of the extremities. The patient was hydrated and, as a result, his blood sugar decreased from more than 600 to normal levels. The patient was discharged with the diagnosis of diabetic ketoacidosis, type I, uncontrolled.

What code(s) are assigned for this admission?

Code(s):_____

4.26.   From the health record of a patient requiring thyroid surgery:

History: Patient is a 50-year-old female who noted a swelling in the neck. Workup was done, which included thyroid scan and thyroid sonogram, revealing moderate enlargement of the left lobe of the thyroid gland measuring 1.1 × 2.2 cm, a solid nodule at the anterior aspect of the mid of the left lobe of thyroid measuring approximately 1 × 1.9 cm, a small cyst in the middle of the left lobe of the thyroid measuring 2.4 cm; normal right lobe of the thyroid; a small cyst in the mid of the right lobe measuring 2.3 mm. Thyroid scan showed hot nodule, which is more often than not negative for malignancy. Had fine needle aspiration strongly suspicious for papillary carcinoma.

Impression: Papillary carcinoma of the thyroid

Report of Operation:

Preoperative Diagnosis: Steroid nodule left lobe, rule out papillary carcinoma

Postoperative Diagnosis: Papillary carcinoma of thyroid

Procedure: Left thyroid lobectomy with isthmectomy and frozen section. Subsequently, patient underwent total thyroid right lobectomy.

Anesthesia: General endotracheal

Estimated Blood Loss: 50 cc, Replacement: IV fluids, sponge count, needle count times two correct

Technique: After patient was well anesthetized with general endotracheal anesthesia, a sand bag was placed underneath the shoulder blades. The neck was extended and stabilized and placed on a foam head pillow. Entire neck and anterior chest was prepped and draped in the usual manner. The skin incision site was marked with 2-0 VICRYL® suture with pressure. Preempt analgesia was obtained with infiltration of .25 percent Marcaine®. Transverse skin incision was made in the anterior part of the neck, which was deepened through the subcutaneous tissue and the platysma. Upper and lower flaps were raised, upper flap up to the thyroid cartilage, lower flap up to the sternal notch. Hemostasis obtained with cautery as well as 3-0 VICRYL sutures. Midline fascia was incised. Strap muscles on the left side were separated from the underlying thyroid gland. Strap muscles were retracted laterally with a Green retractor. Middle thyroid veins were identified, divided between the clamps, ligated with 3-0 VICRYL suture. Patient was noted to have palpable thyroid nodule on the left lower part of the thyroid gland. Superior thyroid vessels were identified. External of the superior laryngeal nerve was identified and protected. Superior thyroid vessels were divided close to the thyroid clamp between the Mixter clamp and ligated with 2-0 VICRYL suture. Recurrent laryngeal nerve was identified and protected throughout the procedure. Superior and inferior parathyroids were identified, protected with their vasculature. Inferior thyroid vessels were divided close to the thyroid capsule after its branching to preserve the blood supply to the parathyroid gland. Isthmus was divided between the clamps, and the entire thyroid lobe was removed and sent for frozen section, which was reported to be a papillary carcinoma. After the pathology report, the decision was made to proceed with the total thyroidectomy, which was carried out in the following manner:

Strap muscles on the right side were separated from the right thyroid gland. Middle thyroid vessels were divided between the clamps, ligated with 3-0 VICRYL suture. Superior and inferior thyroid poles were identified. Superior thyroid vessels were divided close to the upper pole. During the procedure, the external branch of the superior laryngeal nerve was identified and protected. The divided vessels were ligated with 2-0 VICRYL suture. Recurrent laryngeal nerve was identified and protected. Inferior and superior parathyroid glands were identified and protected with vasculature. Inferior thyroid vessel branches were divided between the clamps, thereby the blood supply to the parathyroid glands was preserved. Care was taken to protect the recurrent laryngeal nerve throughout the procedure. The right lobe of the thyroid was completely removed after satisfactory hemostasis. No drains were placed. The strap muscles were approximated with interrupted 3-0 VICRYL suture. Platysma and subcutaneous tissue was approximated with interrupted 4-0 VICRYL. Skin approximated with subcuticular 4-0 Dexon. Sterile dressings were applied. At the end of the procedure the vocal cords were inspected. They were moving equally well. The patient tolerated the entire procedure well and was discharged in stable condition to recovery room.

Discharge Information: Patient discharged after two days, with no complications.

Diagnosis: Papillary carcinoma of the thyroid, left and right lobes, with follicular pattern. Papillary carcinoma positive in one cervical lymph node. Will follow up with me in the office.

What are the correct codes in this case?

Code(s):_____

4.27.   This 59-year-old patient has type I diabetes mellitus. He has atherosclerosis and gangrene of the extremities due to the diabetes mellitus. What code(s) are assigned for this case?

Code(s):_____

Disorders of the Genitourinary System

4.28.   From the health record of a patient with urinary retention admitted through the emergency room:

Discharge Summary

Pertinent History: The patient is a 34-year-old female admitted through the ER with severe, stabbing, low-back pain and inability to urinate. The patient has a long history of pelvic inflammatory disease, with three surgical episodes to remove implants. CT scan revealed a mass in the area of the kidneys.

Hospital Course: The patient was admitted, prepped, and taken to surgery. Exploratory laparotomy was done and revealed an area of pelvic inflammatory disease involving both kidneys in dense adhesions. Cultures indicate chlamydia. Both ureters were almost totally blocked. Dense adhesions were painstakingly taken down. This was done very carefully and required several hours of surgery. Care was taken not to sever the kidneys or ureters. INTERCEED® adhesion barrier was applied.

Postoperatively, the patient was pain free.

Discharge Instructions: The patient was discharged home to return to see me in the office in one week.

Diagnosis: Severe pelvic adhesions, chlamydia infection.

Which of the following code sets would be reported for this admission?

a. 614.9, 079.98, 59.02
b. 614.6, 079.98, 59.02, 99.77
c. 614.6, 079.88, 54.59, 99.77
d. 614.3, 079.98, 59.02, 99.77

4.29.   From the health record of a patient requiring radical surgery:

Discharge Summary

Pertinent History: The patient is a 68-year-old female admitted through the ER. The patient's abdomen is enlarged to about 18-week size; however, the patient states she has actually lost 22 pounds over the past few weeks. Patient says her appetite has disappeared. Patient is admitted for workup and definitive treatment.

Hospital Course: The patient's CT scan and MRI revealed a suspicious mass in the pelvis. Patient was taken to surgery, where exploration revealed and pathology report later confirmed ovarian cancer. A radical abdominal hysterectomy was performed with regional lymph node dissection and bilateral salpingo-oophorectomy. The patient tolerated the procedure well.

Discharge Instructions: The patient was discharged home to see me in the office in one week for removal of staples and scheduling for oncologist consultation.

Which of the following code sets should be reported for this admission?

a. 183.0, 68.41, 65.61, 40.3
b. 183.0, 68.69, 65.61, 40.3
c. 198.6, 68.61, 65.61, 40.3
d. 183.0, 68.69, 65.61, 40.59

4.30.   This 80-year-old female patient was admitted with fever, malaise, and left flank pain. A urinalysis was performed and showed bacteria more than 100,000/ml. This was followed by a culture, showing E. coli growth as the cause of the UTI. Patient is also on current medication therapy for hypertension, ASHD, and COPD. What codes are assigned for this encounter?

Code(s):_____

4.31.   This 65-year-old male was admitted to the hospital in acute urinary retention. A transurethral resection of the prostate was performed and the diagnosis made of benign nodular hyperplasia of the prostate. When the pathology report was reviewed, there was documentation of BPH and a microscopic foci of adenocarcinoma of the prostate, which was confirmed by the physician. What codes are reported?

Code(s):_____

4.32. This 38-year-old mother of four children has been treated for nearly 20 years with severe cystic breast disease. The patient has elected to have her breasts removed to relieve the pain. She is also very worried about developing breast cancer. She has had numerous breast biopsies, and each time they are benign. She may consider plastic reconstruction later, but is not interested in it now. She is in good health. She was taken to surgery, and bilateral simple mastectomies were performed. The pathology report shows severe cystic breast disease. What codes are assigned?

Code(s):_____

4.33. This elderly patient has been treated for hypertension for many years. Otherwise he is in relatively good condition considering his age. He was brought to the ER and admitted in acute renal failure. What code(s) are assigned for this case?

Code(s):_____

4.34. The 56-year-old type I diabetes mellitus patient is admitted with acute renal failure. Other diagnosis listed are: hypertension, diabetic nephropathy, and chronic kidney disease stage IV. What codes are assigned?

a. 584.9, 403.91, 250.41, 583.81
b. 584.9, 585.4, 250.41, 583.81, 401.9
c. 584.9, 403.90, 250.41, 583.81
d. 584.9, 403.90, 585.4, 250.41, 583.81

4.35. What code is assigned to show that a 35-year-old patient is having a prophylactic removal of her breasts because of a strong history family of breast cancer?

a. V84.01
b. V16.3
c. 174.9
d. V10.3

Infectious Diseases

4.36. A patient with AIDS was admitted with a chief complaint of shortness of breath of approximately one-week duration. Red/blue skin lesions are noted on his legs and on his external genitalia. He also states that he has had a high fever and chills and has noted a weight loss of approximately 15 pounds within the past month. Chest x-rays reveal extensive bilateral pulmonary infiltrates. A diagnosis of Pneumocystis carinii pneumonia was made. Leg lesions were diagnosed as Kaposi's sarcoma via punch biopsy. Lesions on external genitalia were viewed as Kaposi's sarcoma also. Which of the following is the correct ICD-9-CM code assignment?

a. 042, 136.3, 176.8, 86.11
b. 136.3, 176.0, 176.8, 86.11
c. 136.3, 176.0, 176.8, 042, 86.11
d. 042, 136.3, 176.0, 176.8, 86.11

4.37. The discharge diagnosis for this patient is UTI with sepsis due to streptococcus. Urine culture and blood cultures were positive for streptococcus. After query to the physician regarding the meaning of the sepsis, an addendum was added to the record with the diagnosis of sepsis with streptococcal septicemia and UTI due to streptococcus B. What codes are assigned?

Code(s):_____

4.38. This 25-year-old patient was admitted with difficulty breathing. She has AIDS and is in the 21st week of pregnancy. Workup shows Pneumocystis carinii pneumonia. What codes are assigned in this case?

Code(s):_____

4.39. This 36-year-old male was diagnosed with AIDS eight months ago. He has had a persistent cough, and microscopy confirmed the presence of pulmonary tuberculosis. The physician documentation shows the infiltrating pulmonary tuberculosis is HIV-related. Patient was treated with ethambutol. What codes are assigned?

Code(s):_____

4.40. This 23-year-old female is admitted with pneumonia. She also has multiple bilateral lesions of the vulva and vagina with fluid-filled blisters. The history includes fever, and pain for two days. Sputum cultures show Group A Strep. History also includes pain, particularly on urinating, and itching of the genitals. Physician documents Group A Strep pneumonia, vulvovaginitis due to herpes. What codes are assigned?

Code(s):_____

Disorders of the Skin and Subcutaneous Tissue

4.41. An elderly nursing home patient was admitted for pneumonia. He has frequent aspiration pneumonia because of difficulty swallowing due to a previous stroke. This pneumonia was also felt to be consistent with aspiration-type pneumonia. He was also found to have stage one decubitus ulcer on the hip. The patient received skin care by the nursing staff for this ulcer. What codes are assigned in this case?

Code(s):_____

4.42. This patient had surgery two weeks ago for appendicitis. She is admitted now because of fever, pain, and redness at the operative site. There is evidence of cellulitis of the operative wound, and cultures confirm Staphylococcus aureus as the cause. She received IV antibiotics. She also has type II diabetes mellitus. What codes are assigned?

Code(s):_____

4.43. This nursing home patient was admitted to the hospital with severe cellulitis in the lower extremity. The cultures grew Streptococcus B, and this was documented by the physician as the cause of the cellulitis. Patient was given IV antibiotics. He also has right-sided hemiplegia from an old CVA and was found to have decubitus ulcers in the gluteal region. What code(s) are assigned?

Code(s):_____

4.44. This 85-year-old patient, who is a resident in the skilled nursing facility, was admitted with a severe decubitus ulcer on the right buttock and a small chronic ulcer on the heel. Patient also has Alzheimer's disease. The treatment was an excisional debridement of the heel and an excisional debridement into the muscle of the buttock. What is the code assignment?

Code(s):_____

4.45. This 29-year-old female patient is admitted for wide excision of melanoma on the back. She also has asthma and received nebulizer treatments after surgery. The wide excision was performed and a full-thickness skin graft was applied. What codes are assigned?

Code(s):_____

Behavioral Health Conditions

4.46. **Case Scenario:** A patient was admitted for alcohol detoxification and rehabilitation, with more than 12 years of alcohol dependence. On the second day of admission, he began experiencing withdrawal symptoms of sweating and nausea. On the third day, the sweating became more profuse and he developed irregular tremors and tachycardia. The DTs were managed medically. The patient did not experience any seizures. Hallucinations abated by day 4. By day 5, the patient was resting more comfortably, and plans for rehabilitation were initiated. The patient expressed a desire to reduce his alcohol abuse to a "controlled" level. A treatment plan was developed and implemented, with the short-term goal of assisting the patient in reaching a stable level of use; that is, controlled drinking and a long-range goal of motivating the patient to accept a goal of total abstinence. Initially, the patient actively participated in the program, but his motivation waned, and he left the program after signing out AMA without meeting any of the rehabilitation goals.

Which of the following code sets most accurately reflects this case scenario?

a. 291.81, 303.93, 94.63
b. 291.81, 303.90, 94.62
c. 291.0, 303.93, 94.63
d. 291.0, 303.90, 94.62

4.47. This 30-year-old male was admitted after being transferred from the outpatient therapy services because of severe major depressive disorder with psychotic features. After a complete psychologic evaluation, the risks and benefits of ECT were reviewed and explained to the patient and his family. ECT was administered three times per week. The patient tolerated the therapy well and responded quickly with overall improvement in the acute phase of his depressive disorder. After establishing adequate therapeutic levels of lithium, the patient was discharged to be managed as an outpatient. What codes are assigned?

Code(s):_____

4.48. This patient has been living at home, but his dementia has been getting progressively worse. He was diagnosed with Alzheimer's disease over two years ago. The family called the police because he was missing from home. A search was conducted and an observant passerby called in a report of an elderly man who seemed to be disoriented. He was found after several hours and brought to the hospital. He had fallen and had a laceration on his knee that required sutures. What codes are reported in this case?

Code(s):_____

4.49. The patient was brought to the ER and then admitted because of acute alcohol inebriation. The discharge diagnosis is acute and chronic alcoholism, continuous. What codes are assigned?

Code(s):_____

4.50. This 65-year-old chronic smoker was admitted to the hospital with acute exacerbation of her COPD. She has anxiety syndrome due to hypothyroidism, and the hospital environment caused a worsening of her anxiety. A psychiatric consultation was ordered. What codes are assigned in this case?

Code(s):_____

Disorders of the Musculoskeletal System and Connective Tissue

4.51. This patient was admitted for treatment of a left metatarsal fracture. The fracture site was opened and reduced, followed by placement of three internal Kirschner wires. Two pins were then placed and an external fixator frame was connected to the pins to provide pressure and hold them in reduction. Which of the following is the correct code assignment?

a. 825.35, 79.37
b. 825.29, 79.37
c. 825.25, 78.18
d. 825.25, 79.37, 78.18

4.52. A patient is admitted with an infected partial hip prosthesis. The prosthesis was removed and the patient underwent a total hip arthroplasty. What are the correct code assignments?

    a. 996.66, V43.64, 81.53, 81.51
    b. 996.66, V43.64, 81.53
    c. 996.67, 81.51
    d. 996.67, 81.53, 81.51

4.53. A patient was admitted for recurrent dislocation of the shoulder. The operation included debridement of the acromion, subacromial bursectomy, division of the coracoacromial ligament, and an abrasion acromioplasty with Mitek suture placement. Which of the following is the correct code assignment?

    a. 718.31, 81.82
    b. 718.31, 81.82, 83.5
    c. 831.00, 81.82, 83.5
    d. 831.00, 81.82, 83.5, 80.41

4.54. This 25-year-old was lifting heavy boxes at the shop where he works when he felt severe low back pain and numbness in the leg. He was brought to the hospital and admitted with herniated intervertebral disc of the lumbosacral area with myelopathy. A laminotomy was performed with excision of the disc. What codes are assigned?

    Code(s):_____

4.55. This 70-year-old female has been treated for progressive increasing pain in her back. She is to the point that she is unable to move. She was brought to the ER and admitted after x-ray shows severe compression fractures of the lumbar vertebrae due to her senile osteoporosis. An injection of anesthetic was done into the spinal canal. What codes are assigned?

    Code(s):_____

4.56. This 45-year-old male patient has failed conservative treatment for degenerative disc disease of the lumbar spine. He came to the hospital and the discectomy was performed at L5 and total spinal disc prosthesis inserted to restore disc function and anatomy. What procedure code(s) are assigned?

    a. 80.51
    b. 80.51, 84.65
    c. 84.65, 80.51
    d. 84.65

4.57.   What procedure code(s) are assigned for a patient with limb deformity due to trauma? An implantation of an internal limb lengthening device with kinetic distraction was performed on the tibia.

a. 84.53, 78.37
b. 84.53
c. 78.37
d. 84.54, 78.37

Neoplasms

4.58.   From the health record of a terminal oncology patient:

Discharge Summary

History of Present Illness: The patient is an 80-year-old white female with a known history of advanced metastatic carcinoma of the breast, widely metastatic. The patient was admitted because of increasing shortness of breath and severe pain. The pain, which was worse in her left chest, was associated with increasing shortness of breath. At the time of admission, the patient was in so much pain that she was unable to remember her history. The patient initially presented for congestive heart failure over a year ago. This was subsequently found to be secondary to metastatic breast cancer, post left mastectomy, three years ago. The patient had previously been on chemotherapy.

Lab Data and Hospital Course: The patient was treated initially with IV pain medication to control her pain. Subsequently, she became able to be stable on oral medication. By the time of discharge, the patient was stable on oral Vicodin®, and she was able to eat. Blood sugars were improved, and her Tolinase® was withheld. Lab at time of discharge included BUN 17, creatinine 1, sodium 141, potassium 4.5, chloride 105, CO_2 25, alkaline phosphatase elevated at 170 with GGT 267, SGOT 68. Admission BUN was up to 38 with creatinine 1.3 secondary to dehydration. By the time of discharge, these had improved. Admission glucose 225, down to 110 at discharge. Patient treated with Lanoxin® and Lasix® for CHF.

Medications at Discharge Include: Aldactone®, 25 mg twice a day; Lanoxin, 0.125 mg daily; Metamucil, 5 cc in four ounces of juice twice a day; Tolinase, 250 mg half tablet b.i.d. (but hold if preceding Accu-Chek® is less than 125); Reglan®, 10 mg p.o. a.c.; Pepcid®, 20 mg b.i.d.; Lasix, 40 mg daily (only if pedal edema is present); Vicodin tablets, 1 every 3 hours p.r.n. for pain.

Discharge Diagnoses: 1. Uncontrolled pain, secondary to widely metastatic breast carcinoma
2. Dehydration
3. Type II diabetes mellitus, uncontrolled
4. Congestive heart failure

Which of the following is the correct ICD-9-CM code assignment?

a. 199.0, V10.3, 276.51, 250.02, 428.0
b. 174.9, 276.51, 250.02, 428.0
c. 786.59, V10.3, 276.51, 250.02, 428.0
d. 786.59, 199.0, 276.51, 250.02, 428.0

4.59. This 60-year-old male was admitted with a diagnosis of bone metastasis originating from the right upper lobe (RUL) of the lung. The pathology was consistent with oat cell carcinoma. This admission is for chemotherapy that was administered. What codes are assigned for this admission?

Code(s):_____

4.60. This patient with terminal carcinoma of the breast, metastatic to the liver and brain, was admitted with dehydration. Patient rehydrated with IVs and discharged, with no treatment given to the cancer. What are the codes assigned?

Code(s):_____

4.61. This 45-year-old female patient was diagnosed with right breast carcinoma three years ago, at which time she had a mastectomy performed with chemotherapy administration. She has been well since that time with no further treatment but yearly checkups. She had metastasis in three axillary lymph nodes. She is admitted now with visual disturbances, dizziness, headaches, and blurred vision. Workup was done that revealed metastasis to the brain. What is the correct code assignment for this admission?

Code(s):_____

4.62. This patient was admitted for chemotherapy following recent diagnosis of cancer of the small intestines. The tumor was in the area where the duodenum and jejunum join. It was resected a month ago and she has been receiving chemotherapy. After the chemotherapy administration, the patient developed severe nausea and vomiting, which led to dehydration and an extra day's stay. Medications were given for the nausea and vomiting. IV fluids were given to rehydrate the patient. What codes are assigned?

Code(s):_____

4.63. This patient was admitted with a large pelvic mass and underwent an exploratory laparotomy. Pathology confirmed carcinoma of the left ovary with extensive metastasis to the omentum. A total omentectomy, excision of left ovarian mass, and radical abdominal hysterectomy with bilateral salpingo-oophorectomy were performed. What codes are assigned?

Code(s):_____

4.64. This 55-year-old male patient was diagnosed with prostate cancer three years ago. He has been treated and followed with bone metastasis, and last year the CT scan showed extensive liver mets. He has been having increasing amounts of pain. He is admitted now to have a PORT-A-CATH® VAD inserted because of intractable pain from his liver cancer. What codes are assigned in this case?

Code(s):_____

Disorders of the Nervous System and Sense Organs

4.65. This is one of multiple hospital admissions for this 37-year-old white male with a history of meningoencephalitis 20 years ago. He developed obstructive hydrocephalus and underwent ventriculoperitoneal shunting of the right lateral ventricle using a high-pressure valve. The patient is now complaining of numbness in his right leg, headaches, and diplopia. The patient had CT head scan which showed a slight increase in the hydrocephalus involving the fourth ventricle. Cisternogram was done, and the dye went into the fourth ventricle but never into the lateral ventricles. Impression was shunt malfunction. He is admitted this time for VP shunt revision. Ventricular shunt was replaced and was functioning well at the time of discharge. Which of the following is the correct ICD-9-CM code assignment?

a. 996.2, 331.4, 326, 02.42, 87.02, 87.03
b. 331.4, 326, 02.42, 87.02, 87.03
c. 996.63, 331.4, 02.42
d. 996.2, 02.42, 87.03

4.66. This 32-year-old female patient was admitted with intractable complex partial epilepsy after an MRI showed medial temporal sclerosis on the right side with hippocampal atrophy. The neurosurgeon carried out a selective amygdalohippocampectomy with intraoperative electrocorticography. The rest of her hospital stay was uneventful. What codes are assigned?

Code(s):_____

4.67. This 19-year-old college student was brought to the ER and admitted with high fever, stiff neck, chest pain, cough, and nausea. A lumbar puncture was performed, and results were positive for meningitis. Chest x-ray revealed pneumonia. Sputum cultures grew pneumococcus. Patient was treated with IV antibiotics and was discharged with the diagnosis of pneumococcal meningitis and pneumococcal pneumonia. What codes are assigned?

Code(s):_____

4.68. This patient was admitted when MRI revealed cerebral aneurysm. After admission, a cerebral angiogram was performed and showed nonruptured arteriosclerotic aneurysm of the anterior cerebral artery. An aneurysmectomy by anastomosis was performed using Marlex® graft replacement. What codes are assigned?

Code(s):_____

4.69. This 64-year-old patient collapsed at home. He was brought to the ER and admitted and placed into the ICU. A CT scan showed acute cerebrovascular embolus with cerebral infarction. Dysphagia and left hemiparesis are present. The patient is right-handed. Patient also has a history of hypertension and his current medications include captopril. At the time of discharge, the dysphagia had cleared, but the hemiparesis is still present. He will be discharged to a rehabilitation center. What codes are assigned?

Code(s):_____

Newborn/Congenital Disorders

4.70. A six-month-old baby with a left-sided, incomplete cleft lip and palate is admitted and undergoes surgical repair of both deformities.

Which of the following codes would be correct?

a. 749.02, 749.12, 27.62, 27.54
b. 749.22, 27.54, 27.63
c. 749.02, 749.12, 27.69
d. 749.22, 27.62, 27.54

4.71. A woman at 40-weeks gestation is admitted in labor. The baby is found to have the umbilical cord wrapped tightly around its neck. The baby is quickly delivered, resuscitated because of moderate asphyxia, and given oxygen in the NICU for the first 40 minutes of life. There are no further complications and the mother and baby are discharged on the second day postpartum.

Which of the following answers would be coded for the baby?

a. V30.00, 762.5, 93.93, 93.96
b. V30.00, 768.6, 93.93, 93.96
c. V30.00, 762.5, 768.6, 93.93, 93.96
d. 762.5, 768.6, V30.00, 93.93, 93.96

4.72. A 27-week-gestation infant is born by cesarean section. The baby weighs 945 grams. The baby's lungs are immature, and the baby develops respiratory distress syndrome, requiring a 25-day hospital stay in the NICU. Discharge diagnosis: Extreme immaturity, with 27-week gestation, with respiratory distress syndrome, delivered by cesarean section.

Which of the following diagnosis codes would be correct?

a. V30.01, 765.03, 765.24
b. 756.03, 769
c. V30.01, 765.03, 765.24, 769
d. V30.01, 769

4.73. The patient is a six-month-old infant born with the US2 type of Usher syndrome. He was admitted for bilateral cochlear hearing implants to treat his mixed hearing loss. The day after admission the patient was taken to surgery and the implants were inserted without incident. The patient tolerated the procedure and anesthesia without incident. The patient was discharged home on the second postop day to be followed in the office.

Which of the following answers is correct to code this admission?

a. 389.9, 20.96
b. 389.2, 759.89, 20.96, 20.96
c. 389.2, 759.89, 20.95
d. 389.2, 20.96, 20.96

4.74. This full-term female infant was born in this hospital by vaginal delivery. Her mother has been an alcoholic for many years and would not stop drinking during her pregnancy. The baby was born with fetal alcohol syndrome and was placed in the NICU. What codes are assigned?

Code(s):_____

Pediatric Conditions

4.75. A child has second- and third-degree burns of the lower leg and second- and third-degree burns of the back. Which of the following is the correct code set for reporting this diagnosis?

a. 945.34, 942.34
b. 945.34, 945.29
c. 945.34, 945.24, 942.34, 942.24
d. 946.3

4.76. Patient admitted with cervical lymphadenopathy. Lymph node biopsy confirmed Hodgkin's sarcoma disease. Megavoltage radiotherapy begun.

Which of the following is the correct code set?

a. 201.21, 40.40, 92.29
b. 201.91, 40.40, 92.29
c. 201.21, 40.11, 92.24
d. 201.91, 40.11, 92.24

4.77. This seven-year-old child was brought to the emergency room with difficulty breathing. He did not respond to aminophylline and was placed in the ICU with acute asthma attack with bronchospasm. Discharge diagnosis was refractory asthma with persistent bronchospasm. What codes are assigned?

Code(s):_____

4.78. This four-year-old child was brought to the ER because of high fever, cough, and chest pain. Diagnosis made of diffuse bronchopneumonia. Gram stain of the sputum shows numerous, small Gram-negative coccobacilli. Child was treated with IV antibiotics and was markedly improved by day five. He did develop moderate dehydration due to the fever and was treated with IV fluids for rehydration. Discharge diagnosis: H. influenzae pneumonia, dehydration. What codes are assigned?

Code(s):_____

4.79. This three-month-old infant was brought to the ER by the babysitter after she did not wake up from a nap. The babysitter admits to shaking the baby because she would not stop crying earlier in the day. She was admitted to ICU and was unconscious for 8 hours. Diagnosis at discharge: Shaken infant syndrome, subdural hematoma, loss of consciousness for 8 hours, and total retinal detachment, right eye. What codes are assigned?

Code(s):_____

Conditions of Pregnancy, Childbirth, and the Puerperium

4.80. The patient presented through the ED with severe abdominal pain, amenorrhea. Serum hCG was lower than normal. There were also endometrial and uterine changes. Patient diagnosed with tubal pregnancy. A unilateral salpingectomy with removal of tubal pregnancy was performed. Which of the following is the correct code assignment?

a. 633.80, 66.62
b. 633.10, 66.62
c. 633.10, 66.4
d. 633.10, 66.02

4.81. From the health record of a patient experiencing a spontaneous abortion:

Diagnosis: Incomplete spontaneous abortion

Postoperative Diagnosis: Same

Operation: Dilatation and curettage

History: This 22-year-old female, Gravida IV, Para II, AB I, comes in today because of crampy abdominal pain and passing fetal tissue at home. Apparently her last menstrual period was 9 weeks ago, and she had been doing well, and this problem just started today.

Procedure: The patient was placed on the operating table in lithotomy position, prepped, and draped in the usual manner. Under satisfactory intravenous sedation, the cervix was visualized by means of weighted speculum, grasped in the anterior lip with a sponge forceps. Cord was prolapsed through the cervix and vagina, and a considerable amount of placental tissue was in the vagina and cervix. This was removed. A sharp curet was used to explore the endometrial cavity, and a minimal amount of curettings was obtained. The patient tolerated the procedure well.

What codes are assigned?

a. 635.91, 69.09
b. 634.91, 69.09
c. 634.91, 69.02
d. 635.91, 69.02

4.82. This 25-year-old female was admitted in labor. She has had a normal pregnancy and this is a term delivery. The single liveborn infant was delivered with spontaneous delivery. A first-degree perineal laceration was repaired. What codes are assigned?

Code(s):_____

4.83. This is a 26-year-old patient who had previous cesarean section for delivery for fetal distress. She had normal antepartum care and has had no complications. We are going to attempt a VBAC for this delivery. She is admitted in her 39th week in labor. The fetus is in cephalic position and no rotation is necessary. The labor continues to progress and five hours later she is taken to delivery. During the delivery she was fatigued, so outlet forceps were required over a midline episiotomy. A single liveborn infant was delivered. What codes are reported?

Code(s):_____

4.84. This patient was admitted in labor at 39-weeks gestation. She has had gestational diabetes during her pregnancy. The labor was very difficult, and finally a low cervical cesarean section was performed because of obstructed labor due to an unusually large baby causing disproportion. What codes are assigned in this case?

Code(s):_____

Disorders of the Respiratory System

4.85. The patient was admitted with increasing shortness of breath, weakness, and ineffective cough. Treatment included oxygen therapy. Final diagnoses listed as acute respiratory insufficiency and acute exacerbation of COPD. Which of the following is the correct ICD-9-CM diagnostic code assignment?

a. 491.21
b. 491.21, 518.82
c. 518.81, 491.21
d. 518.82, 491.21

4.86. A ventilator-dependent patient (due to COPD emphysema) is admitted to the hospital at 10 a.m. on January 1. He is admitted for dehydration and is placed on the hospital's ventilator upon admission. The patient is discharged January 5 at 1 p.m. What is the appropriate code assignment?

a. 492.8, 276.51, 96.72
b. 276.51, 492.8, V46.11, 96.72
c. 276.51, 496, V46.11, 96.71
d. 492.8, 276.51, V46.11, 96.72

4.87. From the health record of a 69-year-old male patient:

Discharge Diagnoses: 1. Status asthmaticus
2. Chronic obstructive pulmonary disease

Hospital Course: The patient is a 69-year-old male who presented with gradual increase in shortness of breath, which was unresponsive to his home nebulizer treatments. In the emergency room, he received more respiratory treatments; however, he failed to improve. Therefore, he was admitted to the hospital. At the time of his admission, the theophylline level was 5.9. His chest x-ray showed no evidence of active infiltrates. He was bolused with intravenous steroids and started on frequent respiratory therapy treatments. IV aminophylline boluses and drip were used to increase his theophylline level to therapeutic range. The patient gradually cleared, and by the next day was much better. His IV aminophylline was changed to p.o. The Ventolin® treatments were decreased to q. 4 h., like he uses at home, and his steroids were rapidly tapered back to 10 mg of prednisone p.o. q. day. At the time of discharge, the patient's theophylline level was 14.8.

Discharge Medications: (1) Theo-Dur® 400 mg p.o. b.i.d. (2) prednisone 10 mg p.o. q. i.d. (3) Ventolin nebulizer treatments 0.5 cc in 2 cc or Ventolin inhaler. (4) Atrovent® two puffs t.i.d.

What is the correct ICD-9-CM diagnostic code assignment?

Code(s):_____

4.88. This nursing home patient presents with aspiration pneumonia with superimposed staphylococcal pneumonia. The patient aspirated food particles in the nursing home because of his dysphagia after a CVA last year. Treatment included clindamycin 600 mg IV q. 6 hours. Condition resolved with treatment and patient discharged home. The correct code assignment is:

Code(s):_____

4.89. A 75-year-old male was admitted to the hospital in acute respiratory failure. He has emphysema due to his continuous smoking for over 50 years. Sputum cultures showed Streptococcus A pneumonia. He was intubated in the ER and started on mechanical ventilation. Thirty-six hours later he was extubated and was able to breathe on his own. Diagnosis: Acute respiratory failure, pneumonia due to Streptococcus A, and emphysema. What codes are assigned?

Code(s):_____

Trauma and Poisoning

4.90.   From the health record of a high school athlete:

Discharge Summary: The patient is a 16-year-old male who received a hard tackle while playing football. He was unconscious at the playing field and was brought by ambulance to the Emergency Department. MRI showed a right subdural hematoma. Repeat MRI an hour later showed the hematoma to be growing. The patient remained unconscious. Vital signs were continuously monitored and remained within normal limits. The patient was taken to the OR, where the hematoma was evacuated. Postoperative course has been uneventful. The patient awakened and stated he was hungry. He has no memory of the event or the period of the football game. The patient is now discharged on the seventh postoperative day.

Which of the following code sets would be correct for this scenario?

a. 852.23, E886.0, 01.31, 88.91, 88.91
b. 852.26, E886.0, 01.31, 88.91, 88.91
c. 852.33, E886.0, 01.39, 88.91, 88.91
d. 852.26, E886.0, 01.39, 88.91, 88.91

4.91.   From the health record of a patient requiring continuing care after surgery:

Discharge Summary: The patient is a 32-year-old male who was admitted for revision of the amputation site above the knee on the right leg. He sustained the amputation in a motorcycle accident eight years ago and now presents with a neuroma of the stump. The patient was taken to surgery, where the boney stump was revised and nerve and scar tissue were removed without event. The patient has undergone this type of revision several times since the accident. The patient was discharged on the second day postop.

Which of the following would be coded?

a. 997.61, E929.0; 84.3
b. 905.9, E929.0; 84.3
c. 997.61, 905.9, E929.0; 84.3
d. 997.61, V49.76; 84.10

4.92.   This 35-year-old female patient was a driver involved in an automobile accident when she was rear-ended by another driver. She was seen in the emergency room complaining of pain in the arm and neck. She was brought into the hospital by the EMTs on a backboard and after proper splinting to the right arm. It was evident that there was a compound fracture present. After a CT scan of the head and neck, the patient was removed from the backboard.

She was admitted to the hospital for an open reduction, internal fixation of the radius and ulna. The surgery was completed without problems. Postoperative x-rays show the radial and ulnar shafts in good alignment. Patient was advised to wear a collar for her cervical strain.

Final Diagnoses, in Order of Significance:

Compound radius and ulna shaft fractures

Cervical spine strain

What are the correct codes to report for this service?

Code(s):_____

4.93. This 32-year-old patient was brought to the emergency room after a gas leak caused an explosion at his home. He was admitted with third-degree burns of the back involving 20 percent of the body surface. What codes are assigned?

Code(s):_____

4.94. This nursing home patient is admitted with extensive cellulitis of the abdominal wall. The examination performed reveals that his existing gastrostomy site is infected. He had a feeding tube inserted four months ago because of carcinoma of the middle esophagus. The physician confirms that the responsible organism is S. aureus.

Code(s):_____

4.95. This patient was walking along the railroad tracks when a train hit him. He is a vagrant and walks along the railroad tracks and hops on trains from time to time. He was taken to the Medical Center by ambulance. Surprisingly, there were no internal injuries, and the only injury sustained was significant trauma to both legs. Discharge diagnosis was bilateral traumatic amputation. He had a long hospital stay because of delayed healing, which was appropriately treated. A revision of the traumatic amputation with reconstruction was performed on both legs.

What are the correct ICD-9-CM codes?

Code(s):_____

4.96. From the health record of a patient who is status post joint replacement:

Discharge Summary: The patient is an active 61-year-old male, who underwent right total hip arthroplasty approximately three years ago. The patient is very active and walks several miles every day and enjoys playing golf. He has recently experienced several instances of failure of the right hip prosthesis. This is well documented in several ED visits for dislocation of the prosthetic hip. The patient was now admitted for scheduled replacement of the right hip arthroplasty. The patient was taken to surgery, where the old prosthesis was found to be eroded and bent, causing the repeated dislocations. The prosthesis was removed and replaced with a titanium prosthetic without incident. The patient was begun on physical therapy for gait training while in the hospital to help regain mobility. The patient was discharged on the fifth day postop to continue the physical therapy as an outpatient.

Which of the following codes would be used to report the above scenario?

Code(s):_____

4.97.   From the health record of a patient sustaining a fracture:

Discharge Summary: The patient is a 50-year-old female who fell down the icy front steps of her house and sustained a closed trimalleolar fracture of the medial and lateral malleolus, confirmed by x-ray done in the ED. She also hit her head on the concrete step and suffered a slight concussion but no loss of consciousness. The patient was admitted and taken to surgery, where open reduction and pinning was accomplished with good alignment of fracture fragments. Postop course was uneventful and the patient was discharged home with daily physical therapy.

What codes are assigned in this case?

Code(s):_____

Chapter 5

Case Studies from Ambulatory Health Records

> **Note:** Even though the specific cases are divided by setting, most of the information pertaining to the diagnosis is applicable to most settings. Even the CPT codes in the ambulatory and physician sections may be reported in the same manner. The differences in coding in these two settings may involve modifier reporting, evaluation and management CPT code reporting, and other health plan reporting guidelines unique to settings. If you practice or apply codes in a particular type of setting, you may find additional information in other sections of this publication that may be pertinent to you.
>
> Every effort has been made to follow current recognized coding guidelines and principles, as well as nationally recognized reporting guidelines. The material presented may differ from some health plan requirements for reporting. The ICD-9-CM codes used are effective through September 30, 2007, and the HCPCS (CPT and HCPCS Level II) codes are in effect through December 31, 2006. The current standard transactions and code sets named in HIPAA have been utilized, which require ICD-9-CM Volume III procedure codes for inpatients.
>
> **Instructions:**
>
> Assign all applicable ICD-9-CM and CPT codes appropriate for the setting for the case studies presented. Some of the cases provide multiple-choice answers, and the reader must select the appropriate code set. In other instances, the reader is expected to assign codes without any prompts.
>
> The scenarios are based on selected excerpts from health records without reproducing the entire health record. However, in practice, the coding professional should have access to the entire health record. Health records are analyzed and codes are selected only with the physician's complete and appropriate documentation available. According to coding guidelines, codes are not assigned without physician documentation.
>
> The objective of the cases and scenarios reproduced in this publication is to provide practice in assigning correct codes, not necessarily to emulate full-record analysis. For example, the reader may be asked to assign codes based only on an operative report, when in real practice a coder has access to documentation in the entire medical record.

Disorders of the Blood and Blood-Forming Organs

5.1.   This 35-year-old patient was brought to the ER for GI bleeding. He was given three units of packed red cells. He was taken to the same-day surgery suite and colonoscopy showed angiodysplasia of the transverse colon, which was controlled with laser. What codes are assigned for this case?

a. 569.85, 45382, 36430
b. 578.9, 569.84, 45382, 36430, 36430, 36430
c. 578.9, 45382, 36430
d. 569.84, 578.9, 45382

5.2.   This 20-year-old female came to the outpatient procedure area with a diagnosis of anemia. A bone marrow aspiration was performed in the following manner.

Manubrial area was prepped with Betadine®. Skin and periosteum anesthetized with 2 percent Xylocaine®. Skin incision was made with #11 Bard Parker blade, and marrow aspirations performed with U of IL sternal needle. Patient tolerated the procedure with no complaints or no complications. Advised to resume normal activity.

Diagnosis: Iron deficiency anemia

Pathology Report

Specimen Received: Bone marrow aspiration and biopsy

Pathologic Diagnosis: Slightly hypercellular marrow with diminished iron consistent with iron deficiency anemia

Microscopic Description: The bone marrow specimen is adequate. The marrow appears to be slightly hypercellular with a cell to fat ratio of 60/40. Megakaryocytes are easily found. Most of them are of normal morphology. There is nothing to suggest a primary or metastatic neoplastic proliferation. Granuloma is not found. The maturation of myeloid cells is complete. A Prussian blue stain obtained on both specimens shows diminished stainable iron. The specimen appears to be marrow aspiration. Bone trabecula are not seen in any of it. A reticulin stain was obtained. There is no evidence of significant increase in reticulin in the marrow stroma.

The marrow smears show adequate number of spicules. The complete maturation of myeloid cells is confirmed. Hemoglobinization of erythroid cells is slightly deficient. There is no evidence of excessive number of blasts. The myeloid/erythroid ratio is within normal limits. Plasma cells amount to less than 1 percent of the cells counted.

A review of the peripheral blood smear received shows no abnormal morphological changes in any of the cell lines.

What would be the correct codes assigned in this case?

a. 285.9, 38220
b. 280.9, 38220
c. 285.9, 38220, 38221-59
d. 280.8, 38230

5.3. This patient with abnormal blood test underwent bone marrow aspiration from the sternum. The area was cleaned with antiseptic solution and a local anesthetic was injected. The needle was inserted beneath the skin and rotated into the cortex and the sample taken. The needle was repositioned slightly, and a new syringe attached, and a second sample was obtained. These were sent to the laboratory for analysis. The results show acute lymphocytic leukemia. How is this coded?

Code(s):_____

5.4. A 40-year-old female has recently had surgery for melanoma of the left arm, documented as Clark level IV. She has no obvious signs of metastasis or adenopathy, but staging needs to be done. Under general anesthesia, a sentinel node biopsy of the deep axillary nodes is performed with a gamma counter probe. An injection of isosulfan blue dye was performed, and the nodes followed carefully to the single bright blue node. This node was excised and sent for frozen section, which proved to be positive for melanoma. Before the procedure, lymphoscintigraphy was performed. What are the appropriate codes to report in this case?

Code(s):_____

5.5. This 12-year-old male African-American patient is admitted to the ER with chest pain and pulmonary infiltrates. He has sickle-cell anemia. Treatment was aimed at reducing the chest pain to improve breathing. He was transferred to a larger children's hospital for admission for his sickle-cell crisis and acute chest syndrome. What code(s) would be assigned for the diagnosis in this case?

Code(s):_____

Disorders of the Cardiovascular System

5.6. A patient with severe varicose veins presents to the ambulatory surgery center for stripping of the long saphenous veins in the right leg, and the long and short saphenous veins in the left leg. She has had increasing pain and edema in her legs and has not responded to conservative therapy. What codes will be submitted on the claim form for this service?

a. 454.9, 37718-50
b. 454.8, 37722-50
c. 454.8, 37722-50, 37718-LT (Use modifier -59 if HCPCS modifiers not recognized)
d. 454.2, 37722-50, 37718-50

5.7.   A pediatric patient requires a transesophageal echocardiogram to evaluate an atrioventricular canal defect present since birth. Which codes are reported for this outpatient service?

a. 745.4, 93315
b. 745.69, 93315
c. 745.69, 93312
d. 429.71, 93312

[handwritten: 93315]

5.8.   This 45-year-old patient is scheduled for the ambulatory surgical center to have an INFUSAID pump installed. He has primary liver cancer and the pump is being inserted for continuous administration of 5-FU.

The right subclavian vein was cannulated without difficulty and the guidewire passed centrally. The subcutaneous tunnel and pocket was then created, and the catheter passed through the tunnel. The central venous catheter was placed and connected to the secured pump. The pump was filled with the chemotherapy agent provided by the hospital, and the patient is observed for adverse reaction and then is discharged home.

What codes are assigned for this episode?

Code(s):_____36563_____

5.9.   This patient has a history of unstable angina, hypertension, and chronic systolic heart failure. He is seen in the ER after prolonged chest pain that was not relieved by medication. Cardiac enzymes are elevated, and EKG shows anterior infarct. A decision was made to perform a cardiac catheterization and coronary angiography. Left heart catheterization was performed in order to perform a left ventriculogram. He tolerated the procedure well and will be discharged. Diagnosis: Acute anterior myocardial infarction, chronic systolic heart failure, hypertension. What are the correct codes?

Code(s):_____93510 , 93556_____

5.10. This 82-year-old male patient was shoveling snow and collapsed in his driveway. He arrived in the emergency department unresponsive and in asystole. A "code blue" was called and CPR was administered without a return to consciousness. The final diagnosis on the ER record was "Cardiopulmonary arrest, probably secondary to an acute myocardial infarction induced by exertion." Which diagnosis codes are reported?

[handwritten: 427.0]

Code(s):_____92950_____

5.11. Under local anesthesia and ultrasound guidance, a patient underwent radiofrequency ablation of an incompetent greater saphenous vein in the left lower extremity. Assign the appropriate CPT code(s).

a. 36475-RT
b. 36475-RT, 36000
c. 36478-RT
d. 36475-RT, 76942

Disorders of the Digestive System

5.12. From the health record of a female patient:

Outpatient Operative Report

This patient with hiatal hernia is admitted to same-day surgery for repair.

Description of Procedure: The patient was placed under satisfactory general endotracheal anesthesia. She was then placed in the lithotomy position. Foley was placed. Orogastric tube was inserted. The abdomen was prepped and draped in normal sterile fashion. A supraumbilical incision was made to the midline and the fascia was incised to enter the abdomen. Under direct visualization, a 0 VICRYL stitch was placed on each side of the fascia, and a blunt Hasson trocar was inserted. The abdomen was insufflated with CO_2. Under direct visualization, two 11 mm ports were placed in the left subcostal region, and 11 mm and 12 mm ports were placed in the right subcostal region.

The liver bed was then lifted up off the gastrohepatic ligament. The gastrohepatic ligament was taken down with harmonic scalpel. The right crus of the diaphragm was identified and dissected out with harmonic scalpel and blunt dissection. I dissected out the phrenicoesophageal ligament anteriorly and came around identifying the left crus. I then took down the short gastrics from the midportion of the greater curvature of the stomach up to the GE junction, using harmonic scalpel and taking care to not damage the spleen. Once we had adequately taken down the short gastrics, the posterior ligament was then mobilized behind the esophagus, and the stomach easily pulled through with no tension and no twist on the esophagus and easily laid in place.

The hiatal hernia was then repaired with a posterior cruropexy stitch of 0 ETHIBOND®. The wrap was then brought around and was placed approximately 2 cm into the esophagus with a horizontal mattress pledgeted 0 ETHIBOND stitch. A second interrupted stitch was placed just through-and-through on the stomach below this. At the end of the procedure, there was no tension or twist on the esophagus and no bleeding apparent. All ports were removed under direct visualization and there appeared to be hemostasis. The fascia at the supraumbilical incision was closed with 0 VICRYL. The skin was anesthetized with local anesthetic and then closed with 4-0 subcuticular MONOCRYL®.

Which codes are reported for this case?

a. 553.3, 39502
b. 553.3, 43280
c. 551.3, 43280
d. 553.3, 43324

5.13. This 59-year-old female patient came into the emergency room because of passing melanic stools. The emergency room physician initially saw her. The gastroenterologist was called into consultation. Because of the massive amounts of bleeding, it was decided to proceed with endoscopy. The endoscope was passed into the esophagus, stomach, and duodenum. Blood and clots were noted. This patient could possibly have a duodenal ulcer, but because of the amount of blood, it was difficult to delineate an ulcer crater. Diagnosis: Gastrointestinal hemorrhage, melanic stools, and possibly duodenal ulcer. What codes are assigned in this case?

Code(s):_____43235_____

5.14. This patient is having an endoscopic-directed percutaneous endoscopic gastrostomy tube placed because of moderate malnutrition. The patient has had a stroke, with residual right dominant-sided hemiparesis. Assign the codes that the hospital would use to bill this service, including the radiologic supervision and interpretation.

Code(s):_____43750, 74350 43246_____

5.15. A 39-year-old male has been treated for symptomatic cholelithiasis without improvement. Patient comes to outpatient surgery for a laparoscopic cholecystectomy. Due to previous abdominal surgery, some adhesions were encountered. During the course of the laparoscopic cholecystectomy procedure, the adhesions were lysed, but this did not prolong the procedure. What codes are assigned?

Code(s):_____47562_____

5.16. From the health record of a surgical patient:

Preoperative Diagnosis:	Rectal mass Change in bowel habits
Postoperative Diagnosis:	Rectal prolapse Colonic polyps. Biopsies × 2 Significant sigmoid diverticulosis with nonspecific colitis
Procedure:	Colonoscopy performed to the level of the cecum, 110 cm

Procedure: The patient was prepped in the usual fashion, followed by placement in the left lateral decubitus position. I administered 3 mg of Versed. Monitoring of sedation was assisted by a trained RN. Next, the Pentax® Video Endoscope was passed through the rectal verge after a negative digital exam and advanced to the level of the cecum. The scope was then slowly retracted with a circular tip motion. There was mild nonspecific colitis noted. She did have significant sigmoid diverticulosis and several small polyps just inside the rectum, as well as a large prolapsing mass of mucosa approximately 5 cm inside the rectum. This appears to have prolapsed previously. Two of the small polyps were biopsied using the cold biopsy forceps and sent to pathology for exam. The remainder of the exam was unremarkable. The patient tolerated the procedure well.

Pathology Report:

Clinical Information: Change in bowel habits. Colonoscopy performed.

Gross Exam: The specimen is labeled polyps × 2 at 3 cm. Submitted are two fragments of tan tissue measuring tip to 0.3 cm in greatest dimension.

Microscopic Exam: Sections examined at multiple levels show two fragments of rectal mucosa in which the surfaces and subjacent crypts show no evidence of adenomatous or neoplastic changes.

Diagnosis: Rectum, biopsies at 3 cm: rectal polyps

What codes are assigned in this case?

Code(s):_____45380_____

5.17. From the health record of a surgical patient:

Preoperative Diagnosis: Right inguinal hernia

Postoperative Diagnosis: Right inguinal hernia, direct and indirect

Procedures: Repair of right inguinal hernia with mesh

Procedure: This 45-year-old male was prepped in the usual manner for an initial hernia repair. After satisfactory spinal anesthesia, the inguinal area was draped in the usual sterile manner. A transverse incision was made above the inguinal ligament and carried down to the fascia of the external oblique, which was then opened, and the cord was mobilized. The ilioinguinal nerve was identified and protected. A relatively large indirect hernia was found. However, there was an extension of the hernia, such that one could definitely tell there had been a long-standing hernia here that probably had enlarged fairly recently. The posterior wall, however, was quite dilated and without a great deal of tone and bulging, and probably fit the criteria for a hernia by itself. Nonetheless, the hernia sac was separated from the cord structures, and a high ligation was done with a purse-string suture of 2-0 silk and a suture ligature of the same material prior to amputating the sac. The posterior wall was repaired with Marlex mesh, which was sewn in place in the usual manner, anchoring two sutures at the pubic tubercle tissue, taking one lateral up the rectus sheath and one lateral along the shelving border of Poupart's ligament past the internal ring. The mesh had been incised laterally to accommodate the internal ring. Several sutures were used to tack the mesh down superiorly and laterally to the transversalis fascia. Then the two limbs of the mesh were brought together lateral to the internal ring and secured to the shelving border of Poupart's ligament. The mesh was irrigated with gentamicin solution. The subcutaneous tissue was closed with fine VICRYL, as was the internal oblique. Marcaine was infiltrated in the subcutaneous tissue and skin. The wound was closed with fine nylon. The patient tolerated the procedure well.

Pathology Report

Gross Description

Specimen: Right inguinal hernia sac

The specimen consists of a pink to blue gray membranous piece of tissue measuring 5.5 cm in maximum dimension. Blocks are made.

Clinical: Right inguinal hernia

What codes would be assigned?

Code(s):_____49505 - RT_____

5.18.   From the health record of a patient requiring cholecystectomy:

Preoperative Diagnosis: Chronic cholelithiasis

Postoperative Diagnosis: Chronic cholelithiasis
Subacute cholecystitis

Operation: Laparoscopic cholecystectomy
Intraoperative cholangiogram

Procedure: The patient was brought to the operating room, placed in supine position, and underwent general endotracheal anesthesia. After adequate induction of anesthesia, the abdomen was prepped and draped in the usual fashion. The patient had several previous lower midline incisions and right flank incision; therefore, the pneumoperitoneum was created via epigastric incision to the left of the midline with a Verres needle. After adequate pneumoperitoneum, the 11 mm trocar was placed through the extended incision in the left epigastrium just to the left of the midline. The trocar was placed, and the laparoscope and camera were in place. Inspection of the peritoneal cavity revealed it to be free of adhesions, and an 11 mm trocar was then placed under direct vision through a small infraumbilical incision. The scope and camera were then moved to this position, and the gallbladder was easily visualized. The gallbladder was elevated, and Hartmann's pouch was grasped. Using a combination of sharp and blunt dissection, the cystic artery was identified. The gallbladder was somewhat tense and subacutely inflamed. Therefore, a needle was passed through the abdominal wall into the gallbladder, and the gallbladder was aspirated free until it collapsed. One of the graspers was held over this region to prevent any further leakage of bile. Again, direction was turned to the area of the triangle of Calot. The cystic duct was dissected free with sharp and blunt dissection. A small opening was made in the duct, and the cholangiogram catheter was passed. The cholangiogram revealed no stones or filling defects in the bile duct system. The biliary tree was normal. There was good flow into the duodenum, and the catheter was definitely in the cystic duct. The catheter was removed, and the cystic duct was ligated between clips, as was the cystic artery. The gallbladder was then dissected free from the hepatic bed using electrocautery dissection, and it was removed from the abdomen through the umbilical port. Inspection of the hepatic bed noted that hemostasis was meticulous. The region of dissection was irrigated and aspirated dry. The trocars were removed, and the pneumoperitoneum was released. The incisions were closed with Steri-Strips™, and the umbilical fascial incision was closed with 2-0 Maxon. The patient tolerated the procedure well; there were no complications. She was returned to the recovery room awake and alert.

What codes would be assigned?

Code(s):_____47562~3_____

5.19.   A patient is being assessed for possible colon cancer. He undergoes a colonoscopy into the ascending colon with biopsy of a suspicious area in the transverse colon using the cold biopsy forceps. In addition, a colonic ultrasound of the area is performed, with transmural biopsy of an area of the mesentery adjacent to the transverse colon. Assign the appropriate CPT codes.

a. 45384, 45342
b. 45380, 45391
c. 45384, 45392
d. 45380, 45392

Endocrine, Nutritional and Metabolic Diseases, and Immunity Disorders

5.20. A 28-year-old diabetic at 38-weeks gestation presents to the ED this evening with concerns that the fetus has not moved at all today. The patient was instructed at her last clinic visit to count fetal movements during a 30-minute period daily and seek prompt attention if she noticed a sudden decrease in fetal movement.

This is the patient's first pregnancy, and control of her type II diabetes has been fairly adequate throughout the pregnancy. Blood glucose level in the ED is 120. A limited ultrasound examination demonstrates fetal movements with a normal heart beat recorded.

The patient's obstetrician was contacted by phone and findings were reviewed.

The patient is discharged home, with instructions to rest on her left side through the night and report to the obstetrical clinic at 9 a.m. tomorrow morning.

Which of the following code sets is accurate for reporting the diagnosis on this visit?

a. 655.73, 648.83
b. 655.73, 648.03
c. 648.03, 250.00
d. 655.73, 648.03, 250.00

5.21. This patient is an 18-year-old white female, diagnosed with Addison's disease four years ago, who subsequently developed diabetic ketoacidosis, diagnosed with type I diabetes mellitus three months after that. She also has positive thyroid antibodies. She presented to the ED with diabetes out of control, with glucose ranging from 70s to nearly 400 on the previous Accu-Chek.

Current medications in addition to daily insulin regimen include:

Hydrocortisone 20 mg q. a.m. and 10 mg q. p.m.

Florinef® 0.1 mg q. d.

Birth control pills one q. d.

Blood glucose in the ED was 350. She was placed on IV insulin drip and transferred to Memorial Hospital to her regular physician's care for SCII pump therapy.

Discharge Diagnoses: 1. Diabetes, type I, out of control
2. Addison's disease

Which of the following is the correct ICD-9-CM diagnosis code set?

a. 250.11, 255.4
b. 250.13
c. 250.01
d. 250.03, 255.4

5.22.   From the health record of a patient with Cushing's disease:

History: This is a 56-year-old female who has had hypertension and palpitations of several years' duration. Ultrasound is done today in consideration of the possibility of a mass. Catecholamine studies have been normal. Dr. White had obtained a 24-hour urinary free cortisol, ACTH, and short suppression tests, all of which confirmed the presence of Cushing's syndrome. The patient was not diabetic. She did report weight gain, some shift in body configuration, and easy bruising of several years' duration. The easy bruising is confirmed on exam today.

Findings: On ultrasound today, a 4–5 cm right adrenal mass was identified. The mass appears well circumscribed and rounded. See the ultrasound report.

Plan: Surgery will be scheduled.

Assessment: Right adrenal tumor with Cushing's syndrome secondary to tumor.

Which of the following is the correct ICD-9-CM code set for this outpatient visit?

a. 239.7, 255.0
b. 239.7, 401.9
c. 255.0, 198.7
d. 255.0, 239.7, 401.9

5.23.   This 57-year-old female patient with known type I diabetes mellitus presents for laboratory work for evaluation of blood sugar levels. What is the correct coding and/or sequencing for this encounter?

Code(s):_____

5.24.   A 45-year-old female presents with a complaint of neck swelling. On the initial physical exam the physician notes diffuse swelling of the neck with enlargement of the thyroid gland. The patient exhibits no signs of hyperthyroidism. The physician suspects lymphoma and a biopsy is scheduled. A large, hollow core needle is passed through the skin into the thyroid. Tissue is sent for histopathology. A diagnosis of nodular lymphoma is confirmed and chemotherapy is planned.

What is the correct code assignment?

Code(s):_____

Disorders of the Genitourinary System

5.25. A female patient with stress incontinence requires repair for midline cystocele and incomplete vaginal prolapse. The physician elects to perform a paravaginal defect repair on both sides. An abdominal incision is made and entry into the space of Retzius is gained. Six sutures are placed through the anterior lateral edge of the vaginal wall and then through the fascia condensation over the obturator internus muscle from the inferior aspect of the pubic bone along the arcus tendinous to the ischial spine. Additional anchors were placed at the level of the urethrovesical junction on both sides to correct the cystocele.

Which of the following code sets is reported for this service?

   a. 625.6, 618.01, 618.2, 57284, 51840
   b. 625.6, 57284-50
   c. 618.02, 57240
   d. 618.01, 625.6, 57284

5.26. This male patient is a nursing home patient who is stress incontinent and continually leaks urine. To treat this, the urologist introduces a mechanical obstruction in the urethra that prevents leakage. Using an endoscope, the physician injects a solution of polytetrafluorethylene into the region of the distal sphincter of the urethra; then inserts an inflatable bladder neck sphincter with pump, reservoir, and cuff. Which of the following code sets is reported for this surgery?

   a. 788.37, 53445, 51715
   b. 788.39, 51715
   c. 788.37, 53440
   d. 788.37, 53445

5.27. This 35-year-old male has renal calculus diagnosed per x-ray. Endoscopes are used to pass through the patient's urethra into the bladder and then the ureter with a renal calculus. An electrohydraulic lithotriptor probe is used to pulverize the stone. An indwelling double-J stent is placed to facilitate passing of any residual stones.

Which of the following code sets will be reported for hospital-based outpatient surgery?

   a. 592.1, 52353, 52332
   b. 592.0, 52353-RT
   c. 592.0, 52353, 52332
   d. 592.0, 52352, 52332-51

5.28. This patient has adenoma of the prostate. The urologist inserts an endoscope in the penile urethra and dilates the structure to allow instrument passage. After endoscope placement, a radiofrequency stylet is inserted, and the diseased prostate is excised with radiant energy. Bleeding is controlled with electrocoagulation. Following instrument removal, a catheter is inserted and left in place. Which of the following code sets will be reported for this service?

a. 600.20, 53852
b. 600.20, 52601
c. 600.00, 53852
d. 222.2, 53850

5.29.   A new patient presents to the hospital-based urgent care center with back pain and burning with urination. The physician on call orders an automated urinalysis with microscopy. Due to the presence of white blood cells in the urine, a culture and sensitivity (quantification and colony count) is ordered, which is positive for E. coli. The physician's diagnosis per the clinic note is "urinary tract infection—cystitis." The patient was referred to her primary care physician for follow-up, and a sample of broad-spectrum antibiotics was provided until her appointment.

What codes are reported by the facility? Do not include E/M codes in this example, but do include laboratory codes, even though they would be reported by the billing system software.

Code(s): __81001 , 87086__

5.30.   A nursing home patient with a history of urinary tract infections is brought to the emergency room, after developing a fever and vague abdominal pain. The patient has senile dementia with delirium and is unable to communicate. The history was obtained from nursing home transfer records. Nonautomated urinalysis with microscopy was performed but was not remarkable. The physician's assessment stated "fever of unknown origin." The patient was treated with Tylenol® and started on a broad-spectrum antibiotic and referred to her primary care physician for follow-up first thing in the morning. What codes are reported in addition to the E/M facility code for ER services?

Code(s): __99281 , 81000__

5.31.   A type 1 diabetic patient with diabetic nephropathy and end-stage renal disease requires dialysis. A Cimino-type direct arteriovenous anastomosis is performed by incising the skin of the left antecubital fossa. Vessel clamps are placed on the vein and adjacent artery. The vein is dissected free and the downstream portion of the vein is sutured to an opening in the artery using an end-to-side technique. The skin incision is closed in layers.

What codes are reported for this service?

Code(s): __36821__

5.32.   A 28-year-old patient has a history of abdominal surgery and is experiencing abdominal pain. Diagnostic workup has presented no etiology, so her physician scheduled an exploratory laparoscopy and discovered adhesions around the fallopian tubes and ovaries, which were taken down during the procedure. What codes will be reported?

Code(s):_____ 58660 _____

5.33. A 59-year-old male has been having increasing difficulty in urinating. A transurethral resection of the bladder neck is performed to treat urinary obstruction and retention due to vesicourethral obstruction with benign prostatic hypertrophy. What codes are reported?

Code(s):_____ 52500 _____

5.34. A patient with advanced renal cell carcinoma is admitted to the IVR Department to undergo percutaneous radiofrequency ablation of four tumors of the right kidney. Assign the appropriate CPT code for this procedure.

Code(s):_____ 50592 - RT _____

Infectious Diseases

5.35. A patient presents to the emergency room with symptoms of right upper quadrant pain, fever, profound malaise, and bloody diarrhea. An infectious consultation was obtained and diagnosis was made of acute Entamoeba histolytica dysentery. What code(s) are assigned in addition to the E/M code?

Code(s):_____

5.36. A patient presents to the hospital emergency room with a vesicular eruption on the penis, scrotum, buttocks, and groin. He complains of severe itching, particularly at night. The assessment recorded in the chart indicates infestation with Sarcoptes scabiei. PMS-Lindane is applied to the affected area and a prescription provided for treatment of the entire household.

What diagnosis code is reported for this encounter?

Code(s):_____

5.37. This three-year-old patient presents to the emergency department with history of sudden bloody diarrhea. The stool culture demonstrated E. coli. The patient went swimming with his child care center the previous day at a nearby water park. The physician documented: acute enteritis, due to enterotoxigenic E. coli. What is the correct ICD-9-CM diagnostic code for this encounter?

Code(s):_____

5.38. This 15-year-old patient presents to the emergency department with symptoms consisting of fever, abdominal pain and cramping, and severe diarrhea. Stool culture demonstrated Salmonella enteritidis bacterium. Upon questioning the patient, he attended a family picnic yesterday and consumed some type of salad, as well as homemade ice cream. Physician diagnosis is Salmonella gastroenteritis. He is instructed to report any worsening symptoms. What is the correct ICD-9-CM diagnostic code?

Code(s):_____

Disorders of the Skin and Subcutaneous Tissue

5.39. A patient who has had a lesion removed returns for a wide excision of a malignant melanoma on the back. The area excised consists of a 3 cm diameter area. A layer closure is required to close the defect. The pathology report shows clear margins.

What are the correct codes to report? The procedure is performed in the outpatient surgery suite at the hospital.

a. 172.5, 11603
b. 709.9, 11603
c. 172.5, 11603, 12032
d. V76.43, 11603, 13121

5.40. An operative report for ambulatory surgery states that a patient receives a full-thickness graft of the cheek following lesion removal of a basal carcinoma. The lesion plus margins are documented to be 3.2 cm in diameter. A 10 sq cm graft is applied with donor skin from her thigh; closed by suture.

Which of the following code sets is correct for this surgery?

a. 173.3, 15240, 11646
b. 173.3, 15240, 15000
c. 173.3, 15350, 15000, 11644
d. 173.3, 15240, 11644

5.41. A patient presents to the urgent care center with a laceration to the elbow that occurred 10 days ago and was not treated. An infected gaping wound is found with resulting cellulitis to the forearm and upper arm. Closure was not attempted pending resolution of the infection. Culture of the wound revealed streptococcus. The patient received 1,200,000 units of Bicillin® C-R IM and is to return in three days for follow-up.

What codes would be assigned for reporting the facility services? In this example, do not assign E/M codes or the laboratory codes.

Code(s):_____ 85499   90772 J0540

5.42. A patient presents to the hospital outpatient surgery center for surgery. Destruction was performed on eight viral warts on the left arm. Destruction was done using cryosurgery and curettement. What codes are reported?

Code(s):_____ 17000, 17003x7

5.43. This four-year-old boy was helping his father, who was installing a new window. The window fell, with some of the glass cutting the boy. He received a 2 cm laceration on his left hand, a 3 cm laceration on his left arm, and a 2.5 cm laceration on his leg. The lacerations on the hand and arm were repaired with a simple repair. The laceration on the leg was deeper and required a layered repair. What procedure codes are assigned for this ER visit?

Code(s): _____ 12002, 12031 _____

5.44. This 40-year-old female has a mole on the left calf. It has been getting progressively darker. An excision of the lesion is performed. The lesion is 1.5 cm. The margins on each side are .5 cm. The pathology report confirms malignant melanoma and the patient is scheduled for wide excision the following week. What codes are reported?

Code(s): _____ 11603 _____

5.45. A patient underwent a left lumpectomy and placement of an afterloading balloon catheter into the breast. Assign the appropriate CPT code(s).

   a. 19297
   b. 19160, 19297
   c. 19160, 19198
   d. 19120, 19197

5.46. A 75-year-old female patient has a sacral decubitus and a small decubitus on her buttock. She has had an excisional debridement done on the sacral decubitus. What diagnosis code(s) are assigned?

   a. 707.0
   b. 707.03
   c. 707.09
   d. 707.03, 707.05

Behavioral Health Conditions

5.47. A 35-year-old patient presents to the Community Mental Health Center for group therapy. A psychiatrist provides group therapy for obsessive-compulsive disorder. Which of the following code sets would be reported?

   a. 301.4, 90853
   b. 300.3, 90857
   c. 300.3, 90853
   d. 300.3, 90847

5.48. A patient in a community mental health center receives individual insight-oriented psychotherapy for over 25 minutes. What CPT codes(s) would be reported for the professional services rendered by the employed clinical psychologist?

Code(s): _____ 90876   90804 _____

5.49.   A young male is seen in the ED for a failed suicide attempt. Both wrists required suturing for lacerations from a razor. A 24-hour hold was instituted and the patient was transferred for psychiatric care. What diagnosis codes are assigned?

Code(s):_____

5.50.   This 25-year-old female was brought to the ER because of an overdose of drugs. Her roommate found her and called 911. She has been treated recently for depression, and her bottle of amitriptyline was empty. The roommate also reports that her bottle of diazepam was empty, and she estimates that there may have been about 20 pills in the bottle. According to the evidence, it looks like she used alcohol to take the pills, and this was confirmed during drug screen. She left a suicide note stating that she could not go on living. Aggressive measures were performed in the ER, but she could not be revived and was pronounced dead. What diagnosis codes are assigned in this case?

Code(s):_____

Disorders of the Musculoskeletal System and Connective Tissue

5.51.   A patient fell from a ladder at his home, which resulted in a nondisplaced compression fracture of L1 and L2 vertebral bodies. The patient was placed in a back brace and will be followed for complications. Do not code the supply in this example.

Which codes are appropriate for reporting?

a. 805.5, E881.0, 22325
b. 805.4, E881.0, E849.0, 22310
c. 806.4, E881.0, E849.0, 22315
d. 805.01, 805.02, E881.0, E849.0, 22326

5.52.   From the health record of a patient requiring fracture care:

Operative Report

Preoperative Diagnosis: Displaced comminuted fracture of the lateral condyle, right elbow

Postoperative Diagnosis: Same

Procedure: Open reduction, internal fixation

Description: The patient was anesthetized and prepped with Betadine. Sterile drapes were applied, and the pneumatic tourniquet was inflated around the arm. An incision was made in the area of the lateral epicondyle through a Steri-Drape™, and this was carried through subcutaneous tissue, and the fracture site was easily exposed.

Inspection revealed the fragment to be rotated in two planes about 90 degrees. It was possible to manually reduce this quite easily, and the judicious manipulation resulted in an almost anatomic reduction. This was fixed with two pins driven across the humerus. These pins were cut off below skin level. The wound was closed with some plain catgut subcutaneously and 5-0 nylon in the skin. Dressings were applied to the patient and tourniquet released. A long arm cast was applied.

Which of the following is the correct code assignment? Do not code the supply in this example.

a. 812.52, 24577, 29065
b. 812.42, 24579, 29065
c. 812.42, 24579-RT
d. 812.52, 24579-RT

5.53. An elderly patient fractures the radius shaft in her arm when she is driving a car involved in a collision with another car. A static short arm splint is provided by the ER physician to provide stabilization until it can be evaluated and treated by an orthopedic surgeon. What codes are used to report this facility service for Medicare reimbursement? Do not assign an E/M code in this practice case, but include the supply.

Code(s): _____ 29125 _____ A4570 _____

5.54. This 52-year-old male was brought to the same-day surgery area for treatment of an open fracture of the distal phalanx caused by a food-processing machine in a factory. The patient had open treatment performed to remove the fracture fragments without any internal or external fixation hardware used. What code(s) are reported?

Code(s): _____ 26765 _____

5.55. This 32-year-old male had an ORIF of a fractured metacarpal done three months ago. The fracture has completely healed, and he is scheduled for removal of deep internal fixation hardware involving the metacarpals. The plate and pins were removed without incident. Which codes would be reported for this service in a hospital-based outpatient surgery center where anesthesia is available?

Code(s): _____ 26320 _____ 20680 _____

5.56. The procedure that involves transplantation of a piece of articular cartilage and attached subchondral bone from a cadaver donor to a damaged region of the articular surface of the knee joint is called a(n):

a. Osteochondral autograft
b. Osteochondral allograft
c. Autologous chondrocyte implantation
d. Anterior cruciate ligament repair

Neoplasms

5.57. A patient has squamous cell carcinoma of the posterior pharyngeal wall and metastasis to the cervical lymph nodes. Following consultation with the oncology team, the patient refused surgical intervention and elected to begin radiation therapy daily on a 6 MV linear accelerator. The radiation was delivered by hyperfractionation technique. Each field was treated twice each day, through a pair of large opposing lateral head and neck fields covering the primary cancer, the suspected areas of extension, and the lymph nodes in the neck. (Three separate treatment areas are involved, and customized shielding blocks are employed to shield normal tissue and shape the field to follow the anatomic boundaries.) Prior to the encounter under consideration, the clinical treatment parameters and dosimetry calculations have been completed, and the simulation-aided field settings have been accomplished.

Which of the following codes will be reported by the hospital for the encounters for radiation therapy, keeping in mind the number of treatments that will be reported in the unit's field on the UB-92?

   a. V58.0, 77413
   b. 149.0, 77408
   c. V58.0, 149.0, 196.0, 77413
   d. 149.0, 196.0, 77412

5.58. A patient with a lung mass discovered on prior x-ray presents to the outpatient surgery area for a diagnostic bronchoscopy. Following anesthetic to the airway, a fiberoptic bronchoscope is introduced into the bronchial tree. A needle is advanced through a channel in the scope, and tissue is aspirated from the lung mass for pathologic evaluation under fluoroscopic guidance. The pathologic diagnosis is oat cell carcinoma.

Which of the following is the correct code assignment?

   a. 162.9, 31629
   b. 162.9, 31629, 76003
   c. 162.9, 31625
   d. 235.7, 31629, 76003

5.59. A Medicare patient is scheduled for breast biopsy of a palpable lump in the right breast and a much smaller lesion in the left breast that is identified by a radiological marker shown on mammography. An excisional biopsy is performed on both sides. The specimen on the right is diagnostic for breast malignancy with clear margins, while the small lesion in the left breast is found to be only fibrocystic disease, without evidence of malignancy. Which of the following is reported?

   a. 174.9, 610.1, 19120-RT, 19125-LT, 19290-LT
   b. 611.72, 610.1, 19120-50
   c. 174.9, 610.1, 19120-50, 19125-50, 19290-50
   d. 174.9, 610.2, 19120, 19125-59, 19290

5.60. A 50-year-old male patient with a personal history of colonic polyps presents to the outpatient surgery department for a colonoscopy to rule out colon cancer. The patient has been experiencing rectal bleeding for about six weeks and has lost a significant amount of weight. A colonoscopy to the terminal ileum is performed. Just beyond the rectal vault, two polyps are found and excised by hot biopsy forceps. Further up into the sigmoid colon, a lesion was biopsied. The pathology report confirms a diagnosis of colon cancer in the lesion found, and the polyps were found to be villous adenoma.

What codes are assigned in this case?

Code(s):_____

5.61. A patient presents to the hospital outpatient department for chemotherapy treatment. She is a 15-year-old female with acute lymphocytic leukemia. The chemotherapy agent is listed as an injection of lyophilized cyclophosphamide, 200 mg IV push. What codes would be reported?

Code(s):_____

Disorders of the Nervous System and Sense Organs

5.62. A Medicare patient presents to the emergency department with a cerebral seizure. Past history includes congestive heart failure and adverse (allergic) reaction to contrast media. A CT scan is performed without contrast material, followed by low osmolar contrast material (200 mg) and further sections. The final assessment by the physician states cerebrovascular accident (CVA) without evidence of embolism. Which of the following code sets is required for appropriate reimbursement? Do not assign the E/M code to this case.

   a. 436, 780.39, 70450, 70460
   b. 434.91, 428.0, V14.8
   c. 780.39, 428.0, V15.08
   d. 434.91, 428.0, V15.08, 70470, A4645

5.63. A patient with Lou Gehrig's disease presents to the hospital-based neurology department for EMG testing. A needle electromyography of the legs and both of the eyes was conducted. Which of the following code sets would be reported?

   a. 335.20, 92265-50, 95861
   b. 335.24, 95868-59, 95861
   c. 335.20, 95861, 92265
   d. 335.2, 95870, 95861, 99201

5.64. From the health record of a patient requiring eye surgery:

Operative Report

Preoperative Diagnosis: Type I diabetes patient with severe retinal microaneurysmal diabetic retinopathy

Postoperative Diagnosis: Same

Operation: Vitrectomy followed by laser photocoagulation

Description of Procedure: An Ocutome® is used to go behind the iris and cut and suction the vitreous mechanically. After the vitreous removal, a laser is used to treat the remaining retinal disorders in all four retinal quadrants and prevent further retinal hemorrhage.

Which of the following code sets is reported for this service?

a. 250.51, 362.01, 67040
b. 362.01, 362.81, 67040
c. 250.50, 362.02, 67039
d. 250.51, 362.02, 67105, 67145

5.65. From the health record of a patient with cataracts:

Operative Report

Procedure: Extracapsular cataract extraction with intraocular lens implantation, left eye

Diagnosis: Bilateral cataracts

Technique: The patient was given a retrobulbar injection of 2.5 to 3.0 cc of a mixture of equal parts of 2 percent lidocaine with epinephrine and 0.75 percent Marcaine with Wydase®. The area about the left eye was infiltrated with an additional 6 to 7 cc of this mixture in a modified Van Lint technique. A self-maintaining pressure device was applied to the eye, and a short time later, the patient was taken to the OR.

The patient was properly positioned on the operating table, and the area around the left eye was prepped and draped in the usual fashion. A self-retaining eyelid speculum was positioned and 4-0 silk suture passed through the tendon of the superior rectus muscle, thereby deviating the eye inferiorly. A 160° fornix-based conjunctival flap was created, followed by a 150° corneoscleral groove with a #64 Beaver blade. Hemostasis was maintained throughout with gentle cautery. A 6-0 silk suture was introduced to cross this groove at the twelve o'clock position and looped out of the operative field. The anterior chamber was then entered superiorly temporally, and after injecting Occucoat, an anterior capsulotomy was performed without difficulty. The nucleus was easily brought forward into the anterior chamber. The corneoscleral section was opened with scissors to the left and the nucleus delivered with irrigation and gentle lens loop manipulation. Interrupted 10-0 nylon sutures were placed at both the nasal and lateral extent of the incision. A manual irrigating aspirating setup then was used to remove remaining cortical material from both the anterior and posterior chambers.

At this point, a modified C-loop posterior chamber lens was removed from its package and irrigated and inspected. It then was positioned into the inferior capsular bag without difficulty, and the superior haptic was placed behind the iris at the twelve o'clock location. The lens was rotated to a horizontal orientation in an attempt to better enhance capsular fixation. Miochol® was used to constrict the pupil, and a peripheral iridectomy was performed in the superior nasal quadrant. In addition, three or four interrupted 10-0 nylon sutures were used to close the corneal scleral section. The silk sutures were removed, and the conjunctiva advanced back into its normal location and was secured with cautery burns at the three and nine o'clock positions. Approximately 20 to 30 mg of both gentamicin and Kenalog® were injected into the inferior cul-de-sac in a subconjunctival and sub-Tenon fashion. After instillation of 2 percent pilocarpine and Maxitrol® ophthalmic solution, the eyelid speculum was removed and the eye dressed in a sterile fashion. The patient was discharged to the recovery room in good condition.

What codes are assigned in this case?

Code(s): _____ 66984 _____

5.66. This 45-year-old female was admitted through the emergency room with a grand mal seizure. She did not respond to treatment and was transferred with the diagnosis of intractable epilepsy. What diagnosis code is reported?

Code(s): _____ 99285 _____

5.67. The patient has known chronic glaucoma, more severe in the left eye. She is brought to the outpatient procedure suite and anesthetized with a periocular anesthetic. The left eye is prepared and sterilely draped, followed by insertion of a lid speculum. A clear corneal incision is made temporally with the diamond blade approximately 3.4 mm in width. Viscoelastic material is injected into the anterior chamber over the pupil and lens to increase and maintain anterior chamber depth. Viscoelastic is then injected under the iris for 180° to visualize the ciliary body processes with the endoscope. The endoscope is inserted through the temporal incision viewing the nasal ciliary processes. The ciliary processes are coagulated through the endoscope with the endpoint of shrinkage and whitening.

Assign the appropriate CPT code for the described procedure.

a. 66710
b. 66711
c. 66720
d. 66700

Newborn/Congenital Disorders

5.68. A baby was born in the hospital to a woman who lacked prenatal care and contracted Rubella during pregnancy, passing it on to her fetus. The baby was born with multiple deformities, including a congenital cortical and zonular cataract of the left eye. The baby is now seven months old and ready for extracapsular phacoemulsification with intraocular lens replacement.

Which of the following code sets would be reported for the surgery?

a. 743.30, 760.2, 66984
b. 366.03, 66984
c. V30.00, 771.0, 743.32
d. 743.32, 66984

5.69.   A newborn female is born with polydactyly of the right foot with a total of five normal toes and two extra digits that do not contain bony structures. Which of the following code sets would be reported by the ASC facility tying off and removing these digits at the age of two weeks?

a. 755.02, 11200
b. 755.02, 11200-RT, 11200-59
c. 755.00, 28899
d. 755.02, 26587

5.70.   A baby boy is born with hypospadias. At seven months of age, the first stage of surgical correction is undertaken, which requires transplantation of the prepuce, but no skin flaps. What are the correct codes for this ambulatory surgery, as reported by the hospital?

Code(s):_____

5.71.   This child was born with a bilateral hydrocele. He also has reducible inguinal hernias on both sides. The condition has become troublesome, and the parents and pediatrician have decided that surgical correction is warranted for this three-year-old.

When the surgeon reports the surgical service including bilateral hernia repair with hydrocelectomy, which CPT codes are used?

Code(s):_____

Pediatric Conditions

5.72.   A three-year-old child was brought to the ER with fever, cough, and chest pain. Chest x-ray reveals diffuse bronchopneumonia. Gram stain of sputum shows numerous, small Gram-negative coccobacilli. Patient treated with ampicillin 250 mg orally t.i.d. Diagnosis: H. influenzae pneumonia. Which of the following is the correct ICD-9-CM diagnostic code assignment?

a. 487.0, 482.2
b. 487.0
c. 482.2, 487.0
d. 485, 482.2

5.73.   A child with chronic suppurative otitis media has a bilateral myringotomy performed in the outpatient surgery department. Goode T-tubes were placed without problems.

Which of the following is the correct code set?

a. 382.3, 69436-50
b. 382.3, 69436-LT, 69436-RT
c. 382.9, 69421
d. 382.9, 69421-50

5.74.   From the health record of a patient requiring hernia repair:

Outpatient Surgery

Preoperative Diagnosis: Right inguinal hernia

Postoperative Diagnosis: Same

Operation: Right inguinal herniorrhaphy

Indications: The patient is a 13-year-old male with reducible right inguinal hernia who now presents for definitive care.

Procedure: The patient was brought to the operating room and placed in the supine position. After the adequate general endotracheal anesthesia, a 4 cm incision was made in the right inguinal region. The subcutaneous tissues were divided and hemostasis achieved with electrocautery. The external oblique fascia was identified and cleaned using Metzenbaum scissors. An incision was made in the external oblique and carried down to the external ring using Metzenbaum scissors. The external oblique was freed from the underlying cord using two pair of forceps. The cremasteric fibers were divided and the hernia sac grasped. Pulling the hernia sac up on some tension, we were then able to tease off the cremasteric fibers, as well as the vas and vessels. At this point, we were able to control the hernia sac between the two hemostats. We then teased it off of the vas and vessels as we dissected proximally toward the internal ring. At this point, the sac was twisted, sutured, ligated times two, amputated, and then the sac was allowed to fall back into the peritoneal cavity. We continued the dissection distally. The anterior wall was opened using electrocautery. At this point, we placed the cord back into the inguinal canal. The external oblique fascia was closed using interrupted 4-0 silk sutures. The external oblique fascia and the structures below it were infiltrated using .05 percent Marcaine. The Scarpa's fascia was closed using 5-0 VICRYL. The skin was closed using interrupted 5-0 subcuticular stitches. Steri-Strips were applied. The patient was taken to the recovery room in satisfactory condition.

Which of the following code sets is correct for reporting this surgery?

a. 550.91, 49520-RT
b. 550.90, 49525-RT
c. 550.92, 49505-50
d. 550.90, 49505-RT

5.75. This four-year-old child was brought to the ER because of cough and fever. The mother was worried about pneumonia, and the physician's office was closed for the weekend. X-ray was negative. Diagnosis: upper respiratory infection with bilateral acute conjunctivitis. What diagnosis code(s) are assigned?

Code(s):_____

Conditions of Pregnancy, Childbirth, and the Puerperium

5.76. A patient at 26-weeks gestation had a one-hour glucose screening test. Results of this test showed a blood sugar level of 160 mg/dl. Subsequently, the patient presents to the outpatient laboratory department with a physician order for a three-hour glucose tolerance test. The reason for the test as documented on the order is: abnormal glucose on screening, rule out gestational diabetes. What is the correct code set for this outpatient ancillary services encounter?

a. 790.22, V22.2, 82951
b. 648.83, 82951
c. 648.83, 82950
d. 648.80, 82951, 82952, 82952

5.77. This 26-year-old gravida 1, para 0 female has been having spotting and has been on bedrest. She awoke this morning with severe cramping and bleeding. Her husband brought her to the hospital. After examination it was determined that she has had an incomplete early spontaneous abortion. She is in the 10th week of her pregnancy. She was taken to outpatient surgery, and a dilatation and curettage was performed. There were no complications from the procedure. She is discharged home with instructions to follow up with the physician in the office.

Which of the following is the correct code set?

a. 637.91, 58120
b. 634.91, 59812
c. 634.91, 58120
d. 634.92, 59812

5.78. This 23-year-old female is expecting her first child. She comes in for an antenatal ultrasound to confirm the gestational age of the fetus and rule out fetal growth retardation. A real-time image was taken of the fetus estimated to be at 16 weeks. What diagnosis codes and associated CPT codes (even though they may be chargemaster-assigned codes) are assigned?

Code(s):_____76805_____

5.79. This patient has a history of infertility and has been seeing her OB/GYN physician for over two years. It was elected to perform a hysterosalpingogram to assess the patency of the fallopian tubes.

Procedure Report

The patient was prepped and draped in the usual manner. The cervical os was cannulated and Sinografin® injected in retrograde fashion under fluoroscopic control. The body of the uterus appears normal. No filling defects are seen. There is no evidence of synechiae. The right fallopian tube is occluded approximately 1 cm from the body of the uterus. The left fallopian tube is patent and demonstrates free spill of contrast into the peritoneal cavity.

What codes are appropriate for this case?

Code(s):_____58340_____

Disorders of the Respiratory System

5.80. A patient with chronic obstructive asthma and an acute exacerbation of chronic bronchitis presents to the ED in respiratory distress.

Which answer represents the correct diagnosis coding for this case?

a. 493.22
b. 493.21, 491.21
c. 493.20
d. 491.21

5.81. This 65-year-old smoker with hemoptysis and chronic cough is scheduled for an outpatient bronchoscopy with an endobronchial biopsy of the lesion in the bronchus. The pathology report states "well-differentiated oat cell carcinoma of the upper bronchus." What codes would be reported?

Code(s):_____

5.82. This 59-year-old male patient presents to the emergency room with severe epistaxis, causing him to nearly choke on blood in the back of the throat. Extensive bilateral anterior cautery and packing is required to control the hemorrhage. What codes are reported? Do not assign E/M codes here.

Code(s):_____

Trauma and Poisoning

5.83. A 10-year-old is rushed to the emergency department choking on a small latex balloon, which is lodged in the trachea just past the larynx and threatening to obstruct her breathing. The piece of latex balloon is carefully removed from the trachea by use of biopsy forceps through flexible fiber-optic laryngoscope following administration of topical anesthesia.

Which codes are reported for this service in addition to the ED visit code?

a. 934.0, E912, 31577
b. 934.0, E912, 31511
c. 784.99, E912, 31530
d. 933.1, 31577

5.84.   A child is brought to the ED after he is found chewing up children's Tylenol tablets. The physician administers ipecac syrup to induce vomiting, and the child is monitored to be certain that the stomach is adequately emptied. No signs or symptoms of toxicity are noted. A blood draw is performed to check the blood level of acetaminophen. The lab results are normal, and the child is released with detailed instructions given to his mother as to what signs would indicate a need for further medical care.

Which of the following code sets is correct for reporting this visit to the ED in addition to the lab test, which is assigned via the chargemaster? Do not assign E/M codes in this case.

a. 965.4, E850.4; 36415
b. 965.4, E850.4; 99175, 36415
c. 995.29, E935.4; 99175, 36415
d. 995.29, E935.4; 99175

5.85.   This 32-year-old female was burned by hot grease in her kitchen. She is seen in the hospital-based outpatient clinic for large dressing changes on both upper extremities following second-degree burns to both arms. This is accomplished without requiring anesthesia.

What codes are assigned for this service?

Code(s):_____

5.86.   A physician performed an aspiration via thoracentesis on a patient in observation status in the hospital. The patient has advanced lung cancer with malignant pleural effusion. Later the same day, due to continued accumulation of fluid, the patient was returned to the procedure room and the same physician performed a repeat thoracentesis.

Which codes would be applicable in this case?

Code(s):_____

5.87.   A patient is treated in the ER for multiple wounds of the right forearm, hand, and knee. The physician sutured the following: single-layer closure, 3 cm, forearm; layered closure 1.5 cm, hand; 2.0 simple repair, knee.

What codes are assigned? Do not include the E/M code.

Code(s):_____

Chapter 6

Case Studies from Physician-based Health Records

Note: Even though the specific cases are divided by setting, most of the information pertaining to the diagnosis is applicable to most settings. Even the CPT codes in the ambulatory and physician sections may be reported in the same manner. The differences in coding in these two settings may involve modifier reporting, evaluation and management CPT code reporting, and other health plan reporting guidelines unique to settings. If you practice or apply codes in a particular type of setting, you may find additional information in other sections of this publication that may be pertinent to you.

Every effort has been made to follow current recognized coding guidelines and principles, as well as nationally recognized reporting guidelines. The material presented may differ from some health plan requirements for reporting. The ICD-9-CM codes used are effective through September 30, 2007, and the HCPCS (CPT and HCPCS Level II) codes are in effect through December 31, 2006. The current standard transactions and code sets named in HIPAA have been utilized, which require ICD-9-CM Volume III procedure codes for inpatients.

Instructions:

Assign all applicable ICD-9-CM and CPT codes appropriate for the setting for the case studies presented. Some of the cases provide multiple-choice answers, and the reader must select the appropriate code set. In other instances, the reader is expected to assign codes without any prompts.

The scenarios are based on selected excerpts from health records without reproducing the entire health record. However, in practice, the coding professional should have access to the entire health record. Health records are analyzed and codes are selected only with the physician's complete and appropriate documentation available. According to coding guidelines, codes are not assigned without physician documentation.

The objective of the cases and scenarios reproduced in this publication is to provide practice in assigning correct codes, not necessarily to emulate full-record analysis. For example, the reader may be asked to assign codes based only on an operative report, when in real practice a coder has access to documentation in the entire medical record.

Anesthesia Services

> **Note:** The reporting of the anesthesia section code versus the CPT code is a payer-specific policy. For these exercises, the anesthesia section code is to be reported for practice in assigning these codes. The exercises in this section are not based upon payer-specific requirements.

6.1.   Correctly apply the anesthesia code for 19367, a breast reconstruction with TRAM flap. Use your CPT book and/or Anesthesia Crosswalk, if available. Do not assign modifiers in this example.

   a. 00404
   b. 00406
   c. 00402
   d. 00400

6.2.   An epidural was given during labor. Subsequently, it was determined that the patient would require a C-section for cephalopelvic disproportion because of obstructed labor. Assign the correct anesthesia code and ICD-9-CM codes. Modifiers are not used in this example.

   a. 660.11, 653.41, 64475
   b. 660.11, 653.01, 01961
   c. 660.11, 653.41, 01967, 01968
   d. 660.11, 653.91, 01996

6.3.   A three-year-old child came to the outpatient surgery center to have dental caries filled and caps placed on his teeth due to nursing bottle decay syndrome. Anesthesia was provided by an anesthesiologist. Assign the correct CPT and ICD-9-CM codes for the anesthesia services. Modifiers are included in this example.

   a. 521.00, 00170-AA-23
   b. 521.00, 00170-AA, 99100-23
   c. 520.7, 00170-P1-23-AA
   d. 521.30, 00170, 99100-23-AA

6.4.   A five-year-old patient was brought into the emergency room with a deep 2 cm laceration of his scalp. The child was combative and would not allow staff to cleanse the wound. The mother held the child in her lap while the ED physician administered 10 mg of Versed intranasally. When the child was sufficiently sedated, one of the ED nurses monitored the patient's vital signs, and the physician performed a layered repair of the laceration. The intraservice time for the procedure did not exceed 30 minutes.

Assign the correct CPT code for the Versed and modifier, if appropriate, for this case:

a. 99143
b. 99144
c. 12031-47
d. 12031-QS

6.5. A two-month-old infant is brought to the operating room for repair of coarctation of the aorta with pump oxygenator. Anesthesia is provided by an anesthesiologist. The infant is in critical condition and may not survive. Assign the correct ICD-9-CM and CPT codes, including physical status, Level I and II modifiers, and qualifying conditions for this procedure.

Code(s): _____ 00561-AA-P5 , 99100, 99144

Disorders of the Blood and Blood-Forming Organs

6.6. This patient with abnormal blood test underwent bone marrow aspiration from the sternum. Results show acute lymphocytic leukemia. How is this coded?

a. 204.90, 38221
b. 208.00, 20220
c. 204.90, 38220
d. 204.00, 38220

6.7. A patient is admitted with cervical lymphadenopathy. A needle biopsy of a cervical lymph node is performed and confirmed Hodgkin's sarcoma disease. Which of the following is the correct code assignment?

a. 201.21, 38505
b. 201.91, 38505
c. 201.21, 38500
d. 785.6, 38510

6.8. From the physician services documentation of a 39-year-old male:

History of Present Illness: The patient is a 39-year-old, African-American male who has a known history of sickle-cell anemia. He was admitted to the hospital with diffuse extremity pains with minor complaints of pain along the right inguinal area. They started on Friday, became a little bit better on Saturday, then improved, and started again in the last 24 hours. He denies any problems with cough or sputum or production. He denies any problems with fever.

Past Medical History: See recent medical records in charts. He does have a new onset of diabetes, probably related to his hemochromatosis. He does have evidence of iron overload with high ferritins.

Review of Systems: Otherwise unremarkable except for those related to his pain. He denies any problems with any fever or night sweats. No cough or sputum production. Denies any changes in gastrointestinal or genitourinary habits. No blood per rectum or urine.

Physical Examination: This is a 39-year-old, African-American male who is conscious and cooperative. He is oriented × 3 and appears in no acute distress. Vital signs are stable. HEENT is remarkable for icterus present in oral mucosa and conjunctivae, which is a chronic event for him. The neck is supple. No evidence of any gross lymphadenopathy of the cervical, supraclavicular, or axillary areas. The heart is irregularly irregular in rate without any murmurs heard. Lungs are clear to auscultation and percussion. The abdomen is soft and benign without any gross organomegaly. Extremities reveal no edema. No palpable cords. He does have some tenderness along the inner aspects of his right lower extremity near the inguinal area; however, no masses were palpable and no point tenderness is noted.

The patient was treated for his painful sickle crisis with IV fluids and pain medications. He had a problem with his right inguinal area. He had evidence of pain. There was some pain on abduction of his right lower extremity. The examination really was unremarkable. There was no evidence of any Holman, no palpable cords, no masses were palpable.

Because of his sickle-cell anemia, rule out the possibility of avascular necrosis of the femur. Complete x-rays of his femur and hip were carried out. However, these were both negative. Patient is being discharged after improvement. To follow up with me in one week.

Diagnoses: 1. Painful sickle-cell crisis
2. Type II diabetes mellitus
3. Chronic atrial fibrillation

Condition on Discharge: Stable

What diagnosis codes would the physician report on this case?

a. 282.61, 789.09, 427.31, 250.00
b. 282.62, 733.42, 427.31, 250.00
c. 282.62
d. 282.62, 427.31, 250.00

6.9.   This established patient comes to the physician office and after evaluation requires a glucose tolerance test. The physician drew the three specimens and performed the test at the office. What would be the correct procedure codes assigned in addition to the E/M visit?

Code(s):_____

6.10.   A patient was given 3 units of packed red blood cells and 3 units of fresh frozen plasma. How is this correctly reported?

Code(s):_____

Disorders of the Cardiovascular System

6.11.   Patient admitted through the ED with diagnosis of CVA. CT scan of the brain showed a thrombotic infarction of the brain. Patient has a history of hypertension and was continued on captopril. Patient experienced residuals of hemiplegia and aphasia, but they were not present at the time of discharge. Which of the following is the correct diagnostic code assignment?

a. 436, 401.9
b. 434.01, 401.9
c. 434.00, 436, 401.9
d. 434.01, 342.90, 784.3

6.12. From the health record of a 63-year-old female patient:

Admission Date: 11/19/XX

Discharge Date: 11/24/XX

Final Diagnoses: 1. Coronary artery disease
                     2. Sick sinus syndrome

Procedures: 1. Permanent AV sequential pacemaker insertion
                     2. Percutaneous transluminal coronary angioplasty

History of Present Illness: The patient is a 63-year-old female who was admitted to another hospital on 11/19/XX, after experiencing tachycardia. At that hospital, she underwent a cardiac catheterization, showing the presence of severe single-vessel coronary artery disease. The patient has a history of sick sinus syndrome. She was transferred to our hospital to undergo a percutaneous transluminal angioplasty.

Physical Examination: No physical abnormalities were found on the cardiovascular examination. Pulse 50, blood pressure 100/66. HEENT: PERRLA, faint carotid bruits. Lungs: Clear to percussion and auscultation. Heart: Normal sinus rhythm with a 2.6 systolic ejection murmur. Extremities and abdomen were negative. Laboratory data: Unremarkable.

Hospital Course: To manage the patient's sick sinus syndrome, a permanent AV sequential pacemaker was implanted by transvenous technique on 11/19. On 11/20, the patient underwent a PTCA without complications and good results were obtained. Postoperatively, the patient was stable and was subsequently discharged. Patient was discharged on the following medications: Cardizem, 30 mg p.o. q. 6 hours; ASA, 5 grains q. a.m.; Metamucil and Colace p.r.n.; Nitro paste $^{1}/_{2}$ inch q. 6 hours.

Which of the following is the correct code assignment for the procedures performed?

a. 427.0, 414.01, 92982, 33206
b. 414.01, 427.81, 92995, 33208
c. 414.01, 427.81, 92982, 33208
d. 427.81, 414.01, 92982, 33200

6.13. A patient is seen in the hospital with a diagnosis of congestive heart failure due to hypertensive heart disease. The patient responds positively to Lasix therapy. The patient also has chronic kidney disease stage V and is a type I diabetic. Assign the correct diagnostic codes.

Code(s):_____

6.14. This 55-year-old male was brought to the ER with chest pain. The final diagnostic statement on the patient's record stated "preinfarction syndrome." What is the correct diagnostic code?

Code(s):_____

6.15. A patient had an implantable vascular access device placed seven weeks ago for chemotherapy administered each week in the ambulatory surgery department of the hospital. The full cycle is now complete and it is no longer needed. The physician surgically removed the centrally tunneled central venous catheter. No services for the carcinoma of the sigmoid colon are provided. The cancer has not been resected yet, because the chemo was utilized in an attempt to shrink the tumor before surgery was initiated. The correct codes for reporting by the physician will be:

Code(s):_____

Disorders of the Digestive System

6.16. This 30-year-old male patient has exhausted all types of conservative treatment for his morbid obesity. He has been treated by me in this clinic for three years. He has also been treated for hypertension and hypercholesterolemia. With these risk factors and with careful review of his condition and symptoms and with multiple consultations with him regarding the risks and benefits of the surgery, it is decided to perform a vertical-banded gastroplasty.

What diagnosis and procedure codes are used in this surgical case?

a. 278.00, 43842, 43846-51
b. 278.01, 401.9, 272.0, 43842
c. 278.01, 401.1, 272.0, 43842, 43843-59
d. 278.01, 43848

6.17. This 25-year-old woman has been treated for Crohn's disease of the small intestine since 18 years of age. She has had several exacerbations but has been maintained on drug therapy. She is being seen now for extreme pain, which on x-ray shows small bowel obstruction. Patient is taken to surgery immediately. During the surgery, a partial excision of the terminal ileum is performed to release the obstruction. There is also a section of the jejunum that is very inflamed. This section is also resected. An end-to-end anastomosis is completed on all segments. The patient tolerates the procedure well. Which of the following is the correct code assignment?

a. 560.89, 555.0, 44120, 44121-51
b. 555.0, 560.89, 44120, 44121-51
c. 555.0, 560.89, 44120, 44121
d. 555.2, 560.89, 44020

6.18. During a colonoscopy, the surgeon biopsies an inflamed area in the ascending colon and removes a polyp in the descending colon with use of hot biopsy forceps. What is the correct CPT coding assignment?

Code(s):_____

6.19. This 11-year-old patient had a bilateral tonsillectomy and adenoidectomy performed due to adenotonsillar hyperplasia. What codes are assigned?

Code(s):_____

6.20. This 50-year-old male patient had a cholecystectomy done with exploration of the common duct for stones. During the procedure an incidental appendectomy was performed. How are the procedure codes reported if the payer requires that both procedures be reported?

Code(s):_____

6.21. The patient has thrombosed external hemorrhoids. The surgeon incises two hemorrhoids. What codes would be assigned?

Code(s):_____

6.22. A laparoscopic cholecystectomy with cholangiography was performed on a 35-year-old female patient due to symptomatic cholelithiasis. The pathology report showed acute and chronic cholecystitis with lithiasis and was documented by the physician. What codes would be assigned?

Code(s):_____

6.23. Patient Betty Jones's gastric band has been adjusted so many times that it is losing its elasticity and starting to slip on her stomach and migrate up around her esophagus. She enters to undergo removal of her current gastric band and placement of a new adjustable band. Her weight loss has been steady and appropriate. Assign the CPT code(s) for the procedure of laparoscopic removal and replacement of an adjustable gastric band.

 a. 43773
 b. 43771, 43770
 c. 43774, 43770
 d. 43888

Evaluation and Management (E/M) Services

6.24. A 45-year-old patient was found unconscious in a park and was brought to the emergency department by the police. A comprehensive physical examination was performed, and the medical decision making was of high complexity. The ED physician documents that he was unable to obtain a history due to the condition of the patient.

[handwritten margin notes: CPT primary by procedure, OUPT - procedures, ICD inpt - procedures, R principle DX]

What is the correct E/M code assignment for the physician's services for this encounter?

a. 99284
b. 99285 *(circled)*
c. 99285-52
d. 99291

6.25. Dr. Jones saw Mr. Stone at the VA domiciliary *[handwritten: -assisted living]* after the patient had an episode of severe choking at the noon meal. He did not aspirate any food. The patient stubbornly refused to go to the clinic but agreed to be seen if the doctor came over. Mr. Stone has had several episodes of choking in the past few days, which he attributed completely to his sinus medication causing a very dry mouth. Dr. Jones documented a problem-focused interval history and an expanded problem-focused examination. Medical decision making was of low complexity. Another medication was substituted. He was advised to drink liquids with his meals and take smaller bites. Give the correct ICD-9-CM and CPT codes for this visit.

a. 784.99, 783.3, 99335
b. 933.1, 99334
c. 933.1, 99335 *(circled)*
d. 783.3, 99334

6.26. A 59-year-old male patient is scheduled for his routine physical exam; however, the physician finds a mass in the abdomen, schedules an abdominal CT scan, and orders lab for blood work and a UA. The physician performs a detailed history and examination with medical decision-making of moderate complexity. The patient has been a patient of this physician for several years. What E/M codes are assigned?

Code(s): __99396__ *[handwritten: for additional work ordered for mass]* __99214-25__ *[handwritten: modifier to show additional E/M service provided on same day]*

6.27. An elderly patient is brought to the emergency department by an ambulance due to a cardiac arrest suffered at home. The ED physician provides critical care services to the patient for a total duration of two hours before the attending physician admits the patient to the cardiac care unit.

What codes are assigned for the ED physician?

Code(s): __99291   99292 x 2__

6.28. From the clinic record of a family practice physician:

Subjective: Amy is a 12-month-old female patient of mine *[handwritten: established]* who presents to the clinic today with a possible ear infection. She has been waking up at night and is irritable. She has had some cold-like symptoms as well as some purulent drainage from her eyes over the past four days or so. She has had a fever since last night. This morning it is near normal. She has had a couple of ear infections *[handwritten: infection]* in the past. No cough, and appetite has been slightly decreased.

Objective: In no acute distress; alert and interactive. Temperature is 100.7°F

[handwritten: alert]   *[handwritten: signs]*

HEENT: Lids and sclera are normal. No erythema noted. She does have some purulent drainage mostly on the left lower lid. She also has a purulent nasal discharge that is yellow to green. TMs are erythematous bilaterally, bulging and with purulent effusions. Oropharynx is nonerythematous without lesions. Tonsils are unremarkable. Two teeth on the bottom.

Neck: Neck is supple with good ROM. Positive cervical adenopathy

Lungs: Clear

Heart: Regular rate and rhythm without murmurs

Assessment: 1. Acute bilateral suppurative otitis media
2. Upper respiratory infection

Plan: She was placed on Augmentin® 40 mg/kg divided t.i.d for 10 days. I recommended lots of fluids and rest, decongestants, and elevating the head of the bed for symptomatic control. I believe the eyes are due to backup from her nose and not due to conjunctivitis at this point. They will need to contact the clinic if she develops any erythema or persistent drainage. They are comfortable with this plan and will contact the clinic with any further questions or concerns. The history is detailed, the examination is expanded problem focused, and the medical decision making is of moderate complexity.

What ICD-9 and CPT codes would be reported for this visit?

Code(s):_____99214_____

6.29.   Dr. Smith sees his patient, Bob Jones, in the nursing home where he has resided for eleven months. Bob is pretty stable and happy, and Dr. Smith performs an annual physical examination and completes the minimum data set instrument. He performs and documents a detailed interval history, comprehensive examination and performs medical decision making of low complexity. Assign the appropriate CPT code.

a. 99304
b. 99308
c. 99318 *Other nursing facilities services – annual assessment*
d. 99313

Endocrine, Nutritional and Metabolic Diseases, and Immunity Disorders

6.30.   A six-year-old child, an established patient, is seen in the pediatrician's office for routine immunization. The physician speaks with the child's father about national immunization recommendations, risks and benefits of vaccine provided, and gives follow-up instructions for possible side-effect treatment. The patient receives a DtaP immunization IM. Assign the appropriate code(s).

a. 90467, 90700
b. 99213, 90465, 90700
c. 90465, 90700
d. 90465

6.31. A 35-year-old male was referred to the endocrinology clinic for symptoms that involved headaches, deepening voice with enlargement, and coarsening of facial features, hands, and feet gradually appearing over the past 3 years. The patient was referred by his dentist, who noticed increased spacing between his teeth over the same time period. Growth hormone levels tested by the endocrinology clinic were elevated for an adult male. Follow-up IGF-1 tests confirmed the diagnosis. The patient was scheduled for a CT scan of the brain to rule out pituitary tumor. Diagnosis after the second clinic visit was acromegaly and ruled out pituitary adenoma. Give the correct ICD-9-CM code for the second clinic visit.

   a. 253.0, 225.0
   b. 253.0
   c. 227.3
   d. 253.0, 227.3

6.32. A 62-year-old postmenopausal female is seen in the clinic for a refill of her estrogen patch. On ROS she relays that she has no complaints. Physical exam is unremarkable and prescription for the estrogen patch is refilled.

Assessment: Menopause

Assuming documentation meets the requirements for a level II visit, which of the following is the correct code set for this clinic visit?

   a. V07.4, V49.81, 99212
   b. 627.2, 99212
   c. 256.31, 99212
   d. V58.69, V49.81, 99212

6.33. This 45-year-old female diabetic patient comes in for her quarterly evaluation of her condition. She has type I diabetes, which has been in good control now. She has diabetic nephropathy and retinopathy. What diagnosis codes are assigned?

Code(s):_____

6.34. From the hospital record of a patient requiring diabetic management:

Hospital Course: This 49-year-old female patient has a history of type I diabetes mellitus and is on 15 units of NPH and 10 of Regular in the morning, and 10 units of NPH and 5 of Regular in the evening. The patient started having symptoms of nausea and vomiting. The patient at the same time had increased frequency of urination and polydipsia. The patient was severely dehydrated on admission. There was no evidence of thrombophlebitis, varicosities, or edema on examination of the extremities. The patient was hydrated and, as a result, her blood sugar decreased from more than 600 to normal levels. The patient was discharged with the diagnosis of diabetic ketoacidosis, dehydration, polydipsia, and increased frequency of urination.

What diagnosis codes would be assigned for this admission for the physician's services?

Code(s):_____

6.35. Assign the code(s) for a patient with type II diabetic gastroparesis who is presently on insulin.

    a. 250.60, 536.3, V58.67
    b. 250.60, 586.3, 337.1, V58.67
    c. 250.61, 536.3
    d. 250.62, 536.3, V58.67

6.36. A 65-year-old female patient has a long history of type II diabetes mellitus with diabetic retinopathy. She is being seen today for her retinal ischemia and diabetic macular edema. What codes are assigned for this proliferative retinopathy?

    a. 250.50, 362.07
    b. 250.50, 362.06, 362.07
    c. 250.50, 362.02, 362.07
    d. 362.02, 363.07

Disorders of the Genitourinary System

6.37. A patient in end-stage renal failure requires outpatient hemodialysis three times a week while he is awaiting kidney transplant. He has an A-V fistula in his left arm for vascular access. Which of the following code sets is appropriate for reporting physician services for this 55-year-old male for the month of August?

    a. 585.6, 90925
    b. V56.0, 90921
    c. 585.6, V56.8, 90999
    d. 585.6, 90921

6.38. From the health record of a patient receiving endoscopy services:

The patient presents to the hospital outpatient department for follow-up cystoscopy for a history of high-grade bladder cancer. This was resected seven years ago and was found to be Grade III with superficial muscle invasion. A cycle of chemotherapy was provided, but no radiation. No recurrence has been noted since then. CT scan of the pelvis six months ago was negative for masses. Sometimes the patient experiences painful ejaculation, but no hematospermia has been found. Cytology to date has been negative, so a biopsy will not be performed, because there has been seven years without recurrence.

Cystoscopy examination today shows a normal anterior urethra and prostatic urethra. There is some lateral lobe prostatic hypertrophy, just barely touching in the midline. The bladder is nontrabeculated. There are no tumors, stones, or carcinoma in situ evident on examination. There is clear efflux from each orifice. The area of resection was around the right ureteral orifice, which appears a little atrophic, but patent.

Impression: Stable transitional cell of the bladder without recurrence with mild benign prostatic hypertrophy.

Which of the following code sets is appropriate for this case?

a. V67.6, V10.51, 600.00, 52000
b. 188.9, 600.0, 52000
c. 600.00, V10.51, 52010
d. V67.00, 188.9, 52000

6.39. This 40-year-old with ureterolithiasis will have a planned cystourethroscopy with stone removal performed. One stone is removed, and after several attempts, the second stone cannot be removed through the scope. Ultrasonic fragmentation is then used on the second stone. What codes would be assigned in this case?

Code(s): _____52310, 52325_____

6.40. This 35-year-old female has had four cesarean births in the past six years and has decided to proceed with sterilization.

Operative Report

Procedure: Laparoscopic tubal ligation with application of Falope-Rings

Diagnosis: Multiparity; desired sterilization

Anesthesia: General

Under general anesthesia and in the supine lithotomy position, the patient was prepped and draped in the usual sterile fashion. A two-puncture laparoscopy was performed in the usual manner with insufflation through a Verres needle inserted infraumbilically. Through the first puncture, a trocar was inserted infraumbilically, followed by the laparoscope. A second trocar was inserted suprapubically in the midline, followed initially by a probe and then a Falope-Ring applicator. Both tubes were ligated in their mid-segment. On the left side, two rings were applied because of the round position of the Falope-Ring director. The right tube was singly ligated. The operation was completed, and the trocar sites were closed with subcuticular sutures of 2-0 VICRYL. The patient was transferred to the recovery room in good condition.

What are the correct codes to assign for this service?

Code(s): _____58671_____

6.41. This 35-year-old male patient has had an eruption of molluscum contagiosum on the penis for several months. He finally sought medical attention. He was advised to have these lesions removed. He is here now for the procedure. The patient had destruction of a penile molluscum contagiosum performed by cryosurgery and laser surgery. What are the correct code(s)?

Code(s): _____54056, 54057_____

Infectious Diseases

6.42. This seven-year-old child patient was seen for cramping abdominal pain, fever, and bloody diarrhea. He has been relatively healthy in the past and has been a patient of mine since his birth. A detailed history and exam were performed, with medical decision making of low complexity done. Results of stool specimen indicate Entamoeba histolytica. Diagnosis: Acute amebiasis. Patient was given iodoquinol, and mother was instructed to return if there was not sufficient improvement. He is to have a reexamination in two weeks. What codes are assigned?

Code(s):_____

6.43. The employees of this clinic who work in the patient care areas are receiving the vaccination for hepatitis B in the employee health clinic. What codes would be reported for this service given as an IM injection?

Code(s):_____

6.44. This five-year-old child is here in the office for her routine annual child exam. She has been healthy, and there were no problems encountered. Active immunization with live measles, mumps, and rubella virus vaccine was given during her annual preventive medicine visit for this established patient. What are the correct codes?

Code(s):_____

Disorders of the Skin and Subcutaneous Tissue

6.45. An elderly patient has an abscess formation around a pacemaker pocket on his chest wall that requires that the device be removed and the pocket reformed in another location. Which of the following code sets is appropriate for this outpatient surgical service? Do not assign E codes in this example.

a. 996.61, 682.2, 33222
b. 682.2, 33222
c. 996.61, 33233
d. 996.72, 682.2, 33999

6.46. This 18-year-old male patient has pustular acne that requires periodic opening and/or removal of milia and comedones from his face in the dermatology clinic on a recurring basis. These visits do not include medical history or examination by the physician—only the procedure. What codes might be assigned for this service?

Code(s):_____

6.47. This 54-year-old female has noticed areas of raised skin on her face, mostly on her forehead. She states that they have grown quickly with the size almost doubling in three weeks. She has concerns that this may be skin cancer and wants an evaluation. She is scheduled for surgery and the physician abraded six areas on the patient's face. They were determined to be keratoses. What codes would be assigned for the surgery episode of care?

Code(s):_____

6.48. A patient with significant second and third degree burns over his back and buttocks underwent debridement of approximately 175 sq cm of necrotic eschar tissue and application of 325 sq cm of Mediskin®. Assign the appropriate CPT code(s).

Code(s):_____

6.49. This patient received 45 sq cm of TranCyte® to an ulcer of the lateral left foot. Assign the appropriate CPT procedure code(s).

Code(s):_____

Behavioral Health Conditions

6.50. A patient in a clinic received individual insight-oriented psychotherapy for more than 25 minutes. The physician also provided E/M services that included a problem-focused history, problem-focused examination, and straightforward level of medical decision making. What CPT codes(s) would this physician report?

a. 90805
b. 90804, 99212
c. 90811
d. 90810, 99212

6.51. A young adult who is self-referred presents as a new patient in the clinic with complaints of an increasing inability to concentrate and complete tasks. He states that he has always been easily distracted and often leaves tasks uncompleted, but in recent years his restlessness has increased. He is perceived as unreliable at work and is concerned about future job advancements. The physician takes a comprehensive history and exam and performs medical decision making of moderate complexity. The physician's diagnosis is attention deficit disorder, DSM-IV 314.9, and the plan of treatment is to begin Ritalin and to follow up to assess dosage and efficacy. The physician documents that he spent 45 minutes in counseling with the patient.

What are the correct ICD-9-CM and CPT codes to report this encounter?

a. 314.00, 99214
b. 314.00, 99204
c. 314.01, 99204
d. 314.9, 99214

6.52. This 25-year-old man is admitted to the hospital for acute alcohol inebriation. He was brought in by the police because he was causing a disturbance. He is well known to me due to his continuous alcoholism. He has refused treatment or admission to alcohol rehab. What diagnosis code(s) are assigned in this case?

Code(s):_____

6.53. Physician progress note states: This patient is a 75-year-old female who has severe Alzheimer's disease. The patient shows no acute change in mental status from her last visit. She requires continuous care because of her dementia, but the family is insistent on keeping her at home. She has made repeated attempts to leave and has wandered off in the past, hence the need for continuous care. She at times recognizes her daughter, the primary caregiver, but most of the time she is unaware of her identity. What diagnosis codes are reported for this visit?

Code(s):_____

Disorders of the Musculoskeletal System and Connective Tissue

6.54. A patient had an osteopathic physician as a primary care provider. The patient suffered from sternoclavicular somatic dysfunction. An evaluation was done using a detailed history and an expanded problem-focused exam, with low medical decision making. The physician performed osteopathic manipulation to the affected body region. What codes should be assigned to this office visit?

a. 739.7, 99213-25, 98925
b. 739.2, 98925
c. 786.59, 99212-25, 98925
d. 739.8, 99213

6.55. From the health record of a young athlete:

Preoperative Diagnosis: Fracture of fibula, left

Postoperative Diagnosis: Left distal fracture of fibula

Procedure: Reduction of fibular fracture

Indications and Description: This 14-year-old gymnast felt pain in her leg after vaulting at practice. She is unable to bear any weight on her left leg.

Physical examination revealed foot and ankle to be normal. The neurovascular status of the foot is normal. The ankle is nontender and not swollen. Findings are confined to the distal fibula, two inches proximal to the lateral malleolus. There is point tenderness in this area. An x-ray of the tibia and fibula shows a displaced fracture of the distal fibula.

The fracture was reduced, and the patient was put in a short leg splint with extensive padding placed over the fracture site. Crutches were provided, and she is instructed not to place any weight on the foot. She was given a supply of Tylenol 3 for pain and will follow up at the clinic in 10 days.

Which of the following is the correct code assignment?

a. 824.8, E917.0, 27788, 99070
b. 824.2, E917.0, 27788, 29515-51
c. 823.81, E917.0, 27786, L4350
d. 824.4. E917.0, 27810, 29515-51, L4396

6.56. This 16-year-old was tackled during a football game 3 weeks ago and received fracture care with a cast for a fracture of the fibula. He is coming in today for a walking cast, which was applied after an x-ray in the clinic. This converted an existing cast to one that did not require crutches. What are the codes that will appear on the CMS-1500 form that is sent to the insurance company?

Code(s):_____

6.57. This 42-year-old male was the driver of an automobile that hit a tree. He was brought to the ER for treatment. After examination, the only injury was a left supracondylar femur fracture. He was taken to surgery for ORIF.

Preoperative Diagnosis: Left supracondylar femur fracture

Postoperative Diagnosis: Comminuted left supracondylar femur fracture

Report of Operation: Open reduction and internal fixation

What codes are assigned by the surgeon?

Code(s):_____

6.58. This 70-year-old patient is seen for his follow-up care for his arthritis. He has generalized degenerative arthritis mostly of his knees, hip, and the lumbosacral spine. It is getting progressively worse. He has been on Relafen® and has been somewhat stable. He refuses surgery and is not a prime candidate because of his arteriosclerotic heart disease and hypertension. An expanded problem-focused history and exam were performed with medical decision making of moderate complexity. A prescription was written to renew his Relafen and his other medications for his ASHD and hypertension. What codes are assigned for this visit?

Code(s):_____

6.59. When back pain is due to a psychological condition, how is this coded?

a. 724.5
b. 724.5, 307.89
c. 307.89
d. 307.89, 724.5

Neoplasms

6.60. A non-Medicare patient with carcinoma of the oral cavity and lip is receiving daily intramuscular injections of interferon alfa-2a (3 million units) in the outpatient cancer center. Which of the following will be reported for this service? The payer does accept HCPCS level II codes for drugs.

a. V58.11, 149.8, 96401, J9213
b. 149.8, 90772, J9213
c. 145.9, 140.9, 90772
d. V58.11, 96549

6.61. This 32-year-old female with asthma and known cervical dysplasia is admitted for an endoscopic cervical biopsy with endocervical curettage. The procedure was performed without incident. The pathology report shows carcinoma in situ of the cervix. What codes are assigned?

Code(s):_____

6.62. This patient had a history of carcinoma of the colon five years ago without reoccurrence or metastasis. After several tests he is admitted now for probable renal cell carcinoma, thought to be a new primary. Laparoscopic partial nephrectomy of the kidney was performed without incident. Frozen-section pathology report reveals a lipoma. What codes are assigned for the procedure performed in the hospital?

Code(s):_____

6.63. This 56-year-old female recently had an abdominal sonogram performed for elevated liver enzymes and abdominal pain. This showed a mass in the liver and a needle biopsy was done. The patient is now admitted with hepatocellular carcinoma. Wedge resection is performed without incident. What are the appropriate codes for this hospital admission?

Code(s):_____

6.64. This 42-year-old female patient has known ovarian carcinoma, and she is being admitted for right oophorectomy. Patient has type I diabetes mellitus, and during her stay we had a hard time controlling her blood sugar. Right oophorosalpingectomy with lymph node samplings and peritoneal biopsies was completed to stage the cancer. Diagnosis: Ovarian carcinoma, without metastasis, and diabetes out of control. What are the correct codes for this admission?

Code(s):_____

Disorders of the Nervous System and Sense Organs

6.65. A patient has right trigeminal neuralgia, and it is decided that Gamma knife stereotactic radiosurgery will be performed. A Leksell® stereotactic head frame was placed prior to the procedure, which consisted of a single shot to a total dose of 7,500 centigrade delivered to the 50 percent isodose line.

What are the CPT level I procedure codes reported for this service?

a. 61793, 20660
b. 61793
c. 64600, 61795
d. 61795

6.66. From the health record of a surgical patient:

A Medicare beneficiary has a procedure to promote nerve regeneration at a pain management center. The patient is placed in a prone position, and a midline incision overlying the affected vertebrae is made. The fascia is divided and the paravertebral muscles are retracted. The physician places the inductive electrode pads in the epidural space proximal to the damaged spinal segment. The pulse generator is sutured over the muscles, just below the skin, and closed with a layer closure.

Which of the following HCPCS/CPT codes will be reported for the surgical service?

a. E0756
b. 63685, E0756
c. 63650
d. 63650, E0756

6.67. From the health record of a patient having eye surgery:

Operative Report

Preoperative Diagnosis:	Open-angle glaucoma, right eye; diabetes mellitus, type I
Postoperative Diagnosis:	Same
Operation:	Initial trabeculectomy, right eye
Anesthesia:	Local

Procedure: Full-thickness lid speculums were placed. A fornix-based, conjunctival flap was performed in the superior temporal quadrant. An angulated blade breaker was used to make grooves at the site of the future scleral flap at approximately the ten o'clock position. Next, a three-sided, partial-thickness, scleral flap was created using a #64 Beaver blade. A trabeculectomy was performed using a sharp blade. A peripheral iridectomy was performed. The scleral flap was irrigated and found to be free flowing. The conjunctiva was closed using two 8-0 collagen sutures at the twelve o'clock position and one 8-0 collagen at the nine o'clock position. Decadron® 10 mg was injected subconjunctivally in the inferior fornix. Maxitrol ointment, patch, and shield were applied.

What are the correct codes for this procedure performed in the hospital surgery center?

a. 365.9, 250.00, 66172-RT
b. 365.11, 250.01, 65850
c. 250.51, 365.44, 66170-52
d. 365.10, 250.01, 66170-RT

6.68. From the health record of a patient having office-based surgery:

Operative Report

Preoperative Diagnosis:	Bilateral entropion
Postoperative Diagnosis:	Bilateral entropion
Operation:	Repair of entropion of right eye
Anesthesia:	Local

Procedure: The patient was sterilely prepped and draped for ocular solution of 2 percent lidocaine, mixed in equal proportions with 0.75 percent Marcaine with the addition of Wydase, and given a modified Van Lint technique to the right eye. Incision was made in the inferior lid margin extended inferiorly. This consisted of a diamond shape, with 6 mm lengthwise incisions interconducted. Hemostasis was obtained using wet-field cautery. The incision was then sutured using a tapered needle. The first suture was placed through the approximate lash line, in addition to one suture through the area of the meibomian gland. Using the tapered needle, the tarsal plate was approximated and reapproximated. The incision was then reapproximated with subcuticular sutures. This was followed by implantation of approximately four interrupted skin sutures using 6-0 nylon.

What are the correct codes for this procedure performed in the hospital surgery center?

a. 374.00, 67921-RT
b. 374.00, 67921-50
c. 374.10, 67921-RT
d. 374.00, 67923

6.69. This 71-year-old male had a stroke six months ago. He is being followed during his therapy for the residuals of his stroke with evaluation of progress. He has right-sided hemiplegia and aphasia. He also has hypertension and diabetes mellitus, type II. What diagnosis codes are assigned?

Code(s):_____

Newborn/Congenital Disorders

6.70. A neonatologist is treating a spontaneously delivered newborn with respiratory failure and erythroblastosis fetalis due to Rh antibodies. An exchange transfusion is required to stabilize this critically ill baby receiving services in the neonatal intensive care unit. The baby remains on CPAP to assist breathing and prevent further respiratory failure.

Which of the following code sets is reported by the neonatologist for this second day of care following birth?

a. 773.0, 770.84, 99296
b. V30.00, 99295, 36450, 94657
c. V30.00, 773.0, 770.84, 99296, 36450
d. 773.0, 770.84, 99296

6.71. A baby boy is born with hypospadias. At six months of age, the first stage of surgical correction is undertaken, which requires transplantation of the prepuce, but no skin flaps. Which of the following codes are reported for this ambulatory surgery?

a. 752.61, 54304
b. 607.9, 54300
c. 752.61, 54322
d. 753.8, 54304

6.72. A congenital bilateral hydrocele has become troublesome, along with reducible inguinal hernias on both sides, and the parents and pediatrician have decided that surgical correction is warranted for their two-year-old son.

When the surgeon reports the surgical service, including bilateral hernia repair with hydrocelectomy, which of the following CPT codes are used?

a. 49495-50, 55041-51
b. 49500-50
c. 49500-RT, 49500-LT
d. 55041, 49500

6.73. A hospital-based pediatric clinic is treating a newborn with talipes equinovarus by manipulation and short leg casting. Which of the following code sets is reported for a visit where the condition is evaluated with a problem-focused history and examination and parents' questions are answered, followed by foot and ankle manipulation and replacement of the plaster cast?

a. 754.69, 29450
b. 736.71, 29405
c. 754.51. 29405
d. 754.51, 99212-25, 29450

6.74. From the health record of a newborn delivered in a birthing room setting:

This infant was born in the New Beginnings Birthing Center adjacent to Children's Hospital at 10:58 a.m. on September 1. He weighed 8 lbs 5 oz and was 21 inches long with Apgars of 9 and 9. Dr. Smith performed a history and examination immediately following his vaginal delivery with no abnormal findings. Parents declined circumcision or administration of hepatitis B. Ricky was discharged at 6:30 p.m. with his mother.

Which of the following code sets is appropriate for Dr. Smith's services on September 1?

a. V30.2, 99431, 99238
b. V30.00, 99435
c. V30.2, 99431
d. V30.2, 99435

Pediatric Conditions

6.75. A six-month-old infant, born prematurely, presents for his monthly injection for RSV. The nurse documents Synagis® 40 mg, IM.

Which of the following code sets is correct for reporting this office visit?

a. 99212, 90378, 90772
b. 90378, 90471
c. 99212, J1565
d. 90378, 90772

6.76. This five-year-old female patient presents to the office for bilateral ear drainage, fever, and ear pain. There is a large perforation in the left eardrum visible. She was given Augmentin twice a day for seven days and will be seen in follow-up.

Diagnosis: Acute suppurative otitis media. An expanded problem-focused history and examination was performed, with medical decision making of moderate complexity.

What are the correct codes for this case?

Code(s):_____

6.77. The same patient in item 6.76 comes in now after the acute otitis media has resolved. We will place ventilating tubes for her chronic problems.

Preoperative Diagnosis:	Chronic recurrent suppurative otitis media
Postoperative Diagnosis:	Same
Operation:	Bilateral myringotomy, placement of permanent ventilating tube
Anesthesia:	General

Procedure: A standard myringotomy incision was made and a copious amount of serous fluid suctioned from the middle ear cleft. A Goode T-tube was placed without problems. The procedure was then repeated on the left side in the same manner.

What are the codes reported by the surgeon for this procedure performed in the hospital surgery center?

Code(s):_____

6.78. This seven-year-old child with an acute attack of his childhood asthma is taken to ER. Post-bronchodilator spirometry reveals continued bronchospasm with intractable wheezing. An expanded problem-focused history and examination were performed with moderate medical decision making. He is subsequently admitted to the hospital. What codes are assigned by the ER physician?

Code(s):_____

Conditions of Pregnancy, Childbirth, and the Puerperium

6.79.   This 29-year-old female has had two spontaneous abortions because of incompetent cervix. Because of this, she had a cervical cerclage placed in the third month of this pregnancy. She is coming in now to have the cerclage removed under general anesthesia. She was taken to surgery, and the cerclage was removed without complication. She was discharged that evening. There are no signs of labor, and the membranes are intact. She was instructed on the signs of labor and will see me in the office in two days. Estimated due date is in two weeks, but labor could begin at any time.

What are the correct code assignments for this case?

a. 654.53, 59871
b. 654.53 (The cerclage removal is part of the global package.)
c. 622.5, with appropriate E/M procedure
d. 622.5, 59871

6.80.   This 29-year-old patient is being admitted for evacuation of uterus for blighted ovum. She is in her second month of pregnancy and has had 2 antepartum visits. What are the correct codes to report?

a. 632, 59820
b. 632, 59851, 59425
c. 631, 59820
d. 631, 59820, plus appropriate E/M code

6.81.   This 26-year-old gravida 1 para 1 female has been having spotting and has been on bedrest. She awoke this morning with severe cramping and bleeding. Her husband brought her to the hospital. After examination, it was determined that she has had an incomplete early spontaneous abortion. She is in the 12th week of her pregnancy. She was taken to surgery, and a dilation and curettage was performed. There were no complications from the procedure. She is to follow up with me in the office. She has had four antepartum visits during her pregnancy.

What are the correct codes to assign?

a. 637.91, 59812
b. 634.91, 59812, 59425
c. 634.91, 58120
d. 634.92, 58120, 59425

6.82.   This 30-year-old female comes to the clinic because of excessive vomiting. She has been vomiting for three days. She has had no problems with vomiting in her early pregnancy. She is now estimated to be in her 24th week. What is the correct ICD-9-CM diagnostic code assignment for this case?

Code(s):_____

6.83. This 29-year-old female is admitted to the hospital with pneumonia due to Pneumocystis carinii. She is in her 30th week of pregnancy and has AIDS. What codes are assigned?

Code(s): _____87281_____

Disorders of the Respiratory System

6.84. A patient is respirator dependent and has a tracheostomy in need of revision due to redundant scar tissue formation surrounding the site. Under general anesthesia and establishing the airway to maintain ventilation, the scar tissue is resected and then repair is accomplished using skin flap rotation from the adjacent tissue of the neck. What codes will be used to report this procedure performed in the hospital short-stay surgery area?

a. 519.00, V46.11, 31614
b. V55.0, V46.11, 31614
c. V55.0, 31610
d. 519.00, 31613

6.85. This 60-year-old patient was admitted with emphysematous nodules. A thoracoscopic wedge resection was performed in the left lung to remove the lung nodules. A resection was done in the upper and lower lobes. Which of the following answers is correct?

a. 518.89, 32657
b. 492.8, 32657, 32657-51
c. 518.89, 32500
d. 492.8, 32657

6.86. From the health record of a patient newly diagnosed with a malignancy:

Preoperative Diagnosis: Suspicious lesions, main bronchus

Postoperative Diagnosis: Carcinoma, in situ, main bronchus

Indications: Previous bronchoscopy showed two suspicious lesions in the main bronchus. Laser photoresection is planned for destruction of these lesions, because bronchial washings obtained previously showed carcinoma in situ.

Procedure: Following general anesthesia in the hospital same-day surgery area, with a high-frequency jet ventilator, a rigid bronchoscope is inserted and advanced through the larynx to the main bronchus. The areas were treated with laser photoresection.

Which codes are reported for this service?

a. 231.2, 31641
b. 162.2, 31641, 31623-59
c. 231.2, 31641, 31623-59
d. 162.2, 31641

6.87. This 80-year-old male presented to the ER with acute pulmonary edema after experiencing a three-day history of increasing shortness of breath and cough. He was admitted to the critical care unit with a diagnosis of congestive heart failure and treated with Procardia®, Nitro Paste, and Lasix with resolution of his respiratory distress.

The patient responded to treatment with increasing nitroglycerin and Lasix. The patient was also given intravenous fluids and low-dose dopamine to maintain an adequate wedge pressure and cardiac output.

Final Diagnosis: Acute pulmonary edema with congestive heart failure.

What diagnosis code(s) are reported?

Code(s):_____

6.88. This 82-year-old nursing home patient presents with aspiration pneumonia. The patient aspirated food particles. Treatment included clindamycin 600 mg IV q. 6 hours. He also has superimposed staphylococcal pneumonia. The condition resolved with treatment, and patient transferred back to the nursing home. What is the correct diagnosis code assignment?

Code(s):_____

6.89. Under conscious sedation, administered by the endoscopist, a patient underwent a bronchoscopy with biopsy of the walls of the left upper lobe bronchus and left mainstem bronchus, dilation of the left mainstem bronchus and placement of a bronchial stent in the left mainstem bronchus. Assign the appropriate CPT codes.

a. 31622, 31625, 31636, 96144
b. 31628, 31632, 31636
c. 31625, 31636
d. 31625, 31636, 96144

Trauma and Poisoning

6.90. Assign the correct ICD-9-CM diagnosis codes for a 29-year-old burn victim with deep third-degree burns of the chest and right leg. He was the victim of a house fire. He has 25 percent of his body burned with third-degree burns.

Code(s):_____

6.91. The patient in item 6.90 was treated with skin grafting over a period of time until his burns healed. Six months later, he is being seen with severe scarring due to third-degree burns of his right leg and chest received in a house fire. What ICD-9-CM codes are assigned for this case?

Code(s):_____

6.92. This 79-year-old patient had a gastrostomy performed because of dysphagia due to a stroke. He has been doing fairly well but is now admitted with extensive cellulitis of the abdominal wall. Examination reveals that the existing gastrostomy site is infected. The physician confirms that the responsible organism is S. aureus. What codes are assigned?

Code(s):_____

6.93. What CPT code(s) would be assigned for a simple repair of a 1.5 cm laceration of the left upper arm and an intermediate repair of a 1 cm laceration of the left hand?

Code(s):_____

6.94. What codes are reported for an encounter in which the patient received a crushing injury of the left toes, foot, and ankle? He was crushed in a metal rolling mill machine at work.

Code(s):_____

Part III

Advanced Coding Exercises

Chapter 7

Case Studies from Inpatient Health Records

Note: Even though the specific cases are divided by setting, most of the information pertaining to the diagnosis is applicable to most settings. If you practice or apply codes in a particular type of setting, you may find additional information in other sections of this publication that may be pertinent to you.

Every effort has been made to follow current recognized coding guidelines and principles, as well as nationally recognized reporting guidelines. The material presented may differ from some health plan requirements for reporting. The ICD-9-CM codes used are effective through September 30, 2007, and the HCPCS (CPT and HCPCS Level II) codes are in effect through December 31, 2006. The current standard transactions and code sets named in HIPAA have been utilized, which require ICD-9-CM Volume III procedure codes for inpatients.

Instructions:

Assign all applicable ICD-9-CM codes appropriate for the setting for the case studies presented. Some of the cases provide multiple-choice answers, and the reader must select the appropriate code set. In other instances, the reader is expected to assign codes without any prompts.

The scenarios are based on selected excerpts from health records without reproducing the entire health record. However, in practice, the coding professional should have access to the entire health record. Health records are analyzed and codes are selected only with the physician's complete and appropriate documentation available. According to coding guidelines, codes are not assigned without physician documentation.

The objective of the cases and scenarios reproduced in this publication is to provide practice in assigning correct codes, not necessarily to emulate actual health record analysis. For example, the reader may be asked to assign codes based only on an operative report or discharge summary. Labeled excerpts are used as source documentation for coding skill practice.

Disorders of the Blood and Blood-Forming Organs

7.1. The following documentation is from the health record of an 87-year-old female patient.

Discharge Summary

History of Present Illness: The patient is an 87-year-old female who was admitted from a nursing home with dehydration and pleural effusion, as well as urinary tract infection and thrombocytopenia with petechial hemorrhage. On admission, she was found to have a platelet count of 77,000 and a Hematology consult was done. The patient denied any bleeding diathesis in the past. She stated that she had recent bruising of the hands related to needle sticks but otherwise has not had any past history of any bleeding disorder. She stated she was taking aspirin on a regular basis. No specific history of hematuria, hematemesis, gross rectal bleeding, or black stools.

Past Medical History: Significant for congestive heart failure, diabetes

Medications: Coreg®, isosorbide, aspirin, Actos®, digoxin, glyburide, hydralazine, furosemide, Ditropan®, and potassium

Family History: No family history of any bleeding disorder

Physical Examination: She is an elderly appearing white female, somewhat short of breath, using supplemental oxygen. Examination of the head and neck revealed no scleral icterus. Throat was clear. Tongue was papillated. There was no thyromegaly or JVD. There was no cervical supraclavicular, axillary, or inguinal adenopathy. Chest examination revealed rales, bilaterally. There were decreased breath sounds at the right base. There were coarse rales heard in the right midlung field. Heart exam showed rhythm was irregularly irregular. Abdomen exam was difficult to perform. I was unable to palpate the liver or spleen. Bowel sounds were active. Extremities revealed no clubbing, cyanosis, or edema. There were diffuse ecchymoses, especially in the dorsum of the right hand.

Laboratory Studies: Hematocrit was 43, white count 9,000 with 82 percent neutrophils, and the platelet count 77,000. The MCCV was 102. Creatinine was 1.7. Bilirubin was 1.7. The alkaline phosphatase was 122. AST 498, ALT 493, and albumin 3.6. The prothrombin time was 18 seconds, the PTT was 25 seconds. The chest x-ray showed a right pleural effusion.

Course in Hospital: The patient was admitted and started on IV fluids. Her diuretics were increased, and she showed a good response with a resolution of her pleural effusion and better control of her congestive heart failure. Hematology consult recommended holding platelet transfusion unless there was evidence of active bleeding. No platelets were given during this admission.

The patient was discharged back to the nursing home on day 6 in improved condition to continue with the same medication regimen as previous to hospitalization.

Final Diagnoses: 1. Pleural effusion from congestive heart failure
2. Dehydration
3. Primary thrombocytopenia with petechial hemorrhage and hematoma of the eyelids and arms and hands
4. Urinary tract infection
5. Type II diabetes mellitus

Which of the following code sets would be correct for this hospitalization?

a. 428.0, 276.51, 287.39, 599.0, 250.00
b. 428.0, 276.51, 287.5, 599.0, 250.00
c. 428.0, 511.9, 276.51, 287.39, 599.0, 250.00
d. 276.51, 511.9, 428.0, 287.39, 782.7, 599.0, 250.00

7.2.   The following documentation is from the health record of a 76-year-old female patient.

Discharge Summary

History of Present Illness: The patient was a 76-year-old female who was admitted in acute distress. The patient had apparently been taking Coumadin® for her atrial fibrillation and got confused about the dosage. She was supposed to be taking 4 mg one day and 6 mg the next. She has apparently been taking 4 mg in the morning and 6 mg in the evening.

Past History: She had a myocardial infarction three years ago. She has had a cholecystectomy in the remote past.

Physical Examination: She was well developed and well nourished. Head and neck: Head was normal shape. The ears and nose were clear. The pupils reacted well to light and accommodation. The patient wore glasses. The mouth was normal. The patient did not have any carotid bruits. The trachea was midline. No palpable lymph nodes. Lungs: Clear. Heart: Regular tone and irregular rhythm. The blood pressure was 142/66 mmHg. The pulse was regular at 54.

Abdomen: Soft, nontender. No masses on palpation. The patient did not have any active bleeding that we could see. Liver and spleen were not enlarged. Upper extremities: Normal. Lower extremities: Normal. No edema. No varicosities.

Laboratory Tests: INR was over 10.

Hospital Course: The patient was admitted and treated with 3 units of fresh-frozen plasma (FFP). The patient's response was excellent. The patient will be discharged in improved condition. I spent several sessions with her explaining her Coumadin regimen and the patient voices an understanding.

Discharge Medications: Coumadin, diazepam, Valium®, Lanoxin, atenolol, Premarin®

Final Diagnosis: Hypocoagulation state due to Coumadin

Which of the following would be correct for the above case?

a. 964.2, E858.2, 412, 99.07
b. 790.92, 286.7, E858.2
c. 964.2, 286.7, 427.31, 412, E858.2, 99.07
d. 286.7, 964.2, 790.92, 427.31, 412, 99.07

Disorders of the Cardiovascular System

7.3.   The following documentation is from the health record of a 66-year-old male patient.

Discharge Summary

Admission Date: 6/19/XX

Discharge Date: 6/28/XX

History of Present Illness: This patient is a 66-year-old man admitted on 6/19 because of unstable postinfarct angina. He underwent cardiac bypass surgery here 15 years ago. He did well until 1989, when he developed angina and underwent angioplasty here. On 6/9, he was awakened with severe chest pain and was taken to a nearby community hospital where he was found to have a small anterior wall myocardial infarction, with the CPK only slightly elevated.

Because of this small infarction, he was referred here for consideration for further coronary arteriography. He was discharged from the hospital on 6/16. On 6/19, as the patient was walking from the car to the office, he developed quite significant chest pain and was therefore admitted to rule out further infarction.

Hospital Course: He was taken to the cardiac catheterization laboratory the day after admission. At that time, complete left heart catheterization, left ventricular cineangiography, coronary arteriography, and bypass visualization were performed. We found that his left ventricle showed severe anterior hypokinesis, although it did still move. The left main coronary artery was narrowed by about 70 percent.

The bypass to the circumflex looked good, but the bypass to the left anterior descending had a very severe stenosis in the body of the graft. There was a very large, marginal circumflex artery that had an orificial 80 percent stenosis. I felt that he was not a candidate for angioplasty but should have bypass surgery. He was seen in consultation by Dr. Reed, who agreed with this, so he was taken to the operating room on 6/21 for that procedure.

Using extracorporeal circulation, the left internal mammary artery was anastomosed to the left anterior descending coronary artery and a venous graft was placed from the aorta to the marginal circumflex. It was found that the old venous graft to the main circumflex was in excellent condition with very soft, pliable walls so that vessel was left intact. There were no complications of this surgery.

His postoperative course was singularly uncomplicated. He never had any arrhythmia problems, his wounds healed nicely. He had a tiny left pleural effusion that never needed to be tapped. He was walking about the ward participating in the cardiac rehab program at the time of discharge.

Discharge Instructions: Discharge medications will simply be aspirin grains 5 q. d, Tylenol with Codeine 1 or 2 p.r.n. for pain, Lopressor 50 mg a day, and Colace, as necessary. He was instructed to contact his private physician upon return home for resumption of his medical care. He is to call me here at the medical center if there are any questions or problems that he wishes to discuss.

Discharge Diagnoses:
1. Unstable angina (intermediate coronary syndrome)
2. Recent incomplete anterior wall myocardial infarction
3. Coronary atherosclerosis, three vessel
4. Successful double-bypass surgery

What are the correct codes for this admission?

a. 414.01, 414.05, 410.12, 411.1, 36.11, 36.15, 39.61, 37.22, 88.53, 88.57

b. 414.01, 414.05, 410.12, 411.1, V45.81, 36.12, 39.61, 37.22, 88.53, 88.57

c. 414.00, 414.05, 410.11, 411.1, 36.11, 36.15, 39.61, 37.22, 88.53, 88.57

d. 414.01, 414.05, 410.12, 411.1, 412, V45.81, 36.11, 36.15, 39.61, 37.22, 88.53, 88.57

7.4. The following documentation is from the health record of an 85-year-old female patient.

Discharge Summary

Admit Date: 12/10/XX

Discharge Date: 12/22/XX

Discharge Diagnoses:
1. Acute pulmonary edema with congestive heart failure
2. Myocardial infarction ruled out
3. Chronic obstructive pulmonary disease
4. Pneumonia
5. Senile dementia

History of Present Illness: This 85-year-old female was admitted via the emergency room from the nursing home with shortness of breath, confusion, and congestion. There was no history of fever or cough noted. Patient has a history of senile dementia and COPD. Prior to admission, the patient was on the following medications: Prednisone, Lasix, Haldol®, and Colace.

Physical Examination: Blood pressure 140/70, heart rate of 125 per minute, respirations were 30, temperature of 101.4°F. The eyes showed postsurgical eyes, nonreactive to light. The lungs showed bilaterally bibasilar crackles. The heart showed S1 and S2, with no S3. The abdomen was soft and nontender. The extremities showed leg edema. The neurological exam revealed no deficits, and she was alert × 3.

Laboratory Data: ABGs were 7.4, PO_2 of 63, CO_2 of 43, bicarbonate 26, saturation of 89. Hemoglobin 11.7, hematocrit was 31.5, platelets of 207,000. Sodium 139, chloride 107, potassium 4.4, BUN 42, creatinine 1.2. The EKG was unremarkable.

Hospital Course: Basically, this patient was admitted to the coronary care unit with acute pulmonary edema, rule out myocardial infarction. Serial cardiac enzymes were done, which were within normal limits; therefore ruling out myocardial infarction. A chest x-ray performed on the day of admission confirmed congestive heart failure and pneumonia.

The patient was started on Unasyn® and tobramycin for the pneumonia, which improved. The congestive heart failure; however, was not improving with administration of Lasix. The patient was not taking foods and liquids well, and, at the family's request, she was made DNR. On hospital day 12, she was found without respirations, with no heart sounds, and pupils were fixed. She was declared dead by the physician, and the family was notified.

Which of the following answers demonstrates the correct code assignment?

a. 428.0, 486, 496, 290.0
b. 428.0, 518.4, 486, 496, 290.0
c. 486, 496, 428.0, 410.91, 290.0
d. 518.4, 428.0, 486, 496, 290.0

7.5.   An inpatient undergoes insertion of an AICD™ and lead testing subsequent to the implant. What is the appropriate code to assign for the lead testing?

a. 37.26 Catheter-based invasive electrophysiologic testing
b. There is no ICD-9-CM code to report a lead check; it is included in the lead insertion.
c. 89.49 Automatic implantable cardioverter-defibrillator (AICD) check
d. Either code 89.49 or 37.26 may be assigned to report the lead check; they are essentially synonymous.

7.6.   A patient is admitted with severe atherosclerosis of the left carotid artery. He undergoes a percutaneous atherectomy of the artery, along with infusion of streptokinase to assist with clot resolution. A carotid artery stent was also inserted to assure that the artery would remain open. Assign the appropriate ICD-9-CM procedure code(s) to report this procedure.

a. 00.61, 99.10, 00.63
b. 00.61, 99.10, 00.64
c. 00.61, 00.63
d. 00.61

7.7.   Joe Jones was admitted to the hospital with severe angina. At cardiac catheterization he was found to have major atheromatous involvement of the left anterior descending coronary artery, with near-total occlusion, but well-preserved flow in the remainder of the coronaries. Because only one vessel was involved, the attending physician decided on a percutaneous treatment and stent placement. Mr. Jones underwent percutaneous atherectomy of the LAD with placement of two sirolimus-eluting stents. Urokinase was injected following the procedure to assist with clot dissolution. Assign the appropriate ICD-9-CM procedure code(s) for the hospital to report this inpatient procedure. Do not assign codes for the cardiac catheterization for this exercise.

a. 00.66, 00.40, 36.07, 36.07, 99.10
b. 00.66, 36.07
c. 00.66, 00.40, 00.46, 36.07, 99.10
d. 36.09, 00.40, 00.46, 36.06, 99.10

7.8.   A patient with severe arterial disease involving the lower abdominal aorta and the iliac bifurcation is admitted to the hospital as an inpatient for endovascular repair. Incisions are made over each femoral artery, and a catheter with modular attachments is inserted via the right femoral artery. The catheter carries a self-deploying endovascular prosthesis, which consists of an aortic component with a modular bifurcated prosthesis to extend into each of the iliac arteries. Via the femoral incisions, the components are aligned and components are noted to be secure. The small incisions are closed and the patient is taken to the recovery area for further observation. Assign the appropriate ICD-9-CM procedure code(s) to describe this procedure.

a. 38.44
b. 39.79
c. 39.71
d. 39.7

7.9.   **History and Physical:** The patient is a 67-year-old male who was transferred from Down-the-Street Hospital where he was admitted with chest pain, shortness of breath, and EKG changes. His cardiac enzymes were elevated and, subsequently, he underwent a cardiac catheterization, which revealed significant four-vessel disease. He was transferred here for a coronary artery bypass procedure once his angina is stabilized.

Past History: Diabetes, hypercholesterolemia and status post appendectomy

Medications: See transfer list

Allergies: None known

Physical Exam:

General: Normal appearing male in no acute distress

Cardio: Rate and rhythm regular

Lungs: Normal

Tests: Chest x-ray normal; EKG nonspecific T-wave changes

Impression and Plan: Unstable angina, coronary artery disease, diabetes mellitus; patient will undergo CABG tomorrow.

Operative Report

Preoperative Diagnosis: CAD

Postoperative Diagnosis: Same

Procedure: Bypass graft of obtuse marginal and posterior descending arteries and left anterior descending artery. Cardiopulmonary bypass

Description of Procedure: After obtaining adequate anesthesia, the patient was prepped and draped in the usual fashion. A primary median sternotomy incision was made and the pericardium was opened. The left internal mammary artery was dissected as a pedicle using electrocautery and small hemoclips at the same time that the greater saphenous vein was harvested from the left lower extremity. Cardiopulmonary bypass was instituted, and the patient was taken to a mild degree of hypothermia.

The aorta was cross-clamped and electrical arrest effect was administered via cold blood cardioplegia. The saphenous vein graft was placed end-to-side with the posterior descending artery, and then a separate graft was placed to the obtuse marginal artery. Each anastomosis was done with running 7-0 Prolene® suture and verified no bleeders were present. The left internal mammary artery was subsequently brought through a subthalamic tunnel and placed end-to-side with the left anterior descending coronary artery.

Following completion of the grafts, warm blood cardioplegia was administered. During this time, two atrial and ventricular pacing wires were attached to the heart's surface; in addition, mediastinal tubes were also placed. The cross clamps were released following this, and sinus rhythm returned spontaneously. The patient was weaned from cardiobypass without incident.

After all grafts were checked for diastolic flow by Doppler interrogation, which revealed no problems, the incisions were closed. The patient was taken to the recovery room in good condition and will be monitored in the intensive care unit for complications.

Progress Notes:

Day 1: Patient progressing well; all vital signs are stable. Will transfer to step-down unit today.

Day 2: Heart rate stable and incision healing nicely. If patient continues to progress will be ready for discharge in a few days.

Day 3: Stable; patient ambulating in hallway without difficulty

Day 4: Continues to progress in ambulation; ready for discharge tomorrow

Day 5: Discharge patient today to follow up with myself next week.

What is the correct code assignment for this admission?

a. 411.1, 414.01, 250.00, 272.0, 36.12, 36.15, 39.61
b. 414.01, 411.1, 250.00, 272.0, 36.12, 36.15, 39.61
c. 414.00, 413.9, 995.89, 250.00, 36.12, 36.15, 39.61
d. 414.01, 411.1, 272.0, 250.00, 36.13, 39.61

Disorders of the Digestive System

7.10. The following documentation is from the health record of an 81-year-old female patient.

Operative Report

Diagnoses: Acute gallstone pancreatitis with acute cholecystitis, evidence of bile duct obstruction.

History: The patient is an 81-year-old female admitted 48 hours ago with evidence of acute gallstone pancreatitis. The patient had some thickening of her gallbladder wall and pericholecystic fluid. The patient had marked elevation of amylase and was given 48 hours of medical therapy with chemical clearance of her pancreatitis. The patient was felt to be a candidate for open exploration of her biliary tract, with concomitant cholecystectomy and possible common duct exploration.

Description of Procedure: After discussion with the patient and her family and obtaining informed consent, she was taken to the operating room, where, after induction of general anesthesia the abdomen was prepped and draped in a standard fashion. Following this, a right upper quadrant incision was used to gain access to the abdominal cavity. Manual exploration revealed no abnormalities of the uterus, ovaries, colon, or stomach. The pancreas was enlarged and edematous in the area of the head. Attention was then turned to the right upper quadrant, where the gallbladder was noted to be somewhat distended. This decompressed with a 2-0 VICRYL pursestring stitch using the trocar.

Following this, dissection of the hepatoduodenal ligament revealed arterial anomaly of the right hepatic artery, coursing from behind the common duct over the top of the cystic duct prior to giving off the cystic artery. The cystic artery was dissected free and double clipped proximally, singly distally, and divided. The duct was then dissected free and subsequently clipped proximally.

Cholangiogram was then obtained by opening the cystic duct and placing a cholangiogram catheter. Real-time cholangiography revealed marked dilation of the bile duct, which was noted prior to placing the catheter. The common bile duct measured roughly 1.5 cm in size. The duct tapered out in the area of the intraduodenal portion of the common duct to near occlusion. There was a very scant amount of contrast, which went beyond the ampulla into the duodenum. With this structure itself, the patient may well have a distal impacted stone. The gallbladder was removed by transecting the cystic duct and removing it in a retrograde fashion. The gallbladder contained no stone.

Following removal of the gallbladder, attention was turned to the common bile duct, which was opened. No stones were retrieved initially from the bile duct. A biliary Fogarty was passed distally and, with some difficulty, was negotiated into the duodenum. On return, no calculus material was obtained. Palpation of the distal duct revealed thickening due to the pancreatic inflammation, which was noted to improve somewhat over the inside portion of the C-loop to the duodenum. The patient was felt to have possible impacted stone or perhaps some other primary common duct process other than inflammation causing her distal duct picture. Choledochoscopy was performed, but distal visualization of the bile duct was not adequate. As such, it was felt that evaluation of the duct from both inside the duodenum and within the duct was profitable. Inspection of the ampulla directly revealed no abnormalities from within the duodenal lumen. Palpation of the ampulla and passage of the biliary Fogarty revealed what appeared to be just diffuse soft tissue thickening and no strong evidence for calculus disease.

Following this, cholangiography revealed some mild emptying of the distal common duct into the duodenum, with filling of the pancreatic duct as well. With the overall picture, it was felt the patient might benefit from a feeding jejunostomy, as she might well sustain postoperative or perioperative complications of respiratory insufficiency or perhaps other imponderables. As such, jejunum was identified roughly one foot beyond the ligament of Treitz, and 2-0 VICRYL purse-string stitches times two were placed. The jejunotomy was performed, and a 16 French T-tube was then placed and brought out through a stab wound in the left upper quadrant. The tube was anchored anteriorly with interrupted 2-0 silk stitches and externally with 2-0 stitches. Jackson-Pratt drain was placed through a lateral stab wound in the right upper quadrant and used to drain the duodenotomy and choledochotomy. This was anchored with several 3-0 silk stitches.

Following this, the wound was irrigated with Kantrex® irrigation, 1 gram per liter, and the wound was closed by closing the posterior rectus sheath with running 1 VICRYL suture. The sub-q was irrigated and the skin was closed with staples. The wound was then dressed, and the patient was taken to the recovery room postop in stable condition. Estimated blood loss was 400 cc. Sponge and needle counts were correct times two.

Code Assignment:

Principal diagnosis:_____

Additional diagnoses:_____

Principal procedure:_____

Additional procedures:_____

7.11.   The following documentation is from the health record of a 77-year-old female patient.

History and Physical

History of Present Illness: The patient is a 77-year-old female patient who presents for evaluation for right-sided abdominal pain.

The patient tells me that she has had a several-month history of right-sided abdominal pain. She tells me that the pain occurs intermittently. It is located in the right side of her abdomen. The pain will sometimes be associated with epigastric pain. She will have nausea sometimes with the pain. The pain sometimes occurs after eating and sometimes does not. She has had no vomiting. Over the past couple of days, she has had persistent right midabdominal pain with nausea.

Now, she has no nausea, but she has continued right-sided abdominal pain. The patient has had a colonoscopy this spring, which was normal. She had a colonoscopy last year showing polyps with apparently some type of atypical pathology, but not cancer. Her brother did have colon cancer.

Past Medical History: History of colon polyps as stated. The patient denies any other known medical problems.

Medications: No regular medications

Past Surgical History: Right knee replacement last year. Colonoscopy with removal of polyps approximately a year and a half ago. No known drug allergies. The patient does not drink or smoke. She lives by herself and is quite active for a woman of her age.

Review of Systems: The patient has had chronic intermittent dizziness in the past. She denies any chest pain or shortness of breath. She has no back pain or flank pain. She has had no vomiting. She has noted no blood in her stool or urine. She does have a chronic problem with fullness in her suprapubic region prior to urinating and difficulty urinating at times. This has been, again, a chronic problem and increased somewhat over the past couple of weeks. She has noted no blood in her stool or urine. She has noted no change in her stools.

Physical Examination: Temperature is 99°F, pulse 100, respiratory rate 18, blood pressure 166/86. There is no palpable neck or supraclavicular lymphadenopathy. Sclera: Nonicteric. Chest: Clear. Heart: Regular rate and rhythm. Abdomen: Soft. Moderate right midabdominal tenderness. No peritoneal irritation signs. The remainder of the abdomen is nontender. Bowel sounds: Normal. Rectal exam: No blood. No masses. Guaiac negative. No gross peripheral edema.

Labs: Pelvic ultrasound grossly normal. No right hydronephrosis. UA: 5 to 10 red blood cells per high-power field with no bacteria. White count 9.6, hematocrit 39.6, platelet count 233,000. Amylase is 76. Liver function tests are all grossly normal, except for total bilirubin of 1.5. BUN and creatinine are 18 and 0.7, respectively. EKG is negative. Chest x-ray is normal. Obstructive series negative.

Impression:

Rule out right renal calculus

Rule out right colon pathology

Rule out chronic pathology

Plan: Admit, n.p.o., pain control, IV fluids, CT scan of the abdomen and pelvis with oral and IV contrast, and delayed KUB now. Further plans pending clinical course and test results. Check urine culture.

I reviewed all of the above in great detail with the patient and her family. They are in agreement with the treatment plan.

Operative Report

Preoperative Diagnosis: Right colon mass

Postoperative Diagnosis: Right colon mass

Surgery Performed: Exploratory laparotomy, right colon resection

Anesthesia: General

Clinical History: Please see the preop note for full details.

Summary: The patient is a 77-year-old female patient who presents with right-sided abdominal pain and right abdominal tenderness. CT scan of the abdomen and pelvis showed a mass/inflammatory process localized to the right side of the colon, no other gross abnormalities. The patient had a previous colonoscopy earlier this year, which was reported to be essentially normal except for some polyps. The patient was initially observed, made n.p.o., given IV fluids, as well as intravenous antibiotics. She continued to have right-sided abdominal tenderness with no fever and no leukocytosis.

She underwent a lower GI, which showed a mass in the right side of the colon, worrisome for carcinoma. Secondary to the patient's lack of response to conservative management, findings in the lower GI and CT scan, and right-sided abdominal tenderness, recommendations were to proceed with exploratory laparotomy and right colon resection.

I had a very detailed discussion with the patient, as well as her family members, reviewing all of the following in great details:

   All clinical lab and x-ray data

   Differential diagnosis

   Possible diagnosis of right colon cancer

   All options

   Recommendations for surgery with the involved details, risk, benefits of recovery

   The risk of surgery can include, but is not limited to, bleeding, postoperative gastrointestinal dysfunction, possible postoperative anastomotic dysfunction, postoperative cardiopulmonary dysfunction, anesthetic risk.

   Possible diagnosis of colon cancer

   The fact that further plans will be pending pathological results

   Basics of colon anatomy in planned procedure

They demonstrated an understanding of the discussion and wished to proceed with the procedure, accepting the involved risks.

Description of Operative Procedure: The patient was taken to the operating room and placed in the supine position. After satisfactory general endotracheal anesthesia had been administered, compression stockings were placed on both lower extremities, and Foley bladder catheter was inserted with return of clear urine. A nasogastric tube was inserted by anesthesia. The abdomen was prepped and draped in the usual sterile fashion.

Midline incision was made and carried down through abdominal wall layers, and the peritoneal cavity was easily entered. The patient had a firm mass in the proximal right colon with inflammatory changes of the serosa. There was no perforation. It was worrisome by palpation for a carcinoma. The liver was grossly normal, with no evidence of metastatic disease. The NG tube was in proper position in the stomach. The small bowel was run and was grossly normal.

There was no gross evidence of metastatic disease within the abdominal cavity. There was no evidence of any small bowel obstruction. The NG tube was palpated via proper position in the stomach. The Bookwalter™ retractor was used for exposure. The terminal ileum and right colon were mobilized. The omentum was dissected off of the proximal transverse colon. The GI stapler was used to transect the terminal ileum, as well as the right colon and the lip of the hepatic flexure. The mesentery was scored, clamped, and divided; the vessels were tied off with 0 VICRYL suture, as well as 2-0 VICRYL suture. Additional 2-0 VICRYL suture ligatures were used for the larger vessels.

A side-to-side, functional end-to-end anastomosis was created between the terminal ileum and the proximal portion of the transverse colon. The anastomosis was found to be airtight, widely patent, and viable. Mesenteric defect was closed with 3-0 silk sutures. The omentum was placed over the anastomosis at the completion of the case. The abdomen was thoroughly irrigated. A 15 BLAKE Drain was inserted via stab incision in the right abdomen and placed in the right gutter, the drain was secured to the skin with 2-0 silk suture and connected to bulb suction at the end of the case.

Lap, sponge, needle, and instrument counts were all reported to be correct. The bowel has been returned in an organized fashion to the abdominal cavity. The fascia was closed with short-interval running segments of 1 VICRYL suture in the midline, as well as figure-eight interrupted #1 sutures. The skin was closed with interrupted metallic staples. Sterile dressings were applied. The BLAKE Drain was connected to bulb suction at the end of the case.

IV Fluids: 2500 cc. Urine output: Approximately 400 cc. Blood loss: Approximately 100 cc.

I had a detailed discussion with the patient's family members about the postoperative findings and reviewed the operative findings, procedure performed, plans, possible outcomes. They demonstrated an understanding of this discussion.

Pathology Report: Severe ulcerative ileocolitis. No signs of malignancy.

Final Diagnosis: Severe ulcerative ileocolitis, postoperative ileus that was treated with NG tube.

Code Assignment:

Principal diagnosis:_____

Additional diagnoses:_____

Principal procedure:_____

Additional procedures:_____

7.12.   The following documentation is from the health record of a 67-year-old female patient.

Clinical Resume

Reasons for Admission:
1. The patient has abdominal pain.
2. The patient has nausea and vomiting.
3. The patient has elevated amylase level, also lipase level.

History of Present Illness: The patient is a 67-year-old white female who has a history of diabetes mellitus, type II, and also hypertension. The patient remained in stable condition until approximately 3 p.m. yesterday afternoon when she was shopping and was not feeling well. Subsequently, the patient went home, and developed nausea and vomiting associated with excruciating abdominal pain; however, the patient did not call for medical attention until almost midnight. The patient was noted to have recurrent abdominal pain. Because of this, the patient was subsequently seen in the emergency room. While she was in the ER, the patient was noted to have amylase level of 2,319. Lipase was 6,312. Because of this, the patient was admitted to the hospital for further evaluation and therapy.

Past Medical History: The patient has diabetes mellitus, type II. Surgical history includes partial hysterectomy 20 years ago. The patient also had surgery done on her left knee. She has also had a cyst removed from her ankle.

Allergies: The patient is not allergic to any medications.

Social History: The patient does not smoke or drink.

Review of Systems: The patient has complained of abdominal pain associated with nausea and vomiting. This has been present for the past 24 hours, but there is no chest pain and no shortness of breath.

Physical Examination: The patient's blood pressure is 134/70. Pulse is 78. HEENT reveals pupils that seem to be reactive. The fundi show sharp disks. There is some exudate, but there is no hemorrhage. Ears: The tympanic membranes are clear. The neck is supple. Thyroid is palpable, but not enlarged. Negative for hepatojugular reflux and negative for jugular venous distention. Chest revealed decreased breath sounds. Cardiac is regular. Abdominal examination is soft. There is only very minimal tenderness on palpation in the right upper quadrant area. Bowel sounds are present. Extremities: There is no cyanosis, there is no clubbing. The deep tendon reflexes seem to be symmetrical and bilateral. Neurological examination: The patient is oriented × 3. The cranial nerves II–XII are grossly intact. Sensory and motor strength are within normal limits. There is no clonus. There is no Babinski. Cerebellar sign is normal.

EKG reveals normal sinus rhythm.

Laboratory Data: The lipase level is 6,312. Amylase level is 2,319. The patient's white blood count is 14.4 with RBC of 4.51, hemoglobin of 13.8 with hematocrit of 40.0, MCV of 88, MCH of 30.7. Platelet count is 279,000. The patient's glucose level is 200, BUN of 19, and creatinine of 0.7, sodium of 136, potassium of 4.0, chloride of 93. Total bilirubin is 1.8. Calcium is 9.6. AST is 435. Total protein is 6.3.

Impressions:
1. Suspected gallstones; rule out possible common bile duct obstruction with stones.
2. The patient has abdominal pain due to pancreatitis.
3. The patient has diabetes mellitus, type II.
4. The patient has hypertension.
5. The patient is obese.

Plan: The patient will be admitted to the hospital. I will get abdominal ultrasound, and GI consultation will be obtained. The patient needs to have ERCP or surgical consultation. Pending above, further diagnostic therapy to follow.

Operative Report

Preoperative Diagnosis: Abnormal liver function tests. Biliary pancreatitis. Chronic cholecystitis with lithiasis.

Postoperative Diagnoses:
1. Dilated common bile duct
2. Small filling deficit in the distal common bile duct, status post sphincterotomy, and balloon extraction of common bile duct stones

Surgery Performed: Endoscopic retrograde cholangiopancreatography with sphincterotomy and balloon extraction of stone.

Anesthesia: Demerol® 100 mg IV, Versed 6 mg IV, glucagon 2 mg IV in intermittent doses

Procedure: After obtaining informed consent, the patient was brought to the fluoroscopy unit. IV Demerol and IV Versed were given in intermittent doses to a total of Demerol 100 mg and 6 mg of Versed, as well as 2 mg of glucagon during the whole procedure.

The Olympus® V-System™ ERCP scope was inserted from the mouth up to the second portion of the duodenum. Duodenal papilla was identified. Using the glow-tipped cannula, the common bile duct and pancreatic duct were cannulated. The pancreatic duct was then slightly dilated. The common bile duct was also dilated, and there were three small filling defects noted in the distal common bile duct causing obstruction. Then the common bile duct was selectively cannulated, and a guidewire was passed. Using a papillotome and current, the sphincterotomy was done. Then the 11.5 balloon was used to sweep the common bile duct. The balloon sweep was done three times. After the balloon sweep, cholangiogram was obtained again, which showed no evidence of any obstruction.

Recommendations: Recommend cholecystectomy for the chronic cholecystitis with lithiasis as soon as possible after acute illness is past. She was discharged after three days in the hospital. We will schedule the cholecystectomy for next week as an outpatient.

Final Diagnoses:
1. Calculus of common bile duct and gallbladder with cholecystitis
2. Biliary pancreatitis
3. Diabetes mellitus, type II
4. Obesity
5. Hypertension

Which of the following is the correct ICD-9-CM code assignment?

a. 574.70, 577.0, 250.00, 401.9, 278.00, 52.93, 51.85, 51.10
b. 574.71, 577.0, 250.00, 401.9, 278.00, 52.93, 51.85, 51.88, 87.53
c. 574.81, 577.0, 52.93, 51.85, 87.53
d. 574.80, 577.2, 250.00, 401.9, 278.00, 52.93, 51.85, 51.88

7.13.   Discharge Summary

Principal Diagnosis: Morbid obesity

Principal Procedure: Open Roux-en-Y gastric bypass, removal of gastroplasty ring, gastric (G) tube prior placement.

History of Present Illness: The patient is a 55-year-old white female with a history of gastroplasty ring placement in 1979 who comes to Dr. Smart for revision by doing a Roux-en-Y gastric bypass because of recurrence of her morbid obesity. Her morbid obesity is complicated by GERD, and obstructive sleep apnea.

Past Medical History: (1) Morbid obesity. (2) OSA. (3) GERD.

Past Surgical History: (1) Gastroplasty in 1979. (2) Laminectomy.

Allergies: Keflex® **Medications:** Pepcid q. d.

Physical Examination: VITAL SIGNS Afebrile, vital signs stable. General: No acute distress. CV RRR. PULMONARY CTAB. Abdomen: Soft, nontender, nondistended.

Impression: A 55-year-old white female with a history of gastroplasty, needing a revision into a Roux-en-Y gastric bypass after morbid obesity not secured.

Hospital Admission: The patient was admitted through same-day surgery and taken to the operating room for open Roux-en-Y gastric bypass with removal of a gastroplasty ring, liver biopsy, and G tube placement. Afterward, she was taken to the ICU because of her obstructive sleep apnea. She was monitored closely, did very well, and afterward, she was transferred to the floor. She was full advanced to activities of daily living through our gastric bypass protocol. She advanced to gastric bypass soft diet by postoperative day 4. She did well with this. On postoperative day 5, she was deemed ready to go home. She understands her discharge instructions and will be given pain medications as well as continue prescription for Zantac® for her GERD and for marginal ulcer prophylaxis.

Condition on Discharge: Stable on postoperative day 5 from open Roux-en-Y gastric bypass.

Disposition: The patient was discharged home with family.

Medications: Resume previous home medications. The patient can resume her Pepcid, or she can continue taking Zantac 150 b.i.d.

Follow-up: The patient will follow up with Dr. Smart.

Diet on Discharge: Gastric bypass soft diet. She has been instructed by a dietician two times already.

Operative Report

Preoperative Diagnosis: Morbid obesity with gastroplasty dysfunction

Postoperative Diagnosis: The same

Operation: Revision gastroplasty to Roux-en-Y gastric bypass and liver biopsy

Indications: This 55-year-old lady had undergone a Silastic® ring gastroplasty by another surgeon in 1979 at a weight more than 250 lb. She had done well for a long time and then had started regaining her weight and also developed significant gastroesophageal reflux disease. A gastric endoscopy done preoperatively showed that the Silastic ring of her gastroplasty had eroded into the gastric lumen with a wide outlet from the pouch and also with a separate dehiscence of the staple line. In the interim, she had developed sleep apnea but did not have hypertension or diabetes. Following the endoscopy and because of being on disability related to a laminectomy and to spinal problems, the excess weight seemed to aggravate her disability and seemed a justifiable reason for a surgical intervention.

Description of Procedure: With the patient supine on the operating table and under satisfactory general anesthesia, we attempted a right and then left subclavian line but had difficulties with the wire guide. Subsequently, a neck central line was placed and the abdomen was prepped and draped in a sterile manner. An upper midline incision was made and carried through the fat by tearing and through the fascia with the cautery. There were adhesions immediately of omentum to the anterior abdominal wall and also to the lower abdominal wall where a paramedian incision had been. These were all lysed, which was not difficult. A Tru-Cut needle was used to obtain a biopsy from the left lobe, which was moderately fatty by examination. The gallbladder was emptied sufficiently to know that there were no stones. The uterus and ovaries were surgically absent. We began by lysing adhesions on the undersurface of the left lobe of the liver to the stomach until we were able to uncover the old gastric pouch and appreciate the location of the staple line. I could also appreciate where the Silastic ring was, separate from the nasogastric tube, which was brought inside. We dissected around the distal esophagus and brought a long Penrose drain around it for retraction purposes. I held up the portion of the stomach near the lesser curve where the Silastic ring was palpable, and we used the cautery to enter into the lumen to find the ring. Its suture was cut and the ring was removed and sent to pathology. The opening made for the gastrotomy was closed with interrupted 2-0 silk sutures. We then dissected a little more proximal to this location along the lesser curve to go around the serosa of the stomach to its backside. A 12 French Robinson catheter was put along this tract and turned around to come to hold the lesser omentum on traction. We also divided some of the gastrocolic omentum to gain access from the lateral side to the posterior lesser sac. We then used a 45 mm blue load endoscopic autosuture stapler to staple and transect the stomach at the lesser curve transversely to create the posterior part of our pouch. When this was done, there was still a small hole into the distal stomach and perhaps into the proximal pouch where the staples had found the tissue too thick to seal completely. On the gastric pouch side, this was managed by an over-and-over suture of 2-0 Prolene from 1 edge to the other. On the gastric side, this was managed with interrupted 2-0 silk sutures. We then dissected behind the stomach up to the angle of His and eventually were able to pass the 12 French Robinson catheter through the angle of His and around the stomach to represent the pathway for the stapler to go at a later time. We lifted the omentum upward and identified the ligament of Treitz. The jejunum was divided a measured 7 $\frac{1}{2}$ in. beyond that ligament, and the mesentery at that level was divided using the endoscopic stapler. The small bowel was then measured from that point to the cecum, which proved to be 204 in., and we selected a 72 in. Roux limb length. The side-to-side jejunojejunostomy was created with the biliopancreatic limb and the Roux limb using an outer running 3-0 Prolene seromuscular layer and an inside GIA stapled anastomosis. The Prolene was continued over the holes made for the stapler and also used to invert the stapled edge of the biliopancreatic limb. The aperture between the 2 mesenteric leaves was closed with a couple 3-0 silk sutures. We then made a channel through the omentum up to the transverse colon and then across the gastrocolic omentum to allow the Roux limb to lie easily antecolic up near the pouch. When this was assured, the Roux limb was fixed to the end of our pouch with 3 interrupted 3-0 silk seromuscular sutures. The cautery was used to make an opening in the jejunum in the gastric wall and the posterior part of the anastomosis was done with interrupted 3-0 VICRYL suture. An opening was made in the Roux limb through which a 10 mm Hegar dilator was passed through the jejunal and gastric sides of the anastomosis. That anastomosis was then sutured with the VICRYL over the dilator and then further reinforced with interrupted 3-0 silk seromuscular sutures. When this was done, we removed the dilator and passed the nasogastric tube through the anastomosis to lie in the Roux limb. The end of the Roux limb was then oversewn with a running 3-0 Prolene suture. After this, we used the 60 mm blue load endoscopic stapler to begin to transect the gastric pouch from the remainder of the stomach, going vertically towards the angle of His. It ultimately took three 45 mm cartridges after the first 60 mm cartridge in order to complete this, but it was done satisfactorily. We used 2-0 Prolene to oversew that vertical staple line throughout its length. We also used the 2-0 Prolene to oversew the gastric staple line throughout its length. The anastomosis in the pouch looked fine, and we assured that the nasogastric tube was movable within the pouch. We then created a gastrostomy to the distal stomach with a 2-0 silk purse-string suture near the greater curve. A 22 French Foley catheter was brought through a left upper quadrant stab wound and on into the stomach and the balloon was filled. A purse-string suture was tied, and a couple of 2-0 silk sutures between stomach and abdominal wall were placed. After this, we irrigated the abdomen with an antibiotic solution containing Kantrex and bacitracin. All of the bowel and omentum was laid back in its normal position, and there was no tension on the Roux limb. The fascia was then closed with a running #1 loop PDS suture. The subcutaneous fat was cleaned with antibiotic solution and the skin was closed with 3-0 VICRYL dermal sutures and 3-0 VICRYL subcuticular sutures. The patient tolerated the procedure well and was taken to the SICU. Estimated blood loss was 350 ml and the sponge count was correct.

What are the correct ICD-9-CM codes for this admission?

a. 996.79, 530.81, 327.23, 44.69, 50.11, 44.13
b. 278.01, 996.79, 530.81, 780.57, 44.39
c. 996.79, 278.01, 780.57, 44.69, 50.11
d. 278.01, 530.81, 327.23, 44.39, 44.99, 50.11, 44.13

Endocrine, Nutritional and Metabolic Diseases, and Immunity Disorders

7.14. This 56-year-old female was admitted for resection of an adrenal mass. The patient has had hypertension and palpitations of several years' duration. Ultrasound was done in consideration of the possibility of a mass, and catecholamine studies have been normal. A 4–5 cm right adrenal mass was identified. Dr. White had obtained a 24-hour urinary free cortisol, ACTH, and short suppression tests, all of which confirmed the presence of Cushing's syndrome. The patient was not diabetic. She did report weight gain, some shift in body configuration, and easy bruising of several years' duration. The easy bruising was identified on exam in the hospital.

Surgery: A 5 cm, well-circumscribed round cortical tumor was resected from the adrenal two days ago.

Allergies: No known drug allergies

Medications on Discharge: Hydrocortisone, rapidly tapering dose, currently on 40 mg daily; Toprol® 50 mg q. a.m.; Prevacid® 30 mg q. d.; Lipitor® 10 mg q. a.m.; Prempro® 0.625/2.5

Physical Exam: Vital signs stable. HEENT: Sclerae and conjunctivae clear. Neck: Supple. No palpable thyroid. Lungs: Somewhat decreased breath sounds currently. There is mild splinting with deep breathing. Abdomen: Tenderness in the incision area. She has active bowel sounds at this time. Extremities: No definite bruises currently. No edema noted.

Discharge Diagnosis: Right adrenal tumor with Cushing's syndrome secondary to tumor

Plan: The patient appears to have tolerated the surgery well. She will require steroid replacement. Excess cortisol output is presumed entirely due to her tumor, and her ACTH was suppressed previously. As with exogenous steroid therapy, there will be contralateral adrenal suppression. The patient will be tapered rapidly to replacement hydrocortisone levels. We will try the remaining hydrocortisone withdrawal over the next six months or so, depending on her ACTH and cortisol responses. She is discharged to home with follow-up in my office in one week.

Which of the following is the correct code set for this hospitalization?

a. 239.7, 255.0, 07.21
b. 198.7, 07.22
c. 227.0, 255.0, 07.21
d. 227.0, 255.0, 07.29

7.15. The following documentation is from the health record of a 57-year-old male patient.

Discharge Diagnoses:
1. Lung cancer currently undergoing chemotherapy with Taxol® and carboplatin with dexamethasone
2. Type 2 diabetes, with neuropathy and nephropathy, not controlled
3. Hyperlipidemia
4. Hepatomegaly

History: This patient is a 57-year-old male who presented for outpatient chemotherapy. He had surgery for lung cancer in September and is now undergoing chemotherapy with Taxol and carboplatin, including dexamethasone as part of his chemo and prophylaxis for nausea. He has done very well with the chemotherapy. When he presented for treatment on the day of admission, he was found to be hypoglycemic. He is a known type II diabetic. His diabetes is complicated by neuropathy and nephropathy. Due to his blood glucose levels, it was decided to postpone this chemo session, and he was admitted for control of his diabetes. Dr. Johnson consulted with the patient to manage his diabetes regimen. He has been on 70/30 insulin, 25 units in the morning and 15 units in the evening. He had problems in the hospital with hypoglycemia several times the first day, with sugars ranging from 30 to greater than 450. An IV insulin drip was started, and he also had q. 1 hour Accu-Cheks. His hepatomegaly has enlarged from the last time that I saw him. Question whether this is fatty infiltration due to poor diabetes control, or whether there is now some involvement with metastatic carcinoma.

Laboratory Data: Sodium 128, potassium 5.5, chloride 89, CO_2 34, BUN 13, creatinine 0.8, glucose range 30–460, with final glucose of 210. Calcium 9.4, WBC 9.8, hemoglobin 11.6, hematocrit 34.3, platelets 277,000.

Plan: One difficulty here is the cyclic nature of his chemo treatment regimen, likely to produce major shifts in his glucose, which is already difficult to control. The patient will need to monitor his glucose levels closely. He is discharged on 70/30 insulin, 35 units in the morning and 20 units in the evening. Dr. Johnson will be managing his diabetes, and the patient has instructions to call into his nurse on a daily basis for the next week. He is to follow up with me for further chemotherapy in the oncology clinic next week.

Code Assignment:

Principal diagnosis:_____

Additional diagnoses:_____

Procedures:_____

Issues to clarify:_____

Disorders of the Genitourinary System

7.16. The following documentation is from the health record of a 58-year-old male patient.

Discharge Summary

Pertinent History: The patient was a 58-year-old male with a more-than-fifty-pack-per-year history of cigarette smoking. The patient had noted urinary frequency, bloody urine, and lower back pain for the past six months. The patient was accompanied by his wife, who was the historian. The patient was adamant that everything was fine. Preadmission workup included a cystoscopy, which revealed extensive bladder cancer. The patient was admitted for bladder removal.

Hospital Course: The patient was admitted, prepped, and taken to the OR. Radical cystectomy and ileal conduit by means of Kock pouch was accomplished. Partial prostatectomy was also done as a prophylactic measure. Pathology report confirmed extensive bladder carcinoma, but no prostate carcinoma. Inguinal lymph node dissection was done and revealed two of seven positive lymph nodes.

Discharge Instructions: The patient was discharged to be followed in the office and scheduled for radiation oncologist consultation.

Which code sets would be reported for the above case?

a. 188.9, 305.1, 57.71, 60.69, 56.51
b. 188.9, 196.5, 305.1, 57.71, 40.24
c. 188.9, 196.5, 305.1, 57.71, 56.51, 40.24
d. 185, 188.9, 196.5, 305.1, 60.69, 57.71, 56.51, 40.24

7.17. The following documentation is from the health record of a 38-year-old female patient.

Operative Report

Preoperative Diagnosis: Left ureteral calculus

Postoperative Diagnosis: Left ureteral calculus

Operative Procedure: Cystoscopy, urethroscopy, stone basketing, and placement of double-J ureteral catheter

This 38-year-old female reported to the ER with a history of severe left flank pain and was admitted for evaluation and treatment. An IVP revealed a large 1.5 cm calculus at the UV junction, which was obstructing. At that time, the patient was taken to the cystoscopy suite and underwent placement of double-J ureteral stent. The patient was now prepared for stone basketing.

The patient was taken to the cystoscopy suite and given spinal anesthetic and placed in the lithotomy position, after prepping and draping in the usual fashion. A #25 French cystoscope was then passed and a 0.038 guide wire was passed up the left ureter. The previously placed double-J catheter was removed. The ureteral orifice was then dilated with bougie dilators under direct vision and fluoroscopic guidance to #15 French, and the urethroscope was then passed alongside the guidewire up to the area of the stone. The stone was nicely identified, and a 2.5 stone basket was passed. The stone was engaged under direct vision and brought down through the ureteral meatus, which was too small to allow its passage. At this time, the urethrotome was passed and a small meatotomy was made at the anterior portion of the intramural ureter for approximately 0.5 cm, and the stone was easily pulled through. A #6 French double-J catheter was then passed over the previously placed guidewire. The guidewire was removed. The KUB showed the stent to be in good position. A Foley catheter was placed. The patient tolerated the procedure well. There were no complications. The patient was taken to the recovery room in stable condition.

Coding Exercise:

The documentation states that the "IVP revealed a large 1.5 cm calculus at the UV junction, which was obstructing." What is the UV junction?

_____

Code Assignment:

Principal diagnosis:_____

Additional diagnoses:_____

Procedures:_____

Issues to clarify:_____

7.18.   The following documentation is from the health record of a 50-year-old female patient.

Discharge Summary

The patient is a 50-year-old female with known carcinoma of the right breast with widespread pulmonary and bony metastases. She has completed a course of outpatient chemotherapy. Initially, the patient was treated with right mastectomy. The patient was now admitted for treatment of fibrous lumps of the left breast. The patient has decided to have a left mastectomy and bilateral insertion of tissue expanders.

The patient was taken to surgery, and a left simple mastectomy was performed. Pathology report revealed benign fibroadenoma. Tissue expanders were inserted under both pectoral muscles, bilaterally, to start the reconstruction process.

The patient was discharged in satisfactory condition to see me in the office in 10 days.

Which of the following code sets will be reported for the above admission?

a. 217, 197.0, 198.5, 85.33
b. 217, 197.0, 198.5, V10.3, 85.41, 85.95, 85.95
c. 610.2, 197.0, 198.5, V10.3, 85.41, 85.95
d. 174.9, 197.0, 198.5, 85.34, 85.95, 85.95

7.19. The following documentation is from the health record of a 14-year-old male patient.

Discharge Summary

The patient is a 14-year-old male with history of renal failure and failed kidney transplant. The patient was admitted for his second kidney transplant.

Prior to surgery, the patient underwent hemodialysis, through the existing AV fistula. The transplant was accomplished within 48 hours of the harvesting of the donor organ. Tissue samples confirmed adequate donor match. The previously transplanted, now failing, kidney was first removed; then the new kidney was placed.

One postoperative dialysis session was required before the transplanted kidney was functioning adequately. Postoperatively, the patient was watched carefully for signs of rejection. Patient's postoperative course was relatively uneventful.

The patient was discharged, to be followed weekly in the office.

Which of the following code sets will be reported for the above admission?

a. 996.81, 586, 55.53, 55.69, 39.95 × 2
b. 586, 996.81, 55.69, 39.95 × 2
c. 586, V42.0, 55.53, 55.69, 39.95
d. 584.9, V42.0, 55.69, 39.95

Infectious Diseases

7.20. The following documentation is from the health record of a 71-year-old male patient.

Discharge Summary

History and Physical Findings: This 71-year-old male is a nursing home resident as a result of a cerebrovascular accident two years ago. He has had numerous hospital admissions for pneumonia and other infectious complications. On the day of admission (4/21), the patient was noted to be clammy, with tachypnea, to have decreased level of responsiveness, and to show increased fever. He was seen in the ER, where evaluation revealed the presence of probable urinary tract infection and sepsis. The patient was also found to have renal insufficiency with BUN and creatinine elevated. His WBC count was 23,000 with decreased hemoglobin and hematocrit. He was admitted for treatment of E. coli septicemia. Physical examination revealed an elderly male who was aphasic. The patient had a right hemiplegia from previous CVA. The heart had a regular rhythm. The lungs were clear. The abdomen was soft.

Significant Lab, X-Ray, and Consult Findings: Follow-up chemistry showed progressive decline in the BUN and creatinine to near normal levels. Initial white blood cell count was 23,700. Final blood count was 9,000. The urinalysis showed white cells too numerous to count. The urine culture had greater than 100,000 colonies of E. coli and Group D strep, which revealed the cause of the UTI. Repeated blood cultures grew E. coli with the same sensitivities as that of the urine. There were no acute abnormalities noted. EKG showed sinus tachycardia and low lead voltage, otherwise was normal and unchanged.

Course in Hospital: The patient was initially started empirically on Primaxin®. He underwent fluid rehydration and his electrolytes were followed closely. Electrolytes improved through his hospital stay. He was continued on IV Primaxin until the date of discharge, when he was changed to Cipro® by tube. All of the bacteria grown in the urine and in the blood were sensitive to the Cipro. The chest x-ray showed no change from previous admissions, and he was followed closely with additional oxygen as needed. The patient does have a history of chronic obstructive lung disease and has required intermittent oxygen therapy at the nursing home. At this time, the patient had reached maximal hospital benefit. He was switched to oral antibiotics. He was to continue on tube feedings, which he was tolerating quite well. The patient was discharged back to the nursing home on 5/4.

Discharge Diagnoses: E. coli septicemia
UTI
Renal insufficiency
Chronic obstructive lung disease
CVA with right hemiplegia

Code Assignment:

Principal diagnosis: _____

Additional diagnoses: _____

Issues to clarify: _____

7.21.   The following documentation is from the health record of a 40-year-old male patient.

Discharge Summary

History of Present Illness: The patient is a 40-year-old male who presents with a newly diagnosed, non-Burkitt's, non-Hodgkin's lymphoma. The patient has a history of homosexuality. He was doing well until approximately one month prior to admission, when he developed watery stool, weight loss, and fatigue. He claims occasional fevers, chills, and diaphoresis but downplays the intensity. He was recently treated for two weeks for oral Candida, which has since resolved. He is positive for HIV. History of hepatitis B in 1986. The patient notes right arm pain and weakness after his lymph node biopsy, which revealed lymphoma of type previously stated.

Significant Lab, X-Ray, and Consult Findings: Labs on admission: Hemoglobin 14.1, MCV 97, hematocrit 41.2, WBC 6.9 with 19 lymphs and 9 monos, platelet count 291,000, urinalysis normal, sodium 144, potassium 4.4, chloride 101, CO_2 27, BUN 11, creatinine 0.9, glucose 94, calcium 9.4, phosphorus 3.3, magnesium 2.1, uric acid 5.3, SGOT 180, SGPT 130, alkaline phosphatase 126, LDH 324, total bilirubin 0.6, direct bili 0.1, total protein of 7.8, albumin 3.9. Chest x-ray was normal. Gram stain of spinal fluid obtained via spinal tap showed no growth at 24 hours and no organisms were seen. No growth on urine culture.

Hospital Course: The patient was admitted with the diagnosis of non-Hodgkin's lymphoma made by lymph node biopsy as an outpatient. He had a bone marrow biopsy done here that revealed slight increase in plasm cells and increase in eosinophils. There were no tumor cells noted. MRI scan of his cervical area revealed a questionable disc herniation at C4–C5. The CT scan of the neck revealed a left cervical node. The CT scan of the chest revealed a mass in the right axilla. The patient received Cytoxan®, vincristine, and prednisone for five days. This regimen is to be repeated every 21 days. The patient also received intrathecal methotrexate.

Approximately three days after admission, the patient developed increasing right-sided numbness with difficulty in respiration. The patient was intubated with endotracheal tube and was transferred to ICU for ventilation. Chest x-ray revealed a paralyzed right hemidiaphragm. The patient also developed bowel and bladder incontinence and lower extremity weakness. The occurrence of cord compression was entertained. A myelogram revealed a myelopathy with partial block at T4 to T6 and a complete block at C3 to C7. The patient received emergent radiation therapy to these areas. He slowly regained function and was able to be extubated after two days and transferred back to the floor. Radiation therapy continued and the patient slowly regained all functions and the paralysis of the hemidiaphragm resolved. The repeat myelogram showed free flow of dye from the cervical to the sacral area. Due to HIV infection, the patient developed thrush during this admission and was treated with nystatin. This did not resolve at the time of discharge and the patient will continue on his medication at home.

Also, the patient developed diarrhea during the hospitalization. Stool analyses were normal. This problem resolved prior to discharge. Medications at the time of discharge include nystatin, Tylenol, and prednisone. The patient is to be admitted in five weeks for further chemotherapy.

Discharge Diagnoses: Non-Hodgkin's lymphoma
Myelopathy
Paralysis of hemidiaphragm, resolved
HIV positive
Thrush
History of hepatitis B

Which of the following code sets will be reported for this hospitalization?

a. V58.11, 202.80, 336.3, 112.0, 042, V02.61, 41.31, 96.04, 96.71, 87.21, 99.25, 92.29, 03.31
b. 202.88, 336.3, 112.0, 042, V02.61, 787.91, 41.31, 96.04, 96.71, 87.21, 03.92, 99.25, 92.29, 03.31
c. 202.80, 336.3, 112.0, 41.31, 96.04, 96.71, 87.21, 03.92, 92.29, 03.31
d. 202.81, 336.8, 519.4, 042, 112.0, 787.91, 41.31, 96.04, 96.71, 87.21, 99.25, 92.29, 03.31

7.22.   The following documentation is from the health record of a two-year-old boy.

Discharge Summary

Admission Date: 7/18/2003

Discharge Date: 7/20/2003

Admitting Diagnosis: Fever of unknown origin

Discharge Diagnosis: 1. Primary herpetic gingivostomatitis
2. Kawasaki's disease
3. Strep pharyngitis

History: The patient is a two-year-old male who presented to the ER this evening from his primary medical doctor's office with four days of fever, rash, cracked lips, and drooling. Mom states that he has had a decreased activity level, decreased p.o. intake, and increased irritability. He has received Tylenol and Motrin® at home. Mom denies vomiting or diarrhea. He has had a sick contact at day care. He also has dysphagia and rhinorrhea.

Past Medical History: Significant for a VSD that has not been repaired. He is followed by a cardiologist and the abnormality is currently stable.

Physical Exam: This young male is quite irritable. He has bulbar conjunctival injection without discharge. His tympanic membranes are dull bilaterally. His tonsils are enlarged. He also has an exudate in his oropharynx. Heart shows regular rate and rhythm with a IV–VI systolic murmur at the left lower sternal border. He has a diffuse maculopapular rash on his lower extremities, trunk, back, and diaper area. He also has perineal desquamation.

Hospital Course: Patient presented to the ER with a four- to five-day history of fever, rash, cracked lips, drooling, and sore throat. Due to lymphadenopathy, perineal desquamation, bilateral bulbar conjunctivitis, and rash found on physical exam, he was treated for Kawasaki's disease with IVIG 2 gm/kg and aspirin 80 mg per day. He was also tested for herpes due to the perioral, paranasal, and oral lesions. His test came back positive for Herpes I virus and he was treated with Kefzol®. Cardiologist performed an echocardiogram to evaluate his VSD. His lesions slowly improved and are largely healed at this time. He remained afebrile for the past four nights. His medications were changed to oral form. He is no longer taking antibiotics and he will be continued on oral acyclovir. Follow-up with cardiologist is in four weeks.

Which of the following is the correct code set for this hospitalization?

a. 523.10, 054.9, 745.4, 446.1, 034.0
b. 054.2, 745.4, 034.0, 446.1, 785.6, 372.30, 782.1
c. 054.2, 745.4, 446.1, 034.0
d. 054.2, 446.1, 034.0

7.23.   **History:** The patient is a 78-year-old female who was initially admitted to the intensive care unit for sepsis and urinary tract infection and decreased level of consciousness. After admission to the intensive care unit, the patient was found to have a massive right-sided cerebrovascular accident, which was felt to be secondary to an embolic phenomenon. The patient was also noted to have endocarditis with a large vegetation noted. It was felt that the patient was not a surgical candidate due to her other multiple medical problems. The vegetation was noted on her mitral valve. It was described as a 4 cm length defect. The patient also had severe mitral regurgitation, moderate tricuspid regurgitation, and an elevated pulmonary artery systolic pressure of 71mmHg. CT of the head revealed an acute left middle cerebral arterial infarction involving the temporal and parietal lobes with localized mass effect and mild midline shift. No hemorrhage was seen.

The patient's sepsis was treated with IV antibiotics as was her urinary tract infection. Discussion was undertaken with the patient's next of kin as to the patient's resuscitation status. The patient was made a Do Not Resuscitate. Decision was made to keep the patient comfortable, and she was transferred to a medical bed. The patient's antibiotics were adjusted by an Infectious Disease Group. Her renal failure was continued to be followed by nephrology. Neurology was consulted for the patient's cerebrovascular accident. They did an EEG, which showed marked slowing; however, there was no total absence of brain activity. Cardiology consultation was obtained because of new onset atrial fibrillation. Cardiology felt that no aggressive intervention was needed; however, she would be given medicine to control her ventricular rate. The patient remained unresponsive. She was started on tube feeding and her antibiotics were continued. The patient was noted to have some thrombocytopenia as well as her continued renal failure and anemia. Diuresis was attempted with IV diuretics by nephrology in an attempt to help the patient's congestive heart failure. The patient was retaining copious amounts of fluid despite the diuretics. Her prothrombin time eventually normalized. Her blood sugar was elevated, and she was placed on once a day insulin at bedtime to cover her tube feedings. The patient was found without audible or visible respirations and no heart tones. She was pronounced dead at 12:40 and her body was released to the funeral home.

Which of the following code sets would be assigned by the hospital for this admission?

a. 038.9, 995.91, 599.0, 434.11, 394.1, 397.0, 398.91, 427.31, 287.5, 285.9
b. 995.91, 599.0, 586, 434.11, 424.0, 397.0, 428.0, 427.31, 287.5, 285.9
c. 038.9, 995.92, 599.0, 586, 434.11, 424.0, 397.0, 398.91, 427.31, 287.5, 285.9
d. 434.11, 038.9, 995.92, 586, 428.0, 424.0, 397.0, 427.31, 287.5, 285.9

7.24.   **Discharge Diagnosis:**   1. Escherichia coli and staphylococcus aureus urinary tract infection with sepsis.
2. Sepsis syndrome
3. Advanced dementia
4. Hypothroidism
5. Hypertension
6. Protein calorie malnutrition
7. Dysphagia

Discharge Medications: Levoxyl® 88mcg p.o. q. a.m., Paxil® 20mg p.o. q. a.m., Namenda® 10mg p.o. q. a.m., and Ativan® .5 q. 8 hours agitation, Augmentin 500mg p.o. b.i.d. for 15 days, and Megace® 400 mg p.o. b.i.d.

Discharge Disposition: Improved and home with home health

History of Present Illness: The patient is an 85-year-old female who was apparently brought into the emergency room by her family this evening for multiple problems. According to the family, she has not been eating recently and has been getting extremely weak. She has not been unable to stand without assistance for quite some time now. The patient, although awake and alert, will not answer any questions. All history is obtained from the computer records, as well as the ER staff and ER physician. Initial workup reveals significant urinary tract infection. She is also most likely septic secondary to her presentation given her hypotension and acute encephalopathy.

Laboratory/Radiology: Admission labs significant for a white count of 9.8, hemoglobin 14.9, platelets of 328,000 with a BUN of 29 and creatinine of 1.4. Urinalysis was small bilirubin, 15 mg ketones, large blood, 100 mg protein, positive nitrates, large leukocytes, and too many WBCs to count, with many bacteria and many red cells. CT of the head was normal. Portable chest x-ray showed hyperexpanded lung fields but no mass.

Hospital Course: The patient was admitted to the general medical floor with the diagnosis of sepsis. After discussion with family, she was made DNR III and was hydrated and started on IV ciprofloxacin. She has a significant advanced dementia and does not speak but was somewhat more encephalopathic secondary to her sepsis, and this improved to her baseline. Her BUN and creatinine normalized, and she was continued on her usual medications for dementia. Her hydrochlorothiazide was held, but she was continued on her Toprol. Levoxyl was held and a TSH was within normal limits. She was continued on her Paxil. Subsequently, her urine culture grew out E. coli, pan sensitive and S. aureus, pan sensitive, and she was changed from ciprofloxacin to Augmentin 500 mg p.o. b.i.d., which she tolerated well. Speech therapy was consulted, and an MBS was performed. Diet with thin liquids was recommended. She does have protein calorie malnutrition.

Disposition: The daughter has been contacted as the patient is stable for discharge. She is discharged to her daughter's care with physical and occupational therapy.

What codes should be assigned in this case?

Principal Diagnosis:_____

Secondary Diagnosis:_____

Behavioral Health Conditions

7.25.   In the following case scenario, a 26-year-old white male was admitted after being transferred from the outpatient evaluation service with severe homicidal and suicidal ideation. Admitting diagnosis was severe major depressive disorder with psychotic features. Pharmacological treatment was initiated and suicide precautions were instituted. After a thorough psychologic evaluation, the risks and benefits of ECT were reviewed. Due to the severity of the psychotic episode and the patient's delusional state, it was determined that ECT was warranted. Extensive efforts were made to secure informed consent from the patient, and a course of ECT was begun.

ECT was administered three times per week, and the course of therapy was completed in a three-week period. On the fourth treatment of ECT, postictal observation was notable for cardiac arrhythmia, which subsided without sequelae. Otherwise, the patient tolerated the therapy well and responded quickly with resolution of the psychotic features and overall improvement in the acute phase of his depressive disorder. Suicide precautions could be lifted after the fifth treatment with ECT. After establishing adequate therapeutic levels of Lithium, the patient was discharged to be managed as an outpatient.

Discharge Diagnosis: Severe major depressive disorder with suicidal ideation, stabilized after a course of ECT.

Which is the correct code set for reporting this case scenario?

a. 296.24, V62.84, 94.27, 94.22, 94.08
b. 296.23, V62.84, 94.27, 94.22, 94.08
c. 296.24, V62.84, 427.9, 94.26, 94.22, 94.08
d. 296.23, V62.84, 997.1, 427.9, 94.27, 94.22, 94.08

7.26. The following documentation is from the health record of a 56-year-old male patient.

Final Diagnosis

Axis I: Chronic schizophrenia, paranoid type with acute exacerbation, improved

Axis II: None

Axis III: Cardiomyopathy secondary to hypertension
            COPD
            Type 2 diabetes mellitus

Axis IV: Psychosocial and environmental stressors are severe

Axis V: Admission GAF 25 to 30
            Discharge GAF 55

Physical Examination: For pertinent findings on medical examination, see the medical doctor's dictation.

Pertinent Laboratory Results: Electrolyte panel within normal limits. Digoxin level was 0.6, hemoglobin A1C 6.5, triglycerides 138, CBC unremarkable. TSH 1.3, urinalysis negative. EKG showed normal sinus rhythm.

Hospital Course: This is a 56-year-old male who was admitted due to decompensating at his apartment where he thought people were trying to get into his apartment, and he continued to decompensate with his paranoia and persecutory-type delusions, so it was felt he needed longer hospitalization. During this time he also switched his medications from Zyprexa® to Seroquel® to Risperdal®, and then he came in on Prolixin®. We reviewed his records, and it appears he did quite well on Risperdal so he went back to taking that, and he was titrated up to 30 mg q. h.s. of Risperdal and 100 mg of trazodone. These two medications helped significantly to eliminate his delusions and paranoid ideation. He slept better. Patient started going on therapeutic passes that went well. His sister reports that he is doing the best that she has seen him in quite some time. During his stay here his mother passed away from a long medical illness, and he was able to go to the funeral and dealt with that loss in an appropriate way. He continued to show improvement and was placed on Level E. He continued to go to psychosocial programming. A discharge meeting was held, and it was agreed that he could get most of his services through the outpatient program. It was felt by everyone that the patient was stable enough to be discharged, and discharge was scheduled.

Pertinent Findings on Mental Status at Discharge: 45 minutes spent in the final examination with the patient. Appearance: Pleasant, white male who looks his stated age. Behavior is cooperative, fair eye contact. Speech is of normal rate and volume. Not rapid or pressured. Mood euthymic, affect appropriate. Thought process is goal directed, decreased paranoid ideation. Negative for racing thoughts and flight of ideas. Thought content: He denies signs of active psychosis, denies current suicidal or homicidal intent. Insight and judgment improved. Impulse control is fair.

Prognosis: Fair. The main problem is that the patient is on so many medications for his medical problems. He did do well with the pill organizer and self-meds, but his mental illness may be exacerbated if his medical conditions are not well controlled.

Discharge Medications: Digoxin .25 mg q. d., Glucotrol® 2.5 mg a.m. and 7.5 mg q. 5:00 p.m., potassium 10 mEq q. a.m., spironolactone 25 mg q. a.m., an aspirin 325 mg q. a.m., Lasix 10 mg q. d., lisinopril 2.5 mg q. d., Atrovent inhaler two puffs q. i.d., isosorbide dinitrate 10 mg t.i.d., beclomethasone inhaler four puffs b.i.d., Risperdal 3 mg q. h.s., Colace 100 mg b.i.d., and trazodone 100 mg q. h.s.

Aftercare Recommendations: The patient will be discharged to his apartment. Social services will follow the patient. He will follow up with a psychiatrist and medical care through the outpatient program. Also, a home health nurse will come to see the patient.

Which of the following code sets is correct for reporting this inpatient hospitalization?

a. 295.34, 425.4, 401.9, 496, 250.01, 94.25
b. 295.32, 402.90, 496, 250.01, 94.25
c. 295.34, 402.90, 496, 250.00, 94.25
d. 295.84, 402.90, 496, 250.00, 94.25

7.27.   The following documentation is from the health record of a 17-year-old male patient.

History of Present Illness: The patient is a 17-year-old white male who was brought to the ED after being found passed out in the town park. The patient was in restraints and accompanied by two police officers. The patient was combative and aggressive, threatening physical harm to himself as well as the physician and hospital staff. The patient has a long history of alcohol and drug abuse, was in the local treatment center, and walked off campus two days ago.

Allergies:	NKDA
PMH:	Attention deficit hyperactivity disorder (ADHD), drug and alcohol dependence, aggressive behavior
Family History:	Noncontributory
ROS:	As above

Physical Examination: Vital signs: Temp. 100.1 degrees; BP 144/88 mmHg; General: Alternating between lethargy and combativeness; HEENT: Pupils pinpoint, 1 mm bilaterally; Skin: Cool, clammy to touch, feet and hands cold, slightly diaphoretic; Heart: Rate tachy, no murmurs; Lungs: Clear, respiratory rate 28 and shallow; Abdomen: Benign; Neurological: Mental status as above; follows commands inconsistently, responds to voice; cranial nerves: pupils as noted, gag intact; Motor: Moving all four extremities with equal power; Sensory: Responds to touch in all four extremities; deep tendon reflexes +3 throughout, but plantar reflexes down going bilaterally.

Laboratory: U/A shows 2+ blood, done after Foley catheter was placed; drug screen positive for amphetamines; ETOH 0.30; ABG within normal limits; EKG sinus tachycardia.

Hospital Course: Family was contacted, IV fluids were initiated, and the patient was admitted to ICU with suicide protocol, Ativan 1–2 mg IV q. 2 hours p.r.n. He was maintained on soft restraints with checks every 15 minutes and monitored with telemetry and neuro checks through the night. By the morning he was no longer tachycardic. By hospital day 3 he was medically stable, but still saying he wants to "kill himself." Psychiatric consult requested; see dictated report.

Disposition: Discharge to psych. Psychiatric liaison service agreed to accept him in transfer to the inpatient adolescent psychiatric unit at children's hospital.

Discharge Diagnoses:	Drug overdose with amphetamines and alcohol
	Apparent suicide attempt
	Continued verbalization of suicidal ideation

Which of the following code sets would be correct for this case?

a. 969.7, 785.0, 304.40, E950.3, 980.0, 303.00, E950.9, 314.01, 312.00
b. 785.0, E939.7, 305.90, 314.01, 312.00
c. 969.7, 785.0, 304.00, E980.3, 303.00, 314.01, 312.00
d. 785.0, 303.00, 304.40, 969.7, E950.3, 980.0, E950.9, 314.01, 312.00

Disorders of the Musculoskeletal System and Connective Tissue

7.28.   The following documentation is from the health record of a 42-year-old male patient.

Discharge Summary

Hospital Course: This is a 42-year-old male admitted through the ED with a right thumb crush injury, the result of a farm accident. See ED report and admitting H&P

for details of the accident. The patient was admitted and taken to surgery for repair. Postoperative course was uncomplicated.

Prognosis: Long-term prognosis is mixed because of the severity of injury. The patient had severe crush injury and is at high risk for partial- or full-thickness skin loss, entire loss of thumb, stiffness, osteoarthritis, sepsis, osteomyelitis, septic arthritis, and generalized dysfunction of thumb. The patient may require further reconstructive surgery at a later date. Discharge medications include Lortab® 5 p.r.n., Anaprox® DS prn for pain, and Duricef® 500 mg for infection. The patient will be followed in my office in three to five days.

Discharge Diagnoses: Right thumb crush injury
Open fracture of proximal phalanx
Pollicis longus tendon transection

Operative Report

Pre- and Postoperative Diagnosis: 1. Open articular fracture of head of
Right thumb crush injury   proximal phalanx
2. Extensor pollicis longus tendon
transection

Procedure Details: The patient was taken to the operating room. Given preoperatively a gram of Ancef® and 80 mg of tobramycin IV in the emergency room. Axillary block was previously administered, as well as a standard metacarpal block, by myself. Standard prep and drape was done. The extremity was exsanguinated and tourniquet was inflated to 250 mmHg. The entire procedure was performed with 3.5 loupe magnification.

The complex, radially based laceration was opened, vigorously irrigated with normal saline and bacitracin. Neurovascular bundle identified, visualized, and noted to be intact, though contused. Laceration was extended dorsally to facilitate exposure. Because of the complexity of the fracture, the entire fracture was opened. Fracture site was irrigated and debrided. Fracture site was curetted. Multiple loose bone fragments were removed. The linear complex radial intra-articular fracture was stabilized to the proximal ulnar fracture with 0.35 crossed K-wires, resulting in excellent bony fixation. The split T-condylar fracture was then anatomically reduced and transfixed with transverse 0.35 K-wires. Anatomic reduction of the articular surface was achieved. This was confirmed clinically and then with intraoperative AP and lateral C-arm. Fracture was clinically stable and anatomically reduced.

The area was irrigated with normal saline with bacitracin again. All potential bleeders were electrocauterized. The distal interphalangeal joint was stabilized in 0 degrees of extension with a 0.45 K-wire that was originally driven retrograde followed by antegrade with excellent purchase. Extensor pollicis longus was formally repaired with interrupted 4-0 MERSILENE® followed by 6-0 nylon epitenon repair. Strong anatomic repair was achieved. The area was again irrigated. Skin was closed with interrupted 4-0 and 5-0 nylon with no skin loss.

At this point, the hand was cleansed with hydrogen peroxide. Proximal metacarpal and median nerve block was performed with 0.5 percent Marcaine. The hand was then further dressed with Neosporin®, Adaptic®, 4x4, 1-inch TubeGauz®. A complex static volar splint was then applied, which was forearm based and covering the thumb. Tourniquet was released. Patient tolerated the procedure well and was transferred to the recovery room in stable condition. Estimated blood loss was none.

Which of the following is the correct ICD-9-CM code assignment?

a. 816.01, 813.18, 79.24, 79.22
b. 816.01, 813.08, 79.34, 79.32, 82.45
c. 816.11, 813.18, 79.24, 79.22, 82.45
d. 816.11, 813.18, 79.34, 79.32, 82.45

7.29. The following documentation is from the health record of a 29-year-old male patient.

Discharge Summary

Hospital Course: This is a 29-year-old white male who was involved in a motor vehicle accident on 11/21 and initially taken to Care Community Hospital and thought to have a T-6/7 paraplegia at that time. CT of the head was ordered at that time, but apparently not done. The patient was transferred here for further treatment and evaluation. On evaluation here, a fracture at C 7 was indeed noted. Evaluation revealed a C 7 quadriplegic, Frankel B, with a neurogenic bladder. The patient apparently was already in traction and that was maintained on admission here. There is no mention in the chart of plane x-ray abnormalities at that time, and he was subsequently scheduled for an MRI and CT scan. The patient was also placed on steroid protocol and sub-q heparin, as well as sequential compression hose.

Urology consultation was also obtained, as well as neurosurgical consultation. MRI was done on 11/22, which showed a decreased amount of cord C 7, which suggested a central cord contusion and also a ventral defect at C-6/7. CT contrast also showed a diffuse ventral lesion at C-5/6; however, there was no displacement of the cord, and no cord encasement was identified, so decompression of the cord was not recommended by neurosurgery. The patient was continued on pain medications as needed, and traction via the halo placed at Care Community Hospital was maintained.

An odontoid fracture was also identified on plane films on flexion and extension of the neck. A halo vest was applied, and traction was discontinued on 11/28. X-rays were taken, and good fracture alignment was obtained at that time. Follow-up films were again taken, and, on 12/11, displacement of the odontoid fracture was noted. The halo itself was repositioned the following day on 12/12. Good position was initially confirmed by x-ray; however, after two days' time, the fracture had redisplaced. Once again, the halo was readjusted on 12/14. On review of films on 12/16, for the second time, again, the odontoid had displaced from its initially reduced position. Surgery was recommended for stabilization of the odontoid fracture; however, the patient initially refused to have this done. After several days of encouragement, the patient finally consented to surgery, which was performed on 12/21. He had posterior cervical wiring and fusion with a left iliac crest bone graft C 1 to C 2. He had no intraoperative complications and was followed postoperatively. He experienced no neurologic changes and had a well-healed surgical incision. Follow-up x-rays postoperatively showed good alignment and stable fixation of the fracture. The patient's course was undergoing full-team evaluation and treatment. At this time, nutrition was concerned and good p.o. intake was stressed. Other services were also working with him, including a speech pathologist, who was working with him for trouble swallowing. He was maintained in the halo postoperatively after his fusion, and this was checked periodically.

The hospital course was complicated by several episodes of urinary tract infection that were addressed by practitioners from urology. He was placed on antibiotics for these problems. The patient also had one episode of vomiting coffee ground emesis on 1/24. This was treated with antacids and n.p.o. for a temporary period of time. His hemoglobin and hematocrit were checked and were stable.

On 1/25, the patient was noted to have some left scrotal swelling. Ultrasound of the testicles was done, and diagnosis of epididymitis was obtained. This was followed by practitioners from infectious disease and urology, who placed him on appropriate antibiotics, which were later switched to p.o. Cipro. Organism was pseudomonas. After a few days, this resolved, and he had no further sequelae from his epididymitis.

Follow-up x-rays continued to show good reduction and healing of the fracture. His halo vest was discontinued on 2/14, and he was then maintained on a hard collar for approximately two weeks. It was then later removed on 2/25. The patient continued in a full rehabilitation program during this time. The patient's hospitalization at this point was getting fairly lengthy, and he was becoming impatient with his rehab and did not cooperate with his therapist, as his discharge date was pushed back some; however, he began to be more cooperative and did show a better attitude in meeting his goals. He continued with his rehab and did relatively well, meeting the majority of his goals, however not doing this willingly sometimes. He was subsequently discharged to home on 4/12 to the care of his mother. He will be followed as an outpatient in the clinic at eight weeks postdischarge.

Final Diagnoses: Cervical fracture at C-6/7 with central cord contusion and a ventral defect
C7 Quadriplegic, Frankel B, with neurogenic bladder
Odontoid fracture, C1
UTI
Epididymitis

Procedures: Posterior cervical wiring and fusion with a left iliac crest bone graft C 1 to C 2
Traction maintenance with halo previously placed

Which of the following is the correct ICD-9-CM code assignment?

a. 806.00, E819.9, 344.61, 599.0, 787.2, 604.90, 041.7, 81.01, 93.41, 02.94
b. 806.09, 805.01, E819.9, 344.61, 599.0, 604.90, 81.01, 93.41, 02.94
c. 806.08, 805.01, E819.9, 344.61, 599.0, 787.2, 604.90, 041.7, 81.00, 93.42
d. 806.08, 806.07, 805.01, E819.9, 344.61, 599.0, 787.2, 604.90, 041.7, 81.01, 93.41

7.30. The following documentation is from the health record of an ORIF patient.

Operative Report

Preoperative Diagnosis: Displaced comminuted fracture of the lateral condyle, right elbow

Postoperative Diagnosis: Same

Procedure: Open reduction, internal fixation

Description: The patient, with malignant hypertension and type 1 diabetes mellitus, was anesthetized and prepped with Betadine, sterile drapes were applied, and the pneumatic tourniquet was inflated around the arm. An incision was made in the area of the lateral epicondyle through a Steri-Drape, and this was carried through subcutaneous tissue, and the fracture site was easily exposed. Inspection revealed the fragment to be rotated in two planes about 90 degrees. It was possible to manually reduce this quite easily, and the judicious manipulation resulted in an almost anatomic reduction. This was fixed with two pins driven across the humerus. These pins were cut off below skin level. The wound was closed with some plain catgut subcutaneously and 5-0 nylon in the skin. Dressings were applied to the patient and tourniquet released. A long arm cast was applied.

Which of the following is the correct ICD-9-CM code assignment?

a. 812.52, 401.9, 250.01, 79.32
b. 812.42, 401.0, 250.01, 79.31
c. 812.42, 401.0, 250.01, 78.52
d. 812.52, 401.9, 250.00, 79.32

7.31. ## Discharge Summary

Admission Date: November 15, 20xx

Discharge Date: November 20, 20xx

Description: The patient is a 49-year-old male who was admitted on November 15. He underwent revision laminectomy and stabilization of his lumbar spine with a Dynesys® system. The patient tolerated the procedure well and had an uneventful hospital course, but was slow to progress with physical therapy and pain control.

By postoperative day 5, he was tolerating a regular diet, had obtained pain control, and cleared physical therapy. He was subsequently discharged home with written instructions. He is to follow up in three weeks after discharge. He was given Percocet® and Flexeril® for pain and spasms, as needed.

History and Physical

Admit Diagnosis: Recurrent herniated disc

Procedure: Lumbar laminectomy, disc stabilization with Dynesys

HPI: 49-year-old male with left leg and back pain. Diagnosed with recurrent disc herniation

Past Medical History: Status post laminectomy and diskectomy two years ago

Physical:

Neck: Supple

Heart: Regular rate and rhythm

Lungs: Clear to auscultation

Neuro: Left leg weakness, numbness and pain

Skin: No lesions, masses or rashes

Assessment and Plan: Recurrent HNP L5 to S1

Operative Report

Preoperative Diagnosis: Radiculopathy and degenerative disc disease at L5-S1 with recurrent disc herniation at L5-S1

Postoperative Diagnosis: Same

Procedure Performed: Revision L5 laminectomy, revision S1 laminectomy and diskectomy, stabilization of L5 to S1 with flexible rod Dynesys system.

Anesthesia: General

Blood Loss: Minimal

Complications: Intraoperative dural tear, which was repaired with watertight seal with interrupted 4-0 NUROLON® sutures.

Description of the Procedure: Under sterile conditions, the patient was brought to the operating room and was placed under general endotracheal anesthesia and placed in a prone position. Lumbar spine was then prepped and draped in the usual sterile manner with a Betadine prep. A lateral x-ray was obtained with an 18-gauge spinal needle placed for level localization. Based upon the x-ray, a direct posterior approach to the lumbar spine was performed. This was carried down to the transverse process of L5 and the sacral ala bilaterally. After adequate exposure, complete laminectomy was performed in a subperiosteal fashion with a combination Leksell and Kerrison rongeurs at the L5 and S1 levels. Mobilization of the left S1 and L5 nerve roots was performed, although there was a significant amount of scar tissue. There was a large free L5-S1 recurrent disc fragment, which was removed with a pituitary rongeur. There was a small dural tear within the axilla of the L5 nerve root which was not repaired because of the location and the fact that it was not leaking actively without traction upon the dura. After adequate decompression, attention was brought to stabilization. Using the usual internal and external landmarks, pedicle screws were placed in the L5 and S1 pedicles bilaterally. These were drilled, probed, dilated, and then a combination of 7.2 × 40 millimeter screws and 7.2 millimeter by 45 millimeter screws were placed in the L5 and S1 pedicles bilaterally. AP and lateral x-rays were obtained, noting appropriate placement of the screws. Measuring of the cord device was performed bilaterally. The cord was placed in the usual fashion, tensioned, and then finally tightened. The wound was copiously irrigated with bacitracin solution. No drain was utilized. The fascia was closed with interrupted 0 VICRYL suture. The subcutaneous tissue and skin were closed in three sequential layers. The patient was awakened in the operating room, extubated, and brought to the recovery room in satisfactory condition.

Code Assignment:

Principal diagnosis:_____

Additional diagnoses:_____

Procedures:_____

Neoplasms

7.32. In the following scenario, the discharge summary states: The patient is a 67-year-old male with cancer of the prostate three years ago, which was treated with prostatectomy and radiation therapy. He has also been diagnosed with metastases to the testes and the lymph nodes in the groin. He has been having increasingly severe lower back pain, and a recent radioisotope bone scan showed a "hot" spot in the lower lumbar vertebrae. The patient was admitted five days ago through the ED, complaining of severe lower back pain upon getting out of bed that day. Lumbar x-ray revealed fracture of the L 4 vertebrae. The patient was admitted and placed in Buck's traction for 24 hours in an attempt to relieve his pain, which was unsuccessful. MRI the next day also revealed metastasis to the spinal cord and vertebrae at the L 4 fracture site. The patient was begun on MS Contin® to relieve pain, and arrangements were made for transfer to a skilled nursing facility for palliative care. Hospice services were offered to the patient and family.

Which of the following code sets would be correct for reporting the diagnoses in this scenario?

a. 198.5, 733.13, 198.3, 198.82, 196.5, 185
b. 198.3, 805.4, 198.5, 198.82, 196.5, V10.46
c. 805.4, 198.5, 198.3, 198.82, 196.5, 185
d. 733.13, 198.5, 198.3, 198.82, 196.5, V10.46

7.33. The following documentation is from the health record of a 72-year-old male patient.

Discharge Summary

History of Present Illness: This 72-year-old male was admitted with shortness of breath. The patient had a prior history of right pleuritic chest pain in January, with a chest x-ray that showed right pleural reaction and mass versus infiltrate on the right. The episode of pain resolved. A follow-up chest x-ray in March showed a decrease in the lung infiltrates, as well as a small bleb not seen on prior films. Over the three to four days prior to admission, the patient complained of increasing shortness of breath, dyspnea on exertion, sweats, and myalgias at the legs and arms, with decreased p.o. intake and abdominal soreness. The patient also had chills once in a while. He denied cough, sputum, and chest pain. There was no nausea, vomiting, diarrhea, or constipation, and there was no dysuria. He was a former 50-pack/year smoker.

Physical Examination: Heart rate 96–104, respiratory rate 30–36, temperature 96°F p.o., blood pressure 115/80. Neck showed no nodes or jugular venous distention. Lungs showed resonant breath sounds equally with left basilar rales. Back was nontender. Heart tones are S1 and S2 with a I/VI systolic murmur. Abdomen was soft and he had positive bowel sounds. The patient had positive right upper quadrant and epigastric tenderness with no rebound or guarding. There was a liver edge palpable at 1–2 cm below the right costal margin. Extremities showed no edema, and there was a darkish/bluish tinge to the lips. Neuro: Patient was alert, oriented, and grossly intact. The patient was admitted to the hospital with respiratory distress, left-sided rales, and pallor. Primary consideration at that time was given to infection (pulmonary) versus exacerbation of chronic obstructive pulmonary disease.

Lab Data: Admission blood values were obtained and showed a white count of 14,600 with 83 bands and 10 lymphs. Hemoglobin was 12, hematocrit 36. Platelet count was 430,000. Initial Profile I was within normal limits except for a CO PO_2 of 21, BUN of 36, and glucose of 145. Initial Profile II was remarkable only for an albumin of 3.3. Chest x-ray was obtained, which showed cardiomegaly with no infiltrate or masses seen. Blood gases obtained showed a pH of 7.46, PCO_2 of 22, and PO_2 of 63 on room air. A CAT scan of the chest was obtained, which showed mediastinal adenopathy and a right-sided mass; massive acute pericardial effusion was also visualized.

Hospital Course: The patient had an emergency consultation with Cardiology. An echocardiogram was obtained that showed acute pericardial effusion. The patient was seen by thoracic surgery, and a percutaneous drainage of the malignant pericardial effusion was performed. With drainage, the patient received almost immediate symptomatic improvement in his dyspnea and chest discomfort. Over the next few days, his dyspnea remained stable, he had no more epigastric pain, and there was improvement in his abdominal exam. Pericardial fluid cytology showed an undifferentiated carcinoma. Once the patient was stabilized, he had a pericardial window placed, as well as a bronchoscopy with transbronchial biopsy, which was interpreted as adenocarcinoma of the lung. He subsequently received a course of chemotherapy with mitomycin, Velban®, and platinum. This was tolerated without major difficulty. The patient was discharged hemodynamically stable; to be seen in the office.

Final Diagnoses: 1. Adenocarcinoma of the lung
2. Acute pericardial effusion
3. Chronic obstructive pulmonary disease

What are the correct ICD-9-CM codes for assignment on this case?

Principal diagnosis:_____

Additional diagnoses:_____

Procedures:_____

Issues to clarify:_____

7.34. The following documentation is from the health record of a 71-year-old female patient.

Discharge Summary

History of Present Illness: This patient is a 71-year-old female with carcinoma of the left breast. She was admitted for reexcision of the left breast mass and left axillary dissection with mirror image biopsy of the right breast. The patient has a history of hypertension, COPD, heavy smoking, and alcohol use. She was in her usual state of health until December, when she noted a lump in her left breast that was painless, without discharge, without retraction. Mammography was reportedly within normal limits. The patient was followed closely.

During recheck in July, a repeat mammography revealed a mass in the left breast with calcifications. The patient underwent an excisional biopsy of the left breast mass, which was positive for in situ intraductal and lobular carcinoma. The initial biopsy specimen showed a positive margin. The patient is, therefore, admitted at this time for extended excision of the left breast. Mirror image biopsy of the right breast and a left axillary lymph node resection are also to be done.

The patient had menarche at age 12 and has given birth to a single child. The patient has no family history of breast carcinoma. Past medical history: Positive for hypertension and chronic obstructive bronchitis. Medications include: Aldomet®, 250 mg p.o. b.i.d.; Dyazide®, one p.o. b.i.d.; Theo-Dur; Premarin; and Provera®. Otherwise unremarkable.

Physical Examination: Exam revealed a well-developed, well-nourished female in no apparent distress. The vital signs are stable, afebrile. The HEENT examination is within normal limits. The neck is supple, the trachea is midline. There are no masses or adenopathy present. The lungs are clear to auscultation and percussion. The cardiovascular examination is within normal limits. The left breast shows a contusion with overlying skin incision and surrounding erythema. The right breast is within normal limits. The right axilla is normal without adenopathy. The left axilla reveals small (less than 1 cm), nonfixed, not matted lymph nodes. The abdominal examination is within normal limits. The rectal examination is normal, with guaiac negative stool present in the vault.

Hospital Course: After adequate preoperative preparation, the patient was taken to the operating room. A left breast excision was performed with left axillary lymph node excision. A right breast local excision was performed for the indication of lobular carcinoma in situ of the left breast. The patient's postoperative course was unremarkable.

The patient is discharged with a large Jackson-Pratt in place, continuing to drain from the left axilla. She is on a regular diet. The patient will be followed up in general surgery clinic. Pathology: Small residual of intraductal lobular carcinoma, left breast. Negative nodes in right breast.

Final Diagnoses:
1. Carcinoma left breast
2. Chronic bronchitis
3. Hypertension

Procedures: 1. Local excision, right breast
                   2. Simple excision of left breast with left axillary lymph node
                      dissection

Which of the following is the most accurate ICD-9-CM code assignment?

a. 233.0, 491.9, 401.9, 85.41, 40.23, 85.12
b. 174.9, 491.20, 401.9, 496, 85.43, 85.12
c. 233.0, 491.20, 401.9, V15.82, 85.43, 85.21
d. 174.9, 491.9, 401.9, 85.41, 40.23, 85.21

7.35. The following documentation is from the health record of a 72-year-old male patient.

Discharge Summary

History of Present Illness: The patient is a 72-year-old male with a history of abdominal perineal resection for colon cancer in 1985 and left hemicolectomy in 1995 for splenic flexure recurrence of cancer. Subsequent right nephrectomy, right adrenalectomy, right posterior hepatic wedge resection in February for metastatic colon carcinoma. The patient is admitted with complaints of lower back pain and bilateral thigh pain times two months, increasing in intensity.

Physical Examination: Examination on admission: temperature 99°F, pulse 72, respirations 24, blood pressure 150/90. The examination was remarkable for left lower quadrant colostomy from previous operation, mildly tender lumbar spine, and the patient was barely able to stand. It was also noted that the patient had decreased sharp/dull discrimination on the neural examination of the lateral thighs.

Laboratory Data: On admission the labs were: Urinalysis: Specific gravity 1.021, pH 5; chem. tests were negative; nitrite negative; blood negative, 12 white cells, moderate bacteria. The clinical chemistry results were: Serum sodium 141, BUN 42, potassium 4.9, chloride 104, CO_2 28, glucose 99, creatinine 1.8, SGOT 12, SGPT 16, alkaline phosphatase 68, total protein 6.6, albumin 3.8, total bilirubin 0.7, direct bilirubin 0.0, GGT 87, calcium 10.3, magnesium 2.0, phosphorus 3.2, uric acid 5.7, PT 12.9, PTT 28.4, white count 8.0, hemoglobin 15.0, hematocrit 43.8, platelets 223,000. The CEA level was noted to be 508 nanograms per ml on admission. Metastatic workup for the colon carcinoma revealed no evidence of metastatic disease to the head or the thoracic and cervical spine.

Radiologic Studies: CT and MRI revealed left celiac ganglion node plexus enlarged, diagnosed as metastasis. Multiple small lung nodules, bilaterally, suspicious for metastasis. Pathological fractures of L2 and L4, with compression of L2, effacement of the spinal canal space and apparent cord compression at the L2 level. Subsequent urine culture grew out greater than 10^5 pseudomonas aeruginosa, which was sensitive to ciprofloxacin. The patient was treated for this UTI with ciprofloxacin 500 mg p.o. q. 8 hours and subsequent urine culture showed no growth.

Hospital Course: The patient went to the operating room for L 2 laminectomy with decompression and anterior allograft bone fusion. The postoperative course was marked by slow recovery with nausea and difficulty with pain control. The patient slowly improved and began ambulating eight days later. The patient fell three days later on ambulation but was without significant injuries. Further physical therapy was marked by continued improvement in ambulation with walker and no further setbacks. Clinically, the patient is afebrile without signs and symptoms of infection, no CVA tenderness, and no dysuria. The patient will be discharged home today. Condition on discharge fairly good.

Treatment: The patient will go home on Vicodin p.o. q 4 to 6 hours for pain, and Capoten®. He will resume Capoten b.i.d. dosing per his internist's recommendations for his hypertension, 25 p.o. b.i.d. Prognosis: The long-term prognosis is poor as the patient has extensive metastatic colon CA; short-term prognosis is fairly good with improvement in ambulation. Ambulation is with walker assistance. Follow-up: The patient will return to see me next Wednesday.

Final Diagnoses: Metastatic colon cancer to lung and bone
Pathologic fracture of L2 secondary to
metastasis, with cord compression

What are the correct ICD-9-CM codes for assignment on this case?

Principal diagnosis:_____

Additional diagnoses:_____

Procedures:_____

Disorders of the Nervous System and Sense Organs

7.36.   The following documentation is from the health record of an 86-year-old female patient.

Discharge Summary

This 86-year-old female patient was noted to have three to four falls in the past two months at ABC Nursing Home. Patient fell yesterday and hit the left frontal temporal area of her head causing a contusion. For this reason, the patient was brought to the hospital for observation and further workup. The patient's exam was remarkable for moderate ataxia. Past medical history includes senile dementia-Alzheimer's type, depression, and emphysema. Current medications include Zoloft® and theophylline. CT of the brain noted that the patient had multiple masses in the brain compatible with metastatic disease. It was felt that the patient's ataxia was most likely on the basis of the metastatic disease to the brain. These results were discussed with the patient's niece. After much discussion regarding the options of possible tissue biopsy versus empiric radiation treatment, the niece decided that she did not want her aunt to undergo any further tests and/or evaluation. It was her decision that the patient be transferred back to the nursing home and put under hospice care.

Which of the following is the correct ICD-9-CM diagnosis code assignment?

a. 781.3, 198.3, 492.8, 331.0, 294.11, 920, E888.1, E849.7
b. 191.9, 492.8, 331.0, 294.10, 311, 920, E888.1, E849.7
c. 331.89, 198.3, 492.8, 331.0, 294.10, E888.1, E849.7
d. 198.3, 199.1, 492.8, 331.0, 294.10, 311, 920, E888.1, E849.7

7.37. The following documentation is from the health record of a 67-year-old female patient.

Discharge Summary

This is a 67-year-old lady with complaints of low back pain, with radiation down her right leg to her foot. This pain has been progressively worse over the past six months. She had an MRI scan that showed degenerative disc disease at L2–3, L3–4, and L4–5; L3–L4 with mild central canal stenosis; and facet arthropathy at L3--L4 and L4–L5. She has a past medical history of coronary artery disease, hypertension, and arthritis. Her current medications include Lipitor, Avapro®, Ecotrin®, Imdur®, Lasix, K-Dur®, calcium, and Vioxx®. She had a CABG two years ago. She also had PTCA with cardiac stents placed three years ago. Patient is admitted for lumbar epidural steroid injections for her lumbar radiculopathy—as noted on MRI results.

Which of the following is the correct ICD-9-CM code assignment?

a. 722.52, 721.3, 724.02, 724.4, 414.00, 401.9, V45.81, V45.82, 03.92, 99.23, 88.91
b. 724.4, 414.00, 401.9, V45.81, V45.82, 03.92, 99.23, 88.91
c. 722.52, 721.3, 414.00, 401.9, V45.81, V45.82, 03.92, 99.23, 88.91
d. 722.52, 721.3, 414.00, 401.9, V45.81, V45.82, 03.91, 88.91

Newborn/Congenital Disorders

7.38. The following documentation is from the health record of an 18-day-old baby boy.

Discharge Summary

This is an 18-day-old male infant who was admitted after he was noticed to be developing omphalitis. He was immediately placed on intravenous cefotaxime and ampicillin, later changed to cefotaxime and clindamycin. A culture taken from the umbilical stump grew Staphylococcus aureus and group H Streptococcus.

After the first day, there was great improvement and the patient continued to improve completely. Now there is no redness or swelling whatsoever. The child has remained afebrile and has continued to eat very well. He shows no sign of abdominal tenderness or peritonitis. I feel that we have treated this well. He has had five days of intravenous antibiotics. I will finish the treatment with Keflex by mouth seeing that both Streptococcus pyogenes and Staphylococcus aureus are sensitive. The mother will watch the child closely and let me know if any problems occur. I have instructed her to watch for any more redevelopment of the redness, swelling, or discharge. We will recheck this in two weeks at his one-month checkup.

Which of the following answers contains the correct diagnostic code(s) for this admission?

a. 771.2, 041.09
b. 686.9, 041.11, 041.09
c. 771.4
d. 771.4, 041.11, 041.09

7.39. The following documentation is from the health record of a three-day-old baby boy.

Discharge Summary

The patient is a three-day-old male infant. He was born at home after approximately 38-weeks' gestation and brought to the Emergency Room shortly thereafter with difficulty breathing. The baby's respirations were very quick and shallow. This was the mother's fourth child, all of whom have been born at home. This was the first child born with complications.

The newborn was resuscitated and placed in the NICU under continuous oxygen therapy.

Admission history and physical examination were otherwise unremarkable. Chest x-ray showed wet lungs. Repeat chest x-ray 24 hours later showed the lungs had cleared. PKU specimen was taken and sent to the state laboratory, as required.

By the second day of life, the patient was able to be weaned off the oxygen and discharged from the NICU to a bassinet.

The mother requested that the baby be circumcised. This was accomplished without incident.

The infant is discharged to be seen in the clinic at one month for well-baby visit.

Which of the following answers is correct to code this admission?

a. 770.6, V30.10, V50.2, 96.04
b. V30.1, 770.6, V50.2, 64.0, 93.93, 93.96
c. V30.1, 769, V50.2, 64.0, 96.04
d. V30.10, 768.6, V50.2, 64.0, 96.05, 93.96

7.40. The patient is a three-year-old child with congenital patent ductus arteriosus. The patient has had several open-heart surgeries attempting to correct the defect. The patient was born prematurely at 34-weeks' gestation. The patient continues to be below average on standard growth charts in size and weight, and the mother states the child is not very active.

Recent echocardiogram revealed an area of the aorta leaking blood into the pulmonary artery. The child is now admitted for further corrective surgery.

On the day after admission, the child was taken to the OR. Open-chest surgery was performed through the existing scar, and the ribs were spread to gain access to the operative field. Several areas of communication between the aorta and the pulmonary artery were identified and closed. The chest was then closed. Throughout the procedure, the patient's vital signs were monitored and remained at satisfactory levels. The patient tolerated the procedure well.

The day after surgery, the patient was allowed to be up and walking. The child appeared to have increased energy and was a healthy pink color. The child was eating and asking for more.

The patient was discharged on the third postop day to be followed as an outpatient in the cardiac education center.

Final Diagnosis: Patent ductus arteriosus

Which of the following answers is correct to code this admission?

a. 747.0, 765.10, 765.27, 38.85
b. 745.9, 35.39
c. 747.0, 38.85
d. 745.0, 38.85

7.41. The following documentation is from the health record of a five-year-old girl.

Discharge Summary

The patient is a five-year-old female child born with myelomeningocele spina bifida. The patient has previously undergone several procedures to cover the defect at the bottom of her spine, including the insertion of a ventriculoperitoneal shunt to drain the CSF fluid accumulation from her hydrocephalus.

The patient was admitted this morning through the emergency department with a plugged shunt. The child was rushed to the OR for emergent irrigation of the shunt. Irrigation was attempted several times but was unsuccessful. Therefore, the shunt was removed and replaced with another ventriculoperitoneal shunt.

The patient tolerated the procedure, although she was very anxious about having surgery and being in the hospital. Her parents were very caring and present to calm her at all times.

The patient was discharged on the second day postop to be followed in the office.

Final Diagnoses: Congenital myelomeningocele spina bifida
Plugged VP shunt

Which of the following answers is correct to code this admission?

a. 996.75, 741.03, 02.42
b. 996.2, 741.03, 02.41, 02.42
c. 741.03, V45.2, 02.42, 02.43
d. 996.75, 742.3, 741.00, 02.42

Pediatric Conditions

7.42. The following documentation is from the health record of a 13-year-old boy.

Preoperative Diagnosis: Right inguinal hernia, hypospadias

Postoperative Diagnosis: Same

Operation: Right inguinal herniorrhaphy, repair of hypospadias

Indications: The patient is a 13-year-old male with reducible right inguinal hernia and hypospadias who now presents for definitive care.

Procedure: The patient was brought to the operating room and placed in the supine position. After the adequate general endotracheal anesthesia, a 4 cm incision was made in the right inguinal region. The subcutaneous tissues were divided, and hemostasis achieved with electrocautery. The external oblique fascia was identified and cleaned using Metzenbaum scissors. An incision was made in the external oblique and carried down to the external ring using Metzenbaum scissors. The external oblique was freed from the underlying cord using two pair of forceps. The cremasteric fibers were divided and the hernia sac grasped. Pulling the hernia sac up on some tension, we were then able to tease off the cremasteric fibers, as well as the vas and vessels. At this point, we were able to control the hernia sac between the two hemostats. We then teased off of the vas and vessels as we dissected proximally toward the internal ring. At this point, the sac was twisted, sutured ligated, times two, amputated, and then the sac was allowed to fall back into the peritoneal cavity. We continued the dissection distally. The anterior wall was opened using electrocautery. At this point, we placed the cord back into the inguinal canal. The external oblique fascia was closed using interrupted 4-0 silk sutures. The external oblique fascia and the structures below it were infiltrated using .05 percent Marcaine. The Scarpa's fascia was closed using 5-0 VICRYL. The skin was closed using interrupted 5-0 subcuticular stitches. Steri-Strips were applied.

With this completed, attention was then turned to repairing the hypospadias. Procedure commenced by placing a 4-0 Prolene stay suture through the glans for traction and observing the distal shaft hypospadias without chordee and with a dorsal hooded foreskin.

The urethroplasty was begun by making parallel lines with a marking pen on either side of the urethral meatus, going out to the tip of the glans, connecting these proximally from the meatus for a distance of about 2.5 cm. With a tourniquet used intermittently, an incision was made in these lines to create two rectangular flaps connected at the urethral meatus. On the left side of the meatus there was a small nevus just lateral to the incision line, and the incision was extended around this to excise a small nevus, less than .6 cm in diameter, which will be sent for pathology. After mobilization of both skin flaps, the proximal one off of the shaft and the ventral one off of the underlying tissue of the glans, optical magnification was used to convert these two flaps into a neourethral tube using 6-0 PDS sutures. The neourethral tube came together quite well.

Next, an incision was made in the midline, out to the tip of the glans, through the incision point at the previous site of the distal flap, to accomplish mobilization of the urethra and advance this urethra out to the tip of the glans. Wedge-shaped areas of glandular tissue were excised to make a smooth passageway for the neourethra. Then the neourethra was sutured into position at the tip of the glans with 6-0 and 5-0 PDS sutures.

Next, a second layer was created by approximating the subcutaneous tissue, adventitial tissue, and elements of the corpus spongiosum over the neourethral reconstruction at the corona, and carrying this with a running 6-0 PDS suture proximally to provide a second layer of coverage.

When this was done, the glans itself was approximated with 4-0 PDS sutures, placing about three sutures into position to firmly reconnect the wings of the glans and to keep them from pulling apart. This left an aperture for the neourethra, which was then sutured into position with 4-0 and 5-0 PDS sutures. When this was done, an #11 French Silastic catheter was used, and a portion of its wall was cut out to turn it into a splint. It was positioned into the urethra and sutured into place at the meatus with a 4-0 Prolene suture to hold it into position. The next step was to close the skin defect on the ventral shaft with interrupted 3-0 chromic catgut.

The next part of the operation involved performing circumcision of the redundant dorsal and lateral preputial tissue. First, this was marked with a marking pen, and then an incision was made in the pen lines to allow excision of the redundant foreskin. Hemostasis was obtained with electrocautery, and 3-0 chromic was used to complete the circumcision.

The next step was to consider the ability of this patient to void. Because of his hernial repair and this operation on the prepuce, I was afraid he would be in urinary retention. I, therefore, inserted an #8 French feeding tube through the #11 French Silastic catheter, passed it all the way into the bladder, and allowed it to drain urine freely. Then a light sterile dressing of 1-inch Adaptic roller gauze soaked in tincture of benzoin was loosely wrapped around the shaft for mild compression and hemostasis. The last few wraps of this incorporated the catheter.

The patient was taken to the recovery room in satisfactory condition.

Which of the following code sets is correct for reporting this operative episode?

a. 752.61, 550.91, 752.69, 58.49, 53.02, 64.0, 57.94
b. 752.61, 605, 550.90, 239.5, 58.47, 53.01, 64.2, 57.94
c. 752.61, 550.91, 752.69, 58.49, 53.00, 57.94
d. 752.61, 605, 550.90, 222.1, 58.45, 53.02, 64.0, 64.2, 57.94

7.43.   The following documentation is from the health record of an 11-year-old boy.

Preoperative Diagnoses: 1. Ewing sarcoma, left scapula
2. Down syndrome

Postoperative Diagnosis: Same

Findings: This is an 11-year-old boy with Down syndrome who presented four days ago with a large mass in the left scapular region. X-ray and CT scan showed laminated new bone with a large expansile permeative lesion in the scapular body. It did not appear to involve the glenohumeral joint. Bone scan showed marked increased uptake and questionable area of uptake in the right seventh rib and left first vertebral body. CT of the lungs was reportedly normal. At the time of biopsy, there was obvious stretching of the posterior trapezius and deltoid musculature over the mass and a very soft calcific mass noted within the central area of the substance. Frozen pathology sections showed many small cells, but definitive diagnosis could not be made off the frozen section. Final pathologic diagnosis was malignant bone tumor consistent with Ewing's sarcoma. He will be started on a chemotherapy program, and definitive surgery will be planned.

Procedure: Following an adequate level of general endotracheal anesthesia, the patient was turned to the right lateral decubitus position with the left side up. The left shoulder region was prepped and draped in routine sterile fashion. Before beginning the biopsy, a venous access device, a MediPort® catheter, was inserted on the right side.

A 3 cm incision was then made over the spine of the scapula. Electrocautery was used for hemostasis and the incision deepened with electrocautery. When we were in the area of the soft tissue mass noted on the CT scan, biopsies were taken. The initial biopsies showed primarily muscle fibers, so we deepened the incision at this point and obtained some of the obvious calcific soft tissue mass. These cultures were more consistent with tumor, and, at this point, hemostasis was achieved with a combination of bone wax, packing, and electrocautery. Meticulous hemostasis was achieved prior to closure, and then a two-layer interrupted closure was performed, closing the skin with a running subcuticular suture of 4-0 VICRYL. Bulky dry sterile dressing was applied, and the patient was awakened and returned to the recovery room in good condition.

Which of the following is the correct code set to report this procedure?

a. 170.4, 758.0, 77.41
b. 170.4, 170.3, 170.2, 77.81
c. 170.4, 758.0, 77.61, 86.07
d. 170.4, 758.0, 77.41, 86.07

Conditions of Pregnancy, Childbirth, and the Puerperium

7.44. The following documentation is from the health record of a 19-year-old female patient.

Discharge Summary

Admission Date: 1/5/00

Discharge Date: 1/9/00

Discharge Diagnoses:
1. Term pregnancy with PROM
2. Failed attempt at vaginal birth after cesarean section
3. Arrest of descent, secondary to persistent occipitoposterior position
4. Cephalopelvic disproportion and malposition
5. Nuchal cord x1 with compression

Procedures Performed: Repeat low transverse cesarean delivery

History of Present Illness: The patient is a 19-year-old gravida 3, para 1, A 1 with an estimated date of delivery of 1/24. She is at +37 weeks in her pregnancy. She underwent spontaneous rupture of the membranes on 1/4. Upon admission, the patient's membranes were ruptured. The cervix was fingertip thick, ballotable.

Hospital Course: The patient was started on Pitocin® for induction of labor because of the premature rupture of membranes 26 hours prior. The patient had a slow labor course, eventually establishing a good labor curve. She dilated completely to a zero station but had difficulty pushing. Progress arrested at 0 to +1 station. Failure to descend was felt to be secondary to persistent occipitoposterior presentation with CPD. The decision was made to perform a low transverse cesarean delivery because of the arrest of descent. She underwent a cesarean delivery without complications.

Estimated blood loss was 600 cc. This resulted in delivery of a live male infant weighing 7 lbs 4 oz having Apgars of 7 at one minute and 9 at five minutes.

Postoperatively, the patient did well. She was ambulating and tolerating her diet. She was afebrile and her incision looked clear, so the patient was discharged home on the third postoperative day.

Code Assignment:

Diagnoses:_____

Procedures:_____

7.45. The following documentation is from the health record of a 33-year-old female patient.

OB Record

Admit Note: 2/27/XX

This is a 33-year-old G2 P0, estimated delivery date of 2/28, and estimated gestational age of 40 weeks. She presents for induction secondary to gestational DM. She has required insulin since 28 weeks, with adequate control. PNL: O positive, rubella immune. PE: AVSS, Abdomen FH 40 cm, EFW 3800–4000 grams. Cervix is closed/50 percent/-3/post/ceph. Plan is for Prostin E2® induction and insulin infusion when in active labor.

Progress Note: 2/28/XX, 0915

Patient is having uterine contractions every three to eight minutes. Cervix is 1 cm/100 percent/floating. Patient desires not to start Prostin E2 induction yet. Feels that she is in labor. FHR reactive, baseline 120s with accelerations.

Progress Note: 2/28/XX, 1925

Patient's uterine contractions have resolved. Cervix unchanged. Discussed options, would like to go home to sleep and return in a.m. for Pitocin induction. Discharged home for tonight to sleep. Admit in a.m., start IV Pitocin as per protocol, start insulin drip, clear liquid diet.

Which of the following is the correct code assignment?

a. 648.83, V58.67, 73.4
b. 648.81, V58.67, 73.01
c. 648.83, V58.67
d. 659.13, 648.83

7.46. The following documentation is from the health record of a 32-year-old female patient.

Delivery Record

Admit Note: 7/20: Patient is a 32-year-old female with EDC 7/22 and EGA of +39 weeks. She has been having uterine contractions for two days, mild, more severe this a.m. with contractions every two to four minutes at admission. Cervix is 1 cm/20 percent/-1 station. EFW 3500 grams.

Delivery Record Summary: 7/21: Patient progressed to 5 cm and exhausted! NO sleep for two nights. Also in extreme pain of labor. Vacuum-assisted vaginal delivery of a live male. Episiotomy. Fourth-degree laceration repaired with 2-0 and 3-0 VICRYL. EBL 450 ml.

Progress Note: 7/22: Patient weak, slightly dizzy, sore perineum. VSS, afebrile, fundus firm. H/H 8.5/24.6; A – s/p VD with fourth-degree laceration; postpartum anemia. Slow Fe® #30.

Progress Note: 7/23: PPD #2 – S – feeling better, ambulating without dizziness; O – VSS, afebrile, fundus firm; A – s/p VD with fourth-degree laceration; P – home today, FU four weeks, DC meds Vicodin #20, Colace #20, and Slow Fe #30.

Code Assignment:

Diagnoses:_____

Procedures:_____

7.47. Discharge Summary

Admission Diagnosis: A 38-week intrauterine pregnancy with leaking amniotic fluid

Discharge Diagnosis: Postpartum female—status post classical cesarean section secondary to prolonged second stage of labor, failure to descend, inability to reduce fetal head from pelvis; endomyometritis, postoperative ileus, persistent fever-suspected septic pelvic thrombophlebitis; wound seroma

Operative Procedure: Classical cesarean section

Admission History: This is a 26-year-old gravida 1, para 0 female who presented at 38-weeks gestation complaining of leaking fluid in the morning. She had very mild leaking noted. She had positive nitrazine. She had no gush of fluid at that time and good fetal movement. She had some mild cramping and minimal contractions. No nausea, vomiting, or headache, or shortness of breath. No chest pain. Her pregnancy had been uncomplicated. She has had mildly elevated blood pressures over the last couple of weeks, but otherwise nothing significant.

Past medical and social history is negative

OB-GYN History: She is gravida 1

OB Laboratory Data: Blood type is O positive. Antibody screen negative. HIV negative. GBS negative. Rubella nonimmune. RPR nonreactive. Hepatitis B negative.

Objective

Vital Signs: stable; BP: Elevated at 152/102; it did come down between the 130–140/70–80

Lungs: Clear to auscultation

Heart: Regular rate and rhythm

Abdomen: Soft and nontender

Pelvic: Cervix is 1 cm 70% effaced, and -2 station. The amniotic bag could still be palpated, but it was felt that she might be leaking; therefore, artificial rupture of membranes was performed with clear fluid. Tocol showed irregular contractions.

Assessment and Plan: Term intrauterine pregnancy at 38 weeks with mild leaking fluid. The patient is admitted, and she is given an IV Hep-lock with expectant management.

Hospital Course: The patient did require Pitocin augmentation, as after several hours, she was not contracting adequately. She progressed slowly, but adequately over the next 24 hours. She was completely dilated at approximately 7:00 in the morning. She began pushing. She pushed for 3 hours. The baby progressed from a +1 to a +2–3 station. She had no further progression. She was counseled on the risks regarding cesarean section versus forceps delivery. The patient did elect for a cesarean section. She is, therefore, taken for a C-section, see operative report for details. The patient did undergo a classical cesarean section due to the fact that the fetal head could not be reduced from the vagina, and a classical was performed in order to grab the fetal feet and deliver in a breech fashion.

Postoperatively the patient did become febrile within a few hours, and this was felt to be due to endomyometritis due to the prolonged rupture, prolonged labor, and the significant manipulation of the uterus with cesarean section. The patient was started on Ancef during the procedure and was started on gentamicin within 12 hours of the surgery. The patient continued on IV antibiotics. She continued to spike on a fairly regular basis over the next two postoperative days. She was tolerating a regular diet and ambulating, in addition to passing minimal flatus. On postoperative day 1 she did have a fever as high as 103 degrees with a tachycardic episode in the 160s. She was somewhat light-headed when she was up to the restroom, but improved with rest. Her heart rate did decrease at that point. An EKG was done and this showed sinus tachycardia. She denied any shortness of breath or chest pain. No nausea or vomiting. Her laboratory studies showed her hemoglobin to be 8.9, white count 12, with a morning repeat of 8.8 and a white count of 9. Blood cultures were done at that time, as well.

On postoperative day 2 the patient was beginning to feel distended. Her pain was getting worse secondary to the descent. She denied any shortness of breath or chest pain. She was still passing some flatus, but minimal. No nausea or vomiting. On examination her temperature was 103.3 degrees, which was the maximum. Her abdomen is soft; however, she did have moderate to severe distention at that time. She had good bowel sounds in all the quadrants. Her incision was intact. The extremities showed no calf tenderness. A chest x-ray was done due to the continued temperature, which showed bowel distension and suspected ileus. Abdominal x-rays were then done which did confirm an ileus, but no signs of bowel obstruction. Her hemoglobin was repeated and showed 7.4 with stable platelets. Blood cultures were negative, as well as her urine. BUN and creatinine were normal. The patient was made n.p.o. and given an NG tube for the postoperative ileus. She did note some relief to her abdominal discomfort and pain. She was afebrile throughout most of the day at that time. The NG tube had 250 cc out initially.

On postoperative day 3 the NG tube was continued, and her belly was somewhat less distended. She was passing flatus still and her pain was otherwise controlled. Her temperature was 101.6 degrees, and clindamycin was added to the antibiotic regimen due to the persistent fevers. On examination, her distention was improved. She was still having some bowel sounds, although hypoactive. The incision showed no significant erythema. Blood cultures remained negative, and the NG tube was continued with intermittent suction.

On postoperative day 4, the patient was feeling better and having some stools. No nausea or vomiting or shortness of breath, chest pain, dizziness, or light-headedness. She was having normal lochia and pain was controlled. The NG tube had minimal amount overnight, and her temperature was 101.6 degrees. She was then started on a clear diet and, if tolerated, the NG tube was to be discontinued. Her hemoglobin was 6.9, with a decreased potassium of 3.2. All other lab work was essentially normal. The NG tube was discontinued, and she was given KCL to replace her potassium.

On the fifth day postoperative, she continued to be febrile with a temperature of 101.5 degrees. The abdomen was soft and nondistended. She was appropriately tender, more on the left side than the right. The incision still appeared well. Laboratory studies showed the hemoglobin to be 6.8 and stable. Her potassium continued to decrease to 3.1. At that time, a CT of the abdomen and pelvic was ordered to rule out a pelvic abscess. C. difficile was ordered due to continued diarrhea. Another physician was consulted. A suspicion of septic pelvic thrombophlebitis was then entertained as her fever continued despite adequate antibiotic therapy. The patient was started on Lovenox®, and the CT scan showed normal postoperative changes, but no evidence of an abscess.

On postoperative day 6, she was feeling better and had no further diarrhea. C. difficile was negative and she was tolerating a regular diet. Her incision did show some erythema, and it was probed with some serosangineous drainage from the left side, but no purulent drainage. Her laboratory studies were stable, and she was continued on Lovenox and antibiotics. The incision was to be cleaned twice daily.

Postoperative day 7 the patient continued to improve and was feeling well. She was tolerating a regular diet and was afebrile in which she remained for 27 hours and was, therefore, discharged home.

Consultation Report: The patient is 26-year-old female who is gravida 1, now para 1. The patient required a C-section because of prolonged labor and maternal exhaustion. The patient was ruptured for a little over 24 hours prior to delivery. The C-section was complicated by the inability to reduce the head from the vaginal canal and was converted to a breech extraction; therefore, the patient had a primary low transverse C-section that had to be converted to a classical C-section. The patient had some tachycardia on the date of delivery. Ancef was continued and gentamicin was started. On postoperative day 1 she developed a temperature up to 103 degrees. Urine was done, which was unremarkable, along with blood cultures. A chest x-ray revealed some atelectasis at the bases, which the radiologist ultimately felt was possibly consistent with a bibasilar pneumonia. At that point her Ancef was switched to ceftriaxone, and postoperative day 1 clindamycin was added.

It was noted on the chest x-ray that she had a probable ileus which was confirmed on the abdominal films. She was placed n.p.o. and an NG tube to intermittent suction was started. The fevers persisted with concomitant chills through today, which is postoperative day 5; however, now her temperature spikes are more in the 101 degrees range. The patient's ileus has resolved, and she is tolerating a normal diet. The patient clinically had endometritis after the delivery with a tender lower abdomen. However, this has gradually improved even though her fevers are persisting.

Review of systems performed in addition to physical examination.

Data Interpretation: Laboratory data reviewed; chest x-ray also reviewed by myself revealed some atelectatic changes in the lung bases with bibasilar patchy infiltrates read out as possible hypostatic pneumonia. Follow x-ray three days later revealed definite improvement with less bibasilar infiltrated, now with just some minimal atelectatic changes in the left lung base. CT scan today revealed an enlarged uterus with prominent endometrial stripes, felt to be probably iatrogenic from the surgery. There was some pelvic cobwebbing, but no obvious abscess and some subcutaneous edema anterior in the abdomen with some pockets of gas, also felt to be iatrogenic. With all of these, infection could not be entirely excluded. No obvious evidence of thrombophlebitis was seen.

Assessment: Persistent postpartum fever with clinical evidence of endometritis initially that has improved. The patient has had good broad-spectrum antibiotic coverage and with persistent fever, the possibility of a pelvic septic thrombophlebitis must be entertained.

Diarrhea with negative C. difficile, possibly still related to antibiotics, also Prevacid has been shown to cause diarrhea.

Postoperative anemia—stable

Heart murmur—likely secondary to her anemia and being immediately postpartum

Hypokalemia, which has been difficult to normalize—likely related to GI losses

Plan: She has received appropriate IV antibiotic coverage for her endomyometritis and no other source of infection is identified, would recommend that anticoagulation be initiated for the possibility of pelvic septic thrombophlebitis or ovarian vein thrombosis.

Would recommend continuing on her current antibiotic coverage; however, because the most recent x-ray did not show significant evidence of pneumonia, the ceftriaxone could be discontinued.

Would recommend adding potassium to her IV fluids to try and correct her hypokalemia. The hypokalemia could add to her ileus.

If the patient does not improve in the next couple of days, other considerations would be to add amp or Unasyn to her regimen for possible resistant organism, such as enterococcus. Also agree with continued intermittent blood cultures if she continues to spike.

Her anemia is stable, would recommend continuing to watch for now; however, if it drops or she becomes symptomatic transfuse.

Consider echo if fever persists to rule out endocarditis.

Operative Report

Preoperative Diagnosis: Gravida 1 para 0 female at 38 weeks gestation; prolonged rupture of membranes; prolonged second stage of labor with failure to descent

Postoperative Diagnosis: Same

Operation: Primary cesarean section—classical

Anesthesia: Epidural

Complications: Classical extension of initially low transverse incision

Findings: Viable female infant; complete placenta with three-vessel cord; normal uterus, tubes, and ovaries

Indications: This is a 26-year-old female gravida 1 para 0 who presented at 38 weeks gestation with complaints of leaking fluid. The patient was approximately 1 cm dilated and 80% effaced at that time. She was felt to be having some leaking, although membranes could still be palpated. Therefore, artificial rupture of membranes was performed. The patient progressed very slowly in labor and required Pitocin augmentation. Over the next 24 hours, she progressed to finally complete dilatation and began pushing at that time and pushed for 3 hours. She started at approximately 0 to +1 station and progressed to +2 or 3 station. Fetal head was seen with separation of the labia; however, after 3 hours and maternal exhaustion she made no further progression of the fetal head over the last hour of pushing. The patient was counseled regarding the need for assistance and forceps assistance versus cesarean section were offered. The risk and benefits of both were explained and the patient opted for cesarean section.

Technique: The patient was taken to the operating room and placed under epidural anesthesia. She was prepped and draped in the normal sterile fashion in dorsal supine position with leftward tilt. Pfannenstiel skin incision was made two fingerbreadths above the symphysis pubis in the midline and carried through to the underlying fascia. The fascia was incised in the midline and extended laterally with Mayo scissors. The rectus muscles were dissected off the fascia using both blunt and sharp dissection. Rectus muscles were then separated in the midline. Peritoneum was entered bluntly and extended superiorly and inferiorly. The bladder blade was inserted. Vesicouterine peritoneum was grasped with pickups and entered with Metzenbaum scissors. This was extended laterally, and the bladder flap was created digitally. The bladder blade was reinserted. The lower uterine segment was incised in a transverse fashion with a scalpel and extended laterally with blunt dissection. The infant's head was very low in the pelvis. Attempt to deliver the fetal head was difficult, and we were unable to reduce the fetal head from the vaginal canal. Nursing staff did apply pressure to the fetal head from the vaginal canal, but still was unable to be dislodged. An attempt was made to retract on the shoulders of the infant in order dislodge the fetal head from the vaginal canal, but again this was unsuccessful. For this reason, the uterine incision was extended vertically in a classical fashion, and the feet were grasped and pulled to the uterine incision. The feet were then delivered, and the infant was delivered in a breech fashion. Nose and mouth were suctioned and cord was clamped and cut. The infant was then handed off to the waiting pediatrician.

Cord gas was obtained. The cord blood was inadvertently not obtained. The placenta was removed. The uterus was cleared of clots and debris. The uterus was exteriorized for better visualization; 0 VICRYL sutures were used to close the vertical incision in the uterus in several layers. Two layers were done initially then the transverse portion of the incision was closed. There was a cervical extension distally, and this was also closed with 0 VICRYL sutures. Once the transverse portion of the incision was closed, attention was again turned back to the vertical incision. The uterus was returned to the abdomen and inspection of the incision appeared to be hemostatic. With all the layers being closed and the sponge, lap and needle counts correct times two. The patient tolerated the procedure well and was taken to the recovery room in stable condition.

Progress Notes:

Postop day 1: Patient with episode of tachycardia consistent with endomyometritis

Postop day 2: Abdomen feels distended endomyometritis, suspect ileus

Postop day 3: Endomyometritis, ileus

Postop day 4: Ileus resolved, temperature improving

Postop day 5: Continued fever, endomyometritis, internal med consult

Postop day 6: Prolonged postpartum fever with initial endometritis, probable pelvic septic thrombophlebitis—on Lovenox, postop anemia stable, hypokalemia—improved

Postop day 7: Patient improved will discharge home

Assign the correct codes for this case:

Principal diagnosis:_____

Additional diagnoses:_____

Procedures:_____

Disorders of the Respiratory System

7.48.   The following documentation is from the health record of a 67-year-old female patient.

Brief History: This 67-year-old female was transferred here for further evaluation of continued respiratory failure. She has a long history of asthma and chronic obstructive pulmonary disease. Current medications: Claforan® one gram q. 6 h. Cardizem SR 90 mg b.i.d., Solu-Medrol® 125 mg intravenously q. 8 h., Trental® one p.o. b.i.d., DiaBeta® 1.25 mg p.o. q. a.m. and 2.5 mg q. p.m., Klonopin® 1 mg p.o. q. 6 h. ibuprofen 800 mg p.o. b.i.d., Lortab 5 mg q. 6 h p.r.n. headache, Atrovent and Proventil® inhalers at bedside.

Physical Examination: She was intubated. Admission ABGs were PO_2 40, PCO_2 55, and pH 7.30. Blood pressure 156/89, heart rate 130 beats per minute, temperature 100.7°F. Neck: No jugular venous distention. Carotid normal upstroke without audible bruits. Pulmonary exam: Decreased breath sounds throughout. Expiratory wheezes were auscultated. Cardiac exam: Sinus tachycardiac rhythm. No murmurs or gallops. Extremities: No edema.

Hospital Course: Upon admission, emergent pulmonary consultation was obtained, and a fiber-optic bronchoscopy was performed without difficulty. Copious thin white pus was noted in all of her inflamed airways. She had no cough despite airway suctioning. A #7.5 nasotracheal tube was inserted via her right naris without difficulty, and airways were aspirated clear. The patient was placed on Ventolin 2 mg p.o. q. 6 h. placed on Proventil inhaler 1 mg q. 4 h. and q. 2 h. p.r.n., placed on oxygen, was given intravenous Lasix, and intravenous Solu-Medrol. Dobbhoff NG tube was placed the day after admission without difficulty. Two days later, she developed a temperature of 103°F and developed chills. All cultures obtained on admission revealed no growth thus far, and a chest x-ray was clear.

Infectious disease consultation was obtained, and a workup to rule out sinusitis, viral upper respiratory tract infection, drug fever, collagen vascular disease, or occult abdominal source was ordered. Antibiotic coverage in the form of Unasyn and tobramycin ordered along with yeast coverage. Other problems included hypokalemia, which required potassium repletion, frequent premature atrial contractions, and marked metabolic alkalosis preventing weaning from her intubation. The only source of fever seemed to be the maxillary and ethmoidal sinusitis on the CT scan, and her head was elevated to decrease venous congestion of the sinuses.

GI consultation was obtained when she started developing abdominal distention and coffee-ground emesis; hematocrit had dropped from 37.8 to 24.2, for which she was given two units of packed red blood cells. The consultant felt that a GI bleed could possibly be related to stress or nonsteroidal anti-inflammatory drugs or gastritis and that the abdominal distention was probably aerophagia, related to ventilator. Recommendation was made to stop the tube feedings and decompressing with nasogastric tube and checking stools for hemoccult. Gallbladder ultrasound revealed gallstones in the thick walls of the ducts.

The patient continued to have abdominal pain. Surgical consultation was ordered and confirmed acute cholecystitis, which could be worse secondary to the steroids. The day of consultation, the patient underwent exploratory laparotomy, bilateral salpingo-oophorectomy, cholecystectomy, cholangiogram, and omental biopsy. Cystadenofibroma of borderline malignancy of the right ovary was reported on pathological findings.

The patient developed anasarca and required intravenous diuretics. She underwent another fiber-optic bronchoscopy six days postop, which revealed diffused edema and slight inflammation with yellow plugs in the left upper lobe and right middle lobe, and scant secretions otherwise clear and foamy. She also underwent tube feedings with hyper Osmolite®. Seven days later, she started developing increasing respiratory distress and a tracheostomy was performed. Tracheal aspirate revealed gram-negative herpetic tracheobronchitis. Within 48 hours, she developed bradycardia and increasing ventilation pressures. Emergency tap of the right pleural space was done, which revealed tension pneumothorax. A trocar chest tube was inserted with good air return. Attempts to see airways via left nares with fiber-optic bronchoscopy revealed all mucosa to be obstructed at the level of the retropharynx. A retap of the left chest revealed air not under pressure, opened with scissors, but still unable to ventilate by tracheal tube. Heart rate was zero, and blood pressure was zero. The futility of cardiopulmonary resuscitation for further events, based on inability to ventilate, led to cessation of efforts and the patient was pronounced dead at 11:15 a.m.

Final Diagnoses: Acute respiratory failure
Long history of asthma
Chronic obstructive pulmonary disease
Metabolic alkalosis with ventilator dependence for the last week or more of her hospitalization
Gram-negative herpetic tracheobronchitis
Acute cholecystitis and cholelithiasis
Anemia due to GI bleed from undetermined cause
Maxillary and ethmoidal sinusitis
Pneumothorax
Premature atrial contractions
Cystadenofibroma right ovary
Hypokalemia

Procedures: Intubation, mechanical ventilation
Tracheostomy
Fiber-optic bronchoscopy × 2
Cholecystectomy with cholangiogram
Bilateral salpingo-oophorectomy
Omental biopsy
Thoracentesis and chest tube

Assign the correct codes for this case:

Principal diagnosis:_____

Additional diagnoses:_____

Procedures:_____

7.49.   The following documentation is from the health record of an 80-year-old male patient.

Discharge Summary

History: The patient is an 80-year-old male with a four- to five-week history of pulmonary disease, apparently developing out of an acute influenza-like illness. He was admitted to his local hospital about 22 days ago with right middle lobe and right lower lobe alveolar filling infiltrates. Initial cultures were negative. Treatment with intravenous Ancef was not effective. The patient's hospital course was manifested by progressive pulmonary infiltrates unresponsive to erythromycin, Claforan, and Primaxin. Complications of nasogastric feeding tube placement in the right pleural space and administration of one liter of Osmolite into the pleural space apparently occurred during hospitalization. The patient had a chest tube placed with effective removal of the Osmolite. Because of fatigue, the patient was placed on a ventilator for two periods of time but has been off the ventilator for approximately a week. He has become severely malnourished and was placed on TPN. Diarrhea has intervened with tube feedings. Cultures and ova and parasite findings showed trichomonas.

Because of failure to resolve pneumonia, malnutrition, and persistent fever, he was transferred here.

Physical Examination: The patient is a chronically ill-appearing, thin man, responsive but unable to talk secondary to a very dry mouth. Blood pressure 144/70, pulse rate 110 per minute and regular, temperature 99.4°F, respirations 28. He is on nasal oxygen. Skin is dry. Lymph nodes are negative. Head: No deformity. Eyes: Increased bilateral purulent drainage. Sclerae are not red. Pupils round and equal. Throat very dry with caked secretions on teeth and palate. Neck is supple. Jugular venous pulse flat, carotids equal. Chest nontender. He ventilates with the left chest fairly well with scattered rhonchi. The right chest; however, showed decreased breath sounds with a line of consolidation about halfway up. Scattered rhonchi were noted above the area of consolidation. No friction rub was heard. The patient had evidence of a right pleural effusion versus right pleural thickening. Heart: PMI was at the midclavicular line. A regular rhythm was noted, no significant murmur, gallop, or rub. Abdomen: Soft and scaphoid, no organomegaly or tenderness, bowel sounds active. The patient passed a green watery stool during examination. Rectal: Slightly decreased sphincter tone, no masses were felt. Prostate was +2 enlarged, no nodules. Extremities showed no edema, clubbing, or cyanosis.

Initial Laboratory and X-Ray Findings: Blood gas on 4 liters of nasal oxygen showed pH 7.48, pCO_2 37, pO_2 65. Initial chest x-ray showed bilateral mixed infiltrate and consolidation throughout both lungs, most prominently in the right midlung and right lung base. A left subclavian venous catheter was seen. Initial hematocrit was 40. Within two days after hydration, this was noted to be 27. Sed rate 96 mm per hour. White blood cell count 16,000 with 5 bands, 73 segs, 15 lymphs, 5 monos, 2 eosinophils. Platelets 464,000. PT and PTT negative. SMA profile: Cholesterol 113, triglycerides 110, electrolytes normal except chloride of 96, CO_2 34. Blood sugar 120. BUN 20, creatinine 0.8. Serum osmolality was 338. Urine osmolality was 456. Creatinine clearance was 81 ml per minute. Urinalysis was negative, except for an initial elevated specific gravity of 1.032. The patient was malnourished by low albumin and transferrin levels. IV albumin was ordered. Cryptococcal antigen of spinal fluid positive at a titer of 1:32.

Hospital Course: The day after admission on 1/9, the patient was submitted to bronchoalveolar lavage. His culture showed beta hemolytic Streptococcus A, Proteus mirabilis, and a Gram-negative bacillus that was not further identified. Legionella culture was negative. Stool showed no pathogens. Spinal tap was done with the finding of cryptococcal antigen of 1:32 in spinal fluid, the patient was started on amphotericin B for his meningitis, but he could not tolerate this and was thus switched to fluconazole. On 1/12, it became evident that the large volume of sputum he was required to mobilize and his generally weakened state resulted in increasing fatigue resulting in acute respiratory failure, such that it was necessary to transfer the patient to the ICU, intubate, and place him on ventilatory assistance. Because of continued deterioration, antibiotics were modified to include vancomycin and imipenem. Because of the inability to obtain a fully established diagnosis, the patient was submitted to open-lung biopsy. The open-lung biopsy showed advanced fibrosis and scarring. Despite therapy with aggressive pulmonary toilet and ventilatory support, his condition continued to deteriorate. The patient experienced cardiac arrest on 1/16.

Final Diagnosis: Pneumonia, apparently due to Gram-negative bacteria

Additional Diagnoses: Acute respiratory failure
                              Cardiac arrest
                              Cryptococcal meningitis
                              Severely malnourished

Procedures: Open-Lung biopsy
                              Ventilatory assistance

Code Assignment:

Principal diagnosis:_____

Additional diagnoses:_____

Procedures:_____

Issues to clarify:_____

7.50.   The following documentation is from the health record of a 29-year-old male patient.

Brief History: This patient is a 29-year-old male who presented to the emergency room with cough and shortness of breath. On examination, his skin was very warm and moist. His color was pale. He states he has been coughing and short of breath and febrile for several days. On admission, his temperature was 102.3°F, respirations 26 per minute and regular, pulse 126 per minute, blood pressure 150/90. He appeared ill.

Pertinent Physical Examination Findings: The patient had decreased breath sounds in the left lower lobe with basilar rales in that area. His heart was tachycardiac. There was no significant murmur, gallop, or rub. The abdomen was soft, no organomegaly. Extremities showed no edema, clubbing, or cyanosis.

Laboratory and X-Ray Findings: Chest x-ray showed consolidation involving the basal segments of the left lower lobe, as well as a subsegmental infiltrate involving the anterior segment of the right upper lobe. Hematocrit was 38.9, white count 5,900, 80 percent granulocytes. SMA profile was normal, including a cholesterol of 135, SGOT of 48. UA was clear. Gram stain of sputum showed few Gram-positive cocci in clusters and many polymorphonuclear cells. Final sputum culture showed the usual throat flora. This; however, was taken after the patient had utilized Augmentin orally for several days prior to admission. Blood cultures showed no growth, and urine culture showed no growth. Patient experienced episodes of tachycardia of unknown etiology. This will be followed up on an outpatient basis.

Hospital Course: It was the impression that the patient had lobar pneumonia due to pneumococcus. However, because of the apparent failure of Augmentin, other etiologies were considered, and he was started on ceftizoxime. The patient responded very promptly and felt well enough to be discharged with plans for follow-up in two weeks.

Which of the following is the correct code assignment?

a. 482.89
b. 483.8, 427.2
c. 481, 785.0
d. 482.9, 785.0

7.51. The following documentation is from the health record of a 65-year-old male patient.

Hospital Course: This unfortunate gentleman was discharged from the hospital yesterday after being treated for several days for congestive heart failure. He presented back to the hospital within 24 hours after he developed significant respiratory discomfort and shortness of breath. He was found to be in respiratory failure and have pneumonia. The patient required ventilation in the emergency room. His x-ray showed diffuse infiltrates bilaterally also consistent with possible congestive heart failure. The patient did not have an elevated BNP. He was taken to the intensive care unit for further evaluation and treatment. It was explained to his wife and family that he was critically ill, and his survival was very guarded. The patient required blood pressure support. He was treated for pneumonia and his sputum cultures grew methicillin-resistant Staph aureus. He was treated with vancomycin. He had a stroke while admitted and had right-sided hemiparesis. He was found to have a left-sided internal carotid artery stenosis. He was felt not to be a surgical candidate as he was critically ill. He was placed on Bumex® infusion for his congestive heart failure. His respiratory status remained very tenuous despite maximum medical management. He was placed on TPN. His condition never improved despite all efforts. He remained poorly responsive, and he developed renal failure, as well. On day 15, it was clear that his survival was unlikely. His family asked that his ventilator support be discontinued. Shortly after, the ventilator was discontinued.

Discharge Diagnoses:

Acute respiratory failure secondary to pneumonia and congestive heart failure
Cerebral vascular accident with infarction
Methicillin-resistant Staphyloccoccus aureus infection
Coronary artery disease
Renal failure
Lung mass
Chronic obstructive pulmonary disease
Diabetes mellitus
Paroxysmal ventricular tachycardia
Hemiplegia secondary to stroke
Hyperlipidemia
Anemia

Operative Procedures:

Mechanical ventilation greater than 96 hours

Packed red blood cell transfusion × 2

Placement of central venous line

Assign the correct codes for this case:

Principal diagnosis: _____

Additional diagnoses: _____

Procedures: _____

7.52.   History and Physical Exam

Present Illness: This 74-year-old male who presented to the emergency room last night with complaints of increased weakness and shortness of breath. In the emergency room, he was found to be hypotensive. Blood pressure 83/42 apparently—actually that was the recording at home. In the emergency room, it was 130/80. He was afebrile, tachypneic per usual, respiratory rate of 32, and admitted with acute pneumonia. He was started on Levaquin®. He has a history of purulent sputum for several days. Since admission, he feels better, tachypnea and weakness have improved. His blood pressure readings have somewhat improved. His peripheral edema improved with a diuretic.

Past Medical History: End-stage pulmonary disease, atherosclerotic heart disease and congestive heart failure, gastroesophageal reflux disease, gout, and hypothyroidism.

Family History: Unremarkable

Social History: Has six children and is a widower

Physical Exam: On physical examination, blood pressure 102/70, pulse 90, respirations 28. He is pleasant, alert. Color is good. No JVD.

Chest: He has bilateral rales, which are chronic.

Heart: There is a systolic ejection murmur, grade 3, with an S4 gallop.

Abdomen: The abdomen is soft, nontender. No palpable organomegaly

Extremities: Extremities reveal trace to +1 peripheral edema. He does have some stasis pigmentary changes. He does have clubbing of his fingers.

Musculoskeletal: No atrophic changes

Skin: Unremarkable except as noted

Neurological: He has no focal sensory or motor deficits and reflexes are physiologic.

Impression(s): I suspect he probably just has purulent bronchitis and that is the cause of his deterioration. He is on Levaquin and seems to be improving. We will observe until tomorrow. If still doing reasonably well, we will let him go.

Discharge Summary

History of Present Illness: This 74-year-old male with end-stage pulmonary fibrosis was admitted via the emergency room with increased breathlessness. The admitting diagnosis was pneumonia. While here, he did not develop any significant fever.

Laboratory Studies: An admission P02 58, PCO2 37, pH 7.45 on 3.5 liters, his electrolytes were normal with the exception of BUN 28, creatinine 1.3, white blood cell count 8.6, hemoglobin 11.4, platelet count slightly low 117, urinalysis fairly unremarkable with trace protein, rare red and white blood cells.

Hospital Course: The patient was continued on his Levaquin, which had been started one day previously. His chest x-ray showed decreased cardiac size from the previous exam, chronic infiltrates bilaterally, no acute infiltrates. Electrocardiogram showed sinus rhythm, right bundle branch block, left anterior hemi-block. He did receive intravenous diuretic and with this did achieve significant diuresis. My concern at the time of admission was the possible hypotension, which was recorded at home, but all blood pressure recordings here varied from the 100–130 systolic range.

Discharge Diagnosis: Probably acute bronchitis with perhaps mild congestive heart failure.

What are the correct code sets for this admission?

a. 466.0, 515, 428.0, 414.01, 530.81, 274.9, 244.9
b. 491.22, 428.0, 414.01, 530.81, 274.9, 244.9
c. 491.22, 466.0, 515, 428.0, 414.00, 530.81, 274.9, 244.9
d. 428.0, 466.0, 515, 414.00, 530.81, 274.9, 244.9

7.53. **Admission Diagnosis:** Pneumonia, hypoxemia

Discharge Diagnosis: Bilateral pneumonia, respiratory failure, dehydration, quadriplegia with old C5-C6 fracture, atonic bladder, tobacco use

Disposition: The patient is being discharged to home. Her daughter stays with her full time to care for her. She is to come to our office in one week to get a repeat chest x-ray and then further treatment with her pending results.

Hospital Course: The patient is a 50-year-old female who is quadriplegic following a motor vehicle accident in which she suffered an injury to her C5–C6 fracture. She had a fever two days prior to admission, so we called her in a prescription for Keflex. She did not improve on this medication, and she came to the emergency room on the day of admission complaining of shortness of breath and cough. She reported a two-day history of shortness of breath, fever, and cough productive of green yellow sputum. There was no elevation in her temperature. A chest x-ray in the emergency room showed bilateral lower lobe infiltrates, which may be actually due to CM. She was admitted to the hospital for intravenous antibiotics for her pneumonia and treatment of her hypoxemia. Her pO2 in the emergency room was 50 on room air. Her temperature was 102.6°F.

After admission to the hospital, the patient was placed on Biaxin®, and she did become a febrile and started to feel better. Her caretaker, who is her daughter, felt that she could care for her at home. The patient is being discharged to the daughter's care.

Work up during this admission included a glucose of 81, a BUN of 6, a creatinine of .5. Electrolytes were normal. Her arterial blood gases show a pH of 7.482, a pCO_2 of 33, a pO_2 low at 50, HCO_3 324, and total CO_2 was 55. Her O_2 saturation was only 88 percent on room air. She was started on hand-held nebulizer treatments, and she rapidly improved.

At the time of discharge, she was breathing easy on room air. She was benefiting from her hand-held nebulizer treatments, and she wants to return home.

The work-up during admission, in addition to that above, included serum electrolytes, which were normal, except for potassium of 3.3. This was corrected with additional potassium. Her hemoglobin on admission was 13.5. Hematocrit was 40.1, RBC was 4.40. Her MCV was 91. Her MCH was 33.6. RDW was 12.7. The urinalysis showed a moderate amount of hemoglobin but no red cells. Her chest x-ray did show a definite infiltrate in her left lower lobe and a questionable infiltrate in her right lower lobe. There is question that possibly her paraplegia may affect her ability to breathe, necessitating her seeing us for respiratory infections. The patient is discharged to home. She will be following with Doctor Jones in two weeks after repeat chest x-ray.

What are the correct codes for this admission?

Principal diagnosis:_____

Secondary diagnoses:_____

7.54.   Discharge Summary

Admit Date: 3/19/20XX

Discharge Date: 3/25/20XX

Admitting Diagnoses: Acute exacerbation of asthma, chronic obstructive pulmonary disease, acute bronchitis, hormonal replacement therapy

Discharge Diagnoses: Acute exacerbation of asthma, chronic obstructive pulmonary disease, acute bronchitis, hormonal replacement therapy

Discharge Instructions: Patient is to follow up in the office in one week

Discharge Medications: Spiriva® as directed daily, Pulmicort® inhaler two puffs p.o. every 12 hours, Serevent® Diskus® one puff p.o. every 12 hours, Augmentin 500 mg p.o. three times a day for six days, prednisone 35 mg to decrease by 5 mg every day until gone.

Brief History: The patient is a 57-year-old white female who presents with approximately one-day history of increasing dyspnea to the point where any ambulation required increasing effort as she could not catch her breath. The patient also had mild complaints of sore throat, neck pain, as well as headache. She denied any fever although a low grade one was present on admission. The patient also admitted to a nonproductive cough.

The patient was admitted with an acute exacerbation of asthma and was admitted to observation. However, this did not clear with IV steroids, nebulizer treatments, as well as supportive therapy so she was admitted for inpatient treatment of acute exacerbation of asthma with possible bronchitis and respiratory distress. During her initial two days, she was continued on Z-Pak®, Decadron, as well as albuterol, and Atrovent treatments as her respiratory distress did not significantly improve. The patient had increased anxiety secondary to her nebulized treatments, and her medication was changed to Xopenex® with some improvement.

Chest x-ray was checked on the second hospital day, and a 2-D echocardiogram was ordered in addition to a pulmonary consult. The patient's Zithromax® was changed to Augmentin to better cover H. flu as a possibility. Inhaled steroids were added as the bronchodilators were continued. The patient's respiratory distress subsequently improved with less agitation with continued high-dose Xopenex. The 2-D echocardiogram was normal. The patient's respiratory condition improved with less dyspnea with her lung exam overall cleared. The patient was discharged in stable condition.

History and Physical: This is a 57-year-old female who presents with approximately one-day history of increasing dyspnea to the point where any ambulation required increasing effort, and she could not catch her breath. The patient stated that approximately a month ago some cold medication was phoned in for her, which cleared up her congestion but did feel she totally got well. She was admitted from the emergency room to observation, but her symptoms did not resolve so she is being admitted for inpatient treatment. Patient smokes approximately one pack of cigarettes a day and denies any alcohol use.

Physical Exam:

General: The patient is alert and oriented appearing in mild to moderate respiratory distress

Lungs: Showed decreased breath sounds throughout with no wheezing present

Abdomen: Soft nontender with good bowel sounds present

Extremities: No cyanosis or edema

The patient is currently on 2 liters of nasal cannula with O2 saturations around 92%. Her chest x-ray is unremarkable.

Assessment and Plan: Acute exacerbation of asthma/chronic obstructive pulmonary disease/acute bronchitis—the patient will be continued on Zithromax given at 500 milligrams p.o. q. 24 hours. Continued on 10 milligrams of Decadron q. 8 hours, given albuterol as well as Atrovent treatments as well as continued on a daily basis.

Hormone replacement therapy on Premarin .625 milligrams q. day

Consultant Report:

Reason for Consultation: Asthmatic bronchitis

Impression: Asthmatic bronchitis either representing acute exacerbation of chronic bronchitis and/or asthma. Cigarette use greater than 40-pack years.

Recommendations: Change Zithromax to Augmentin as she has had antibiotics in the past 90 days, and there is a high incident of resistant H. flu and strep pneumon.

Hand-held steroids

Prophylactic H2 blockers and low molecular with heparin

Check sputum for eosinophils

Cigarette cessation

Discussion: The patient has purulent bronchitis and wheezing on top of chronic daily shortness of breath and wheezing. This is compounded by at least 40-pack years of smoking history. It is difficult to tell if this is just chronic obstructive pulmonary disease exacerbation due to infection or whether or not she has a large component of asthma. Whichever the initial diagnosis is, she would benefit with albuterol and Atrovent, inhaled steroids and antibiotics.

On the long term basis, she will need PFTs and a long-acting bronchodilator, Spiriva or Advair® depending on the way she responds on her pulmonary function test abnormalities. Advair is recommended if the FEV1 is less than 50%, Spiriva would be a better choice if this is all chronic obstructive pulmonary disease.

Emergency Room Report: Chief Complaint: Shortness of breath

History of Present Illness: The patient is a 57-year-old female complaining of shortness of breath since yesterday evening. She states that breathing difficulty became very severe to the point that she felt like she could not catch her breath. She could not walk across the room without becoming severely dyspneic. Also complaining of soreness in her neck bilaterally and of a headache.

Impression/Management Plan: Breathing difficulty with marked bronchospasm, possible fever with chills present. Rule out superimposed pneumonia. Symptoms consistent with exacerbation of asthma. Initial oxygen saturation on presentation to the emergency department 89% on room air.

Course in the Emergency Department: The patient received intravenous fluids, Decadron, magnesium. The patient did develop a fever in the emergency department with temperature up to 100.7°F, for which she received Tylenol. The patient received multiple nebulizer treatments in the emergency department and has persistent expiratory wheezes with somewhat labored respirations. Chest x-ray read negative for acute changes by my reading. The patient received initial dose of Zithromax in the emergency department. Decision for further treatment was made with an admission to the observation unit.

Final Diagnosis: Status asthmaticus.

What is the correct code assignment for this admission?

a. 493.91, 305.1
b. 466.0, 493.22, 305.1
c. 493.22, 305.1
d. 493.21

Trauma and Poisoning

7.55. The following documentation is from the health record of a four-year-old male patient.

Case Summary: The patient is a four-year-old male child who, at the age of two, swallowed some drain cleaner while playing in the bathroom. He was found at that time with acid burns of the mouth, throat, trachea, and esophagus. Plastic repair has been performed on the mouth and throat. He is now being admitted by a plastic surgeon for plastic reconstruction and removal of scar tissue to the trachea. The patient was admitted, prepped, and taken to surgery where the scar tissue of the trachea was removed, and plastic repair was accomplished. The patient's recovery was uneventful, and the patient was discharged in satisfactory condition three days postsurgery.

Which of the following code sets is correct for reporting the diagnoses of the most recent admission?

a. 709.2, 909.1, E929.2
b. 478.9, 909.1, 906.8, E929.2
c. 709.2, 909.5, 906.8, E864.2
d. 478.9, 909.5, E864.2

7.56. The following documentation is from the health record of a 22-year-old male patient.

Case Summary: The patient is a 22-year-old male, admitted through the emergency department after the motorcycle he was driving collided with an elk on a mountain highway. The patient was not wearing a helmet and sustained a skull fracture over the left temporal and orbital roof areas with depressed zygomatic arch on the left side. The patient was unconscious at the scene and upon examination in the ED, with a GCS score of 12. Left pupil was blown (fixed and dilated), indicating intracranial injury. Hypoxemia, hypotension, and brain swelling were noted. The patient was admitted to the ICU with monitoring of intracranial pressure. The patient experienced increasing periods of apnea and was placed on a ventilator following endotracheal intubation. The patient also had numerous friction burns all over his body, but no other fractures were apparent. The patient's family (in another state) was notified and arrived two days later. There was no improvement in the patient's status over the next four days. The patient continued to be monitored and was unconscious. Attempts to wean from ventilation were unsuccessful. Brain wave monitoring showed no brain wave function. The family made the decision to discontinue life support and the life-sustaining efforts were discontinued.

Which of the following is the correct code set for this case scenario?

a. 804.45, E815.2; 96.72
b. 803.45, 919.0, E815.2; 96.72, 96.04
c. 801.05, 802.85, 802.45, E815.2; 96.72, 96.04, 01.18
d. 801.45, 802.4, 919.0, E815.2; 96.72, 96.04, 01.18

7.57. The following documentation is from the health record of a 28-year-old female patient.

Case Summary: The patient is a 28-year-old female passenger in a motor vehicle accident. Upon arrival in the ED the patient was complaining of severe abdominal pain. CT scan revealed laceration of the liver and increasing hematoma. The patient was taken immediately to the OR, where exploratory laparotomy revealed a traumatic rupture approximately 2 cm deep. It was felt that the parenchyma could not be adequately repaired, so a lobectomy was carried out with evacuation of the hematoma. The patient's postoperative course was stormy. The patient developed infection and dehiscence of the operative wound, necessitating return to the OR for opening and drainage of the wound. The patient was also given a 10-day course of IV gentamicin. The patient was finally able to be discharged on the 12th day postop in satisfactory condition.

Code Assignment:

Principal diagnosis: _____

Additional diagnoses: _____

Procedures: _____

Issues to clarify: _____

7.58. The following documentation is from the health record of a 32-year-old male patient.

History of Present Illness: A 32-year-old male was brought to the ED via ambulance. He was the unrestrained, front-seat passenger in a single-vehicle crash. The patient was ejected from the vehicle and had a brief, witnessed, loss of consciousness at the scene. Paramedics reported the following vital signs en route: BP 110/palp; heart rate 90, respiratory rate 20. A large bore intravenous access was established, and fluids were begun.

Physical Examination:	Vital signs: Unchanged
	HEENT: 2 cm superficial laceration over left eyebrow
	Lungs: Clear to auscultation
	CV: Regular rate, S1/S2; NSR on EKG monitor
	Abdomen: Mild epigastric tenderness without rebound
	Pelvis: Stable, no crepitans
	Extremities: No deformities
	Neuro: GCS 13, nonfocal exam

Radiology: Chest x-ray, lateral C-spine, and pelvis film are all reviewed by the chief resident on call and noted to be normal. CT scan of the patient's abdomen demonstrated free intra-abdominal fluid, perisplenic hematoma, and splenic laceration. Patient remained hemodynamically stable during the scan.

Because of the patient's young age and hemodynamic stability, nonoperative management of his splenic injury was begun. The patient was admitted to the ICU for hemodynamic monitoring, serial measurement of hematocrit, and serial abdominal examinations. He was transferred to the floor on hospital day 2 and made an uneventful recovery.

Diagnoses: 1. Minor concussion with 10 minutes of loss of consciousness
2. Perisplenic hematoma and splenic laceration of capsule

Which of the following code sets would be correct?

a. 865.11
b. 865.02, 850.9, E819.1
c. 865.02, 850.11, E819.1, 88.01, 87.44, 87.22, 88.26
d. 865.01, 865.02, 850.11, E819.1

Chapter 8

Case Studies from Ambulatory Health Records

Note: Even though the specific cases are divided by setting, most of the information pertaining to the diagnosis is applicable to most settings. If you practice or apply codes in a particular type of setting, you may find additional information in other sections of this publication that may be pertinent to you.

Every effort has been made to follow current recognized coding guidelines and principles, as well as nationally recognized reporting guidelines. The material presented may differ from some health plan requirements for reporting. The ICD-9-CM codes used are effective through September 30, 2007, and the HCPCS (CPT and HCPCS Level II) codes are in effect through December 31, 2006. The current standard transactions and code sets named in HIPAA have been utilized, which require ICD-9-CM Volume III procedure codes for inpatients.

Instructions:

Assign all applicable ICD-9-CM diagnosis and CPT procedure codes for the case studies presented. The majority of the cases provide multiple-choice answers, and the reader must select the appropriate code set. In other instances, the reader is expected to assign codes without any prompts.

The case studies in this ambulatory section are based on selected excerpts from health records without reproducing the entire health record. However, in practice, the coding professional should have access to the entire health record. Health records are analyzed and codes are selected only with the physician's complete and appropriate documentation available. According to coding guidelines, codes are not assigned without physician documentation.

The objective of the cases and scenarios reproduced in this publication is to provide practice in assigning correct codes, not necessarily to emulate real coding practice. For example, the reader may be asked to assign codes based only on an operative report or emergency room documentation, when in real practice a coder has access to documentation in the entire medical record.

Disorders of the Blood and Blood-Forming Organs

8.1.   The following documentation is from the health record of a 39-year-old male patient.

Emergency Department Services

History of Present Illness: The patient is a 39-year-old African-American male who has a known history of sickle-cell anemia who presented to the Emergency Department with diffuse extremity pains and pain along the right inguinal area. The pains started on Friday, became a little bit better on Saturday; then improved, and again started in the past 24 hours. He denies any problems with cough or sputum or production. He denies any problems with fever.

Past Medical History: See recent medical records in charts. He does have a new onset of diabetes, probably related to his hemochromatosis. He does have evidence of iron overload with high ferritins.

Review of Systems: Otherwise unremarkable except for those related to his pain. He denies any problems with any fever or night sweats. No cough or sputum production. Denies any changes in gastrointestinal or genitourinary habits. No blood per rectum or urine.

Physical Examination: This is a 39-year-old African-American male who is conscious and cooperative. He is oriented × 3 and appears in no acute distress. Vital signs are stable. HEENT is remarkable for icterus present in oral mucosa and conjunctivae, which is a chronic event for him. The neck is supple. No evidence of any gross lymphadenopathy of the cervical, supraclavicular, or axillary areas. The heart is irregular in rate without any murmurs heard. Lungs are clear to auscultation and percussion. The abdomen is soft and benign without any gross organomegaly. Extremities reveal no edema. No palpable cords. He does have some tenderness along the inner aspects of his right lower extremity near the inguinal area; however, no masses were palpable and no point tenderness is noted.

IV fluids and pain medications were administered in the ED. He had a problem with his right inguinal area. He had evidence of pain. There was some pain on abduction of his right lower extremity. The rest was unremarkable. There was no evidence of any Holman, no palpable cords, no masses were palpable.

Because of his sickle-cell anemia, rule out the possibility of avascular necrosis of the femur. Complete x-rays of his femur and hip were carried out. However, these were both negative.

Patient is being transferred to a larger facility for treatment of his sickle-cell crisis. Doppler studies should also be carried out to rule out any venous thrombosis.

Diagnoses: 1. Painful sickle-cell crisis
2. Type II diabetes mellitus
3. Chronic atrial fibrillation

Condition on Discharge: Stable on pain meds

What codes would the facility report for this Medicare service? The patient met the fourth acuity level in the facility's criteria for evaluation and management in the ED.

a. 282.61, 789.09, 427.31, 250.00, 99285
b. 282.62, 733.42, 99284, 73550, 73510
c. 282.62, 427.31, 250.00, 73550, 73510
d. 282.62, 427.31, 250.00, 99284-25, 73550, 73510

8.2.   The following documentation is from the health record of a 66-year-old male patient.

Outpatient Hospital Department Services

History: This is a 66-year-old male who had coronary artery bypass graft in February. He did well. He was discharged home. Some time after that when he was home, he had two days of black stools. He mentioned it to the nurse, but I'm not sure anything was done about it. He has not had any other evidence of hematemesis, melena, or hematochezia but was feeling rather weak and fatigued. He had blood work done that showed a hemoglobin of 5.7, hematocrit of 20.9, MCV of 80. Serum iron of 8, 2 percent saturation. No indigestion or heartburn. No abdominal pain of any kind. No past history of anemia or GI bleed.

Past Medical History: General health has been good.

Allergies: None known

Previous Surgeries: Coronary artery bypass graft

Medications: At the time of admission include Glucotrol, Lasix, potassium, and aspirin

Review of Systems: Endocrine: He does have diabetes controlled with medication. Cardiovascular: History of coronary artery disease with coronary artery bypass graft. No recent symptoms of chest pain or shortness of breath. Respiratory: No chronic cough or sputum production. GU: No dysuria, hematuria, history of stones or infections. Musculoskeletal: No arthritic complaints or muscle weakness. Neuropsychiatric: No syncope, seizures, weakness, paralysis, depression.

Family History: Is positive for cardiovascular disease and diabetes in his mother. No history of cancer.

Social History: The patient is married. Never smoked. Doesn't drink any alcohol. Works in a factory.

On physical examination, a well-developed, well-nourished, alert male in no acute distress. Blood pressure: 146/82. Respirations: 18. Heart rate: 78. Skin: Good turgor and texture. Eyes: No scleral icterus. Pupils are round, regular, equal, and react to light. Neck: No jugular venous distention. No carotid bruits. Thyroid is not enlarged. Trachea in the midline. Lungs are clear. Heart: No murmur noted. Abdomen is soft. Bowel sounds present. No masses, no tenderness. Liver and spleen are not palpably enlarged. Extremities: Good pulses. Trace edema of the feet.

Laboratory values show severe anemia with a hemoglobin of 5.7. Hemoccult is also positive. His iron studies showed low iron and low ferritin, consistent with chronic blood loss anemia. His B_{12} and folate levels were normal. His SMA-12 was essentially unremarkable.

Impression: 1. Anemia. Probably he is anemic post bypass and then had stress gastritis with a little bit of bleeding and has never recovered from that. No evidence of acute or active bleeding at this time. The patient is stable. Possibility of occult malignancy or active peptic ulcer disease does exist.
2. Arteriosclerotic heart disease of native vessel, stable

Recommendations: Admit patient as an outpatient for blood transfusion. Patient is being transfused. He should have an esophagogastroduodenoscopy and colonoscopy, possible biopsy or polypectomy, which has been explained to the patient along with potential risks and complications including bleeding, transfusion, perforation, and surgery. These tests will be scheduled as soon as possible.

Discharge Note

Final Diagnoses: 1. Severe blood loss anemia; weakness
2. Type II diabetes mellitus
3. History of coronary artery disease status post coronary artery bypass graft

The patient received three units of packed red blood cells, leukoreduced, CMV negative. He felt better, with subsidence of his shortness of breath and his weakness improved. His last hemoglobin was 8.4 with a hematocrit of 27.7.

The patient was scheduled for EGD to rule out peptic ulcer disease and colonoscopy to rule out occult malignancy in one week. The patient will be discharged home, and he will have clear liquid diet. He is to call for any problems. He will continue with his home medications, and he was placed on ferrous sulfate one tablet twice a day.

What codes are reported for this outpatient encounter? The facility purchases its blood from the blood bank.

a. 280.0, 792.1, 414.01, 250.00, V45.81, 36430, P9051 (3 units)
b. 285.9, 780.79, 36430, P9051 (3 units)
c. 280.0, 578.1, 414.01, 250.00, V45.81, 36430
d. 285.9, 792.1, 414.01, 250.00, V45.81, C1010, P9051 (3 units)

8.3.   The following documentation is from the health record of an 87-year-old female patient.

Emergency Department Services

History: The patient is an 87-year-old white female brought to the ED because of pleural effusion, urinary tract infection, and dehydration. She had been taking medication. She lives at the nursing home and has been doing fairly well. Today she was found to be weak and not eating well. Then she was sent to the emergency room for evaluation and found to have pleural effusion and dehydration, urinary tract infection, also thrombocytopenia with petechial hemorrhage. She was found to have a platelet count of 77,000.

Past History: She has a history of cholecystectomy.

Social History: She is a retired woman. No smoking, no drinking, no allergies.

Family History: Noncontributory

Systemic Review: Otherwise normal

Physical Examination: Today reveals blood pressure is 163/62. Pulse of 80. Respirations of 15. Temperature of 98.6°F. General condition of the patient showed chronically ill, confused, disoriented. No jaundice, no cyanosis. No pallor, no edema. The patient has dehydration +3. Scalp and skull are normal. Eyes showed bluish around the eyes and petechial hemorrhage at the eyelid and conjunctiva. Ears, nose, and throat are normal. Neck showed normal cervical spine. The neck veins are flat. No bruits of the carotid arteries. The trachea is midline. Thyroid gland cannot be palpated. Lymph glands cannot be palpated. Chest shows normal contour. The breasts are normal. Movement of the chest equal on both sides. There is dullness of the chest with some rales and rhonchi. Heart shows apex beat is at the fifth intercostal space, left midclavicular line. No diffuse precordial pulsation, no thrill. Heart rate is 80, regular, with premature ventricular contraction, no murmur. Back is normal. Abdomen showed normal contour, soft, nontender, no guarding, no rigidity. Liver, spleen, and kidneys cannot be palpated, no mass is palpable. Bowel sounds are positive. No fluid thrill. No shifting dullness. No bruits of the abdominal vessels. Extremities show no clubbing of the fingers. No varicose veins. No phlebitis. Hematoma of the right hand. Peripheral pulses are normal. The deep tendon reflexes are normal. Babinski sign is negative.

Laboratory Studies: Hematocrit was 43, white count 9,000 with 82 percent neutrophils, and the platelet count 77,000. The MCV was 102. Creatinine was 1.7. Bilirubin was 1.7. The alkaline phosphatase was 122. AST 498, ALT 493, and albumin 3.6. The prothrombin time was 18 seconds, the PTT was 25 seconds. The chest x-ray showed a right pleural effusion.

Impression:
1. Urinary tract infection
2. Dehydration
3. Pleural effusion from congestive heart failure
4. Primary thrombocytopenia with petechial hemorrhage
5. Type II diabetes mellitus

Plan of Treatment: The patient will be stabilized and started on IV fluids. Also will start IV antibiotic for urinary tract infection.

Patient will be transferred at the family's request to a larger facility. A consult with hematology will be arranged, and a transfusion of platelets may be indicated.

What are the appropriate diagnosis codes for this service?

a. 599.0, 276.51, 428.0, 287.5, 250.00
b. 599.0, 276.51, 428.0, 511.9, 287.5, 250.00
c. 599.0, 276.51, 428.0, 287.30, 250.00
d. 599.0, 276.51, 428.0, 511.9, 287.30, 782.7, 250.00

8.4. The following documentation is from the health record of a 39-year-old female patient.

Hospital Outpatient Department Services

This 39-year-old female was diagnosed with breast cancer two years ago. At that time she had a mastectomy performed, with no evidence of metastases to the lymph nodes. About eight months ago, metastases was discovered in her liver. The patient was given chemotherapy. She has been losing weight and developing increased fatigue. Patient was referred to hospice care program, with a life expectancy of four to six months. Progressive weight loss due to loss of appetite led to cachexia and program of home intravenous hyperalimentation. Progressive, unrelenting abdominal pain led to chronic use of analgesics. Patient is awake, alert, and desires to spend more time with family. Progressive weakness and dropping hemoglobin led to the decision to transfuse the patient every two weeks with two units of packed cells. Patient is stable and more comfortable on this regimen.

She is coming into the outpatient department now for transfusion.

Diagnosis: History of breast cancer, current liver metastases, anemia due to the neoplasm and chemotherapy.

What are the correct diagnosis codes assigned in this case?

a. 285.22, 197.7, V10.3, E933.1
b. 285.9, 197.7, V10.3, E933.1
c. 197.7, 285.22, V10.3, E933.1
d. 285.9, 197.7, V10.3

Disorders of the Cardiovascular System

8.5. The following documentation is from the health record of a 60-year-old male patient.

Outpatient Hospital Diagnostic Services

A 60-year-old white male was given a stress test for recent left arm pain that occurred with exercise the day before. His only medication was Dyazide 1 daily. He was exercised by Bruce protocol for a duration of 6 minutes, 2 seconds, using the treadmill. Maximum heart rate achieved was 137, 85 percent maximum predicted was 136. His blood pressure during the stress test went up to 182/80. He denied any arm pain with the exercise. He did have 2 mm of ST depression at a point of maximum exercise in 2, 3, AVF, but these were all upsloping. Also in V5, V6, he had 1.4 mm ST depression, also upsloping.

Following exercise he was placed at rest. At about 1 minute, 45 seconds post exercise, his STT waves changed. He had STT wave depression with T-wave inversion in the interior and V5 and V6 leads. The patient remained asymptomatic throughout, with no arrhythmias. His blood pressure dropped to a low of 38 systolic over 0 at 6 minutes post exercise and remained low for several minutes. During this time period, an IV was started and D5 ½ normal saline was given to elevate the blood pressure. The patient remained pain-free during this episode and felt fine during the entire episode. At the 10-minute mark, the T-wave inversion started resolving, and the STT waves returned to normal.

Upon consultation with Dr. Jones at Magic Memorial, the patient was advised to report for a cardiac catheterization to rule out ischemic heart disease.

Which codes are reported by the hospital for this outpatient service?

Note: The cardiologist is not employed by the hospital reporting the test.

a. 786.50, 796.3, 93015
b. 729.5, 796.3, 93015
c. 414.8, 458.29, 93017
d. 729.5, 458.9, 93017

8.6.　The following documentation is from the health record of a patient who received hospital outpatient surgical services.

Preoperative Diagnosis:	Hypertensive cardiovascular with end stage renal disease and congestive heart failure
Postoperative Diagnosis:	Same
Procedure:	Placement of AV fistula with Gore-Tex® graft of the right forearm for dialysis access

Description: After placement on the operating table, the patient was premedicated with .05 mg of Versed. The right arm was prepped and draped in the usual sterile fashion. Following the infiltration of 1 percent lidocaine, a transverse incision was made just beyond the antecubital fossa. Dissection was carried down, basilic vein and artery were identified and mobilized, and Silastic loops were placed. Another incision was then made, just above the wrist. After the area was infiltrated with lidocaine, a 6 mm Gore-Tex graft was tunneled through the loop. Anastomosis to the artery was accomplished after the patient received 2,000 units of IV heparin. End-to-side anastomosis was accomplished with 6-0 and 7-0 Prolene sutures. The end areas were interrupted and the edges approximated with running sutures. On removal of the clamps, excellent blood flow was evident. Anastomosis was deemed satisfactory. Venous anastomosis was then accomplished with 6-0 and 7-0 Prolene sutures Flushing and back-bleeding was allowed prior to completion of the anastomosis. Upon completion, excellent flow was evident through the vein. After a period of observation with no bleeding, both wounds were closed with subcutaneous 3-0 VICRYL in a running fashion, and the skin was closed with 4-0 Prolene sutures. Dressings were applied and the patient returned to the outpatient recovery area in stable condition.

Which of the following is the correct code set?

a. 404.92, 36830
b. 404.93, 585.6, 428.0, 36830
c. 585.6, 428.0, 401.9, 36821
d. 404.93, 36821

8.7. The following documentation is from the health record of a patient who received hospital outpatient diagnostic services.

Preoperative Diagnosis: Angina

Postoperative Diagnosis: Patent coronary arteries and grafts, ASHD present

Procedure: Right and left heart cath with coronary angiography

The patient was brought to the cath lab in a fasting state. The right groin was prepped and draped in the usual sterile fashion. After local anesthesia was administered, sheaths were placed percutaneously into the right femoral artery and vein. IV heparin 3,000 units were given.

Using a thermodilution catheter, right heart pressures were measured, and thermodilution cardiac outputs and AV oxygen differences were obtained. A pigtail catheter was inserted into the left ventricular cavity, and simultaneous left ventricular pressures were measured. A pullback was obtained across the aortic valve.

Using a 7R4 catheter, angiography was performed of the right coronary artery and both vein grafts. A 7L4 was used for angiography of the left coronary artery. Additional attempts were made to image the vein graft to the right coronary artery with a right coronary artery bypass catheter. The pigtail catheter was reinserted, and left ventricular angiography and aortic root angiography was performed. The patient tolerated the procedure well and returned to the recovery room in good condition.

Which codes are assigned for this service?

a. 414.00, 413.9, V45.81, 93526, 93543, 93540, 93544, 93555, 93556
b. 414.01, 414.02, 93526, 93543, 93540, 93544, 93555, 93556
c. 414.00, 413.9, V45.81, 93526, 93543, 93540, 93544
d. 414.01, 414.02, 413.9, V45.81, 93510, 93543, 93544

8.8. A patient presents to the emergency department with a history of syncope. In the EP laboratory, a comprehensive electrophysiological study is performed, including right atrial and right ventricular pacing and recording. The patient shows inducible ventricular tachycardia and an ICD and RA and RV leads are placed under fluoroscopic guidance. The ICD and leads are tested after implantation and the patient is taken to the recovery area of the EP Laboratory for postprocedural observation.

Assign the appropriate codes for the hospital to report for the diagnostic and interventional portions of this procedure.

a. 93620, 33249, 71090, 93641
b. 93620, G0300, 71090, 93641
c. 93620, G0300, 93641
d. G0300, 71090, 93641

8.9. A patient with rapid atrial fibrillation that is resistant to medical management is referred to the EP laboratory for AV node ablation. He undergoes placement of catheters in the right atrial septum for mapping and in the right ventricle for temporary pacing. The appropriate location for ablation is mapped and the designated area is ablated to achieve complete heart block. Assign the appropriate CPT code(s) to report this procedure.

a. 93650, 93620
b. 93650, 93620-59
c. 93650
d. 93650, 93620, 93622

8.10. The following documentation is from the health record of a 51-year-old female patient.

Emergency Department Services

The patient is a 51-year-old female with a history of serious illnesses, including ventilator dependency in the past as a result of pulmonary edema and congestive heart failure and type I diabetic complications, including severe peripheral vascular disease of the extremities and a nonhealing ulcer. She presented to the ER via ambulance with chest pain and shortness of breath.

Past history shows cardiac catheterization performed, which was diagnostic for three-vessel coronary disease. Due to the patient's other health problems, surgery was not recommended, so the patient has frequent bouts of angina controlled with nitroglycerin. She has been hypertensive for many years and is currently well controlled on medication.

Impression: 1. Chest pain and shortness of breath
2. Rule out exacerbation of CHF vs. pulmonary embolus
3. Uncontrolled diabetes mellitus, type I with significant peripheral vascular disease
4. Nonhealing ulceration on the left foot of one-year duration

Plan: Transfer to University Hospital

Which diagnosis codes are reported for this ER patient?

a. 786.50, 786.05, 250.73, 440.23
b. 786.50, 786.05, 250.73, 443.81, 707.15
c. 428.0, 415.19, 250.73, 443.81, 707.15
d. 415.19, 428.0, 250.83, 707.10

8.11. The following documentation is from the health record of a patient who received hospital outpatient radiology department services.

Preoperative Diagnosis: Left carotid aneurysm, internal extracranial portion

Postoperative Diagnosis: Same

Procedure: Left carotid artery test occlusion

Procedure Description: With the patient properly prepared and draped in sterile fashion, a 6-French sheath was inserted in antegrade fashion into the right femoral artery. A diagnostic catheter was inserted coaxially through the sheath and used to select the left internal carotid artery. An exchange 018 wire was placed through the catheter and then the catheter was removed. A 6 mm × 2 cm balloon catheter was threaded over the wire and positioned with the balloon across the lumen of the proximal left internal carotid artery. The balloon was inflated to 0.5 atmosphere while slowly injecting contrast through the end of the balloon around the wire. Complete stasis of the carotid artery was documented. Neurologic testing was performed for five minutes. The patient was placed on heparin prior to this procedure, and a 5000-unit bolus was administered in the left carotid artery just prior to balloon inflation. Another 1000 units of heparin were slowly administered through the tip of the balloon over a five-minute period, along with saline. Only a small amount of total fluid was administered, and contrast was found to be static in the carotid artery during the entire period. After 5 minutes, the balloon was deflated and the patient was sent to the recovery area in good condition.

What is the correct code assignment?

a. 437.3, 36100, 37204, 75894
b. 442.81, 36620
c. 442.81, 36100, 37204, 75894
d. 442.81, 61626, 36100, 75894

Disorders of the Digestive System

8.12.   The following documentation is from the health record of a 68-year-old female patient.

Emergency Department and Hospital Observation Services

The patient presented to the ER per ambulance from the nursing home for G-tube placement. According to nursing staff at Happy Acres, there has been a foul-smelling green drainage for the past several days. Today the bulb was deflated and was found lying on the stomach. Nurses attempted to place the tube without success. Patient has redness surrounding the stoma.

Procedure: Gastrostomy tube placement

Date: 11/30/2000

The patient was taken to the GI treatment room where the wound site was scrubbed with Betadine. A wire was placed into the stomach with relative ease. At this point, because the tract appeared to be closed, an 8 mm balloon was then applied across the tract with some dilatation. A 16-gauge MIC tube was attempted to be placed through the site, but could not be accomplished, even with multiple attempts. Therefore, a 12-gauge Foley was attempted, also without much result. The patient will have to proceed with endoscopic replacement of the gastrostomy tube. The patient was sent to an observation bed in good condition, and tube placement was arranged in the GI lab for tomorrow.

Procedure: Esophagogastroduodenoscopy with percutaneous endoscopic gastrostomy tube replacement

Date: 12/01/2000

Record Review: This is a 68-year-old white female with an astrocytoma with seizure disorders who requires feeding by gastrostomy tube due to inability to swallow. Yesterday an attempt was made to replace the feeding tube by manipulation

of the abdominal wound site and use of an MIC tube an^d Foley, both of
which were unable to be placed through the tract, e ith a 10 mm
balloon. The patient is noncommunicative but h rgery other
than the previous placement of the PEG tub^e pressure
of 130/76, pulse 60. Lungs show a few ra¹ en soft,
nontender, with an obvious wound site was
placed.

Procedure Description: The pat
The Pentax upper endoscope was p n
the left lateral decubitus position. Exa as
was relatively normal. The scope was a or
gastrostomy site was seen. The antrum w orus
was normal. The scope was then advanced t the ortion of
the duodenum. The third portion, second port h were normal.
The scope was brought back into the antrum. Th nd site was cleaned
in the usual fashion. After taking a culture of the o chose a site next to the
prior site. However, even after using a 22-gauge spi needle, I was unable to locate
the stomach, even 1 cm away from the prior site. Therefore, because a wire could be
advanced through the prior site, it was decided to place the wire of the gastrostomy
tube kit into the stomach, which went in easily. A snare was used to grab the scope
and pull it out in the usual fashion via the mouth. At this time, a 20-gauge Bard
Mushroom gastrostomy tube was easily pulled out via the prior abdominal wound
site and fixed in the usual manner. Betadine scrub was used to clean the infected
wound. Betadine antibiotic ointment was used around the gastrostomy tube site. The
bumper was applied in minimal fashion, and the patient returned to the observation
bed in good condition.

The patient was held an additional 8 hours to receive IV Ancef to prevent cellulitis;
then transferred to a skilled care bed in the nursing facility. Close observation by
nursing home staff is recommended for signs of infection or other problems. The
wound site was strongly positive for S. aureus.

What codes will be submitted on the UB-92 for the outpatient care of this
Medicare observation patient for services from 11/30 to 12/1?

a. V55.1, 191.9, 345.9, 43246, 43750
b. 191.9, 345.9, V55.1, 43246, 43760-74
c. 536.41, 041.11, 787.2, 191.9, 345.9, 43246, 43760-52
d. 996.69, 041.11, 787.2, 191.9, 345.9, 43246, 43750-53

8.13. A patient reported to the ambulatory surgery department at the request of
her general surgeon.

Operative Report: Hospital Outpatient Surgery Department

Preoperative Diagnoses: 1. Inguinal hernia
                              2. Post colorectal resection for CA

Postoperative Diagnosis: Same

Procedure: Right inguinal herniorrhaphy

Description of Procedure: Under general anesthetic, an incision was made over the anterior wall of the inguinal canal, which was opened. The cord was isolated taking care to protect the nerve. The hernia sac was seen, which has direct hernia on the medial aspect of the wound. This was reduced and held in place using mesh that was stapled into place with a hole being made for the cord. The anterior wall of the inguinal canal was then closed with VICRYL, a hemostasis was achieved, and the wound closed with skin clips. Following this, the attention was turned to a screening colonoscopy, which was performed to the ileocecal valve without difficulty. Ascending, transverse, and descending colon were normal. There was no true evidence of diverticula. The sigmoid was normal, and a retroflex view of the rectosigmoid anastomosis in the rectum shows no gross abnormalities. The patient tolerated the procedure well and will be followed in the office.

Which code set is reported by the facility for this outpatient surgery?

a. 550.90, 562.10, V10.05, 49505-RT, G0105
b. 550.90, V76.51, V10.06, 49505-RT, 45378
c. 550.91, V76.51, V10.05, 49505-RT, 49568-RT
d. 550.90, V10.06, 49520-RT, 45330

8.14.   The following documentation is from the health record of a 70-year-old Medicare patient who received hospital outpatient services.

Operative Report

History and Indications: The patient is a 70-year-old female who has complained of altered bowel habits, abdominal pain, and a 2- to 3-gram documented decline in hemoglobin, confirming blood loss anemia. Her stools are heme negative, but there is suspicion that she may have pathology in the colon. She presents today for a diagnostic colonoscopy.

Procedure: Incomplete colonoscopy

In the endoscopy suite, with appropriate monitoring of pulse, oxygenation, temperature, blood pressure, and respiration, a digital rectal examination was performed. IV sedation was administered. Following the digital exam, the Pentax video colonoscope was inserted through the anus and was advanced almost to the midsigmoid colon. At this point, anatomic factors precluded any further advancement. In this instance, it was felt that a conservative approach was warranted in view of the patient's cardiovascular symptoms, including elevation of blood pressure and tachycardia and generally frail state. We elected to terminate the procedure and removed the air using suction and removed the instrument. The patient stabilized and was sent to recovery in good condition, but the examination was incomplete. No evidence of malignancy was seen in the section of the colon that could be visualized. The patient will be further evaluated using alternative methods.

Which code set will be submitted for this Medicare patient for the services described?

a. 789.00, 787.99, 280.0, 796.2, 785.0, V64.3, 45378-74
b. V71.1, V64.3, 45378-52
c. 789.00, 787.99, 280.0, 796.2, 785.0, V64.3, 45378
d. 789.00, 787.99, 280.0, 997.1, V64.3, 45330

8.15. The following documentation is from the health record of a 65-year-old male patient who received hospital outpatient GI laboratory services.

Endoscopy Record

Preoperative Diagnosis: Guaiac positive stools

Postoperative Diagnosis: Multiple colon polyps, diverticulosis

Procedure: Total colonoscopy with biopsy and polypectomy

Indications: This is a 65-year-old male who was found to have guaiac positive stools on a routine exam, no change in bowel habits or appreciable weight loss.

The patient was brought to the endoscopy suite and placed in left lateral decubitus position. 50 mg of Demerol and 2 mg Versed were administered. Digital rectal exam was performed, which was normal. Olympus colonoscope was inserted and passed under direct vision. A large polyp was seen immediately at 20 cm. This appeared to be pedunculated and approximately 1.5 cm long. Scope was passed all the way to the cecum and then slowly withdrawn. Cecum, ascending colon, hepatic flexure, transverse colon all appeared normal except for fairly extensive diverticula in the cecum and scattered throughout the rest of the sets. At the splenic flexure at 80 cm, there was a lesion, which was biopsied with a hot biopsy probe. At 60 cm, there was another small polyp, which was cauterized at the base with the probe and excised. At 20 cm, the pedunculated rectal polyp was snared and removed. The exam of the base revealed complete excision. The rest of the sigmoid and the rectum were unremarkable.

The pathology report showed mucus polypoid tissue at 80 cm and adenomatous polyps at 60 cm and 20 cm.

Which of the following code sets should be reported?

a. 211.3, 211.4, 562.10, 45385, 45384-59, 45380-59
b. 211.3, 569.0, 45384
c. 211.3, 569.0, 45385, 45384-59, 45380-59
d. 792.1, 211.3, 569.0, 562.10, 45385, 45384

8.16. The following documentation is from the health record of a 40-year-old female patient.

Emergency Department Services

HPI: This is a 40-year-old female with a three-year history of diarrhea and a one-year history of epigastric discomfort. She had a CT scan with a mass on the tail of the pancreas, as well as gastrin level greater than 1000 while taking Prilosec®. She has been amenorrheic for the last four months.

The patient presents to the ED with severe diarrhea and dehydration after discontinuing medications to allow for a repeat gastrin level off medications to eliminate the compounding effect of Prilosec on gastrin levels. Unfortunately, she was unable to stay off medication long enough, and she developed severe diarrhea with dehydration and a creatinine greater than 3, and she was admitted to observation services. Gastrin level is 1023 with VIP of 290.

Patient was rehydrated and orally treated with 200 mEq of potassium. The patient had significantly elevated calcium, which normalized with rehydration. Vitamin D level is pending, and PTH level also has returned elevated, concurrent with a calcium of 9.9. MRI abdomen has revealed multiple lesions in the liver with a density consistent with metastatic malignancy. Additionally on the MRI, a 6 cm pancreatic mass was noted at the tail of the pancreas.

This scenario is most consistent with multiple endocrine neoplasia syndrome (MEN-1) with parathyroid hyperplasia leading to hypercalcemia when dehydrated. Most likely, the recent normal calcium is due to a concurrent hypovitaminosis D, which is, in turn, secondary to chronic diarrhea. Dostinex® has been initiated today at 0.25 mg two times a week. Most likely she has MEN-1 given the current pancreatic and pituitary evidence of adenoma.

She is transferred to Memorial Hospital for CT-guided biopsy of a possible adenocarcinoma and to rule out the possibility of MEN-1.

Discharge Diagnoses:	1. Pancreatic and pituitary adenomas with multiple lesions on the liver consistent with metastasis
	2. Probable carcinoid syndrome (MEN-1)
	3. Hypercalcemia while dehydrated with normalization on rehydration
	4. Severe chronic diarrhea with hypokalemia and hypomagnesemia
	5. Amenorrhea

Discharge Medications: Prevacid 30 mg, one p.o. b.i.d.
Magnesium oxide 400 mg, one p.o. t.i.d.
Sandostatin® ampules 0.5 amp of 1 mg per amp every 8 hours
Trazodone 50 p.o. q. h.s. p.r.n. insomnia
Darvocet N®100 mg p.o. q. 4–6 hours p.r.n.
Dostinex 0.5 mg $^1/_2$ tab every Wednesday and Saturday

Which of the following is the correct ICD-9-CM code set for this observation service?

a. 237.4, 573.8, 275.42, 276.51, 787.91, 276.8, 275.2, 626.0
b. 211.6, 227.3, 197.7, 275.42, 276.51, 787.91, 276.8, 275.2, 626.0
c. 235.5, 237.0, 197.7, 275.42, 276.51, 787.91, 276.8, 275.2, 626.0
d. 237.4, 573.8, 259.2, 275.42, 276.51, 787.91, 276.8, 275.2, 626.0

8.17.   The following documentation is from the health record of a 57-year-old male patient.

Hospital Outpatient Department Services

Diagnoses: 1. Lung cancer
2. Chemotherapy with Taxol and carboplatin with dexamethasone
3. Type 2 diabetes with neuropathy and nephropathy, under poor control
4. Hyperlipidemia
5. Hepatomegaly

This patient is a 57-year-old male who presents to the outpatient department for chemotherapy, which has been complicated by his diabetes because it has been difficult to control. He had surgery for lung cancer in September and has now undergone chemotherapy with Taxol and carboplatin, including dexamethasone as part of his chemo and prophylaxis for nausea. He has done very well with the chemotherapy. His diabetes is complicated by neuropathy and nephropathy. Dr. Johnson consulted with the patient to manage his diabetes. He has been on 70/30 insulin, 25 units in the morning and 15 units in the evening. His hepatomegaly has enlarged from the last time that I saw him. Question whether this is fatty infiltration due to poor diabetes control, or whether there is now some involvement with metastatic carcinoma.

Taxol and carboplatin were infused today, followed by dexamethasone; see infusion sheet. The patient appears to have tolerated the chemotherapy well.

Laboratory Data: Sodium 128, potassium 5.5, chloride 89, CO_2 34, BUN 13, creatinine 0.8, glucose 210, calcium 9.4, WBC 9.8, hemoglobin 11.6, hematocrit 34.3, platelets 277,000.

Plan: One difficulty here is the cyclic nature of his treatment regimen, likely to produce major shifts in his glucose, which is already difficult to control. The patient will need to monitor his glucose levels closely and follow up with Dr. Johnson. The patient has instructions to call in to Dr. Johnson's nurse on a daily basis for the next week. He is to follow up with me for further chemotherapy next week.

Which of the following is the correct ICD-9-CM code set for this outpatient visit?

a. 162.9, 250.62, 357.2, 250.42, 583.81, 272.4, 789.1
b. V58.11, 250.62, 250.42, 272.4, 789.1
c. V58.11, 162.9, 250.62, 357.2, 250.42, 583.81, 272.4, 789.1
d. 162.9, 250.02, 272.4, 789.1

Disorders of the Genitourinary System

8.18.   The following documentation is from the health record of a 22-year-old male patient who received hospital outpatient surgery services.

A patient with chronic benign hypertension and stage V chronic kidney disease requiring chronic dialysis, replacement of a permanent Quinton catheter, and the formation of an arteriovenous graft in the left forearm. Following heparinization, the anastomosis was performed, which resulted in a good pulse, but no thrill. The vein was then explored where an area of stenosis was found. This was opened and a dilator passed, but no more than 2 mm diameter was possible. Therefore, the anastomosis was taken down, a tunnel formed, and a 4×7 Impra® graft used. The graft originated at the antecubital fossa, which was opened transversely. The vein here was about 4 mm, so there were no problems passing a dilator. The graft was then anastomosed over a distance of about 5 mm, resulting in good flow. Wounds were closed in layer fashion with 3-0 VICRYL for deep tissues and continuous suture of 6-0 Prolene.

Following completion of the graft, the patient was reprepped and draped for the changing of the Quinton catheter. Following administration of local anesthesia, an incision was made high in the neck close to the point of insertion in the internal jugular. A guidewire was then tunneled centrally through the existing catheter. The old Quinton was removed and an obturator placed. Then a peel-away introducer was inserted easily. The wounds were then closed and a confirmatory x-ray obtained for placement. This showed the Quinton extended well up into the internal jugular. Dialysis was provided the same day.

Which of the following code sets will be assigned for this ambulatory service (omit chargemaster-assigned codes)?

a. 585.6, 401.1, 36830, 90935
b. 403.90, 36825, 90935
c. 403.11, 585.5, 36830, 36581-59
d. 403.11, 585.6, 36830, 36581-59, 90935

8.19.   The following documentation is from the health record of a patient who received hospital radiology department services.

A patient who has had his bladder removed due to carcinoma without recurrence is ordered to have a radiology procedure to evaluate the patency of his ileal conduit, including a ureteropyelography using contrast media. The chief complaint and reason for service line in the progress note is blank. The entire procedure is performed in the radiology suite with the radiologist's impression of "normal functioning ileal conduit."

Which of the following procedure codes should be reported for the UB-92 in this case? Do not assign ICD-9-CM Volume III procedure codes.

a. V55.6, V45.74, V10.51, 50684, 74425
b. V55.2, V10.51, 74425
c. 596.8, 188.9, 74425
d. Contact the ordering physician to obtain a diagnosis before coding this encounter.

8.20.   The following documentation is from the health record of a 47-year-old female patient.

Hospital Outpatient Surgery Services

Preoperative Diagnosis: Menorrhagia, failure of conservative treatment

Postoperative Diagnosis: Same

Procedure: Hysteroscopy with biopsy, dilatation and curettage

Diagnosis: Menorrhagia

Anesthesia: General

Indications: The patient is a 47-year-old multigravida female with increasing irregular vaginal bleeding. The uterus is very tender, and ultrasound reveals no specific adnexal masses. A Pap smear shows some chronic inflammatory cells. Bleeding has not been controlled in the past month with conservative therapy; thus, the patient is admitted for dilation and curettage, and a hysteroscopy and biopsy will be carried out.

Technique: Under general anesthesia, the patient was prepped and draped in the usual manner with Betadine, with her cervix retracted outward. Secondary uterine prolapse was noted with minimal cystocele, large rectocele, enterocele, and moderate cervical erosions. The vaginal vault appeared to be clear, as did both adnexa. However, the uterus was thought to be slightly enlarged. Sound was passed into the intrauterine cavity after the cervix was found to be 8 cm deep. The cervix was dilated with Hegar dilators up to #5. The 5 mm Wolff scope, with normal saline irrigation, was then inserted. An inspection of the endocervical canal showed no abnormalities.

Upon entering the uterine cavity, some irregular shedding of the endometrium was noted. Endometrial shedding was noted more to be patient's left cornu area than the right. The contour of the cavity appeared to be normal; no bulging masses or septation were noted. The Wolff scope was removed, and the cervix was further dilated with Hegar dilators up to #12. A medium-sharp curette was inserted into the uterine cavity and the uterus was curettaged in a clockwise manner, with a moderate amount of what appeared to be irregular proliferative endometrium being obtained. Again, the contour of the cavity appeared to be normal. Endometrial biopsies also were taken. The patient was transferred to the recovery room in good condition.

Pathology report reveals secretory proliferative endometrium without additional abnormalities noted.

Which of the following code sets will be reported?

a. 626.2, 618.4, 618.6, 616.0, 58558
b. 626.2, 58558
c. 626.2, 618.4, 618.6, 616.0, 58100, 58120
d. 618.4, 618.6, 616.0, 58558

Infectious Diseases/Disorders of the Skin and Subcutaneous Tissue

8.21. The following documentation is from the health record of a 62-year-old female patient.

Hospital Outpatient Surgery Services

The patient is a 62-year-old female who has been in generally good health until last month, when she developed a crusty lesion inside the left naris. She initially treated it with Vicks® ointment. When it failed to heal, she decided to seek medical attention. Her primary care physician biopsied this lesion, and pathologic diagnosis came back squamous cell carcinoma of the left internal nasal ala. She is post hysterectomy (10 years) for endometrial carcinoma. She has smoked $1\frac{1}{2}$ packs of cigarettes each day for the past 40 years.

The patient presented to the outpatient surgery center of the hospital for wide excision of the left internal nasal alar lesion, which is less than .5 cm in diameter. This procedure included a full-thickness resection in the middle and posterior thirds of the lateral cartilage, along with vestibular skin and mucous membrane. Nasal reconstruction was required to provide an acceptable cosmetic appearance following excision. A flap graft composite reconstruction was utilized for primary closure of the defect that was left following excision, using donor tissue from the right arm and requiring primary closure of a 2 cm graft.

Which of the following code sets is appropriate for this case?

a. 173.3. V10.42, 30118, 30400
b. 160.0, V10.42, 305.1, 30150, 15760
c. 160.0, 15760, 30150
d. 173.3, V10.42, 305.1, 14060

8.22. The following documentation is from the health record of a 44-year-old female patient.

Hospital Outpatient Surgery Services

Preoperative Diagnosis: Extensive superficial partial-thickness wounds to the abdomen, secondary to poor wound healing; status post abdominoplasty

Postoperative Diagnosis: Same

Operation: Split-thickness skin graft

History: This is a 44-year-old white female who underwent abdominoplasty for morbid obesity in October 1999, and had poor wound healing after the procedure. The patient underwent several debridements and presently has an extensive superficial, partial-thickness abdominal wound that is granulating well, but it was felt the patient would benefit significantly from split-thickness skin graft to decrease wound pain and decrease convalescence time.

Details of Procedure: The patient was taken to the operating room, prepared, and draped in the usual sterile fashion, preparing the donor site of the right thigh as well as abdominal superficial partial-thickness wound. First, two donor grafts were taken with the Brown dermatome, adjusted to a #10 blade, 10:1000 of an inch size. The grafts were placed over the abdominal superficial partial-thickness wound in the abdomen after it was prepared by a sharp debridement with Bard-Parker #10 blade. The graft was scored with a #10 blade Bard-Parker in a meshing fashion The graft was then sewn into place with multiple 5-0 VICRYL sutures. The wound as well as the donor site were then covered with an Owens dressing. Sutures were placed and the Owens was reinforced with wet saline cotton balls and with a fluff dressing. The stents were then tied in place and covered with a pressure dressing of Elastoplast®, while the donor site received wet-to-dry dressing with ABD burn pad taped into place. The patient was extubated in the operating room. All needle and sponge counts were correct, and the patient was taken to the PAR in stable condition.

Pathology Report: None

Which of the following code sets is correct for this case?

a. 998.59, E878.8, 15100
b. 998.59, 15000, 15100
c. 998.83, E878.8, 15100, 15000
d. 998.83, 278.01, 15200

8.23. The following documentation is from the health record of a patient who received hospital outpatient surgery services.

Preoperative Diagnosis:	1. Biopsy-proven malignant melanoma, Clark Level I, right shoulder
	2. Neoplasm on left heel
Postoperative Diagnosis:	Same
Operation:	1. Wide excision of malignant melanoma, Clark Level I, right shoulder with wide undermining, rotation, and advancement flap reconstruction
	2. Excision of left heel 2 cm × 1 cm × .5 cm pigmented neoplasm, rule out dysplasia versus malignant melanoma, with wide undermining, rotation, and advancement flap reconstruction

Description of Procedure: The patient was placed on the operating table in the prone position with the back and left heel prepped and draped in sterile fashion. Utilizing 1 percent Xylocaine with epinephrine, a block of the two sites was performed.

The right shoulder lesion was outlined with Brilliant Green in the lines of relaxation, excised in full-thickness fashion down to the fascial level. Undermining over the fascial level was then performed with rotation flaps elevated into position and sutured deeply at the fascial level with #5-0 PDS interrupted, #6-0 PDS, superficial dermis, and #6-0 PDS running intracuticular on the skin. Total area slightly over 10.2 sq cm.

Attention was then turned to the left heel where the pigmented neoplasm was outlined with Brilliant Green, excised in full-thickness fashion, and closed at the fascial level with #4-0 PDS interrupted and 4-0 black nylon interrupted on the skin.

The patient tolerated the procedure quite well and was taken to the recovery room.

Pathology Report

Preoperative Diagnosis: Melanoma right shoulder and lesion left heel

Postoperative Diagnosis: Same

Macroscopic: Specimen 1: Received in formalin, labeled "melanoma right shoulder; biopsy proven Clark Level I" is one ellipse of tan skin, 5 × 1.3 × 1.8 cm. In the center is a healing pink ulcer, 0.6 × 0.4 cm.

The specimen is serially sectioned, and the central lesion is totally submitted in multiple cassettes.

Specimen 2: Received in formalin, labeled "lesion left heel" is one ellipse of tan skin, $1.8 \times 0.9 \times 0.4$ cm. In the center is a brown macular lesion that covers much of the center of the specimen. The specimen is totally submitted in multiple cross sections.

Microscopic and Summary

Specimen 1: Right shoulder excision. Healing ulcer of skin overlying eschar. There is mild scarring and focal foreign body response.

Specimen 2: Left heel. Consistent with a giant pigmented dysplastic nevus.

Which of the following codes sets would be reported for this ambulatory surgery?

a. 172.6, 216.7, 14001, 15000
b. 216.7, 216.6, 14000
c. 216.6, 238.2, 14001, 11606, 11423
d. 172.6, 238.2, 14001, 11423, 12041

8.24.   The following documentation is from the health record of a patient who received hospital outpatient surgery services.

Preoperative Diagnosis: Nevus of the left auricle

Postoperative Diagnosis: Nevus of the left auricle

Operation: Excision of nevus, left auricle, with reconstruction with full-thickness skin graft, postauricular area

Description of Procedure: The patient was brought to the operating suite and placed under satisfactory general anesthetic using an indwelling endotracheal tube. The left ear and postauricular areas were prepped with Betadine.

A total of 6 cc of 1 percent Xylocaine with 1:200,000 adrenalin were utilized during the procedure. The lesion measured about 6 mm and was superficially infiltrating at its margins with some variegated color being present as well. The lesion was at a two o'clock position on the auricular helix. Margins of about 5 mm were made around the lesion. The tissues were submitted for permanent section.

The resulting defect could not be closed primarily. The postauricular incision was outlined for development of postauricular skin graft centered at the level of the cephaloauricular groove. The graft measured about 8×10 mm in its form and was elliptical in its orientation. The resulting defect postauricularly was closed in layers with 4-0 VICRYL to the subcutaneous layer and 4-0 nylon in an interrupted fashion to the skin.

The skin graft was placed and sutured in place with four sutures peripherally with 4-0 silk and then was tied over bolster sutures of 4-0 silk with a bacitracin-impregnated section of sponge rubber. The patient is to stay away from any contact sports and to keep a prescription for Duricef 250 mg b.i.d. for 10 days. A prescription for Cap elixir with codeine 1–2 tsp, 8 oz was also given. The patient is to be followed in approximately one week in the office.

Pathology Report

Tissues/Specimen: Skin of external ear, nevus of left auricle

Clinical History: Left ear nevus

Gross Description: Nevus left auricle consists of small 4 mm fragment of skin. Entire specimen submitted.

Microscopic: Sections show the specimen to consist of an ellipse of skin showing a benign compound nevus. There is no evidence of malignancy.

Which of the following code sets will be reported for this service?

a. 216.8, 15240, 15000, 12051
b. 216.2, 15260, 11442
c. 173.2, 15260, 15000, 11442
d. 216.2, 14060

8.25. The following documentation is from the health record of a male patient who received emergency department services.

ED Report

A patient who is a known heroin addict is brought in significant distress to the emergency room by friends. His genitalia are covered with many lesions. Due to his IV drug habit and sexual preference, he is at risk for HIV exposure and hepatitis. He has experienced febrile jaundice for three days. He is unable to provide a medical history, but the physician is able to get some information from his girlfriend. Although severely ill, he is not comatose. Medical decision making was stated to be of high complexity. The ER acuity system used by the hospital for medical visits indicated a Level IV service.

Physical examination reveals multiple excoriations covering the penis and scrotum with fluid-filled blisters. The patient is jaundiced and in significant distress. The last "fix" was 3 hours ago per the girlfriend, and the patient has been using heroin daily for the past two months. A number of laboratory tests were run, and it was determined that the patient should be transferred to a tertiary care center for definitive treatment and an infectious disease consultation and substance abuse rehabilitation when stable.

The physician's dictated report that details the test results shows the following diagnostic assessment:

1. HSV-2 infection, culture confirmed, severe outbreak
2. Hepatitis suspected, pending laboratory results for type, abnormal liver function studies confirmed; febrile jaundice × 3 days
3. HIV seropositive; recommend Western Blot to confirm
4. High-risk lifestyle; sexual habits and drug addict

Which of the following code sets will be reported in addition to chargemaster-reported codes?

a. 054.10, 782.4, 794.8, 042, 99284
b. 054.19, 573.3, 795.71, 305.51, V69.8, 99214
c. 054.13, 054.19, 070.1, 794.8, 795.71, 305.51, V69.2, 99284
d. 042, 305.51, 070.1, 99291

Behavioral Health Conditions

8.26. The following documentation is from the health record of a 26-year-old male patient.

Hospital Outpatient Services

On 1/15, a 26-year-old white male was admitted after being transferred from the outpatient evaluation service with severe homicidal and suicidal ideation. Admitting diagnosis was severe major depressive disorder with psychotic features. Pharmacological treatment was initiated, and suicide precautions were instituted. After a thorough diagnostic evaluation, the risks and benefits of ECT were reviewed. Due to the severity of the psychotic episode and the patient's delusional state, it was determined that ECT was warranted. Extensive efforts were made to secure informed consent from the patient, and a course of ECT was begun.

On 1/23, the psychiatrist reviewed the patient's status noting any changes in his physical condition and his response to the treatment. He performed a problem-focused interval history, a problem-focused examination, and medical decision making of low complexity. At this visit, the psychiatrist again reviewed the treatment options and confirmed the patient's continued consent for ECT. Subsequently on 1/23, the fourth treatment of ECT was administered via placement of a stimulus electrode frontotemporally. Sufficient electrical stimulus was applied to produce an adequate ictal response. A generalized seizure was monitored via EEG. EKG, blood pressure, and pulse remained acceptable throughout. Postictal observation was notable for cardiac arrhythmia, which subsided without sequelae. The patient tolerated the procedure well and was returned to his inpatient room in good condition.

He was discharged to a group home on 1/25 and returned to the hospital as an outpatient for his final planned ECT treatment. Again, sufficient electrical stimulus was applied to produce an adequate ictal response. A generalized seizure was monitored via EEG. EKG, blood pressure, and pulse remained acceptable throughout. Postictal observation was notable for cardiac arrhythmia, which subsided without sequelae. The patient tolerated the procedure well and was held in observation for 4 hours posttreatment; then discharged to the care of his group home supervisor in good condition.

Which of the following code sets is reported for the 1/25 outpatient hospital service?

a. 90870, 296.24
b. 90870, 95812, 93040, 296.24
c. 90870, 99211-25, 296.24
d. 90870, 95812, 93040, 99234-25, 296.24

8.27. The following documentation is from the health record of a 56-year-old male patient.

Emergency Department and Hospital Observation Services

Final Diagnosis: Chronic schizophrenia, paranoid type with acute exacerbation, improved, compensated congestive heart failure

Pertinent Laboratory Results: Electrolyte panel within normal limits. Digoxin level was 0.6, hemoglobin A1C 6.5, triglycerides 138, CBC unremarkable. TSH 1.3, urinalysis negative. EKG showed normal sinus rhythm.

Assessment: This is a 56-year-old male who presented to the emergency room with his sister after decompensating at a hotel where he thought people were trying to get into his apartment, and he continued to decompensate with his paranoia and persecutory-type delusions, so that she felt he needed evaluation for hospitalization. Psychiatric consultation was initiated with Dr. Brown.

Recently, his personal physician has been switching his medications from Zyprexa to Seroquel to Risperdal and then he started Prolixin. We requested and reviewed his records, and it appears he did quite well on Risperdal, so he went back to taking that, and he was titrated up to 30 mg q. h.s. of Risperdal and 100 mg of trazodone. These two medications helped significantly to eliminate his delusions and paranoid ideation. He was admitted to observation status and slept peacefully for 6 hours. His sister reported after the workup that he is doing the best that she has seen him in quite some time, and we were conversing at the time of discharge. After consultation with his psychiatrist about the change in medication, the patient was released in the custody of his sister to follow up with his personal physician next Tuesday.

Pertinent Findings on Mental Status at Discharge: Patient spent 45 minutes in the final examination. Behavior is cooperative, fair eye contact. Speech is of normal rate and volume. Not rapid or pressured. Mood euthymic, affect appropriate. Thought process is goal directed, decreased paranoid ideation. Negative for racing thoughts and flight of ideas. Thought content: He denies signs of active psychosis, denies current suicidal or homicidal intent. Insight and judgment improved. Impulse control is fair.

Prognosis: Fair. The main problem is that the patient did not respond well to medication changes. He did do well with the changes we made, but his mental illness may be exacerbated if his medical conditions are not well controlled or if he is noncompliant with dosages.

Aftercare Recommendations: The patient will be discharged to his sister's care and will be followed by his personal psychiatrist, Dr. Eddings. Social services will follow the patient from his hometown.

The hospital acuity system used showed this to be a Level 4 ER service.

Which of the following code sets is correct for reporting this service?

a. 99201; 295.34, 428.0
b. 99283; 295.32,
c. 99284; 295.34, 428.0
d. 99234; 295.84

8.28. The following documentation is from the health record of a female patient who received psychiatrist treatment services in a hospital outpatient-based clinic.

Date: XX/XX/XX 6:20 p.m. Dialectical behavior therapy (DBT), individual therapy—1:1 × 45 minutes at 5 p.m.

Subjective/Objective: Patient and I reviewed diary card and target hospitalizable behaviors and increased skills to stay out of hospital and complete the outpatient program. Target goals 1 through 3 were reviewed today. Patient did not engage or act on urges for self-harm and urges for suicide after self-injurious behavior on XX/XX/XX. We focused on reinforcing skills of emotion regulation, highlighting times she used these while at work and with family members. Suicidal ideation today was minimal with sense of increased willingness to learn to apply skills. Discussed need to address ETOH dependence because patient notes increased risk of suicidal ideation with ETOH use. She identifies "fear" of "running in panic" will be what keeps her from staying with chemical dependency (CD) program. We addressed treatment plan (see below) to increase skills associated with CD treatment follow-through as well as structuring environment to "keep me in CD treatment."

Assessment: Major depressive disorder, recurrent; posttraumatic stress disorder, ETOH dependent; borderline personality disorder. Continued suicidal risk, patient has had some success over urges but is now coping well with the outpatient treatment where she receives therapy four times a week.

Plan: Patient and I identified targeting emotion regulation and distress tolerance in individual therapy to increase control over urges for suicidal thoughts, as well as follow-through with substance abuse treatment. Extended structuring continues with increased resources for managing son's behavior at home. Patient wants family meeting to orient family to DBT to increase chance they will be supportive of her treatment after discharge as opposed to disparaging, which, per patient, has increased her emotional vulnerability leading to increased suicidal urges. I gave times I would be available for a family meeting.

Addendum: Patient now has few suicidal urges and urges to do target behaviors. She reviewed skills with me to "get through" the rest of her week at home and at work. She notes that level of urges right now is manageable for her, and she believes she is improving.

Which of the following code sets is correct for reporting the outpatient services provided to this patient?

a. 90819; 296.20, 309.81, 303.92, 301.83, 300.9
b. 90845; 296.30, 309.81, 303.90, 301.83, 300.9
c. 90818; 296.30, 309.81, 303.90, 301.83
d. 90818; 296.30, 309.81, 303.90, 301.83, 300.9

8.29.   The following documentation is from the health record of a 45-year-old female patient.

Mental Health Clinic Visit (Facility Services)

The 45-year-old patient is seen today for 20-minute medication review in the Community Mental Health Center. Patient overall continues to be somewhat elevated in her mood with some evidence of grandiosity but overall is goal directed and seems to be doing reasonably well with her subchronic schizophrenia in the structured setting. Patient currently is now off Seroquel and will continue to transition from oral Prolixin to Prolixin Decanoate®. She did receive Prolixin Decanoate 12.5 mg IM on XX/XX/XX. When I try to decrease her oral Prolixin, we notice some more increased grandiosity as well as more impulsive behavior and more thought disorganization, so on XX/XX/XX we increased her Prolixin back to 5 mg q. h.s. orally. On seeing her today, she seems to be improving somewhat on that. Her appetite and sleep pattern were fine over the weekend. She had no evidence of aggressive behavior. I decided at this time to maybe increase her Prolixin Decanoate® to 25 mg IM every two weeks, and that will start today. Will continue with the oral Prolixin for a period of time and then will be able to eliminate that. There is a meeting with her family this upcoming Wednesday and we'll discuss patient's care and how they feel she is doing and also discuss discharge and aftercare planning, if that's appropriate.

Mental Status Exam: Appearance: The patient is a female who looks her stated age. Behavior: Cooperative, fair eye contact. Speech: Normal rate and volume. Mood slightly elevated. Affect less labile. Thought process: More goal directed. Negative for racing thoughts, flight of ideas. Thought content: Has delusional belief system, but it has decreased in intensity. No evidence of auditory, visual, or olfactory hallucinations. Denies current suicide or homicide intent. Insight: Judgment remains impaired. Impulse control improving.

Impression: Axis I: Schizophrenia, paranoid type, acute exacerbation
Axis II: None known
Axis III: Hypercholesterolemia; currently on Lipitor

Plan: At this time will continue on the Prolixin Decanoate but increase to 25 mg IM every two weeks. Will continue with the oral Prolixin at 5 mg q. h.s.

Which of the following is the correct code set for reporting this clinic service?

a. 90862; 295.33, 272.0
b. 90862; 295.30, 272.0
c. 90862, 99231; 295.30, 272.0
d. M0064, 99231; 295.33, 272.0

8.30. The following documentation is from the health record of a female patient who received services in a community mental health center.

Reason for Encounter: The patient has not had any self-injurious behavior or behavioral problems this past week except that she has used marijuana, which she endorses. Today we discussed her treatment and overall she is happy with the DBT program and her chemical dependency program. She and I discussed future care and the need for her to get away from her current living arrangements.

Counseling/Coordination of Care: We reviewed how her DBT is going and what skills she could use when she has high urges to use marijuana. We also discussed that I would be doing periodic drug screens.

Response to/Complications of Current Medications: None. The patient is happy with her medications as they are.

Examination:	WNL	Abnormal
General appearance		X
Muscle strength/tone, gait		
Speech		
Thought process		X
Associations/psychosis		
Suicidal/homicidal ideation		X
Judgment and insight		X
Attention span/concentration		
Orientation		X
Recent and remote memory		X
Fund of knowledge		X
Mood and affect		X

Assessment of Current Status: The patient appears to be stabilizing; however, she does appear to have a need for ongoing chemical dependency treatment and support, perhaps on an inpatient basis if the outpatient treatment plan fails to control relapses.

Diagnosis: Borderline personality disorder; major depression, recurrent; cannabis dependence.

Plan: Continue DBT and chemical dependency treatment. The social worker and the patient should begin to work on alternative living arrangements because the patient is exposed to substance abuse in the current living arrangements and has conflicts with others living in the same apartment. We will not be changing any medications at this time.

Session Time: 25 minutes

Over 50 percent Counseling/Coordination of Care? __ Yes _x_ No

History: Problem focused

Examination: Problem focused

Decision Making: Straightforward

Which of the following code sets is correct for reporting this clinic visit with a psychiatrist?

a. 99214; 301.83, 296.30, 304.31
b. 99212; 301.83, 296.30, 304.30
c. 90805; 301.83, 296.30, 304.30
d. 90805; 301.83, 296.30, 304.31

Disorders of the Musculoskeletal System and Connective Tissue

8.31. The following documentation is from the health record of a 39-year-old female patient.

Hospital Outpatient Surgery Services

Admission Diagnosis: Possible rotator cuff repair

Discharge Diagnosis: Partial rotator cuff tear, right shoulder

Procedure: Arthroscopy, right shoulder, with subacromial decompression and excision of the distal clavicle

Short-Stay History and Physical:

Age, Sex, Diagnosis, Operation: 39-year-old female for right shoulder arthroscopy. Patient has complained of pain in shoulder since injury one week ago.

Past Surgery: D&C in 1986

Anesthetic Complications: None

Allergies: NKDA

Medications: HCTZ for hypertension. Last dose taken before admission.

Respiratory Assessment: Clear, smokes cigarettes, $\frac{1}{2}$ pack per day

Cardiovascular: Normal sinus rhythm, normal heart sounds. BP 168/90 on medication.

Bleeding: Negative history

Renal: No complaints

Hepatic: Negative history

Neuromuscular: Negative, except as above

Metabolic: Negative

Diagnostics: Chest x-ray shows mild cardiomegaly, otherwise normal

Physical Status: Cleared for arthroscopic surgery, pain in right shoulder, possible rotator cuff; monitor blood pressure

Operative Report

Preoperative Diagnosis: Probable rotator cuff

Postoperative Diagnoses: 1. Partial rotator cuff tear and anterior labral tear, right shoulder

2. Chronic bursitis

Procedure Description: The patient was taken to surgery. After adequate induction of general anesthesia, the patient was placed in the left lateral decubitus position and prepped and draped in standard orthopedic fashion. The arthroscope was introduced through a standard posterior portal. On visualizing the glenohumeral joint, the glenoid and humeral head appeared to be normal. The instruments were then transferred to the subacromial bursa. There was evidence of chronic bursitis that was resected away. There was also a large acromial spur with corresponding lesion on the superior surface of the rotator cuff, appearing to be a traumatic-type injury with a partial rotator cuff tear. This was debrided and anterior acromioplasty was performed with the shaver in the lateral and posterior portals. The coracoacromial ligament was excised down to the coracoid, the AC joint was carefully examined, and it was felt the distal clavicle was moderately arthritic and resection of the distal clavicle was accomplished as well. Once this had been completed, the instruments were withdrawn from the shoulder and Marcaine injected into the portals and intra-articularly. Sterile dressing was applied and the patient was sent to recovery in stable condition.

Which of the following is the correct code assignment?

a. 840.4, 29822
b. 726.10, 401.9, 23415-RT, 23120-RT
c. 840.4, 726.10, 29820, 29805-59
d. 840.4, 726.10, 401.9, 29826-RT, 29824-RT

8.32.   The following documentation is from the health record of a 47-year-old male patient.

Hospital Outpatient Surgery Services

Operative Report

Preoperative Diagnosis: Torn medial meniscus and DJD right knee

Postoperative Diagnosis: Large flap tear, posterior horn, medial meniscus; chondral loose bodies; significant degenerative arthritis right knee

Operation: Arthroscopy of the right knee with partial medial meniscectomy; arthroscopy of the right knee, with removal of chondral loose bodies

Procedure Description: This 47-year-old male was taken to the operating room and placed in the supine position. General anesthesia was accomplished without complication. Evaluation under anesthesia of the right knee showed it was stable with a negative Lachman's and firm end point. Negative anterior and posterior drawer, stable to varus and valgus testing. A tourniquet was placed on the midright thigh. The right leg was prepped and draped free in the usual sterile manner. Tourniquet inflated to 325 mmHg. There were loose bodies throughout the knee, which were flushed and removed. The patient had a large flap tear of the posterior horn of the medial meniscus that was unstable. He underwent a partial medial meniscectomy with small basket forceps and small synovial resector removing the torn portion of the meniscus, leaving about a 2 mm rim posteriorly and then saucerizing this to smooth margins anteriorly. The anterior cruciate ligament and posterior cruciate ligament were normal. The lateral compartment could not be entered because of significant arthritis medially. The knee joint was thoroughly irrigated and the portals closed with interrupted 3-0 nylon mattress sutures. Sterile dressing was applied. No complications occurred. The tourniquet was deflated after 20 minutes. The patient went to the recovery room in stable condition.

Which of the following is the correct code assignment?

a. 717.2, 717.6, 715.96, 29881-RT
b. 717.43, 718.16, 29881-RT, 29874-RT
c. 844.8, 717.6, 29881-RT, 29877-RT
d. 717.2, 715.96, 29881-RT, 29874-RT

8.33.   The following documentation is from the health record of a 68-year-old male patient.

Hospital Outpatient Surgery Services

This patient presented to the podiatrist for surgical evaluation at the request of the primary care physician. After surgery was completed, a copy of the evaluation and operative report was sent to the primary care office.

Preoperative Evaluation: This 68-year-old male of Italian descent presents with degenerative arthritis and bunion formation. On 6/30/00, patient was sent by Dr. Brown for bunionectomy evaluation. A problem-focused history was conducted, followed by an expanded problem-focused examination.

Impression: Painful left foot due to: (1) Bunion with degenerative joint disease in the toes. (2) Metatarsus primus varus. (3) Hammertoe second digit. (4) Elongated metatarsal, second digit, left.

Plan: Surgery scheduled for 8:00 a.m. 7/12/00, at Hegg Memorial Hospital

Procedures: Keller bunionectomy; Austin bunionectomy; arthroplasty, second digit; and excision of the metatarsal head, second digit, left foot

Operative Report: The patient was placed in the semisupine position where Dr. Graybeard administered spinal anesthesia. After prepping and draping the patient in the usual aseptic manner and under ankle hemostasis, the left foot was approached. A dorsal linear incision was performed medial to the extensor hallucis longus tendon. Incision was carried through the skin and subcutaneous tissue and extended from midshaft metatarsal to distal proximal phalanx. The superficial fascia was separated from the deep fascia using sharp and blunt dissection techniques. An inverted L capsulotomy was performed and sharp capsular periosteal dissection was performed with a #15 blade to expose the first metatarsal and base of the proximal phalanx. The medial eminence was resected with a micro-oscillating saw.

Next, attention was directed to the base of the proximal phalanx, where the Keller procedure was performed. One-third of the proximal phalanx was resected and excised in toto.

Attention was next directed to the head of the first metatarsal where an Austin osteotomy was performed in the usual manner with screw fixation. The area was flushed with copious amounts of antibiotic flush. The capsular periosteal layer was next closed with 3-0 VICRYL. The subcutaneous tissue was reapproximated with 4-0 VICRYL.

Attention was next directed to the second digit and MPJ area, where a dorsal curvilinear incision was performed. The incision was deepened and the PIPJ was exposed. A transverse incision was performed through the capsular periosteal tissue at the PIPJ. Medial and lateral capsulotomies were performed, exposing the head of the proximal phalanx. The head of the proximal phalanx was resected and excised in toto.

Attention was next directed to the second MPJ. The incision at this area was deepened. A dorsal linear capsulotomy was performed and the head of the second metatarsal was resected and excised in toto. The surgical sites were next flushed with copious amounts of antibiotic flush. The second digit was noted to be aligned without pressure on the neurovascular structures.

Next, a .45 K-wire was placed percutaneously into the hallux distal to proximal. Capsular periosteal closure was next performed with 3-0 VICRYL. Subcutaneous closure was performed with 4-0 VICRYL. The skin was closed in 4-0 nylon. Postop anesthesia consisted of 17 cc 5.0 percent Marcaine plain and 1 cc of Decadron 4 mg/ml. Next, the sterile dressing was applied, which consisted of Betadine ointment, 4 × 4 gauze, and 4-inch Kling. The tourniquet was released, and the patient was returned to recovery in stable condition.

Which of the following is the correct code assignment for this outpatient procedure?

a. 727.1, 735.4, 99242-25, 28202, 28285
b. 727.1, 715.97, 754.52, 735.4, 754.59, 28299-TA, 28285-TI
c. 735.4, 754.52, 28296
d. 727.2, 715.97, 754.52, 735.4, 754.59, 28296-TA and 28292-TA-59, 28285-T1

8.34.   The following documentation is from the health record of a patient who received hospital outpatient surgery services.

Preoperative Diagnosis: Deep laceration, left hand with extensive tendon disruption of the fourth and fifth digits, secondarily of the third digit, middle finger, and open fracture with chip fracture from the MCP joint of the fifth digit; and an open fracture of the middle phalanx of the index finger.

Postoperative Diagnosis: Deep laceration left hand with extensive tendon disruption of the fourth and fifth digits, secondarily of the third digit, middle finger; and open fracture with chip fracture from the MCP joint of the fifth digit; and an open fracture of the middle phalanx of the index finger

Operation: Extensive tendon repair, fourth and fifth digits, third digit longitudinally, index finger second digit with extensor hood, and debridement open-fracture middle phalanx, and intra-articular laceration of fourth and fifth digit

Anesthesia: Intravenous Bier block

The patient was brought to the operating theater and anesthetized with an excellent Bier block. We explored the wound, and the joint capsule to fourth and fifth was excised into the joint. The superior pole of the articular surface of the distal metacarpal on the fifth digit was avulsed, and we excised this because it was impregnated with a lot of dirt.

The tendon of the extensor indices communis to the fifth digit was lacerated. The extensor indices proprius ulnarly was still intact. The extensor hood over the MCP joint of #4 was torn, as was the capsule. The extensor tendon along the central hood of the third digit was torn longitudinally and the point was spared. The index finger had a longitudinal tear of the extensor hood in the central portion of the midphalanx, with the lateral band on the radial side torn. The wound was copiously irrigated with bacitracin saline with a pulsatile lavage. The joint surface of the fourth and fifth were irrigated The open fracture of the fifth was removed. The open fracture of the middle phalanx of the index was debrided and irrigated.

We then began the definitive repairs. We sutured the joint capsule of the fourth and fifth with a 4-0 VICRYL continuous. We sutured the extensor digitorum communis tendon to #5 with 5-0 Prolene and to #4 over the central hood, over the MCP joint with a 5-0 Prolene continuous. The extensor tendon of the third or middle finger was sutured longitudinally, and a lateral band on the radial side was repaired with a 5-0 VICRYL. The longitudinal tear, which was really a split or a double split, was sutured with over-and-over 5-0 VICRYL as well. We then increased her incision in an S-shaped fashion over the index finger to expose the central hood, which was torn, and lateral on the radial aspect, which was torn as well. This was repaired with 5-0 VICRYL and the main extensor hood was repaired with 5-0 Prolene simple sutures. We then irrigated again with a liter of bacitracin Pulsatile figure eight mattress sutures, alternating with simple sutures. A bulky dressing was then applied, with a volar slab with the hand in the position of function, extension of the wrist, extension of the MCP joint, flexion of the PIP, and DIP of 30 degrees. The patient then had the tourniquet deflated fully and was sent to the recovery room in good condition.

Which of the following is the correct code assignment? Report the codes a hospital outpatient surgery department would report for this hand surgery. Do not assign E codes.

a. 882.1. 817.1, 26418, 26735, 26746, 11012
b. 842.12, 817.0, 26746-F4, 11010-F1, 11012-F4
c. 842.12, 817.1, 26418-F1, 26418-F2, 26418-F3, 26418-F4
d. 882.2, 816.11, 26418-F1, 26418-F2, 26418-F3, 26418-F5, 11010-F1, 11012-F4

Neoplasms

8.35.   The following documentation is from the health record of a patient who received hospital outpatient surgery services.

Operative Report

A patient with an elevated (35.7) prostate-specific antigen (PSA) comes to the outpatient surgery center for a transrectal ultrasonic-guided (TRUS) prostate biopsy.

Technique: The patient is placed in the Sims position with the left side down. The anus was generously lubricated with 2 percent Xylocaine jelly. The ultrasound probe was then introduced and scanning initiated. A great deal of calcification was noted in the outer margin of the central zone. The area proximal and anterior to the calcifications was hypoechoic but may have been influenced by the stones. There was very thin peripheral zone tissue available. Three needle biopsies were taken from each side, starting in the periphery and working toward the midline and trying to biopsy anterior to the stones on the more medial biopsies from each side.

The pathology report confirmed carcinoma in situ of the prostate.

Which codes will be reported for this service? This facility does not assign ICD-9-CM Volume III procedure codes to radiologic procedures but reports CPT procedure codes for reimbursement.

a. 185, 55700
b. 233.4, 790.93, 55705, 76872
c. 233.4, 602.0, 55700, 76872, 76942
d. 185, 790.93, 602.0, 55700, 76872, 76942

8.36.   The following documentation is from the health record of an 88-year-old female patient.

Hospital-Based Oncology Department Services

This 88-year-old white female is here to rule out the possibility of myeloma. She has been followed by Dr. Black as an outpatient and has sustained a 13-pound weight loss over a six-week period. She seemed to stabilize at a weight of 82 lbs, but has recently dropped an additional two pounds. She is experiencing recurrent pain in the chest. Three weeks ago, she was treated by Dr. Black for a sinus infection, and sinus films showed lytic lesions of the skull, as well as the left maxillary sinus.

The patient had a left radical mastectomy 38 years ago for carcinoma of the breast without recurrence. The right breast is atrophic and without masses. Laboratory tests are attached and without noteworthy comments, except for urinalysis culture revealing over 100,000 E. coli. A bone scan shows multiple areas of increased bony uptake and two areas of increased rib uptake and present healing osteoporotic fractures. There are multiple areas of increased uptake throughout the bony skull, suggestive of progressive metastatic disease or perhaps myeloma.

This is a delightful elderly woman who has markedly abnormal bone films and severe osteoporosis. General appearance of the bone is metastatic malignancy, supported by the weight loss history. Myeloma is consistent with her symptoms, but a normal sed rate and relatively normal globulin are somewhat against that diagnosis. Certainly light chain myeloma is a possibility. In addition, some other metastatic disease, including the previous breast cancer, could give this appearance, but that seems unusual. I have never seen recurrent breast cancer this late (38 years).

Pertinent studies have been ordered, but I believe it would also be worthwhile to do a Beta II microglobulin, which may be helpful in confirming myeloma. The UTI due to E. coli is being treated with antibiotics. Additional x-rays of the lateral skull and long bones have also been ordered. In addition, I performed a bone marrow aspiration today from the left posterior iliac crest.

At this point, my recommendation is to wait and see what the additional tests show. If we can determine that this is a myeloma, then it would be worth treating her with an alkylator-prednisone combination. In terms of any other metastatic disease, there is little we can do short of palliative radiation therapy. If this looks like recurrent breast cancer; then it may be useful to try tamoxifen. I would probably do that at any rate, if the carcinoma is further collaborated in any fashion by the bone marrow biopsy or other studies.

I cannot make any more definitive recommendations at this point. When I return next week and we see the studies ordered, we will go from there.

Procedure Note

Bone Marrow Biopsy Results: Metastatic poorly differentiated carcinoma and hyperplastic marrow with decreased iron stores

Comment from Pathologist: The features of the tumor do not suggest a definite site or origin. The most common tumors causing extensive lytic lesions of the bone are breast carcinoma, lung carcinoma, and renal cell carcinoma. With regard to the patient's previous history of breast cancer, although late recurrence has been described after more than 20 years, 38 years is an extreme interval.

Which of the following are assigned for the services performed on this date of service?

a. 203.01, 199.1, 38221
b. 198.5, 199.1, 733.19, 733.00, V10.3, 599.0, 041.4, 38221
c. 199.0, 27299
d. 198.5, 203.01, 174.9, 38221

8.37. The following documentation is from the health record of a female patient who received hospital outpatient surgery services.

Operative Report

A 52-year-old female presented with abdominal pain and change in bowel habits. A barium enema suggested a diverticular stricture, so a sigmoidoscopy was performed in the clinic, finding a stricture at 25 cm. The patient was then scheduled for exploratory laparoscopy in the hospital outpatient surgical center to treat the stricture.

Preoperative Diagnosis: Stricture of the sigmoid colon, rule out carcinoma

Postoperative Diagnosis: Carcinoma of the sigmoid with invasion into adjacent tissue and suspected metastasis to the liver

The patient was brought to the surgical suite, and an NG tube was placed in the stomach and a Foley catheter in the bladder. She was placed in the lithotomy position and routine prep and draping performed. A small incision was made in the right upper quadrant directly into the peritoneal cavity with CO_2. Once we had a good tent, we examined the peritoneal cavity and could not really see the liver because we were too close to it, but one view suggested surface lesions. After placement of the three cannulas (12 mm in the RUQ, 10 mm LLQ, and 5 mm in LUQ) we mobilized the sigmoid off the pelvic gutter and dissected down towards the bladder. She had undergone a previous hysterectomy, but there were no adhesions. We could not get the small bowel to easily come up out of the pelvis and lesions were evident surrounding the colon, so biopsies were taken. We then used a colonoscope through the rectum and advanced to 25 cm where we saw, not a stricture, but carcinoma, and biopsies were taken for pathologic evaluation. At this point the colonoscopy was completed with no other pathology found. The surgery was discontinued, the trocars removed, and the patient returned to recovery in stable condition. The patient will undergo full evaluation and consultation with oncology before further treatment is undertaken.

Pathology report confirms invasive adenocarcinoma, moderate to poorly differentiated, of the sigmoid colon with extension to the pericolic adipose.

Which codes are assigned to this surgery?

a. 153.3, 197.4, 49329
b. 153.9, 49321-74, 45380-59
c. 197.4, 153.3, 197.7, 49321, 45380
d. 153.3, 198.89, 49321, 45380

8.38.   The following documentation is from the health record of a male patient who received hospital outpatient surgery services.

Operative Report

Preoperative Diagnosis:	Prophylactic removal of the testes for treatment of carcinoma of the prostate
Postoperative Diagnosis:	Same
Procedure Description:	Bilateral inguinal orchiectomy and placement of testicular prosthesis

The testicles are normal in position and normal to palpation. The patient has elected to have this procedure to increase survival risk for carcinoma of the prostate diagnosed four months ago. The prostate on digital rectal examination has irregular areas and is about grade 1 enlarged.

Following spinal anesthesia, the patient was placed in supine position and prepped and draped in sterile fashion. Suprapubic bilateral inguinal incisions were made just above Poupart's ligament following the skin lines. Dissection was carried down though the subcutaneous tissue, where the spermatic cord was identified. The spermatic cord was isolated from the surrounding tissue and the testicle was pulled up into the wound. Stick tie ligature was placed through the thin spermatic cord so that only the blood vessels were remaining. A #0 Dexon stick tie was placed and doubly ligated, creating constriction and complete occlusion of the blood vessels. The spermatic cord was divided about $\frac{1}{2}$ cm distal to the ligature, and the ends were heavily fulgurated to additionally assure hemostasis. A gel-filled testicular prosthesis, adult size, was dropped into the left scrotal sac from the inguinal incision and placed in normal anatomic position. No effort was made to suture it in place. The subcutaneous tissue was closed with 2-0 VICRYL continuous subcuticular, and the skin was 4-0 VICRYL. A similar procedure was carried out on the opposite side.

Which of the following code sets is assigned?

a. V50.49, 185, 54520, 54520
b. 185, 54690
c. 185, 54520-50
d. V50.49, 54530-50

Disorders of the Nervous System and Sense Organs

8.39. The following documentation is from the health record of a 22-year-old male patient who received hospital outpatient surgery services.

Operative Report

A patient injured his foot using a razor-sharp garden hoe in his yard and severed the superficial branch of the external plantar nerve and the flexor digiti minimi brevis tendon in his left foot. The patient experienced loss of sensation on the outer side of the fifth toe and across the side of the foot, so a neurology consultation was requested, and the patient was taken directly to surgery. Following exploration of the wound and identification of the nerve avulsion, a repair of the nerve was undertaken using a nerve graft from the sural nerve. A lateral incision was made on the lateral malleolus of the ankle. The nerve was identified and freed for grafting, and the proximal and distal sural nerve endings were anastomosed. The wound was dissected, and the damaged area of the nerve was removed. The innervation of the external digital nerve was restored by suturing the 1.5 cm graft to the proximal and digital ends of the damaged nerve, using the operating microscope. Tenoplasty was performed on the tendon injury, and the wound closed in layers.

Which of the following would be correct? Do not assign evaluation and management service codes for the ER visit or consultation service.

a. 956.5, E920.4, E849.0, 64831, 28200
b. 892.2, 956.5, E920.4, E849.0, 64891, 28202, 69990
c. 892.2, 956.5, E920.4, E849.0, 64890-LT, 28200-LT, 69990
d. 956.5, 64890-LT, 28200-LT

8.40. The following documentation is from the health record of a patient who received hospital outpatient surgery services.

Preoperative Diagnosis:	Reflex sympathetic dystrophy
Postoperative Diagnosis:	Same
Operation:	Right stellate ganglion block #1
Location:	Outpatient Pain Clinic Surgery Center
Anesthesia:	Local with conscious sedation

Details: The patient was placed in the supine position to start the IV in his left hand for the sedation of 4 mg of Versed. Then he was positioned using a shoulder roll with the neck extended. Betadine was used for preparation. Following local anesthesia, a #22, 1.5 cm needle was introduced paratracheally at the level of the cricoid cartilage towards the stellate ganglion. Ten cc of .05 percent Marcaine with epinephrine 1:200,000 was injected and the patient tolerated this very well. There was no paresthesia, heme, or CSF detected. The patient swallowed copiously during the procedure, but we were able to obtain an adequate block with the patient's right hand temperature changing from 90.1 to 93 degrees F following the block. He was moved to the outpatient recovery area where he tolerated fluids and nutrition and was able to be discharged home to his caregiver.

Assign the correct diagnosis and procedure codes. Do not assign HCPCS level II codes for the drug(s) injected.

Code Assignment:

Diagnosis code:_____

Procedure code:_____

8.41. The following documentation is from the health record of a 48-year-old female patient.

Emergency Department Services

This is a 48-year-old female presenting to the ER in the middle of the night with a complaint of unexpected right-sided weakness. It occurred during sleep, and the patient awoke and found it difficult to use her right arm or leg. She denies fever, shortness of breath, cough, headache, or other symptoms, and related that she was asymptomatic until this occurred.

Medication: Glucophage® for type II DM control. Has never used oral contraceptives

Allergies: None

Habits: Tobacco, one pack per day; social use of alcohol

Family History: Positive for early stroke in maternal grandmother at 52; father deceased at 53 due to lung cancer

Physical Exam: Patient is alert and oriented times three. HEENT: Pupils are round, regular, equal, and reactive to light and accommodation. Extraocular muscles are intact. Oral mucosa moist and pink. Decreased nasolabial fold on the right side and slight drooping of the angle of the mouth on the right. Neck supple, without lymphadenopathy, carotid bruit, or thyromegaly. She has impaired speech. Chest: Negative. Cardiovascular: Negative. Abdomen: Benign. Neurologic: Mild paralysis evident. Cranial nerves II through XII intact. Marked decrease in power and tone on the right side when compared to the left. Decrease in sensation on the right compared to the left. She has no visual disturbances or vertigo.

CT scan without contrast shows a small infarction in the left basal ganglia near the internal capsule. This is likely a small- to medium-size arterial occlusion causing the stroke.

Plan: Will transfer for further neurologic consultation to University Medical Center for lab work per Dr. Smith on the neurology service. MRI, Carotid Doppler, and 2D echocardiogram were ordered to be completed there also.

Acuity Level: IV

Which of the following code sets will be used for reporting this ER visit for the facility?

a. 436, 99284-25, 70450
b. 434.91, 99283, 70470
c. 434.91, 342.90, 784.5, 305.1, 250.00, 99284-25, 70450
d. 436, 342.90, 784.5, 305.1, 250.00, 99284, 70470

8.42. The following documentation is from the health record of a 35-year-old female patient.

Hospital Outpatient Surgery Services

Operative Report

Preoperative Diagnosis: Right trigeminal neuralgia

Postoperative Diagnosis: Right trigeminal neuralgia

Operation: Right radiofrequency coagulation of the trigeminal nerve

Indications: This is a 35-year-old lady with intractable trigeminal neuralgia causing her considerable pain and inability to eat or speak, who was referred for treatment of her affliction. Indications, potential complications, and risks were explained to the patient and family.

Operative Procedure: After the patient was positioned supine, intravenous sedation with propofol was administered. Lateral skull x-ray fluoroscopy was set. The right cheek was infiltrated dermally with Xylocaine and a small nick in the skin 2.5 cm lateral to the corner of the mouth was performed with an 18-gauge needle. The radiofrequency needle with 2 mm exposed tip was then introduced using the known anatomical landmarks and under lateral fluoroscopy guidance into the foramen ovale. Confirmation of the placement of the needle was done by the patient grimacing to pain and by the lateral x-ray. The first treatment, 90 seconds in length, was administered with the tip of the needle 3 mm below the clival line at a temperature of 75 degrees C. The needle was then advanced further to the midclival line and another treatment of similar strength and duration was also administered. Finally, the third and last treatment was administered with the tip of the needle about 3 cm above the line. The cerebrospinal fluid was noted. The needle was removed. The patient tolerated the procedure well and had adequate tearing and corneal sensation and had reduction, if not complete cure, of her pain by the end of the procedure.

Which of the following code sets is correct?

a. 350.1, 64600, 76005
b. 350.1, 64610, 76005
c. 350.1, 64610
d. 350.1, 64605

8.43.   The following documentation is from the health record of a 33-year-old female patient.

Hospital Outpatient Surgery Services

Operative Report

Preoperative Diagnosis: Left frontal lesion

Postoperative Diagnosis: Left frontal lesion

Operation: Stereotactic biopsy of left frontal lesion

Indications for Procedure: The patient is a 33-year-old female transferred to the university neurosurgical service for outpatient treatment from Blank Memorial Hospital, where she is an inpatient. She presents with neurologic deterioration, nausea, neck pain, and headache. A CT and magnetic resonance scan revealed a left frontal cystic mass. It was recommended that the patient undergo stereotactic biopsy and aspiration. The risks and benefits of the procedure were explained to the patient and her family in detail, who requested the procedure be performed and the patient returned to Blank for further therapy.

Procedure: The patient was first taken to the CT suite, where a stereotactic halo was placed on the patient's head with the four-pin system using local anesthesia. The stereotactic CT was then performed, and the patient was transported to the operating room. The patient was placed on the operating room table in the supine position. General endotracheal anesthesia was smoothly induced. The left frontal area was then clipped and shaved, and the area was then prepped and draped in the usual sterile fashion. The stereotactic arm was then brought into the field and placed on the stereotactic ring. The localizing arm and the pointer were used to mark the left frontal area for skin incision. The area was then infused with 1 percent lidocaine with epinephrine, and a 2 cm skin incision was created in the left frontal region. The self-retaining retractor was placed, and hemostasis was obtained. The pointer was again used to mark the spot on the skull to make the burr hole, and a perforator was used to create a left frontal burr hole. The dura was coagulated and incised using a #15 bladed knife. The pia was then also coagulated and nicked with a #11 blade knife. The biopsy needle was then placed into the stereotactic localizing arm. The coordinates were dialed into the arm, and the biopsy needle was advanced to the appropriate depth. Upon entering the lesion, 25 cc of yellowish fluid was withdrawn from the cyst. The fluid was sent for cytology and bacteriology. The biopsy needle was then removed, and the incision was irrigated with bacitracin irrigation. The self-retaining retractor was then removed, and the incision was closed using #00 Dexon for the galea and staples for the skin. Estimated blood loss was 15 cc. No transfusion was given. The sponge, needle, and instrument counts were reported as correct at the end of the case. The patient was removed from the stereotactic halo ring. She was allowed to wake up and was extubated and taken to the recovery area. She will be transferred by ambulance back to Blank as soon as she has recovered from the anesthesia.

Assign the correct CPT codes for this procedure.

Code(s):_____

Newborn/Congenital Disorders

8.44. The following documentation is from the health record of a three-year-old child.

Hospital-Based Clinic Outpatient Services

Parents bring their three-year-old boy, who was born with hydrocephalus, to the pediatric neurology clinic at University Hospital to have the child evaluated by the pediatric neurologist and have his VP shunt lengthened to accommodate a growth spurt. Their pediatrician requested a consultation to evaluate the shunt and replace the peritoneal catheter if needed. Outpatient surgery had been previously scheduled tentatively pending this evaluation for the afternoon.

The catheter used in the shunt was removed and replaced in the outpatient surgery suite following a follow-up consultation, which included a detailed interim history, a detailed examination, and medical decision making of moderate complexity. Findings documented in the consultation include "Assessment: Shunt valve malfunction requiring replacement." The VP shunt valve was replaced, along with a new peritoneal catheter in a longer length.

Which of the following code sets will be reported for this service by the physician performing the assessment and surgery?

a. V53.01, 62230
b. 996.2, 742.3, 99243-57, 62230
c. 742.3, V53.01, 99243-57, 62225
d. 742.3, 62230

8.45. The following documentation is from the health record of a four-week-old baby.

Emergency Department Services

A four-week-old baby is rushed to the hospital after the parents checked and found her cyanotic. While in the ER, she suffered respiratory arrest followed by cardiac arrest and was given cardiopulmonary resuscitation. The baby was born at 36-weeks gestational age with a birth weight of 2400 grams. Her current weight is 2700 grams. An emergency intubation was performed, and then she was placed on a ventilator and transferred to the neonatal intensive care unit at the university hospital across town for monitoring and further workup. The ER physician provided 1 hour and 20 minutes of critical care, not including the cardiopulmonary resuscitation. His final diagnosis for the ER service is "Hypoxia with respiratory failure in a preterm infant—etiology unknown."

Which of the following code sets (diagnoses and CPT codes) will be reported for the ER physician and then the hospital emergency room encounter?

a. Diagnoses: 770.84, 765.19; Physician: 99291, 99292, 92950; Hospital: 99285
b. Diagnoses: 770.84, 779.89, 427.5, 765.18; Physician: 99291, 99292 92950, 31500; Hospital: 99291, 92950, 31500
c. Diagnoses: 770.84, 779.89, 765.18; Physician: 99295, 92950; Hospital: 99295, 92950
d. Diagnoses: 770.84, 779.89, 427.5, 765.18; Physician: 99291, 99292; Hospital: 99291

Pediatric Conditions

8.46. The following documentation is from the health record of a male patient who received emergency department services.

Chief Complaint: Tommy was playing basketball today, fell, and hurt his left wrist. He is right-hand dominant.

Allergies: NKA

Examination: Tenderness and swelling of the wrist, especially the volar aspect. There is a slight abrasion over the swelling. The x-ray shows a fracture of the ulnar styloid and distal radial epiphyseal plate fracture with slight posterior displacement of the distal fragment of about 4 mm. CMS is intact. Short arm cast is applied for comfort measures.

Diagnosis: Colles' fracture

Condition: Good

Disposition: He is to follow up with the orthopedist in the next day or two to determine if reduction is necessary and return if problems occur. Tylenol 3 q. 4 h. p.r.n. pain.

Which is the correct code set for this emergency service, in addition to the codes for the x-ray and cast supplies captured via the chargemaster?

a. 813.41, 29075, 99283
b. 813.44, 29075, 99283-25
c. 813.44, 25600, 99283-25
d. 813.41, 25600, 99283-25

Conditions of Pregnancy, Childbirth, and the Puerperium

8.47. The following documentation is from the health record of a 33-year-old female patient who received hospital observation services.

Observation patient

Admit Note: 2/28/XX 0730

This is a 33-year-old G2, P0, estimated delivery date of 2/28 and estimated gestational age of 40 weeks. She presents for induction secondary to gestational DM. She has required insulin since 28 weeks with adequate control. PNL: O positive, rubella immune. PE: AVSS, abdomen FH 40 cm, EFW 3800 – 4000 grams. Cervix is closed/50 percent/-3/post/ceph. Plan is for ProstinE2 induction and insulin infusion when in active labor.

Progress Note: 2/28/XX 0915

Patient is having uterine contractions every 3 to 8 minutes. Cervix is 1 cm/100 percent/floating. Patient desires not to start Pitocin yet. Feels that she is in labor. FHR reactive, baseline 120s with accelerations.

Progress Note: 2/28/XX 1925

Patient's uterine contractions have resolved. Cervix unchanged. Discussed options, would like to go home to sleep and return in a.m. for Pitocin induction. Discharged home for tonight to sleep. Admit in a.m., start IV Pitocin as per protocol, start insulin drip, clear liquid diet.

Which of the following is the correct code set for this outpatient encounter?

a. 648.81, 250.01, V58.67, 99235
b. 648.83, 250.81, 99235
c. 648.83, V58.67, 99235
d. 648.83, 790.29, V58.67, 99235

8.48. The following documentation is from the health record of a female patient who received hospital outpatient surgery services.

Procedure Performed: Cervical cerclage by the McDonald method

Diagnosis: 14-week gestation with cervical incompetence and history of preterm labor and delivery

Findings: The cervix was large and patulous with evidence of prior cerclage and incompetence. The cervix itself was open to approximately 1 cm and long. After the cerclage was performed, the os was seen to be tightly closed.

Description of Procedure: The patient was brought into the OR, where following administration of spinal anesthetic, she was placed into the dorsal lithotomy position and prepped and draped in the usual sterile fashion. A weighted vaginal speculum was placed; then a wide-angled retractor was also placed to visualize the cervix. The edges of the cervix were gently grasped with a ring clamp; then the cerclage performed in the usual fashion for a McDonald cerclage using the 5 mm MERSILENE band with the double-headed blunt needle. The knot was tied anteriorly and the edges of the MERSILENE trimmed to approximately 1 cm. Exam after the knot had been tied showed a tightly closed cervical os. The patient tolerated the procedure well without complication and was not having any bleeding. Fetal heart tones were auscultated afterward at 140 beats per minute.

Which of the following is the correct code set for this outpatient surgery?

a. 654.53, V23.41, 59320
b. V23.41, 654.53, 57700
c. V23.5, 59320
d. 654.53, 644.23, 59320

8.49.   The following documentation is from the health record of a 36-year-old female patient.

Hospital Outpatient Surgery Services

Preoperative Diagnosis: Left ectopic pregnancy

Postoperative Diagnosis: Same

Anesthesia: General

Operation: Diagnostic laparoscopy
Left salpingostomy with removal of ectopic pregnancy

Rationale for Surgery: This patient is a 36-year-old gravida III, para I, AB I, who has a positive pregnancy test with left adnexal mass that is a gestational sac with FHTs, and left ectopic pregnancy diagnosis was made. She was admitted at this time for laparoscopy with removal of this left ectopic pregnancy. We did talk about possibly sacrificing the tube on that side if we did get into problems with bleeding. This patient has a history of having pelvic adhesions with blocked right tube. She is aware that we may have to sacrifice the left tube and that essentially she would be unable to become pregnant in all probability if we're not able to save the tube. She is also aware of the risks and benefits of surgery, including hemorrhage, bowel and bladder injury, and infection.

Procedure: With the patient in the lithotomy position and under satisfactory general anesthesia, the patient's abdomen and perineum were prepped and draped in the usual manner. A weighted speculum was placed in the vaginal vault. Anterior lip of the cervix was grasped with a single-toothed tenaculum. The uterus was sounded to about 9 cm, and it was retroverted. The endocervical canal was dilated with Pratt dilators, and Zumi™ uterine manipulator was placed and the bulb insufflated with about 8 cc of air. A red rubber catheter was placed to gravity and attached to the Zumi uterine manipulator. Attention was then turned to the abdominal area, where a small skin incision was made with a scalpel. Large trocar was placed in the direct insertion technique, and pneumoperitoneum was established without difficulty. It is noted she did have some blood in the cul-de-sac. The right tube and ovary looked grossly within normal limits except the fimbriated end on the right was somewhat blunted. The ectopic pregnancy was really at the fimbriated end and had a small clot that was extruded from the fimbriated end. She also had the ovarian cyst on that side, which was not complicating this pregnancy. It was opened and drained. She also had a peritubular cyst, which I left intact. I isolated the ectopic pregnancy and then made a small cut using the needle coagulator over the ectopic pregnancy and extruded this with the needle nose forceps. Had some oozing along the fimbriated end. I did put Avitene™ in this area and then topped it with some Surgicel®. We watched it for several minutes, and it seemed to control the small amount of oozing. We irrigated the pelvic region with copious amounts of irrigation and then aspirated it. We again checked the operative field, and it seemed to be dry. We watched it as we deflated the abdominal pressure. I then removed all the instruments, used .25 mg of Marcaine injection at the injection sites, and closed the incisions with staples. Vaginal instruments were removed. She was taken to recovery room in good condition. Estimated blood loss about 50 cc. Sponge and needle count was correct times two. Patient did tolerate the procedure well and left the operating room in good condition.

Which of the following is the correct code set for this outpatient surgery?

a. 633.20, 620.2, 59121, 49320
b. 633.10, 620.2, 620.8, 59150, 58662
c. 633.10, 620.2, 58673, 49320
d. 633.20, 654.43, 58673, 58662

Disorders of the Respiratory System

8.50. A patient is respirator dependent and has a tracheostomy in need of revision due to redundant scar tissue formation surrounding the site. Under general anesthesia and establishing the airway to maintain ventilation, the scar tissue is resected, and then repair is accomplished using skin flap rotation from the adjacent tissue of the neck. What codes will be used to report this procedure, which was performed in the hospital outpatient surgical department?

Code Assignment:

Diagnosis code(s):_____

Procedure code(s):_____

8.51. The following documentation is from the health record of a 72-year-old female patient.

Hospital-Based Clinic Services

This 72-year-old female presented to the hospital-based urgent care clinic with a chief complaint of recurrent epistaxis for three days prior to admission. The bleeding occured in the right nostril. She also complained of weakness and dizziness when standing. At the last clinic visit, hematocrit was 35, and this morning it is 27. Her past medical history is positive for COPD, with a negative surgical history.

A right anterior limited nasal pack was placed in the clinic treatment room. Because of the weakness and dizziness, we decided to admit the patient to an observation bed. In the evening, the anterior pack required replacement with extensive cauterization because of refractory bleeding. Due to falling hematocrit, two units of packed red cells were transfused for the blood loss anemia resulting. The next morning, the patient was still experiencing some bleeding around the anterior nasal pack. For this reason, she was taken back to the treatment room, and a posterior nasopharyngeal pack was placed by another physician. No further bleeding occurred throughout the day, and the patient was discharged to home health care follow-up following pack removal.

Which of the following should appear on the UB-92 claim for the outpatient services rendered to this Medicare patient? **Note:** The facility purchases its blood from the blood bank.

a. 784.7, 30901, 30903, 30905, 36430
b. 784.7, 280.0, 496, 30901, 30901-76, 30905-77, P9021
c. 784.7, 285.9, 30901, 30903-59, 30905-77, 36430, P9021 (2 units)
d. 784.7, 280.0, 496, 30901, 30903-59, 30905-59, 36430, P9021 (2 units)

8.52. The following documentation is from the health record of a three-year-old male patient.

Emergency Department Services

The patient is a three-year-old male, presenting to the ER with a two-day history of fever, cough, and wheezing. His mother has been treating him at home with Ventolin and erythromycin syrup prescribed for his sister who has otitis media. An albuterol aerosol treatment was given, and arterial blood gases (pH and calculated oxygen saturation) and a routine single-view chest x-ray were performed. Past medical history is significant for two previous hospital admissions for extrinsic asthma and pneumonia. Both parents and a grandmother smoke in the household.

The chest x-ray was negative for infiltrates or consolidation. The patient was placed on albuterol aerosol treatments and prescribed prednisone, 20 mg b.i.d., and Tylenol 150 mg, q. 4–6 hours, for fever control. A prescription was given for erythromycin syrup to continue to treat this acute exacerbation of asthma with acute bronchitis.

Which of the following represents correct coding for this service, including the chargemaster-assigned codes?

a. 493.00, 466.0, 71010, 82803, 94664
b. 493.02, E869.4, 71010, 82803, 94664
c. 493.02, E869.4
d. 493.02, 466.0, E869.4, 71020, 82803, 94640

8.53. The following documentation is from the health record of a patient who received hospital outpatient surgery services.

Operative Report

Preoperative Diagnosis:	Chronic sinusitis
Postoperative Diagnosis:	Sinusitis of the maxillary, ethmoid, and sphenoid sinuses
Procedure:	Bilateral endoscopic sinusotomies, anterior and posterior ethmoidectomies, sphenoidotomy, with debris removal in all sites

EBL: <100 cc

Description of Operation: The patient was placed in supine position after appropriate preparation, draping, and induction of endotracheal anesthesia. The nose was cocainized and injected with Xylocaine 2 percent with 1:100,000 epinephrine.

The endoscope was then used to examine the maxillary sinus structures on the left side. There were several polyps present, and these were carefully injected with Xylocaine 0.5 percent with 1:200,000 epinephrine and removed. The maxillary sinus opening was identified by blunt dissection and was then opened, and with various rongeurs, the tissue was debrided. We then started through the posterior of the middle meatus region involving the ethmoid floors. Care was taken to preserve the parietal mucosa, while performing the ethmoidectomies; then we proceeded posteriorly and entered into the sphenoid posteriorly and inferiorly. Gelfilm® was folded and placed in the areas involved.

Attention was then directed to the right side in similar fashion. Again, polyps were removed from the maxillary sinus. The uncinate was prominent and was resected, and more polyps were debrided. We then identified the maxillary sinus opening on the right and opened it in a satisfactory manner. We then proceeded anterior through posterior ethmoidal cells into the sphenoid cavity posteriorly, opening and removing large amounts of polypoid mucosa, polyps, and some mild purulence. When this was completed to our satisfaction, Gelfilm was folded and placed. The posterior throat was suctioned clear, and the patient was awakened and taken to recovery in good condition.

Which codes will be reported for this ambulatory surgery service?

a. 473.9, 31256-50, 31287
b. 473.0, 473.2, 473.3, 471.8, 31256-50, 31287-50
c. 473.0, 473.2, 473.3, 471.8, 31255-50, 31267-50, 31288-50
d. 473.0, 473.2, 473.3, 471.8, 31255, 31267

Trauma and Poisoning

8.54. The following documentation is from the health record of a 25-year-old female patient.

Emergency Department Services

A 25-year-old female fell off of her horse in the morning, sustaining an injury and fracture of the spinal cord and vertebra at the C4 level. The patient was brought to the nearest ED by ambulance in a full-body air splint. CT scan revealed the injury to be a complete injury to the spinal cord (tetraplegia). The patient was having some difficulty breathing, and, after endotracheal intubation, ventilator support was initiated. Vital signs were unstable in the ED. The patient had no feeling below the level of the injury. The patient was closely monitored throughout her stay in the ED. Later that day, when it was felt that she was stable enough for transport, she was transferred to the neurosurgical intensive care at the teaching hospital downtown for definitive treatment at the fracture site.

Critical care services were provided according to the acuity system. The ED physician who managed this patient recorded extensive progress notes, which included the specific time he spent with the patient on and off throughout the day. Times noted included the following:

0800–0900

1000–1030

1100–1115

1300–1315

1500–1600

Which of the following sets of codes would be appropriate for facility reporting of this ED service in addition to the CT scan, 72125, assigned via the chargemaster?

a. 99291, 99292 × 4, 31500; 805.04, 344.01, E828.2
b. 99291, 31500, 94656; 805.04, 344.01, E828.2
c. 99291, 31500, 94656; 806.01, E828.2
d. 99291, 31500, 94656, 22305; 806.01, E828.2

8.55.   The following documentation is from the health record of a male patient with a stab wound.

Hospital Outpatient Surgery Services

A patient was stabbed in the right hand during a street fight. Examination showed a sensory deficit of the thumb and index finger due to an injury to the common digital nerve, and a tendon laceration involving the abductor pollicis and first dorsal interosseous. He was taken immediately to the operating room for repair.

General anesthesia was given, a tourniquet was applied, and the wound was explored. The common digital nerve to the thumb was identified and found to be divided at the level just proximal to the first metacarpal. The digital nerve to the radial aspect of the index finger was also divided. The abductor pollicis and the first dorsal interosseous tendons were then repaired with 3-0 VICRYL to the fascia.

Following this, the operative microscope was used to repair both digital nerves using interrupted 9-0 nylon, suturing epineurium to the epineurium. When completed, the wound was thoroughly irrigated with saline solution and the skin was closed with interrupted ETHILON®. A dorsal splint was applied to the thumb and remains in IP flexion at about 30 degrees and slight adduction. Tourniquet time totaled 190 minutes.

Which of the following code sets is appropriate for this service?

a. 883.2, 955.6, E966, E849.5, 64831-F5, 64832-F6, 69990, 26989
b. 955.6, E920.3, 64831, 64832-59, 26356
c. 883.2, E966, E849.5, 64831-RT, 26989
d. 955.6, 955.6, 883.2, 64831, 64832, 69990, 26989

Chapter 9

Case Studies from Physician-based Health Records

Note: Even though the specific cases are divided by setting, most of the information pertaining to the diagnosis is applicable to most settings. If you practice or apply codes in a particular type of setting, you may find additional information in other sections of this publication that may be pertinent to you.

Every effort has been made to follow current recognized coding guidelines and principles, as well as nationally recognized reporting guidelines. The material presented may differ from some health plan requirements for reporting. The ICD-9-CM codes used are effective through September 30, 2007, and the HCPCS (CPT and HCPCS Level II) codes are in effect through December 31, 2006. The current standard transactions and code sets named in HIPAA have been utilized, which require ICD-9-CM Volume III procedure codes for inpatients.

Instructions:

Assign all applicable ICD-9-CM codes appropriate for the setting for the case studies presented. Some of the cases provide multiple-choice answers, and the reader must select the appropriate code set. In other instances, the reader is expected to assign codes without any prompts.

The scenarios are based on selected excerpts from health records without reproducing the entire health record. However, in practice, the coding professional should have access to the entire health record. Health records are analyzed and codes are selected only with the physician's complete and appropriate documentation available. According to coding guidelines, codes are not assigned without physician documentation.

The objective of the cases and scenarios reproduced in this publication is to provide practice in assigning correct codes, not necessarily to emulate real coding practice. For example, the reader may be asked to assign codes based only on an operative report, when in real practice a coder has access to documentation in the entire medical record.

Anesthesia Services

9.1. A neonatal patient is brought to the operating room for repair of complete transposition of the great arteries under cardiopulmonary bypass. The infant is in critical condition and may not survive. Assign the correct ICD-9-CM diagnosis codes and CPT codes to report the administration of anesthesia, including physical status, Level I and II modifiers, and qualifying conditions for this procedure.

   a. 745.10, 00562-AA-23, 99100
   b. 745.11, 00561-AD-P5, 99140
   c. 745.10, 00561-AA-P5
   d. 745.19, 00563-AA-P5, 99100, 99140

9.2. A patient came into the pain clinic for management of chronic neck and shoulder pain following a car accident one year ago. The pain extended down into her left hand, and the patient had difficulty lifting or moving anything with that hand. She also reported inability to sleep well due to pain. Her attending physician requested a consultation with Dr. Jones, a pain specialist. Dr. Jones performed a brief history and expanded problem-focused physical exam with medical decision making of low complexity. He and the patient discussed the injection of Marcaine and steroids into the cervical plexus for relief. The patient agreed to this, and, after consents were signed, the injection was performed. The patient noted approximately 40 percent relief in pain almost immediately. Dr. Jones requested that the patient come back in one week and again in two weeks for another injection.

   Diagnosis: Cervicobrachial syndrome, due to auto accident one year ago.

   Assign the correct ICD-9-CM and CPT codes for this scenario, keeping in mind that the –25 modifier may or may not be necessary depending on the payer.

   a. 723.3, 907.3, E929.0, 99241, 64413
   b. 907.3, 723.3, E929.0, 99242, 64413
   c. 723.3, 907.3, E929.0, 99212, 64415
   d. 907.3, E929.0, 99245, 64470

9.3. A 55-year-old patient is brought into the operating room for elective decompression of the median nerve for carpal tunnel syndrome. She is in excellent health otherwise. The surgeon places an Esmarch bandage on the arm, and the arm is exsanguinated. A tourniquet is then placed and the surgeon administers Bier block anesthesia.

   Tourniquet time was approximately 50 minutes. Assign the ICD-9-CM diagnosis code and CPT surgical and anesthesia codes with any applicable modifiers.

   a. 354.0, 64719, 01995
   b. 354.0, 64722-47, 01995
   c. 354.0, 64721-47
   d. 354.1, 64721, 01810

Disorders of the Blood and Blood-Forming Organs

9.4. A 32-year-old female has recently had surgery for melanoma of the right arm, Clark level IV. She had no other signs of metastasis or adenopathy. Under general anesthesia, a sentinel node biopsy of the deep axillary nodes was performed with a gamma counter probe. An injection of isosulfan blue dye was performed and the nodes followed carefully to the single bright-blue node. This node was excised and sent for frozen section, which proved to be negative for melanoma. Before the procedure, the radiologist performed a lymphoscintigraphy. Which of the following code sets would the surgeon report? (Do not report supplies.)

a. 173.6, 38525
b. 172.6, 38525, 38792
c. 172.6, 38525, 38792-51, 78195
d. 172.9, 38525, 38790-51

9.5. The following documentation is from the health record of a male patient.

History: This is a 66-year-old male who had coronary artery bypass graft in February. He did well. He was discharged home. Some time after that when he was home, he had two days of black stools. He mentioned it to the nurse, but I'm not sure anything was done about it. He has not had any other evidence of hematemesis, melena, or hematochezia but was feeling rather weak and fatigued. He had blood work done, which showed a hemoglobin of 5.7, hematocrit of 20.9, MCV of 80. Serum iron of 8, 2 percent saturation. No indigestion or heartburn. No abdominal pain of any kind. No past history of anemia or GI bleed.

Past Medical History: General health has been good.

Allergies: None known

Previous Surgeries: Coronary artery bypass graft

Medications: At the time of admission include Glucotrol, Lasix, potassium, and aspirin

Review of Systems: Endocrine: He does have diabetes, controlled with medication. Cardiovascular: History of coronary artery disease with coronary artery bypass graft. No recent symptoms of chest pain or shortness of breath. Respiratory: No chronic cough or sputum production. GU: No dysuria, hematuria, history of stones, or infections. Musculoskeletal: No arthritic complaints or muscle weakness. Neuropsychiatric: No syncope, seizures, weakness, paralysis, or depression.

Family History: Is positive for cardiovascular disease and diabetes in his mother. No history of cancer.

Social History: The patient is married. Never smoked. Doesn't drink any alcohol. Works in a factory.

On physical examination, a well-developed, well-nourished, alert male in no acute distress. Blood pressure 146/82. Respirations 18. Heart rate 78. Skin: Good turgor and texture. Eyes: No scleral icterus. Pupils are round, regular, equal, and react to light. Neck: No jugular venous distention. No carotid bruits. Thyroid is not enlarged. Trachea in the midline. Lungs are clear. No heart murmur noted. Abdomen is soft. Bowel sounds present. No masses, no tenderness. Liver and spleen are not palpably enlarged. Extremities: Good pulses. Trace edema of the feet.

Laboratory values show severe anemia with a hemoglobin of 5.7. Hemoccult is also positive. His iron studies showed low iron and low ferritin, consistent with chronic blood loss anemia. His B_{12} and folate levels were normal. His SMA-12 was essentially unremarkable.

Impression: 1. Anemia. Probably he is anemic post bypass and then had stress gastritis with a little bit of bleeding and has never recovered from that. No evidence of acute or active bleeding at this time. The patient is stable. Possibility of occult malignancy or active peptic ulcer disease does exist.
2. Arteriosclerotic heart disease of native vessel, stable.

Recommendations: Admit patient as an outpatient for blood transfusion. Patient is being transfused. He should have an esophagogastroduodenoscopy and colonoscopy, possible biopsy or polypectomy, which has been explained to the patient along with potential risks and complications, including bleeding, transfusion, perforation, and surgery. These tests will be scheduled for a later date.

Discharge Note

Final Diagnosis: Severe blood loss anemia, weakness, diabetes mellitus, history of coronary artery disease status post coronary artery bypass graft.

The patient received three units of packed red blood cells, he felt better with subsidence of his shortness of breath, and his weakness improved. His last hemoglobin was 8.4, with a hematocrit of 27.7.

The patient was scheduled for EGD to rule out peptic ulcer disease and colonoscopy to rule out occult malignancy in one week. The patient will be discharged home, and he will have clear liquid diet. He is to call for any problems. He will continue with his home medications, and he was placed on ferrous sulfate one tablet twice a day.

What diagnosis codes are reported for this hospital outpatient encounter reported by the physician?

a. 280.0, 792.1, 414.01, 250.00, V45.81
b. 285.9, 780.79
c. 280.0, 578.1, 414.01, 250.00, V45.81
d. 998.11, 285.1, 792.1, 414.01, 250.00, V45.81

9.6.   The following documentation is from the health record of a female patient.

History: The patient is an 87-year-old white female brought to the ED because of pleural effusion, urinary tract infection, and dehydration. She had been taking medication. She lives at the nursing home and has been doing fairly well. Today she was found to be weak and not eating well. Then she was sent to the emergency room for evaluation and found out to have pleural effusion and dehydration, urinary tract infection, also thrombocytopenia with petechial hemorrhage. She was found to have a platelet count of 77,000.

Past History: She has a history of cholecystectomy.

Social History: She is a retired woman. No smoking, no drinking, no allergies.

Family History: Noncontributory

Systemic Review: Otherwise normal

Physical Examination: Today reveals blood pressure is 163/62. Pulse of 80. Respirations of 15. Temperature of 98.6°F. General condition of the patient showed chronically ill, confused, disoriented. No jaundice, no cyanosis. No pallor, no edema. The patient has dehydration, +3. Scalp and skull are normal. Eyes showed bluish around the eyes and petechial hemorrhage at the eyelid and conjunctiva. Ears, nose, and throat are normal. Neck showed normal cervical spine. The neck veins are flat. No bruits of the carotid arteries. The trachea is midline. Thyroid gland cannot be palpated. Lymph glands cannot be palpated. Chest shows normal contour. The breasts are normal. Movement of the chest equal on both sides. There is dullness of the chest with some rales and rhonchi. Heart shows apex beat is at the fifth intercostal space left mid clavicular line. No diffuse precordial pulsation, no thrill. Heart rate is 80, regular with premature ventricular contraction, no murmur. Back is normal. Abdomen showed normal contour, soft, nontender, no guarding, no rigidity. Liver, spleen, and kidneys cannot be palpated, no mass is palpable. Bowel sounds are positive. No fluid thrill. No shifting dullness. No bruits of the abdominal vessels. Extremities show no clubbing of the fingers. No varicose veins. No phlebitis. Hematoma of the right hand. Peripheral pulses are normal. The deep tendon reflexes are normal. Babinski sign is negative.

Laboratory Studies: Hematocrit was 43, white count 9,000 with 82 percent neutrophils, and the platelet count 77,000. The MCV was 102. Creatinine was 1.7. Bilirubin was 1.7. The alkaline phosphatase was 122. AST 498, ALT 493, and albumin 3.6. The prothrombin time was 18 seconds, the PTT was 25 seconds. The chest x-ray showed a right pleural effusion.

Impressions:
1. Urinary tract infection
2. Dehydration
3. Pleural effusion from congestive heart failure
4. Primary thrombocytopenia with petechial hemorrhage
5. Type II diabetes mellitus

Plan of Treatment: The patient will be stabilized and started on IV fluids. Also will start IV antibiotic for urinary tract infection.

Patient will be transferred at the family's request to a larger facility. A consult with hematology will be arranged, and a transfusion of platelets may be indicated.

A detailed history and examination was performed, with medical decision making of moderate complexity.

What are the appropriate diagnosis codes and E/M code for this service?

a. 599.0, 276.51, 428.0, 287.5, 250.00, 99284
b. 599.0, 276.51, 428.0, 511.9, 287.30, 250.00, 99284
c. 599.0, 276.51, 428.0, 287.30, 250.00, 99284
d. 599.0, 276.51, 428.0, 287.30, 782.7, 250.00, 99285, 36430

Disorders of the Cardiovascular System

9.7. A patient who is six weeks post anterior MI with congestive heart failure has been taking Lanoxin and is experiencing nausea and vomiting and profound fatigue. The evaluation and treatment were focused on adjustment of medication only. Blood levels show 4 ng/ml. Which of the following diagnosis codes will be reported?

    a. 972.1, E858.3, 787.01
    b. 410.12, 428.0
    c. 787.01, 780.79, E858.3
    d. 787.01, 780.79, E942.1, 410.12, 428.0

9.8. The following documentation is from the health record of a female patient.

History: This is a 70-year-old female who had noted exertional tachyarrhythmia described as palpitations, diaphoresis, and presyncope. She had noted no frank syncopal episodes. Prior to this admission, she had been on Lopressor, Norpace®, and Lanoxin in combination but was still experiencing breakthrough atrial flutter.

Hospital Course: Upon admission, the patient underwent echocardiography. This revealed moderate left ventricular dysfunction, mild to moderate atrial regurgitation, mild mitral regurgitation, and the left atrium proved to be within the upper limits of normal. At that time, it was recommended that the patient begin on amiodarone therapy due to drug refractory atrial flutter. Pulmonary function test and thyroid function test were also performed. Thyroid function test results proved within normal limits. Pulmonary function test revealed normal lung volumes with mild loss of alveolar capacity. Amiodarone loading continued. The patient was taken to the electrophysiology lab, and overdrive pacing was attempted. This was unsuccessful. The patient therefore underwent direct-current external atrial cardioversion and at that time converted to normal sinus rhythm. The patient was discharged with a scheduled follow-up in one month.

Final Diagnoses: 1. Drug refractory atrial flutter
                       2. Successful cardioversion to normal sinus rhythm

Which of the following is the correct code assignment?

    a. 429.9, 424.0, 92961
    b. 429.9, 394.1, 33240
    c. 427.32, 394.1, 429.9, 33211
    d. 427.32, 396.3, 429.9, 92960

9.9. The following documentation is from the health record of a 66-year-old male patient.

Discharge Summary

Admission Date: 6/19/XX

Discharge Date: 6/28/XX

History of Present Illness: This patient is a 66-year-old male admitted on June 19 because of unstable postinfarct angina. He underwent cardiac bypass surgery here 15 years ago. He did well until 1989, when he developed angina and underwent angioplasty here. On 6/9, he was awakened with severe chest pain and was taken to a nearby community hospital where he was found to have a small anterior wall myocardial infarction with the CPK only slightly elevated. He had cardiac catheterization performed at that time. Because of this small infarction, he was referred here for consideration for further surgical intervention. He was discharged from the hospital on 6/16. On 6/19, as the patient was walking from the car to the office, he developed quite significant chest pain and was therefore admitted to rule out further infarction.

Documentation of recent cardiac catheterization showed that complete left heart catheterization, left ventricular cineangiography, coronary arteriography, and bypass visualization were performed. The left ventricle showed severe anterior hypokinesis; although it did still move. The left main coronary artery was narrowed by about 70 percent. The bypass to the circumflex looked good, but the bypass to the left anterior descending had a very severe stenosis in the body of the graft. There was a very large, marginal circumflex artery that had an orificial, 80 percent stenosis. He was felt to not be a candidate for angioplasty but should have bypass surgery.

Surgical Procedure: Using extracorporeal circulation, the left internal mammary artery was anastomosed to the left anterior descending coronary artery, and a venous graft was placed from the aorta to the marginal circumflex. It was found that the old venous graft to the main circumflex was in excellent condition with very soft, pliable walls so that vessel was left intact. There were no complications of this surgery. His postoperative course was singularly uncomplicated. He never had any arrhythmia problems; his wounds healed nicely. He had a tiny left pleural effusion that never needed to be tapped. He was walking about the ward participating in the cardiac rehab program at the time of discharge.

Discharge Instructions: Discharge medications will simply be aspirin grains 5 q. d., Tylenol with Codeine 1 or 2 p.r.n. for pain, Lopressor 50 mg a day, and Colace, as necessary. He was instructed to contact his private physician upon return home for resumption of his medical care. He is to call me here at the medical center if there are any questions or problems that he wishes to discuss.

Discharge Diagnoses:
1. Unstable angina (intermediate coronary syndrome)
2. Recent incomplete, anterior wall myocardial infarction
3. Coronary atherosclerosis, three vessel
4. Successful double-bypass surgery

What are the correct codes for this admission?

a. 414.01, 414.05, 410.12, 411.1, V45.81, 33517, 33533, 33530
b. 414.01, 414.05, 410.12, 411.1, V45.81, 33510, 33533
c. 414.00, 414.05, 410.11, 411.1, V45.81, 33530
d. 414.01, 414.05, 410.12, 412, V45.81, 33518, 33530

9.10. The following documentation is from the health record of an 85-year-old female patient.

Admission Date:	12/10/XX
Discharge Date:	12/22/XX
Discharge Diagnoses:	1. Acute pulmonary edema with congestive heart failure
	2. Myocardial infarction ruled out
	3. Chronic obstructive pulmonary disease
	4. Pneumonia
	5. Senile dementia

History of Present Illness: This 85-year-old female was admitted via the emergency room from the nursing home with shortness of breath, confusion, and congestion. There was no history of fever or cough noted. Patient has a history of senile dementia and COPD. Prior to admission, the patient was on the following medications: Prednisone, Lasix, Haldol, and Colace.

Physical Examination: Blood pressure 140/70, heart rate of 125 per minute, respirations were 30, temperature of 101.4°F. The eyes showed postsurgical eyes, nonreactive to light. The lungs showed bilaterally bibasilar crackles. The heart showed S1 and S2, with no S3. The abdomen was soft and nontender. The extremities showed leg edema. The neurological exam revealed no deficits, and she was alert × 3.

Laboratory Data: ABGs were 7.4, PO_2 of 63, CO_2 of 43, bicarbonate 26, saturation of 89. Hemoglobin 11.7, hematocrit was 31.5, platelets of 207,000. Sodium 139, chloride 107, potassium 4.4, BUN 42, creatinine 1.2. The EKG was unremarkable.

Hospital Course: Basically, this patient was admitted to the coronary care unit with acute pulmonary edema, rule out myocardial infarction. Serial cardiac enzymes were done, which were within normal limits; therefore, ruling out myocardial infarction. A chest x-ray performed on the day of admission confirmed congestive heart failure and pneumonia. The patient was started on Unasyn and tobramycin for the pneumonia, which improved. The congestive heart failure, however, was not improving with administration of Lasix. The patient was not taking foods and liquids well, and, at the family's request, she was made DNR. On hospital day 12, she was found without respirations, with no heart sounds, and pupils were fixed. She was declared dead by the physician and the family was notified.

Which of the following answers demonstrates the correct ICD-9-CM code assignment?

a. 428.0, 486, 496, 290.0
b. 428.0, 518.4, 486, 496, 290.0
c. 428.0, 410.91, 486, 496, 290.0
d. 518.4, 428.0, 486, 496, 290.0

 9.11. Dr. Hiram performs an endovascular repair of a very long aneurysm of the descending thoracic aorta, with placement of two distal extension components due to the extensive length of the aneurysm. The left subclavian artery was not covered during this procedure. Assign the appropriate CPT code(s) to report this procedure.

a. 33880
b. 33779
c. 33881
d. 33881, 33883, 33884

9.12. Kathy Jones has a pseudoaneurysm of her left iliac artery that has developed proximal to an area of occlusion. She is admitted to Community Hospital for an endovascular repair. She undergoes a percutaneous transluminal balloon angioplasty of the area of occlusion, with placement of a drug-eluting stent, and an endovascular graft placement to repair the area of the pseudoaneurysm. An endovascular ultrasound is performed after the procedure to assure patency of the vessel. Assign the appropriate CPT code(s) that her surgeon, Dr. Vessel, would report. You do not need to assign modifiers for this exercise.

a. 35454, 34900, 37205, 37250
b. 35473, 34900, 37205, 37250
c. 35454
d. 35492, 34900, 37205

9.13. In the cardiac catheterization laboratory of Big City Hospital, Dr. Hart performed a PTCA on a patient's right coronary artery, with placement of a drug-eluting stent. He also performed a PTCA of the left circumflex coronary artery and placement of two stents. The patient had undergone a complete diagnostic cardiac catheterization at an outlying hospital the previous day, so complete cardiac catheterization was not performed. Dr. Hart performed the procedure via femoral artery cutdown without left heart catheterization. Assign the appropriate CPT codes and HCPCS Level II modifiers that Dr. Hart would use to report these procedures. You do not need to assign CPT modifiers for this exercise.

a. 93508, 92982-RC, 92984-LC, 92980-RC, 92981-LC
b. 93508, 92982-RC, 92984-LC, 92980-RC, 92981-LC × 2
c. 93510, 92982-RC, 92984-LC, 92980-RC, 92981-LC
d. 93510, 92982-RC, 92984-LC, 92980-RC, 92981-LC × 2

Disorders of the Digestive System

9.14. A 48-year-old man came in to the emergency department complaining of vomiting coffee-ground material several times within the past hour. He has abdominal pain and has been unable to eat for the past 24 hours. He is dizzy and light headed. Two stools today have been black and tarry. While in the emergency department, he vomited bright-red blood and some coffee-ground material. A nasogastric tube was inserted by the ED physician and attached to suction. An abdominal exam showed a fluid wave consistent with ascites. An IV of lactated ringers was started, and CBC and clotting studies were drawn. A detailed history and physical exam with high-complexity medical decision making were documented. A GI consultant was called and the patient was taken to Endoscopy for further evaluation of upper GI bleeding. Diagnosis: Hematemesis, rule out esophageal varices; blood loss anemia, acute; ascites.

Which of the following is the correct code assignment for the independent ED physician?

a. 578.0, 285.1, 789.5, 99285, 43752
b. 578.0, 789.00, 780.4, 99284-25, 91105
c. 789.50, 578.0, 280.0, 99284, 43752
d. 578.0, 285.1, 789.5, 99284-25, 43752

9.15. This 35-year-old man has had a history of diverticulosis with frequent bleeding in the past. He came in to have a colonoscopy and rule out any other pathology, such as carcinoma. During the colonoscopy, severe diverticulosis was noted. This is definitely the cause of the bleeding. Also noted were a polyp at the splenic flexure and a polyp in the transverse colon. The polyp at the splenic flexure was removed by hot biopsy, and the second polypectomy was done by snare technique. The polyps were both classified as adenomatous polyps with no signs of malignancy. What are the correct codes for this case?

a. 562.12, 211.3, 45385, 45384-51 or 45384-59
b. 211.3, 562.10, 578.1, 45384
c. 562.12, 211.3, 578.9, 45385
d. 562.12, 211.3, 45384

9.16. The patient had a laparoscopic Nissen fundoplasty performed for gastroesophageal reflux with esophagitis. He also has Barrett's esophagus. These conditions have not been responding to conservative treatment, and the patient wishes to undergo surgery at this time. The patient has also had many instances of treatment for chronic cholecystitis. It has been decided to pursue a laparoscopic cholecystectomy at the same time that the fundoplasty is done. Which of the following is the correct code assignment?

a. 530.81, 530.85, 47562, 43289-51
b. 530.11, 530.85, 574.10, 43324, 47600-52
c. 530.11, 530.89, 575.11, 43326
d. 530.11, 530.85, 575.11, 43280, 47562-51

9.17. This 52-year-old female has chronic cholecystitis with cholelithiasis. She has been having increasing abdominal pain. A laparoscopic cholecystectomy was performed, and an ERCP was also done to rule out obstruction of the common bile duct. The findings showed an obstructed common bile duct with stones. A sphincterotomy was performed, and then lithotripsy of the stones was done. The largest particles of stones were removed. Which of the following is the correct code assignment?

a. 574.11, 47564
b. 574.70, 47562, 43265-51
c. 574.71, 47562, 43265-51, 43264-51
d. 574.71, 47562, 43265-51, 43262-51, 43264-51

9.18. The following documentation is from the health record of a 33-year-old female patient.

History and Physical

The patient is scheduled for surgery today.

Chief Complaint: Anal pain with bleeding

History of Present Illness: This is a 33-year-old woman with a two-year history of anal pain and bleeding, which has been markedly worse lately. Has been on stool softener, sitz baths, and it has not improved. She presents for ligation of internal hemorrhoids.

Past History: General health is good. There are no major medical illnesses. She has had a tubal ligation in the past.

Family History and Review of Systems: Otherwise noncontributory

Physical Examination: HEENT: Grossly intact. Neck: Supple. Chest: Clear. Heart: Regular rate and rhythm. Abdomen: Soft, without mass, tenderness, or organomegaly. Anal exam: There is marked posterior tenderness and pain.

Impression: Bleeding, prolapsed internal hemorrhoids, not responding to conservative therapy

Recommendations: Internal rubber band ligation. The procedure has been explained in detail to the patient, and she understands and accepts.

Operative Report

Preoperative Diagnosis:	Internal prolapsing hemorrhoids
Postoperative Diagnosis:	Same
Surgery Performed:	Proctosigmoidoscopy, rubber band ligation of the internal hemorrhoids, done with an anoscope

Procedure: The patient was placed on the operating table in a sitting position. The patient was placed in prone jackknife position and the buttocks were retracted. Proctosigmoidoscopy was then carried out to 20 cm and was normal except for the anal findings mentioned above. The proctoscope was withdrawn, and the anus was prepped and draped in antiseptic fashion. A field block with Marcaine 0.25 percent was then placed. Anoscope was inserted. There was a prolapsing hemorrhoid in the anterior midline. This was rubber-band ligated above the dentate line by applying two bands. In the posterior midline, there was another hemorrhoid, which was banded in the same manner. Bleeding was checked, and none was noted.

The patient was taken to the recovery room in stable condition. Blood loss was negligible. Counts correct; no drains.

Which of the following is the correct code assignment?

a. 455.2, 46221, 45300-51, 46600-51
b. 455.2, 46221, 46221-59, 45300
c. 455.0, 46945, 45300
d. 455.8, 46934, 45300-51, 46600-51

Evaluation and Management (E/M) Services

9.19. Dr. Bill admitted a patient to observation after seeing him in the emergency department with severe nausea, vomiting, and dizziness from dehydration. IVs were started, and the plan was to hydrate the patient and discharge him to home the next morning. The patient, however, had not improved enough the next day (day 2) and was kept an additional 24 hours. On day 3, the patient was discharged home.

[handwritten note: Do not code E/M separately when put in Hosp. Observation Care from Emergency Room.]

Assuming documentation guidelines have been met, choose the correct sequence of CPT codes for Dr. Bill's services.

a. 99219, 99231, 99217   *[handwritten: Initial Observation, Subsequent Hosp. Care, Observation Care Discharge Services]*
b. 99219, 99499, 99217
c. 99283, 99219, 99217
d. 99283, 99231, 99217

9.20. Dr. Smith sent a patient to observation care at the local hospital following his visit to the nursing facility. The patient was admitted for observation to rule out stroke due to a change in mental status. The next morning, Dr. Smith left town, and his partner, Dr. Johnson, admitted the patient to inpatient care because of sudden worsening symptoms. The patient expired later the same day. Assuming documentation guidelines were met, how would E/M services for these two physicians be coded?

a. Dr. Smith: 99315, 99219; Dr. Johnson: 99236
b. Dr. Smith: 99219; Dr. Johnson: 99217, 99236
c. Dr. Smith: 99219; Dr. Johnson: 99236   *[handwritten: Initial Observation Care Observation or Inpt. Care Services (Including Admission + Discharge Serv)]*
d. Dr. Smith: 99315, 99222; Dr. Johnson: 99238

9.21. An 85-year-old patient of Dr. Smith's was brought to the clinic from her home after her family failed to get her to respond to their phone calls. She was poorly nourished, dehydrated, and confused. Dr. Smith admitted her to the hospital to stabilize her, then discharged her to a nursing facility the next day. Assuming that all documentation guidelines for each level of service have been met, assign the correct CPT codes for Dr. Smith's services.

a. 99214, 99222, 99239, 99305
b. 99222, 99239, 99305
c. 99214, 99235, 99305
d. 99222, 99305

9.22. Dr. Donahue had an elderly Hispanic male come to his office for an initial visit. The patient had multiple medical problems and had not had any care for at least 10 years. The patient brought his 12-year-old granddaughter to interpret; however, she was of minimal assistance due to her unfamiliarity with medical terms and problems. Dr. Donahue's nurse called the local hospital and requested the services of their Spanish-speaking interpreter. By putting the interpreter on speakerphone, Dr. Donahue was able to finish his examination of the patient, prescribe medications, and give instructions for follow-up care. He documented a comprehensive history, comprehensive physical, and medical decision making that was moderate. He spent an additional 50 minutes counseling and coordinating the care of this patient, for a total of 95 minutes of care.

Assign the correct CPT code for Dr. Donahue's services.

   a. 99204, 99354
   b. 99205-21, 99354
   c. 99205, 99354
   d. 99204-21

9.23. The following documentation is from the health record of a 56-year-old female patient.

Preventive Medicine Visit

This patient is a 56-year-old female who comes in today for a complete physical, which is covered by her insurance company. Patient is known to me, although has not been in to see me since last year.

Past Medical History:

1. History of proctosigmoiditis, probably ischemic, treated 1/93
2. History of TAH-BSO for endometriosis
3. History of NSVD × 2
4. History of correction of bunion and hammertoe, 1996

The only concern that she has is that she has had some problems with headaches in the frontal area in the morning. It seems to be worse fairly consistently in the morning. She has also had some problems with hips aching, and her eyes occasionally have been a little blurry. Other than that, she has no other concerns on ROS. She has no jaw claudication, joint pains, etc.

Family History: Her mother died of CVA and colon cancer at age 76. Her father died of heart disease at age 80.

Social History: She has been married for 25 years. She has two children and is a homemaker. She does not smoke or drink. Her husband is a farmer.

Allergies: No known allergies

Medications: ASA, Premarin, Caltrate®

ROS is otherwise entirely unremarkable.

Physical Exam:

She appears to be in no acute distress.

HEENT: Head is normocephalic. PERRLA: Fundi benign. TMs are clear. Pharynx is negative. There is no temporal artery tenderness.

Neck: Without adenopathy or thyromegaly

Lungs: Clear

Heart: Showed a normal S1, S2, with regular rate and rhythm and no murmur

Breasts: Without masses. Self-breast examination was taught and encouraged on a monthly basis. Axillary is unremarkable.

Abdomen: Soft and nontender with no hepatosplenomegaly present

Genitalia: External genitalia normal. Cervix was absent. Vaginal Pap smear was done. Bimanual exam revealed an absent uterus and nonpalpable ovaries. Rectal exam was normal.

Neurological: Exam intact

Assessment: 1. Headaches, exact etiology not clear. I am going to check her sed rate. If that is normal, then will proceed with CT scan of the head.
2. Routine physical

I will write to her with the test results. If she does not hear from me in two-weeks' time, she will give me a call. Otherwise see her right after her head CT.

Assign the correct ICD-9-CM and CPT codes for this visit:

Preventative med · *office/Other outpt additional*
services 25- required.
services

a. V72.31, V76.47, V45.77, 99396; 784.0, 99213-25
b. V70.9, 99396, 784.0, 99213
c. V76.2, V76.47, V45.77, G0101, Q0091; 784.0, 99213-25
d. 784.0, V72.31, V76.47, V45.77, 99214

9.24.   The following scenario involves a female patient in the intensive care unit.

Hospital Visit Services

Progress Note

2 a.m. to 3 a.m. – Emergent

Subjective: I was called regarding endotracheal tube cuff leak and copious secretions suctioned through ETT. N/G sounds not heard in stomach per nurse, though no evidence by exam that N/G was withdrawn partially. Dark gray green material suctioned. Anesthesia called in. Pt is very afraid of losing airway.

Objective: Vital signs stabilized after new tube placed. Pt panicky but calmed when I arrived. Postsuctioning had good breath sounds bilaterally with few mild right expiratory rhonchi. Cor 50s–60s. O_2 SATs remained in the 90s. Endotracheal tube replaced by anesthesia and verified with good bilateral breath sounds.

Assessment:	1. Respiratory failure: Holding own; chest x-ray ordered
	2. Congestive heart failure: Retaining fluid despite increased diuretics
	3. Nutrition: Improved
	4. Heart: Remains in normal sinus rhythm
	5. Atelectasis and pneumonia: Now afebrile, still needs frequent pulmonary toilet
	6. INR 1.9
Plan:	1. Transfer out of ICU tomorrow
	2. Increase Coumadin
	3. Continue respiratory care and IV antibiotics
	4. Increase diuresis: She is above her dry weight.

Determine the correct E/M code for the scenario above.

a. 99233
b. 99291, 99292
c. 99233, 99354
d. 99291

9.25. The following documentation is from the health record of a female patient.

Office Consultation

Reason for Consult: Recurrent right costal margin pain from about the midclavicular line in the midline. Recurred four- to five-weeks ago. Pain daily. The patient tends to vomit if she eats much, so she hasn't been eating well. Describes the pain as "just a continuous pain. Sometimes it doubles me up. It goes through to my back" (that is, to the right medial lower posterior thoracic region). She has had an extremely thorough evaluation for right upper quadrant pain in the past. Her last study and treatment was the ERCP with sphincterotomy 11/7/96. Recurrence of pain suggests that this procedure was a failure. While this is most likely due to the fact that pain is not related to sphincter of Oddi dysfunction, it is not entirely out of the question that sphincterotomy might have been inadequate or that she might have had scarring of the sphincterotomy site.

Review of Systems: She took a week off from work because of pain, and since then she has missed parts of some days because of pain. She doesn't know what pain pills she is taking, but she takes 3–4 of them per day and notes that if pain is real bad, she is allowed to double up on her pills. She notes that when she vomits, pain is worse, and "it seems to be sharper."

For the past several weeks, at least, she has had dizziness. This is probably vertigo because it bothers her when she lies flat in bed and also when she rolls over in bed. Her head has been hurting all of the time, "but it's not like a headache." Light bothers her at times. She has been on 2 meclizine 25 mg pills four times a day, without much improvement.

Allergies: Sulfa and Tylenol 3

Medications: Meclizine 25 mg pills 2 q. i.d. and two medicines, the names of which she doesn't know

Physical Exam:

Chest: Clear

Heart: Regular rate and rhythm

Abdomen: Manifests a midline scar from about the midepigastrium down to the pubis. Extending across the right lower quadrant is a horizontal scar that reaches to the midline and extends across both lowermost abdominal regions. There appears to be a small hernia through the medial aspect of the horizontal RLQ scar. I can't feel liver, spleen, or masses. There is mild to moderate tenderness in the right medial epigastrium. This feels quite localized. I can't feel a clear-cut defect. There is no tenderness along the rib margin in this region. I can create tenderness, however, by pushing both downwards and upwards underneath the rib margin, and I think that this tenderness is coming from abdominal wall structures rather than from something within the abdomen.

Impression:

1. Recurrent right medial epigastric pain of four- to five-weeks' duration, etiology uncertain. This pain may well be of abdominal wall origin. She may have a trigger point in the right medial epigastric region. Another possibility is that she might have a small midline hernia, though I doubt that.
2. Small incisional hernia, RLQ
3. Vertigo of a number of weeks' duration, etiology uncertain. There is some associated headache.

Recommendations: *Complete blood count,*
CBC, sed rate, chemistry panel, amylase

Refer to anesthesiology for consideration of injection therapy directed at right medial epigastric region. Refer to neurology for headaches and vertigo.

I spent 25 minutes interviewing and examining this patient and another 40 minutes discussing the etiology of her problem and answering multiple questions she had.

Give the correct CPT code for this service.

a. 99242
b. 99244
c. 99243
d. 99245

Endocrine, Nutritional and Metabolic Diseases, and Immunity Disorders

9.26.   A 13-year-old male patient is being evaluated in the children's clinic for growth problems. He is 4'1" and does not exhibit any signs of puberty or secondary sexual characteristics. His parents wonder if the necrotizing enterocolitis that he had at birth is the cause of his short stature. Other than his short stature, the patient seems perfectly normal. Blood tests were drawn and indicated a deficiency of growth hormone. The patient came back to the clinic for follow-up of test results and parents were given the option of starting him on growth hormone treatments. Diagnosis on the second visit is HGH deficiency. Give the ICD-9-CM codes for both the first and second visits.

a. First visit: 259.4, 259.0; second visit: 253.3
b. First visit: 783.43, 259.0; second visit: 253.3
c. First visit: 259.0; second visit: 253.4
d. First visit: 259.4; second visit: 253.4

9.27. An 18-year-old male was referred to an endocrinologist by his family doctor, with symptoms of gynecomastia, hypogonadism, and failure to develop secondary sexual characteristics. The family reported no exposure to industrial chemicals and lived in a town far from any large industrial areas. The patient's mother reported that the family did live on a farm briefly when the patient was a small child, and there was a large amount of crop dusting that took place at that time. The endocrinologist reviewed the case and performed a physical exam that confirmed the findings of the family doctor. The endocrinologist initiated several diagnostic studies. Assessment: Gynecomastia, hypogonadism, and failure to develop secondary sexual characteristics, possible pesticide exposure, etiology pending further study.

Which of the following is the correct code set for this initial visit to the endocrinologist?

a. 611.1, 257.2
b. 257.1, 611.1, 259.0
c. 257.8, 909.1
d. 257.2, 259.0

9.28. The following documentation is from the health record of a 69-year-old female patient.

HPI: The patient is a 69-year-old female with a large pituitary tumor found after lymph node biopsy that demonstrated lung cancer. The lung cancer is apparently nonsmall cell adenocarcinoma. This is being followed by Dr. Smith who is planning chemotherapy, I believe, for the future. The pituitary gland appears to be nonfunctioning. She underwent transphenoidal surgery three days ago and is doing well without complaints.

Physical Exam: Vital signs normal. General: Elderly white female in no acute distress. HEENT: Normocephalic and atraumatic. Pupils are equal, round, and reactive to light. Lids and conjunctivae are normal. Throat unremarkable. No blurred vision. Lungs: Clear, but with decreased basilar breath sounds. Cardiac: Regular rate and rhythm without any murmurs. Abdomen: Positive bowel sounds. Soft and nontender, without hepatosplenomegaly. Extremities: Negative; no edema. Neuro: Oriented × 3. Cranial nerves II–XII intact.

Lab Data: WBC 6.9, hemoglobin 12.1, hematocrit 36.2, platelets 314,000.

Glucose 116, BUN 9, creatinine 0.7, sodium 134, potassium 3.9, Chloride 85, CO_2 26, calcium 8.2

Assessment and Plan: Pituitary tumor, status post resection. Currently on steroids, 50 mg q. 8 hours. Wean to 20 mg in the morning and 10 mg in the evening starting tomorrow. Recommend follow-up in two weeks with Dr. Smith; he will further evaluate that. We will watch urine output and be aware for any evidence of diabetes insipidus.

Which of the following is the correct ICD-9-CM code set for this physician?

a. 227.3, 162.9, V77.1
b. 194.3, 162.9
c. 239.7, 162.9, 253.5
d. 239.7, 162.9

Disorders of the Genitourinary System

9.29.   A patient has a transrectal ultrasound-guided placement of prostatic radiation palladium seeds with a cystoscopy for localized adenocarcinoma of the prostate.

Procedure Description: The patient was given general anesthesia, placed in the lithotomy position, and prepped and draped in sterile fashion. The bladder was drained, and 100 cc of half contrast and half saline were placed into the bladder. The scrotum was then draped up out of the way. The BUK 7.5 MHz transrectal ultrasound probe was then introduced into the rectum, and the prostate was imaged. The probe was placed into the stabilization bar mechanism. We then centered the prostate image on the template screen and established our base image. Stabilization needles were then put into position. We then passed the needles, using a perineal approach at the corresponding positions to the corresponding depth, using ultrasound and fluoroscopy for guidance. After satisfactory placement of all the needles, the ultrasound probe and needles were removed. A total of 60 palladium seeds were put in place. We had good distribution of the seeds and good images on the ultrasound. Using the #22 French cystoscope, a cystoscopy was performed, and the bladder was fully inspected with the 30- and 70-degree lenses without notable findings. The bladder demonstrated no tumors, lesions, or other abnormalities, and there were no seeds present and very minimal bleeding. The bladder was drained and the patient was taken to the recovery room in stable condition.

Which of the following code sets would be reported for this service in addition to the HCPCS Level II supply codes for the implants and contrast used? The procedure was performed in the cancer center.

a. 233.4, 55859, 52000, 77763, 76965, 76000
b. 185, 55859, 77778, 76965, 76000
c. 185, 55859, 77784, 76872, 77790
d. 185, 52000, 77762

9.30.   A Medicare patient is scheduled for breast biopsy of a palpable lump in the right breast and a much smaller lesion in the left breast that is shown on mammography and identified by a radiological marker. An excisional biopsy is performed on both sides. The specimen on the right is diagnostic for breast malignancy with clear margins, while the small lesion in the left breast is found to be only fibrocystic disease without evidence of malignancy. Which of the following is reported? The procedure is completed at the hospital surgery center.

a. 611.72, 610.1, 19120-50
b. 174.9, 610.1, 19125-50, 19290-50, 19120-50
c. 174.9, 610.1, 19125-LT, 19290-LT, 19120-RT
d. 174.9, 610.2, 19120, 19125-59, 19290-59

9.31. The following documentation is from the health record of a 48-year-old female patient.

Surgical Procedure

A 48-year-old female patient presents to the hospital-based ambulatory surgery center for laser ablation of cervical dysplasia CIN-III. Following intravenous sedation, the patient was brought to the operating room and placed in the dorsolithotomy position. A vaginal speculum was placed and colposcopy proceeded. No abnormalities were noted during colposcopic exam. Next, 100 watts were used with a 2 mm laser beam to ablate the cervix. The endocervix was buttonholed. No blood loss was appreciated, and the patient tolerated the procedure well and was returned to the recovery room in stable condition.

Which codes does the surgeon assign?

a. 622.10, 57513, 57452
b. 233.2, 57510, 57452
c. 180.0, 57513, 70.21
d. 233.1, 57513

9.32. The following documentation is from the health record of a female patient.

Operative Report

Preoperative Diagnosis: Recurrent right ureteral malignancy

Postoperative Diagnosis: Same

Description of Procedure: Under satisfactory standby anesthesia, the patient was placed in dorsolithotomy position. Her external genitalia were prepared and draped in sterile fashion for a cystourethroscopy examination.

Two percent Xylocaine jelly was instilled into the urethra for topical anesthesia. Using a #20 Wappler panendoscope sheath, right angle, and four oblique fiber-optic telescopes, a cystourethroscopy was performed with a normal urethra noted. The bladder was also unremarkable but showed evidence of past reimplantation of one of the right ureters. Using a flexible ureteroscope, retrograde ureteroscopy was performed all the way to the renal pelvis. Two tumors were found in the upper ureter, one at the ureteropelvic junction and one below. Each was less than .5 cm in size. Using the rigid ureteroscope, the tumors were reached and, using a Bugbee electrode, fulguration of the tumors was carried out. Tissue that remained on the Bugbee was retained and sent to pathology for microscopic study. All of the instruments were removed, and the patient was moved to recovery in good condition. She will receive

Bactrim® 1 b.i.d. for 10 days and will be watched closely by nurses on the floor in the observation unit. Discharge is expected in the early morning, barring any complications.

Pathology Results: Carcinoma of the ureter, recurrent

Which of the following code sets is reported for the surgeon for this hospital-based ambulatory surgical service?

a. 188.6, 52354
b. 188.6, 52224
c. 189.2, 52354
d. 189.2, 52354, 52330

9.33.   The following documentation is from the health record of a male patient.

Operative Report

A patient with an elevated prostate-specific antigen (PSA) of 35.7 comes to the surgery center for a transrectal, ultrasonic-guided (TRUS) prostate biopsy.

Technique: The patient is placed in the Sims position with the left side down. The anus was generously lubricated with 2 percent Xylocaine jelly. The ultrasound probe was then introduced and scanning initiated. A great deal of calcification was noted in the outer margin of the central zone. The area proximal and anterior to the calcifications was hypoechoic but may have been influenced by the stones. There was very thin peripheral zone tissue available. Three needle biopsies were taken from each side, starting in the periphery and working toward the midline and trying to biopsy anterior to the stones on the more medial biopsies from each side.

The pathology report confirmed carcinoma in situ of the prostate.

Which codes will be reported for this service? The facility bills for the technical and professional components and also reports procedure codes for radiologic procedures for reimbursement. Do not include surgical supplies in this example.

a. 185, 55700
b. 233.4, 790.93, 55705, 76872
c. 185, 790.93, 602.0, 55700, 76872, 76942
d. 233.4, 602.0, 55700, 76872, 76942

Infectious Diseases/Disorders of the Skin and Subcutaneous Tissue

9.34.   A new patient presented to the urgent care center with a laceration to the elbow that occurred 10 days ago and was not treated. An infected gaping wound was found, with resulting cellulitis to the forearm and upper arm. Extensive irrigation and debridement using sterile water were performed, but closure was not attempted pending resolution of the infection. Culture of the wound revealed streptococcus. The patient received 1,200,000 units of Bicillin C-R IM and is to return in three days for follow-up. The history and physical examination were problem focused.

Which of the following code sets is appropriate for reporting the services?

a. 881.11, 682.3, 041.00, 99201, 90722, J0540
b. 881.11, 682.3, 11040
c. 884.0, 041.00, 99201
d. 881.01, 99281, 90722, J0540

9.35.   The following documentation is from the health record of a 13-year-old male patient.

Physician Office Record

This 13-year-old male was chasing his brother when he fell through a sliding glass door sustaining three lacerations—one on his left knee, one on his right knee, and one on his left hand.

Left knee: 5.5 cm laceration, involving deep subcutaneous tissue and fascia, was repaired with layered closure using 1 percent lidocaine local anesthetic.

Right knee: 7.2 cm laceration was repaired under local anesthetic with a single-layer closure.

Left hand: 2.5 cm laceration of the dermis was repaired with simple closure using DERMABOND® tissue adhesive.

Assessment: Wounds of both knees and left hand requiring suture repair

Plan: Follow-up in 10 days for suture removal. Call office if there are any problems or complications.

What are the correct ICD-9-CM and CPT procedure codes? Do not code the anesthesia administration in this example.

a. 891.0, 882.0, E920.8, E849.0, 12005
b. 891.1, 882.0, 12002, 12032-51, 17999-51
c. 894.0, 12032, 12002, E/M code for the DERMABOND adhesive
d. 891.0, 882.0, E920.8, E849.0, 12032, 12004-51

9.36.   An operative report provides the following information:

Excision lesion on right shoulder, 2.5 × 1.0 × .5 cm, including circumferential margins. Excision lesion, skin of left cheek, 1.0 × 1.0 × .5 cm, including margins. Pathology report states that the skin lesion on the right shoulder is a lipoma, and the lesion on the left cheek is a squamous cell carcinoma. The physician progress note states that the right shoulder was sutured with a layered closure, and the cheek was repaired with a simple repair.

What are the correct code sets?

a. 173.3, 214.1, 11641, 11403-51, 12031-51
b. 173.3, 214.9, 11403, 11441-51
c. 214.1, 195.0, 11603, 11641-51, 12031-51
d. 173.3, 11643, 12031-51

9.37. The following documentation is from the health record of a patient who received outpatient surgical services.

Operative Report

Preoperative Diagnosis: Full-thickness burn wound to anterior left lower leg

Postoperative Diagnosis: Same

Operation: Split-thickness skin graft, approximately 35 centimeters; preparation of the wound

Anesthesia: General

Procedure: The left lower leg was prepped and draped in the usual sterile fashion. The ulcer, which measured approximately 8 × 4 to 4.5 cm, was debrided sharply with Goulian knife until healthy bleeding was seen. The bleeding was controlled with epinephrine-soaked lap pads. Split-thickness skin graft was harvested from the left lateral buttock area approximately 4.5 to 5 cm × 8 cm at the depth of 14/1000 of an inch. The graft was meshed to 1 to 1.5 fashion and placed over the prepared wound. This was stabilized with staples, and then Xeroform dressings and dry dressings, wrapped with gauze and finally immobilized in a posterior splint. The donor site was covered with Xeroform and dry dressings.

What are the correct procedure codes reported by the physician for this procedure performed in the hospital outpatient surgical suite?

a. 15220, 15221-51, 15000-51
b. 15100
c. 14021, 15000-51
d. 15100, 15000-51

9.38. The following documentation is from the health record of a patient who received outpatient surgical services.

Operative Report

Preoperative Diagnosis: Basal cell carcinoma of the forehead

Postoperative Diagnosis: Same

Procedure: Excision of basal cell carcinoma with split-thickness skin graft

The patient was given a local IV sedation and taken to the operating room suite. The face and left thigh were prepped with pHisoHex® soap. The cancer was outlined for excision. The cancer measured approximately 2.5 cm in diameter. The forehead was infiltrated with 1 percent Xylocaine with 1:1,000,000 epinephrine.

The cancer was excised and carried down to the frontalis muscle. The area of the excision measured 5 × 4 cm in toto. A suture was placed at the twelve o'clock position. The specimen was sent to pathology for frozen section.

Attention was then turned to the skin graft. A pattern of the defect was transferred to the left anterior thigh using a new needle. A local infiltration was performed on the thigh. Using a free-hand knife, a split-thickness skin graft was harvested. The thigh was treated with Tegaderm™ and a wraparound Kerlix® and ACE® wrap. The skin graft was applied and sutured to the forehead defect with running 5-0 plain catgut.

Xeroform with cotton soaked in glycerin was sutured with 4-0 silk. A sterile dressing was applied. The patient tolerated the procedure well with no complications or blood loss.

What are the correct codes reported by the physician for this procedure performed in the hospital outpatient surgical suite?

a. 195.0, 15120
b. 173.3, 15120
c. 173.3, 15120, 11646
d. 195.0, 15000, 15120

9.39. A nursing home patient with an indwelling Foley catheter is diagnosed with a serious urinary tract infection due to E. coli caused by the catheter. The catheter is removed, and a urine culture and sensitivity is performed. The catheter is replaced through the urethra, and aggressive antibiotic therapy is begun in the emergency room of the hospital. Which of the following code sets will be reported by the emergency room physician? No medical evaluation was performed because the patient was evaluated by her primary care physician via telephone with the nursing home staff, and orders were called in to the hospital.

a. 599.0, 041.4, 51701
b. 996.64, E879.6, 51703, 99281
c. 996.64, 599.0, 041.4, E879.6, 51702
d. 599.0, 996.64, E878.8, 51010

9.40. An eight-year-old boy was brought to the ER by a social worker who discovered him alone in throat spasms and seizures. The social worker relates that the child's older sister told her the boy was bitten on the hand by a raccoon he played with 11 days ago. No treatment was sought for the injury at the time, but the area was inflamed and hot. According to the social worker, the mother is a drug addict and often leaves the children unattended. Illness actually began two days ago with a headache and restlessness and inflammation at the wound site. The child expired due to cardiorespiratory failure before any effective treatment could be administered. CPR was performed but was not successful. The physician's diagnosis was listed as rhabdovirus from infected raccoon bite, not treated due to child neglect. Critical care was provided for 60 minutes. Which of the following code sets will be reported?

a. 071, 882.1, E906.3, E968.4, E967.2, 995.52, 99291, 92950
b. 079.89, 99285
c. 799.1, 780.39, 780.6, 882.1, E906.3, E968.4, E967.2, 92950
d. 071, 780.39, 780.6, 92950

Behavioral Health Conditions

9.41. A patient was brought into the emergency department by her mother after she was found to be groggy with an intentional overdose of a "handful" of aspirin approximately ½ hour before. The mother thought the bottle was almost empty. The patient was beginning to experience dizziness and loud ringing of the ears. The physician inserted a gastric tube. The patient was stabilized in the ED, during which time bleeding studies and urinalysis were completed. A detailed history and physical examination were performed, and medical decision making was of moderate complexity. The diagnosis was suicide attempt with unknown quantity of aspirin, dizziness, and tinnitus. A psychiatric consult was arranged, and the patient was transferred to the psychiatric hospital by ambulance.

What are the correct ICD-9-CM and CPT codes for this visit?

a. 965.1, 780.4, 388.30, E950.0, 99284, 91105
b. 965.1, 780.4, E980.0, 99284
c. 780.4, 388.30, E935.3, 99284, 43752
d. 780.4, 388.30, 965.1, E935.3, 99284, 43752

9.42. A 20-year-old patient was brought into the emergency department in nearly comatose condition following an evening of drinking beer and vodka with friends. Vital signs were depressed. A blood alcohol was drawn, which was reported as 0.38. The patient had vomited several times before passing out. There was a 1 cm laceration on the patient's eyebrow. This was treated with a Steri-Strip. An IV was started and pulse oximetry and blood pressure monitors were placed. The patient was stabilized in the emergency department for 1 ½ hours and admitted to intensive care by the Internal Medicine physician on call. Documentation in the ED record supports a level 5 emergency department visit. Diagnosis was alcohol poisoning, acute alcohol intoxication, and 1 cm laceration, right eyebrow.

What is the correct ICD-9-CM and CPT code assignment?

a. 303.00, 980.9, 99291, 99292
b. 980.9, 305.00, 99285-25, 12011
c. 980.0, 305.00, 873.42, E860.0, 99285
d. 980.0, 303.00, 99291, 12011

9.43. A physician was asked to conduct psychological testing on a 19-year-old female who was admitted to the hospital following a suicide attempt. The physician reviewed prior psychiatric treatment and medical records and administered the MMPI-2™ and WAIS–R tests. After scoring the tests, the physician completed his interpretation of the tests and recorded diagnostic impressions and treatment recommendations. The physician documented time spent as approximately 3 hours. What CPT code(s) would be reported for this service?

a. 96101
b. 96101, 96101, 96101
c. 90818, 96101, 96101
d. 96116, 96116, 96116

9.44. The following documentation is from the health record of a 22-year-old female patient.

Date of Admission: 02/10/XX

Date of Evaluation: 02/12/XX

Amount of Time of Evaluation: Patient participated in a direct interview for 40 minutes.

Sources of Information: The patient participated in a 40-minute direct interview. Patient's commitment documents from ABC were also reviewed. Patient's records from Dr. S. were also reviewed.

Chief Complaint: "I came here because someone was hurting me, and they thought that I wasn't eating enough and that I was throwing up too much."

History of Present Illness: The patient is a 22-year-old female with a past history of anorexia nervosa and attention deficit disorder. She was committed after a six-week stay at ABC. Her parents brought her to this facility after her mother noticed that she was fasting and vomiting and was not sleeping. Her mother also noted that she was more weak than usual and was only able to work her job for 1 or 2 hours rather than a full day. It was also noticed that she was losing track of time, appearing confused, fearful, and angry. Patient notes that, prior to admission, she was actually sleeping fairly normally for her, about 5 hours of sleep per night, though she does agree that she was eating rather little and vomiting because of some abuse that was troubling her. On admission, she was noted to be withdrawn and refused to talk to staff and was very tearful. Later that day, however, she did not remember this incident of being tearful. On admission, she was noted to be 84 pounds at a height of 5 feet tall. She at that time admitted to vomiting as much as three times a day and that she had to have her teeth resurfaced due to purging. At ABC facility, staff noted she was hoarding condiments in her room and was also noted to purge in front of staff during her stay there. The patient, however, does not feel that her purging was due to eating disorder; rather, she felt that it was due to stress and anxiety over a previous abuse. Previous records reveal potassium levels as low as 2.0. She states that the low potassium is due to a kidney disorder; however, a nephrologist felt that the low potassium was most likely due to her purging behavior. Her weight at discharge from ABC was 85.5 pounds. Patient notes that her sleep has not been disrupted prior to her hospital stay. She states that she usually gets about 5 hours of sleep per night, which is normal for her. She notes that her appetite has been decreased for the past several months because of stress regarding prior abuse. She denies any thought racing or excessive energy for the past several months. She also denies any suicidal thoughts or behaviors. She also denies any obsessive-compulsive actions. She denies feeling hopeless or depressed.

Chemical Dependency History: Patient denies any current or previous use of alcohol or drugs.

Current Prescribed Medications: Claritin® 10 mg p.o. q. d.; potassium chloride 20 mEq t.i.d. to q. i.d. p.r.n. hypokalemia; Dexedrine® SR 40 mg t.i.d.

Past Psychiatric History: Patient has a history of problems with eating disorders that goes back to the age of 14. Over the past eight years she has been involved in a variety of treatment programs. She was first treated in an inpatient setting at the age of 14. She was subsequently hospitalized at the age of 15, age 16 × 2, and age 17. From the age of 17 to 18 she was placed in foster care. She has attempted suicide three times in her life. Each time the attempt was made by trying to overdose on her asthma medication, theophylline. She has been hospitalized five times for hypokalemia. She notes that she currently sees a psychiatrist and a psychologist as an outpatient. In the past, she has exhibited some features of self-injurious behavior. She burned a cross into her arm at age 13. She also has a past history of scratching her arm.

Family Psychiatric History: She notes that her younger sister attempted to overdose one time in the past and that her father has been treated for depression with ECT, which was successful.

Mental Status Examination: The patient is a petite, too-thin young female who appears younger than her stated age of 22. She is clean, well groomed, and dressed in jeans and a large hooded sweatshirt. Her general behavior is noted to be normal and appropriate throughout the interview. She is cooperative throughout our question-and-answer session. Her mood is somewhat subdued, and she seems slightly anxious. Her affect is rather flat throughout the interview. No abnormal movements are noted during the interview. Her speech is fairly soft and rather monotone in nature. Speech is noted to be of normal speed. Stream of mental activity is normal and appropriate. The form of thought processes appears to be normal without any tangential thinking. Thought content appears to be normal as well. She denies delusions, hallucinations, and suicidal or homicidal ideation at present. She does not seem to be impulsive in her speech or thought processes throughout the interview. She does seem to have some insight into her illness in that she is able to name her illness as anorexia. She states that her weight now is OK. Her judgment, concentration, orientation all appear to be within normal limits. Recent and remote memory appears intact. Her general fund of knowledge is above average. Her calculations, abstractions, proverbs, similarities, are all within normal limits. Estimated IQ would be 120 based on education background and verbal skills. The patient does not appear to be dangerous or suicidal at present.

Biopsychosocial Discussion and Discussion of Differential Diagnosis: The patient is a 22-year-old female with a past history of anorexia and subsequent hypokalemia. She notes that recent exacerbation in her anorexia and vomiting seems to be due to stress over abuse in the past by a physician with whom she had previous professional contact and subsequently became friends. She has limited insight into her eating disorder in that she is able to name it as anorexia now. In the past, however, she has denied the existence of an eating disorder. In the past, she has had suicidal attempts. However, at this time she does not appear to be depressed and does not indicate any suicidal thoughts or plans. At this time, she does not indicate feeling particularly anxious but, rather, regards her main symptom as stress. She states that her only fear right now is that of being in the hospital for her first commitment. She appears to have a long history of hospitalizations for her eating disorder and subsequent hypokalemia. Her family history does appear to have a history of mental illness, with depression in her father and suicide attempt in her younger sister. She also was noted to have burned a cross into her arm as a young child, as well as a history of scratching her arm. There is a possibility that she has a personality disorder with borderline features. Though she does not seem to be in danger of suicide right now or hurting others, it is felt that because of her history of severe hypokalemia and history of anorexia, as well as purging behavior, she will require a long-term inpatient hospitalization for her safety.

Admitting Diagnosis:

Axis I	1. Anorexia nervosa, purging type
	2. Attention deficit hyperactive disorder
Axis II	Personality disorder with predominant borderline features
Axis III	1. History of hypokalemia
	2. Asthma
	3. Hypokalemic periodic paralysis (per patient report)
Axis IV	Severe with stresses incurred due to previous abuse
Axis V	Current GAF – 50 to 60

Prognosis: Guarded due to her history of multiple hospitalizations for her eating disorder

Strengths:
1. Patient is very intelligent.
2. Patient is enrolled in school and has had a high level of education.
3. Patient has a therapeutic relationship with her therapist and psychiatrist as an outpatient.
4. Patient's weight is near her target weight already.
5. The patient has some insight into her eating disorder.

Problems:
1. Patient lacks a deep insight into her eating disorder.
2. Patient clings to a diagnosis of hypokalemia periodic paralysis, which she claims is a kidney disorder that she has. Nephrologist cannot corroborate this theory.
3. Patient has a high rate of recidivism in the hospital system for treatment of her eating disorder.

Short-Term Goals:
1. Patient will identify and discuss high-risk situations.
2. She will listen.
3. She will demonstrate four alternative coping skills to purging.
4. She will seek out assistance from staff before acting on urges to purge.
5. Patient will identify triggers.
6. Patient will be able to discuss short- and long-term consequences of her eating disorder.
7. Patient will complete a crisis plan to control purging urges.
8. Patient will maintain personal safety by not engaging in purging.
9. Patient will maintain her current weight or increase that weight up to 90 pounds.

Long-Term Goals:

1. Patient will reduce the frequency of purging.
2. Patient will complete community passes without reports of purging in preparation for transition to home.
3. Patient will develop the ability to control impulses and demonstrate strategies to deal with dysphoric moods.
4. Patient will maintain her current weight or increase that weight.
5. Patient will maintain normal potassium levels and will not require supplemental potassium treatment.

Biopsychosocial Treatment Plan:

1. Because of her anorexia nervosa and possible personality disorder, she would likely benefit from a referral to dialectical behavior therapy.
2. She would also benefit from a referral to the eating disorders group.
3. Because of her history of hypokalemia, we will regularly monitor her potassium level and treat accordingly with supplemental potassium.
4. We will weigh her three times a week in order to monitor her progress here. We will expect that she maintain her current weight or increase it.
5. She will be allowed initially to go to the cafeteria on her own and choose what she eats, assuming that her weight stays at her current level or increases.
6. She will be started at level B privileges.

Discharge Criteria:

1. She will maintain or increase her weight during her stay here.
2. She will maintain normal potassium levels during her stay here.
3. She will participate in dialectical behavior therapy as well as eating disorders group.
4. She will reduce the frequency of her purging behaviors while here.
5. She will complete community passes without reports of purging in preparation for transition to home.

Estimated Length of Stay as Per UM Norms: 45 days

Which of the following is the correct code set for reporting this physician's service?

a. 90801; 307.1, 314.01, 301.83, 493.90, V17.0
b. 90801; 301.1, 314.01, 301.83, 276.8, 493.90, 359.3
c. 99223; 307.1, 314.01, 301.83, 493.90, V17.0
d. 99223; 301.1, 314.01, 301.83, 276.8, 493.90, 359.3

Disorders of the Musculoskeletal System and Connective Tissue

9.45. A Monteggia fracture-dislocation with a large contaminated open wound is treated with open reduction and external fixation, extensive subcutaneous fracture site debridement, and application of a posterior splint. Which codes are assigned for the surgical services?

  a. 813.32, 24650, 11010-51, 20692-51
  b. 813.18, 24685, 11010-51, 29105-51
  c. 813.02, 24635, 20692, 29105-51
  d. 813.13, 24635, 11010-51

9.46. An arthroscopic partial synovectomy for crystal-induced tenosynovitis is conducted with removal of loose bodies in the ankle for a 65-year-old Medicare beneficiary. What codes will be assigned for the surgical procedure?

  a. 712.87, 727.06, 29895
  b. 718.57, 274.0, 29894, 29895-51
  c. 727.06, 718.17, 29894, 29895-59
  d. 275.4, 29894

9.47. The following documentation is from the health record of an elderly female patient.

Hospital Record Entries

The patient underwent left hybrid total hip replacement. She did extremely well during the postoperative period and was ambulating by day 4. Her hemoglobin/hematocrit stabilized to 9 and 29 prior to discharge, and Coumadin maintenance kept her prothrombin times at approximately 15 seconds.

Diagnoses: 1. Posttraumatic arthritis, left hip
                 2. Status post left total hip replacement

Procedure: Left hybrid total hip replacement

Instructions: Regular diet and activity per physical therapist. Physical therapy orders are independent transfers, weight bearing as tolerated with walker assistance.

Medications: Vicodin, 1–2 q. 3 or 4 hours p.r.n. for pain management. Coumadin 2 mg p.o. q. day.

Condition on Discharge: Improved

History and Physical Report

Chief Complaint: Pain, left hip.

Present Illness: This is an elderly white female with a history of bilateral hip fractures. The left femoral neck was fractured around Thanksgiving and was initially pinned. The pins did not hold and two revisions were needed. Since then, she has developed avascular necrosis with collapse of the femoral head. Worsening pain had occurred on the left side with ambulation, requiring assistance with a cane to walk.

Past History: Positive for a hysterectomy in 1974 for carcinoma of the cervix. She had two diskectomies during the 1980s. She had the right hip pinned in 1996. Her only medication at this time is Synthroid® for hypothyroidism.

Family History: Noncontributory

Social History: No drug or alcohol used. Retired teacher, widowed nine years with five adult children who all live nearby and are supportive of her needs.

Review of Systems: Patient denies shortness of breath or cardiovascular disease. No genitourinary complaints. Musculoskeletal: Limited to pain in the left hip. All other systems negative.

Physical Examination: General: Ht. 5′3″, Wt. 114, BP 130/82 . She has a severe antalgic gait on the left side. Oriented × 3. Mood and affect normal. Extremities: Range of motion of the left hip is severely limited with flexion to 85 degrees. No internal rotation. 20 degrees of external rotation; 20 degrees of abduction; 5 degrees of adduction. Neurologic Exam: The left lower extremity is neurovascularly intact. Pulses are present, but barely palpable. She has good feeling in both legs and feet. X-rays: AP pelvis and lateral view of the left femur show collapse of the femoral head on the left with inferior pins possibly protruding.

Impression: Avascular necrosis, posttraumatic in etiology, left hip

Plan: Good operative candidate; hybrid left total hip replacement, cementing the femoral implant with removal of previously placed pins

Operative Report

Preoperative Diagnosis: Posttraumatic arthritis, left hip

Postoperative Diagnosis: Same

EBL: 400 cc

Indications: This is an elderly female who is status post multiple pinnings of her left hip due to fracture and collapse. Because of the collapse of her femoral head, the pins have progressively protruded through the femoral head, causing significant arthritis and pain. Because of this, it was decided to revise the hip with a total hip replacement.

Description of Procedure: After adequate general endotracheal anesthesia was obtained, the patient was prepped and draped in the usual sterile fashion in the right lateral decubitus position. Initial incision was taken down laterally through the subcutaneous tissue to the level of the tensor fascia lata. The tensor fascia lata was divided in line with its fibers. Using an anterolateral approach, a Z-type incision was made in the vastus lateralis, then brought up anteriorly over the trochanter, where the musculature was released to the tip of the trochanter. Once this was accomplished, the capsule was excised in T fashion. The pins were drilled out with the drill, six in all. The femoral neck was cut at a 45-degree angle to the greater trochanter. The labrum was taken off around the acetabulum, the acetabulum reamed to a size 47, and a size 48 sup was impacted in. Once this was done, a neutral high-wall liner was placed.

Attention was then turned to the femur. The femur was progressively reamed to size 13.5. Once this was done, a size 3 broach was impacted in and seated. A calcar reamer was used. Silastic plug size 16 mm was impacted a finger's breadth below the level of the tip of the stem. The canal was copiously irrigated out, dried, and cement applied. A size 3 SML implant was placed in the correct version. A small head was placed on this and the hip relocated. It was found stable in all directions. Leg lengths were found to be approximately equal.

The wound was irrigated copiously. The abductor musculature was repaired through drill holes through the anterior trochanter. Number 1 NUROLON was used to supplement the vastus lateralis and the rest of the abductor musculature. A drain was placed anterolaterally. The tensor fascia lata was closed in layers, subcutaneous tissues were closed in layers, and skin closed with staples.

A sterile dressing was placed on the wound. ACE spica bandage was placed. The patient was returned to the supine position. Radiographs of the hip showed good cement bone interface and excellent position of all implants. The patient was taken to the recovery room in good condition.

Pathology Report Diagnosis: Bone, left femoral head; avascular necrosis

Which of the following is the correct code assignment? Code for surgical services only.

a. 716.15, 244.9, 27132-LT, 27091-LT-59, 99221, 99232, 99232, 99238
b. 733.42, 716.15, V10.41, 244.9, 27132-LT
c. 733.40, 715.95, V10.41, 27132-LT, 99253
d. 715.95. 244.9, V45.89, 27130-LT, 27091-51, 99221, 99232, 99239

9.48.   The following documentation is from the health record of a 42-year-old male patient.

Physician Office Record Entries

Hospital Copy: History and Physical

Admitting Diagnosis: Herniation of intervertebral disc, L5–S1 right side

Present Medical History: Patient is a 42-year-old Native American male, who initially developed problems with his back in July of this year. He was treated with anti-inflammatories and exercise program and improved enough to return to work. About one month ago, he had recurrence of pain, which has become steadily worse in the past week. He noticed some numbness of his right foot, primarily the toes and right heel. The patient was initially evaluated by his family physician and is now admitted to the orthopedic service for microdiskectomy after MRI revealed herniation and protrusion of the disc encroaching on the nerve root.

Past Medical History: Patient denied any known allergies or drug sensitivities. He has been taking Advil® on a p.r.n. basis. Also takes Lotensin® 10 mg daily for hypertension and has a history of incomplete bundle branch block, hyperlipidemia (no meds), hiatus hernia with gastroesophageal reflux.

Previous Surgeries: Tonsillectomy as a child and also tendon repair to the right hand in 1989. Does state that he injured his kidney in a motorcycle accident at age 21 and was hospitalized with viral pneumonia in 1983.

Family History: Father is 62 with heart disease and hypertension problems. Mother is 64 and well, without significant illness. Three siblings, all in good health.

Social History: Patient is employed full-time at the Harley-Davidson® dealership. At the present time, he is divorced and has one child who lives with her mother. He does not smoke, is sexually active, and admits to sporadic alcohol use.

Review of Systems

HEENT: Patient denies any unusual problems with headaches, dizziness, visual, or hearing difficulty. Cardiorespiratory: Denies chest pain; does have occasional asthma symptoms with some wheezing but does not use medications. Hypertension for two years, well controlled on medication. Gastrointestinal: Denies distention, diarrhea, and constipation. Genitourinary: Negative. Musculoskeletal: See present complaint.

Physical Examination: Reveals a well-developed, well-nourished male in no acute distress. Does have a hard time sitting due to pain in the right side. Ht 6'1", Wt 210 lbs, BP 122/90, pulse 72, respiration 20. Skin is clear, normal temperature and texture. HEENT: Head normal cephalic. Pupils are round, equal, and reactive to light accommodation. Canals are clear. Tympanic membranes, nose, and throat are clear of infection. Neck: Supple, thyroid negative. No adenopathy, no distomegaly or carotid bruits. Chest: Symmetrical, lungs clear to P & A. Heart: Normal sinus rhythm, no thrills or murmurs. Abdomen: Soft, no tenderness or masses. No organomegaly. Normal male genitalia. Extremities: Normal development. Patient does have tenderness in the area of the right sciatic knot and in the lower lumbar area on the right side. Has positive leg raising and some decrease in the deep tendon reflexes on the side.

Impression: Herniation of intervertebral disc at L5–S1 right side

Plan: Microdiskectomy tomorrow morning

Operative Report

Preoperative Diagnosis: Herniated nucleus pulposus, right

Postoperative Diagnosis: Same

Operation: Right L5–S1 diskectomy with minifacetectomy foraminotomy

Complications: None

Indications: The patient is an otherwise healthy 42-year-old Native American male who has had six months of disabling right leg pain. He has tried extensive physical therapy, nonsteroidal anti-inflammatory drugs, and an epidural injection, without relief. He has a positive straight leg-raising test on the right side and an absent ankle jerk. MRI scan confirms the disk herniation at L5–S1 on the right side.

Description of Procedure: The patient was brought to the operating room, and general anesthesia was administered in the usual fashion. He was positioned in the prone position onto a well-padded Andrews frame. All pressure points were well padded. The back was prepped and draped in a sterile fashion. He received 1 gm of Ancef prior to the beginning of the case along with 30 mg of IV Toradol®.

Initially, an x-ray was checked that showed we were at the L4–5 interspace, so we went down one level. A 3/4 skin incision was made in the midline of the lumbar sacral spine, and this was carried down to the subcutaneous tissue. The fascia over the L5–S1 lamina was then dissected away. The paraspinal muscles were then elevated above the lamina, and a laminotomy was performed in between the L5 and S1. The superior facet of S1 was the undercut using a Kerrison rongeur. The S1 nerve root was well visualized and this was protected throughout the procedure. Following this, a foraminotomy was performed over the top of the S1 nerve root. The S1 nerve root was then gently retracted medially, and a very large extrusive disk fragment was pulled out from underneath the S1 nerve root. The annulotomy that had been made from the disc herniation was then explored, and no further fragments could be found. The wound was thoroughly irrigated with a bacitracin solution. Gelfoam® and thrombin were placed over the top of the dura, and the deep fascia was closed with interrupted 0 VICRYL sutures. The subcutaneous tissue was closed with 2–0 VICRYL suture, and the skin was closed with 4–0 VICRYL suture. Benzoin and Steri-Strips were applied to the wound. The patient was returned to recovery in stable condition. EBL 10 cc.

Pathologic Diagnosis: Intervertebral disc L5–S1 resection, herniated nucleus pulposus

Which of the following is the correct code assignment? Code for surgical services only.

a. 722.52, 401.9, 63047
b. 722.73, 401.9, 63030
c. 722.10, 63047
d. 722.10, 401.9, 63030

9.49.   The following documentation is from the health record of a male patient.

Operative Report

Preoperative Diagnosis: 1. ACL deficient, right knee
2. Medial and lateral meniscal tear, right knee

Operation: 1. Examination under anesthesia, right knee
2. Arthroscopic-assisted anterior cruciate ligament reconstruction, right knee
3. Partial medial and partial lateral meniscectomy

Anesthesia: General

Complications: None

The patient was identified and taken to the operating room and general anesthesia administered. The patient's lower extremity was examined under anesthesia. The patient had evidence of +2 Lachman and +2 Pivot shift. After examination under anesthesia, the right lower extremity was prepped and draped in the usual sterile fashion. Routine arthroscopic portals were placed. Examination of the patellofemoral joint was fairly unremarkable. Coming down the medial gutter and the medial compartment revealed a complex tear of the posterior horn of the medial meniscus. Using a combination of basket and 4.2 shaver, partial medial meniscectomy was carried out. This resected about 50% of the posterior horn of the medial meniscus. There was a horizontal cleavage component remaining, it was stable to probing and this was left alone. Intercondylar notch revealed a complete tear of the anterior cruciate ligament. Going to the lateral compartment, there was a flap tear of the posterior horn of the lateral meniscus, and, again utilizing of the lateral meniscus, partial lateral meniscectomy was carried out. This resected about 30% of the posterior horn. At this point, the scope was removed from the knee. We did make a longitudinal incision based up the tibial tubercle medially. This was carried down through the skin and down the subcutaneous tissue. We readily identified the hamstring tendon and harvested the gracilis and semitendinosus. These were taken to the back table and a #2 ETHIBOND leader was placed on the leading edge, and the graft was doubled over for quadruple graft. The scope was placed back in the knee. Notchplasty was performed. Subsequently, we made a tibial tunnel utilizing the Arthrex® tibial guide referenced off the posterior cruciate ligament. We then made a femoral tunnel again utilizing the Arthrex femoral guide referenced off the posterior cortex. Both of these were 8 mm tunnels. We subsequently placed the graft on the knee, and we fixed it on the femoral side with 8 × 23 Arthrex bioabsorbable screw. Visualization of the graft revealed no evidence of impingement, no roughing on the medial aspect of the lateral wall. We subsequently held the knee in just short of full extension with appropriate amount of tension and fixed it on the tibial side with an 8 × 28 Arthrex bioabsorbable screw. Examination after placement of the graft revealed a negative Lachman and negative pivot shaft. Multiple intraoperative photos were obtained. At the end of the procedure, subcutaneous tissue was closed with 2-0 VICRYL, the skin with running 2-0 nylon, and portals with 3-0 nylon. Sterile dressing was placed followed by ACE wrap and total thigh and knee immobilizer. The patient tolerated the procedure well and there were no complications.

Assign the correct codes for this case:

Principal diagnosis: _____

Additional diagnoses: _____

Procedures: _____

Neoplasms

9.50. A 63-year-old patient is admitted for colostomy infection. Patient has Stage IV ascending colon cancer that has metastasized to the liver and lung. On the previous admission two weeks ago, the surgeon performed a colon resection with colostomy. The patient now presents with an infection at the colostomy site. Discharge summary states colostomy infection and abdominal cellulitis with Staphylococcus aureus bacterium, which was treated with IV antibiotics. Which of the following is the correct ICD-9-CM code assignment?

a. 153.6, 569.61, 682.2, 041.11, 197.7, 197.0
b. 569.61, 998.59, 153.6, 197.7, 197.0
c. 153.6, 569.61, 197.7, 197.0
d. 569.61, 682.2, 041.11, 153.6, 197.7, 197.0

9.51. A patient with a chronic cough and shortness of breath is scheduled for a pleural biopsy following a chest x-ray that revealed a significant mass in the left lower lobe of the lung. Due to the position of the mass, a pleural biopsy is planned rather than a bronchoscopic biopsy.

Following the administration of local anesthetic in the interventional radiology suite of the hospital, a pleural biopsy needle is passed over the left side of the ribs. Fluoroscopic guidance is used to guide needle placement into the mass, so that tissue is obtained for pathologic evaluation.

Which of the following code sets would the physician assign for this procedure if carcinoma of the lung is diagnosed?

a. 162.9, 32400, 76003
b. 786.09, 786.2, 32405
c. 162.5, 32405, 76003-26
d. 162.5, 786.09, 786.2, 32405, 76003-26

9.52. A patient with hemoptysis, hoarseness, and chronic cough is scheduled for an outpatient flexible fiberoptic laryngoscopy including a biopsy of the cricoid. The procedure was performed in the hospital outpatient area. Following administration of IV sedation and a topical anesthetic spray, a flexible fiberoptic laryngoscope is inserted and biopsies are taken from multiple sites of the affected areas. The pathology report states "metastatic carcinoma of the arytenoid cartilage and the posterior commissure and well-differentiated carcinoma of the cricoid and extrinsic larynx." The operative note states suspected involvement of the thyroid cartilage with primary malignancy believed to be from the esophagus. The patient experienced an increase in blood pressure after the biopsies were obtained, and the procedure was discontinued. An esophagoscopy will be scheduled after the patient's blood pressure is stabilized.

Which of the following code sets would the physician report?

a. 197.3, 199.1, 796.2, 31576
b. 161.8, 198.89, 401.9, 31510
c. 150.9, 197.3, 197.3, 197.3, 197.3, 997.1, 31576-53
d. 150.9, 161.8, 796.2, 31576

9.53. A Medicare patient with a personal history of colon cancer, considered to be at high risk for recurrent disease, presents to the office for a screening colonoscopy. The gastroenterologist also examines the anastomosis sites following a previous hemicolectomy.

Procedure: The patient was prepped in the usual fashion, followed by placement in the left lateral decubitus position. I administered 3 mg of Versed. Monitoring of sedation was assisted by a trained RN.

A colonoscopy to the terminal ileum was performed with lesions found just beyond the splenic flexure, which were biopsied. In the sigmoid colon, two polyps were found and excised by hot biopsy forceps.

The pathology report showed the descending colon lesions to be a recurrence of the malignancy and the polyps to be adenomatous.

Which of the following code sets would be reported for the procedure performed in the office?

a. 153.2, 45384
b. 153.2, 211.3, 45384, 45380-59
c. V67.09, V10.05, 153.2, G0105, 45384-59
d. 153.9, V10.05, V45.89, 45384, 45380

9.54. A Medicare beneficiary visits the oncology clinic for follow-up. Following a comprehensive history and detailed examination, including pelvic and breast examinations, the physician elects to perform a hysteroscopy with endometrial biopsy to evaluate postmenopausal bleeding and rule out a neoplastic source. The patient also has a suspicious lump (enlarged lymph nodes) under the arm, which is suspected to be a recurrence of breast cancer resected eight years ago that will require a future biopsy to stage. According to the clinic form, the physician's medical decision making was considered moderate complexity. The pathology report from the biopsy indicates primary endometrial cancer.

Which of the following will be reported for this clinic service?

a. 182.0, 627.1, V10.3, 58558, 99214-59
b. 182.0, 785.6, V10.3, 58558, 99214-25
c. 182.0, 785.6, V10.3, 58558-25
d. 182.0, 785.6, V10.3, 58555, 58100, 99214-25

9.55. The following documentation is from the health record of a 78-year-old male patient.

Preoperative Diagnosis: Need for permanent venous access

Postoperative Diagnosis: Same

Description of Procedure: Placement of Infuse-A-Port®, right subclavian vein

The patient is a 78-year-old Hispanic male with disseminated metastatic colon carcinoma under chemotherapy management. His oncologist has requested placement of a permanent venous access catheter.

The patient was brought to the operating room and placed in the supine position. The initial request was for placement in the left subclavian vein. However, after cannulation of the vein and injection of contrast, there was not adequate flow to allow passage of the guidewire through the vein into the superior vena cava. Therefore, the left-sided procedure was aborted.

The right subclavian vein was cannulated without difficulty, and the guidewire was passed centrally down into the superior vena cava. The location was confirmed with fluoroscopy. A subcutaneous pocket and tunnel was then created for the port. The port was placed just above the pectoral fascia. The dilator and peel-away catheter and sheath were passed off the guidewire into the subclavian. The sheath was peeled away, and the catheter that had been previously trimmed to the appropriate length and flushed with heparinized saline was passed through the sheath into the subclavian. The sheath was peeled away, and hemostasis was achieved. The port was sutured into the pocket with 3-0 Dexon. The 2.5 cm wound was irrigated with saline and closed in layers with 3-0 Dexon subcutaneously followed with 4-0 Dexon subcuticular for the skin. Steri-Strips were applied with sterile dressing and tape. Following the procedure, a chest x-ray in the holding area revealed no pneumothorax and the catheter in excellent position.

Which of the following code sets would the surgeon report for this ambulatory surgical service performed at the hospital?

a. 199.0, 153.9, 36561, 36556-59
b. 153.9, 36563, 36410-53
c. 199.0, 153.9, 36561, 36410-59
d. V58.81, 199.0, 153.9, 36561, 12031

Disorders of the Nervous System and Sense Organs

9.56. A patient presents to the neurology clinic for assessment of apraxia at the request of her primary care physician. The patient has a history of CVA and has expressive aphasia. She is unable to carry out purposeful movements, even though she has normal muscle tone and coordination. A full assessment is performed using the Boston Diagnostic Aphasia Examination including interpretation and report (1 hour). The consulting neurologist conducts a detailed history and examination, performs medical decision making of low complexity, and dictates a complete report to the requesting physician, along with the finding of the aphasia assessment.

Which of the following code sets is reported for this service?

a. 438.11, 438.81, 99203, 96105
b. 784.3, 784.69, 99244
c. 438.81, 99243
d. 438.11, 438.81, 99243-25, 96105

9.57. This 35-year-old female patient was admitted with the diagnosis of cerebral aneurysm. The following procedure was performed: Intracranial aneurysm repair by intracranial approach with microdissection, carotid circulation. The patient continued to improve with no residual defects. During the hospital stay, she did experience postoperative pneumonia due to Pseudomonas.

In addition to the E/M codes submitted by the office, what ICD-9-CM codes and CPT codes are assigned?

a. 437.3, 61700
b. 430, 482.1, 61700, 69990-51
c. 437.3, 997.3, 482.1, 61700, 69990
d. 747.81, 997.3, 61703, 69990

9.58. A patient presents to the neurology clinic for a consultation with a neurologist for intention tremors with periodic muscle weakness in the upper body.

Short-latency somatosensory-evoked potential studies were conducted immediately following a comprehensive history, comprehensive neurologic examination, and decision making of moderate complexity. Both arms and the head and trunk were tested. The results of the interpretation of the tests state "Rule out MS," and a report was sent to the requesting physician stating that a diagnosis of multiple sclerosis could not be ruled out at this time and further testing would be undertaken at a later date. Which of the following is correct?

a. 333.1, 728.9, 99244-25, 95925, 95927-51
b. 340, 99245-25, 95927
c. 333.1, 728.9, 99204, 95925, 95927-51
d. 728.9, 781.0, 99244-25, 95927

9.59. A Medicare patient has a persistent pain syndrome of the low back and leg subsequent to an automobile accident five years ago in which he sustained back injuries. The patient is brought to the outpatient surgery center nerve block area and is premedicated so he is relaxed enough to position appropriately. The sacral area is prepped with Betadine and a 25-gauge, followed by a 22-gauge needle, is placed under lidocaine anesthesia in the caudal space. 29 ccs of solution were injected containing 150 cc of Xylocaine and 16 mg of Decadron LA®. The patient remained in good condition in the block room and the recovery area.

Which of the following procedure code sets is reported?

a. 64449
b. 62319
c. 62311
d. 62311, 76005

9.60. This 45-year-old patient has been followed for left ear conductive hearing loss. It was decided to proceed with surgery to correct the condition. The postoperative diagnosis is left ear otosclerosis. During the procedure, a markedly thickened stapes footplate was observed; however, the eustachian tube was intact, and there was normal mobility of the malleus and incus. The left ear stapedectomy with drillout of the footplate proceeded uneventfully. During recovery, the patient experienced atrial fibrillation. This was felt to be due to the surgery because the EKG was normal during the preoperative evaluation. The patient was admitted to the hospital from the outpatient surgical area, and a consultation was requested from the cardiologist. I will continue to follow the patient.

With the exception of E/M codes, what are the correct diagnosis and procedure codes?

a. 387.9, 997.1, 427.31, 69661-LT
b. 387.9, 69661-LT
c. 387.9, 427.31, 69661-LT
d. 387.9, 69660-LT

Newborn/Congenital Disorders

9.61. The following documentation is from the health record of a newborn infant.

Newborn Care

Delivery Note: 11/20/XX, 2300. Called to provide pediatric standby during delivery for suspected nuchal cord. Mother G2, P1. Onset of labor 0730 with normal progression. Entered stage 2 labor at 2100. Fetal monitor showed occasional decelerations. Spontaneous rupture of membranes at 2110, fluid was clear. Noted to have nuchal cord at time of delivery. Otherwise uneventful course.

O: Initial Apgar 8/9. Weight 3340 grams. Approximate gestational age 38 weeks.

General: Pink with lusty cry. HEENT: Normal, moderate molding, minimal caput. Spine intact. Lungs: Clear bilaterally. Cardiovascular: No murmur noted, capillary refill less than 2 seconds.

Assessment: Normal full-term newborn, noted to have nuchal cord with occasional decels, otherwise uneventful delivery.

Plan: No further intervention at this time. Transferred to newborn nursery for routine newborn care and monitoring.

Progress Note: 11/21/yy, 0630

Subjective: Female newborn, gestational age 39 $^3/_7$ wks. Product of full-term pregnancy, NSVD, SROM epidural anesthesia, sl nuchal cord. Initial Apgar 8/9.

Mother is 32-year-old G2 P1. Pregnancy was significant for maternal hypothyroidism and vanishing twin syndrome. See delivery note for labor course. EDC 24 Nov, initial prenatal care at 10 $^3/_7$ wks. Maternal labs: blood type O positive, ABS neg, Rub immune, VDRL nonreactive, HIV neg, GBS neg, 1hr GTT 82, HBsAg neg, GC/Chlm neg.

Objective: Birth wt 7 lb 6 oz, head circ 14″, length 19 3/4″, head: normocephalic, fontanelles soft nonbulging. Mild caput, moderate molding. Skin: Pink and warm. Eyes: + red reflux × 2, PERRL. ENT: Nares patent, palate intact. TMs clear bilaterally. Lungs: Bilateral breath sounds equal, no accessory muscle use noted. Cardiovascular: regular rate and rhythm, no murmur appreciated. Well-perfused, normal pulses. Capillary refill less than 2 seconds. Abdomen: Normal active bowel sounds, soft no masses, three-vessel cord. No erythema or discharge at umbilical stump. Genitalia: Normal female minimal engorgement, anus patent. Neuro: Lusty cry, good suck, reflexes: + rooting, + morrow, + grip, + Babinski's present bilaterally. Skeletal: Clavicle is intact. Spine: No dimples or defects noted. Hips: Normal range of motion, no click noted.

Assessment: Healthy, full-term infant. No defects noted.

Plan: Continue routine newborn care and monitoring. Hearing screen ordered. Check bili, ABO, CBC, and Coombs given Rh+ mother. Continue breast feeding, no supplemental feeding at this time.

Discharge Exam: 11/22/XX, 1000

Subjective: 2 d/o female infant. Breast feeding q. 2 hr., 10 min ea breast; mother denies diff with latching on (+ breast fed previous infant), + lusty cry when hungry, easily consoled. + Wet diapers q. 2–3 hours, + meconium diapers × 3 since birth.

Objective: wt 7 lbs 1.5 oz, afebrile throughout admission

See Newborn D/C Pe Form

Lab: Coombs neg, blood type B neg, bili 12, HTC 37, hearing screen pass, initial PKU pending

Assessment: Normal, healthy term infant, s/p SVD

Plan: D/C to home. Continue breast feeding. Follow up in clinic for wt check and repeat bili in three days. Hep B and 2nd PKU in two weeks. RT ER for temp > 100.5°F, no wet diapers > 12 hours, lethargy, or resp distress. Education given to parents regarding use of car seat, + verbalized understanding.

Which of the following CPT code sets accurately represents the physician's services for this newborn hospital stay?

	11/20	11/21	11/22
a.	99431	99433	99238
b.	99431, 99436	99433	99238
c.	99431, 99360	99233	99238
d.	99436	99232	99238

9.62.   The following documentation is from the health record of a two-year-old boy.

Patient Name: Johnny Jones

CC: Routine checkup

HPI: Johnny is 2 ½-years-old and has Down syndrome and a ventricular septal defect, surgically corrected. Mother reports he is pulling at his ears and has been running a temp of 99 to 100°F in the past two evenings. Tylenol Liquid has been effective in fever resolution according to mother. Development is coming along as expected. Walks with an ataxic gait but does not run. One-word speech pattern. No two-word sentences yet. Appetite is good. Child appears happy, well-groomed, and well-nourished. Mother reports no specific behavior or social-adjustment concerns.

Past History: Normal SVB, 8 lbs 5 oz, 24″ long. Heart surgery at seven months. No known allergies. No medication at this time. Takes daily multivitamins.

Social: Lives at home with mother, father, and older brother. Receives physical, speech, and occupational therapy services from area education services in the home on a periodic basis.

Review of Systems: See patient data sheet and pediatric growth profile chart, not remarkable other than notation concerning recurrent ear infections. No cyanotic episodes, difficulty breathing, or other cardiac symptoms reported. Johnny had a follow-up visit to the cardiologist last month and his findings were reviewed; no significant problems. No voiding or digestive complaints by mother. Child still in diapers. All other systems negative (see detailed history).

Physical Exam: Wt 27 lbs, Ht 36″ HEENT: Both ears positive for redness and otitis media with effusion evident on the left, eyes PERRLA, nose slightly congested clear discharge, neck supple without adenopathy. Throat slightly red. Temp. 99.6°F, BP 108/82, R 15, P 72. Heart regular rate and rhythm; lungs clear to auscultation and percussion, no rales or wheezing. Abdomen soft without tenderness.

Extremities negative. (Detailed)

Assessment: Acute serous otitis media and slight throat infection, likely viral. Inject Bicillin C-R, 600,000 units and follow-up appointment in three days. No immunizations needed at this time. Fifteen additional minutes spent in counseling the mother concerning developmental expectations and reviewing cardiologist findings and answering questions about future cardiac risks.

Which of the following code sets is assigned for reporting the pediatrician's services?

a. 381.01, 462, 758.0, V45.89, 99214, 90772, J0530
b. V20.2, 381.01, 462, 758.0, V45.89, 99392, 99214-25
c. 381.01, 462, 99214, 90772
d. 758.0, V45.89, 99213, J0530

9.63. The following documentation is from the health record of a 10-year-old boy.

Preoperative Diagnosis: Status post palatoplasty, history of bilateral incomplete cleft palate with recurrent tonsillitis

Postoperative Diagnosis: Same

Operation: Second-stage palatoplasty with attachment of pharyngeal flap and incidental tonsillectomy

Indications: 10-year-old patient scheduled for revision of palatoplasty with incidental tonsillectomy requested by pediatrician due to repeated infections

Description of Procedure: The patient was prepped and draped in normal sterile fashion. A midline incision was made through the soft palate, exposing the posterior pharyngeal wall. A flap was then taken by incising the mucosa, submucosa, and underlying muscle, and securely sutured to the soft palate.

Bilateral tonsillectomy was then performed by grasping with a tonsil clamp and capsule dissection. Bleeders were controlled with electrocautery and gauze packing. Sponge and instrument counts were taken and correct, and the patient was transferred to the recovery room in good condition. Follow-up in the office in three days.

Which of the following code sets will be reported?

a. 749.04, 42225, 42825
b. 749.04, 474.00, 42225
c. 749.04, 474.00, 42225, 42825-51
d. V50.8, 749.04, 474.00, 42200, 42826-51

9.64.   The following documentation is from the health record of a 10-month-old baby.

Hospital Outpatient Diagnostic Services

A 10-month-old infant was found to have a heart murmur during the newborn hospital stay. A 2D echocardiogram and Doppler study demonstrated a ventricular septal defect. At the age of three months, congestive heart failure developed, which has been managed by digitalis administration and diuretics. A cardiac catheterization is performed to measure the magnitude of the defect and to assess pulmonary artery pressure and resistance. A right heart catheterization with selective biplane cineangiocardiograms to the femoral vein for pulmonary angiography and aortography were performed in the cardiac catheterization suite of the hospital. Because of the age of the patient, conscious sedation was provided using an intravenous route by the physician.

Which of the following code sets is reported by the pediatric cardiologist reporting this service?

a. 745.4, 785.2, 93530, 93541, 93544, 93556
b. 785.2, 37.21, 88.42, 88.52
c. 745.4, 93530-26, 93541, 93544, 93556-26
d. 745.4, 93530, 93541, 93544, 93556

Pediatric Conditions

9.65.   A three-year-old child was brought to the emergency department after inhaling a peanut. The child had a brassy cough that was not present prior to the incident. X-rays showed congestion in the lungs but no obvious foreign body in the larynx. The child was given Versed intravenously and placed on a papoose board. The emergency department physician could see the peanut on indirect laryngoscopy but could not grasp it with multiple attempts. An ENT specialist was called and took the patient to surgery for removal under anesthesia. An expanded, problem-focused history, problem-focused physical exam, and medical decision making of low complexity were documented.

Give the correct CPT codes for reporting the independent ED physician's service:

a. 99281-25, 31505
b. 99281-25, 31511
c. 99282, 31505
d. 99281, 31511

9.66. A one-year-old child was seen for a well-child check. Growth charts were initiated as she had not been seen previously for a well-child check at this clinic. The physician noted that she had completed the antibiotics that he had prescribed for OM and the ears were clear. The rest of the history and exam were unremarkable. Three shots were given: HepB-Hib, MMR, and IPV.

Which of the following code sets is correct for reporting this office visit?

a. V20.2, V06.8, V06.4, V04.0, 99392, 90748, 90707, 90713, 90471, 90472, 90472

b. V20.2, V06.8, V06.4, V04.0, 99391, 90748, 90707, 90713, 90471, 90472

c. V20.2, V06.8, V06.4, V04.0, 99392, 90744, 90645, 90707, 90713, 90472

d. V20.2, V06.8, V06.4, V04.0, 382.9, 99382, 90748, 90707, 90713, 90472

9.67. The following documentation is from the health record of a boy with a fracture.

Office Visits

3/31 Office Visit (Primary Care Physician)

S: Peter was playing basketball today, fell, and hurt his wrist.

O: Tenderness and swelling of the wrist, especially the volar aspect. There is a slight abrasion over the swelling. X-ray shows a fracture of the ulnar styloid and possibly the distal radius. There is some question of dorsal displacement of the epiphysis. Short arm cast is applied for comfort measures.

A: Fracture of the ulnar styloid

P: I am going to have the orthopedist look at the x-ray and obtain a consult to determine if reduction is necessary. Return to clinic in two days for ortho appt, sooner if problems.

4/1 Office Visit (Primary Care Physician)

S: Peter has pain inside his cast.

O: We thought this was pressure, so I split the cast and it really didn't relieve the pain much at all. I asked him what was hurting about it, and he said it was hurting further up his arm. Then he told me that at the time he had the injury he noticed a great big bulge there. He thought it was the bone poking through, pushed on it, and it sort of went down by itself. His x-ray clearly shows there is no bony injury at that area, but that he has the fracture down by the epiphyseal plate. This is probably a torn muscle.

A: Torn muscle left arm with fracture.

P: Keep the appointment with ortho tomorrow. In the meantime, symptomatic care, and we left the cast split because it is probably going to have to be removed for adequate exam tomorrow anyway.

4/2 Office Visit (Primary Care Physician)

S: Peter injured the left wrist playing basketball. He is right-hand dominant. He is currently in a short arm cast, which had been split previously because it was a bit too snug. With the cast he has wrist in extension at least 15 degrees despite the fact that he has the epiphyseal plate fracture with slight posterior displacement of the distal fragment of about 4 mm. He has seen the orthopod in consultation, who felt that this did not require further reduction.

O: He has intact CMS today. Cast is removed, and he is placed in a short arm cast with anterior flexion of about 10 degrees with very slight ulnar deviation. The position of the distal epiphysis of the radius appears to be about the same as it was on the original x-rays taken a week ago. This position alignment should be quite satisfactory.

A: Distal radial fracture, Colles' type, with ulnar styloid fracture

P: We will continue with the short arm cast for a duration of six weeks. He is to return to see me in two weeks for repeat x-ray through the cast and follow up sooner if any problems.

Which of the following is the correct code set to report these visits with the primary care physician?

a. 3/31: 813.43, 25600, A4580
    4/1: 813.43, 840.9, 99024
    4/2: 813.44, 99024, A4580
b. 3/31: 813.43, 29075, A4580
    4/1: 840.9, 813.43, 99213
    4/2: 813.44, 25600, A4580
c. 3/31: 813.43, 25605, A4580
    4/1: 840.9, 813.43, 99213
    4/2: 813.44, 29075, A4580
d. 3/31: 813.43, 29075, A4580
    4/1: 840.9, 813.43, 99213
    4/2: 813.44, 25605, A4580

9.68.   The following documentation is from the health record of a 14-year-old male patient.

Admission Date: 2/2/XX

Discharge Date: 2/3/XX

Admission Diagnosis: Peritonsillar abscess

Discharge Diagnoses: 1. Peritonsillar abscess
                           2. Chronic tonsillitis
                           3. Mononucleosis
                           4. Type I diabetes

Reason for Hospitalization: This patient is a 14-year-old white male with a history of right peritonsillar abscess in December who presented with a four- to five-day history of progressively increasing sore throat. He had previously been started on amoxicillin as an outpatient, but the severity of his symptoms increased. He presented to the ER on 2/2 with findings consistent with a peritonsillar abscess.

Hospital Course: He was admitted and started on IV Unasyn. Blood glucose levels were drawn and showed only slight hypoglycemia, no doubt as a result of decreased intake due to throat pain. Insulin dosage was adjusted accordingly. An ENT consult was performed, and I&D was recommended. An endocrinology consult was obtained, and he was cleared for surgery. The patient was taken to the operating room that same day. An I&D of the right peritonsillar abscess was performed with a unilateral right tonsillectomy, given his history of recurrent peritonsillar abscesses. The patient was continued on IV antibiotics overnight. The following day, the patient reported significant improvement in his throat pain. He was noted to be afebrile. His Monospot was positive and consistent with acute infectious mononucleosis. Blood glucose levels were adequate. Later, on 2/3, he was seen by the surgeon who felt he was doing well from a surgical standpoint. The patient was tolerating p.o. well, and the decision was made to discharge the patient home later that same day.

The patient is in satisfactory condition at the time of discharge. Discharge medications include Roxicet® p.r.n. for throat pain, Augmentin, and insulin.

He was instructed to comply with a soft diet until further follow-up. Extra time was spent reviewing his insulin regimen and making adjustments (35 minutes with patient and family). Additionally, he was educated about activity restrictions, including no vigorous exercise or contact sports for the next three to four weeks because of his mononucleosis. The patient was instructed to follow up with the surgeon in two weeks.

Which of the following code sets is correct for reporting the attending physician's services on the day of discharge?

a. 475, 474.00, 075, 250.01, 99239
b. 475, 474.00, 075, 250.81, 99238
c. 475, 075, 250.01, 99238
d. 475, 474.0, 075, 250.81, 99239

Conditions of Pregnancy, Childbirth, and the Puerperium

9.69. The following documentation is from the health record of a female patient.

Discharge Summary

Admission Date: 03/12/00

Discharge Date: 03/23/00

Discharge Diagnoses: 1. Term intrauterine pregnancy, delivered, single liveborn.
2. Maternal obesity
3. Iron deficiency anemia
4. Herpes simplex virus type II with spontaneous rupture of membranes
5. Retained placenta
6. Endometritis

Procedures Performed: Right paramedian episiotomy, low outlet forceps vaginal delivery, repair of right paramedian episiotomy with repair of partial fourth degree extension, manual removal of placenta 3/13/00. Dilation and suction curettage 3/22/00.

Hospital Course: This patient presented at 39-weeks gestation with rupture of membranes of clear fluid. She was not in active labor, her cervix was unfavorable for induction. She was initially managed expectantly, and oxytocin was used to facilitate labor. She progressed throughout the active phase of labor without complications. The fetal evaluations were reassuring throughout the labor process.

The fetal head presented on the perineum in the OA position; and because of maternal exhaustion and inability to allow further descent because there was a single nuchal cord released, low outlet forceps were placed after right paramedian episiotomy was performed, and the fetal head was delivered without difficulty. Upon delivery, there was a partial fourth-degree extension just through the anal mucosa. There was retained placenta and manual extraction was required. The episiotomy was repaired by using 000 VICRYL suture, closing the rectal mucosa.

The postpartum course was complicated by the patient developing endometritis. The patient was placed on IV antibiotics and showed some sign of improvement with a dropping white blood count; however, her temperature continued to spike. An initial ultrasound revealed some intrauterine products that appeared to be retained placenta. The following day, however, she passed these retained products without difficulty, and her bleeding subsided. Her temperature, however, continued to develop intermittent fever, and the antibiotics were switched to the IV, and she again showed a good clinical response with decreased uterine tenderness. Because of the fever continuing, however; a follow-up ultrasound was performed, and no placental products were appreciated. However, there were some clots and unidentifiable tissues still remaining in the intrauterine cavity. Thus, a dilation and curettage was performed on 3/22/00, and some amniotic membranes were removed, which appeared to be infected. There were no placental products noted in the curettage.

After removal of the amniotic membrane, her temperature defervesced, and she remained afebrile throughout the remainder of the hospitalization. On discharge, she was tolerating a regular diet, ambulatory without complaints, very scant vaginal spotting, and on oral antibiotics.

It should be noted that because of the excessive blood loss and the preexisting anemic condition prior to delivery, she was given two units of transfusion to maintain hemoglobin from 8–9. She was asymptomatic with this hemoglobin; and thus was placed on iron and Colace throughout the remainder of her hospitalization.

Discharge Medications: Include iron sulfate, Colace, and Augmentin

Which of the following is the correct code set presuming this physician provided the antepartum and postpartum care?

a. 667.02, 648.21, 285.1, 646.62, 670.02, 647.61, 054.9, 646.11, 664.31, 663.31, V27.0; 59400, 59160-78

b. 667.04, 646.62, 670.02, 647.61, 054.9, 646.11, 664.31, 663.31, V27.0; 59400, 59300-51, 58120-78

c. 667.02, 648.21, 285.1, 647.61, 646.11, 664.31, 663.31, V27.0; 59400, 59300, 59160

d. 667.04, 648.21, 285.1, 646.62, 670.02, 647.61, 054.9, 664.31, V27.0; 59400, 58120

9.70. The following documentation is from the health record of a female patient.

Anesthesia: IV sedation by CRNA combined with paracervical block

Preop DX: Anembryonic gestation

Operation: Suction curettage

Postop DX: Anembryonic gestation

History: Problem list includes G4, P2, L2, and missed abortion. Patient has asthma with medications including albuterol p.r.n.

Findings: The laminaria that had been placed in the office yesterday had dilated the cervix, which easily fit a #20 Hanks dilator. The uterus sounded 12 cm. The uterus was 10 weeks size. There was a moderate amount of tissue obtained from the uterine cavity.

Procedure: Under satisfactory intravenous medication, the patient was prepped and draped in the dorsolithotomy position. A speculum was placed. Paracervical block was administered. The laminaria was removed. Using a #9 rigid curved Vacurette, curettage was performed. There was good clamping down effect of the uterus. The intrauterine contents were expelled. There were no complications of the procedure. There was a satisfactory amount of bleeding following the procedure. Estimated blood loss was negligible.

Path report demonstrates histological sections of the uterine contents, which show multiple chorionic villi. This is accompanied by fragments of decidualized tissue and gestational-type endometrium. These histological findings represent products of conception.

Which of the following code sets would be reported for this procedure?

a. 632, 493.90, 59820, 59200-51
b. 630, 493.90, 59870
c. 631, 59856, 59200
d. 631, 493.90, 59820

Disorders of the Respiratory System

9.71. Patient seen in the office with increasing shortness of breath, weakness, and ineffective cough. This patient is seen frequently for this chronic condition. Orders were given for chest x-ray and lab work. Antibiotics were also prescribed. This patient already is on oxygen at home. I will try to manage this patient at home, per his wishes. A detailed history was done with an expanded problem-focused exam, and medical decision making of moderate complexity. Diagnoses listed as acute respiratory insufficiency and acute exacerbation of COPD. Which of the following is the correct ICD-9-CM diagnostic code assignment?

    a. 491.21, 518.82, 99214
    b. 518.81, 491.21, 99213
    c. 518.82, 491.21, 99203
    d. 491.21, 99214

9.72. A patient has recurrent polyposis with right pansinusitis and left anterior polyposis with blocked maxillary ostiomeatal units on both sides. The surgeon performs a bilateral intranasal sphenoethmoidectomy and maxillary antrostomy with polypectomy.

The patient was placed under general anesthesia and appropriately prepped and draped. The nose was anesthetized with cocaine flakes, 200–300 mg, and topical adrenaline 1:1000. A large polyposis on the right side was removed to gain access for more vasoconstriction, using a Robert's snare. Injections of Xylocaine and epinephrine were also used, and the procedure was essentially the same on both sides.

On the left side, there was extensive scarring of the middle turbinate, so through-cutting punches were used to open up the ethmoidectomy bilaterally. While manipulating the left middle turbinate, there was a small CSF leak noted at the junction of the turbinate with the equivaform area. No instrumentation had been done in this area, and it was only a slit-like small leak. This was packed with topical Gelfoam and topical thrombin with Gelfoam at the end of the case and held unto the pack. The nasal antral windows were opened bilaterally and were cannulated, using the right-angle ethmoid curet until palpation showed the natural ostium of the maxillary sinus. The uncinate process was still there from the previous surgery, and this was removed with back-biting forceps and opened into the maxillary sinus widely.

Both sphenoides were widely opened. There was an adhesion from the head of the middle turbinate to the nasal septum on the left side, and this was lysed. A Cottle speculum and the through-cutting forceps were used throughout the case, as well as the 1.7 power magnification operating microscope. The patient had a moderate bout of bleeding bilaterally that was controlled with towel clip pledgets of 1:10,000 of adrenaline. Silastic splints were placed on both sides of the nose to prevent adhesions and were sewn in with 4-0 Prolene sutures. Expandable foam packs were then placed and expanded with 1 gram and 10 cc of Ancef. The procedure was then terminated with estimated blood loss at 300 cc for the entire case. The patient tolerated the procedure well and there were no CSF leaks found at the end of the procedure.

Which diagnosis and procedure codes are assigned for this procedure performed in the outpatient surgical department of the hospital?

a. 473.8, 471.8, 349.81, 31201-50, 31051-50, 31020-50, 69990
b. 473.8, 471.8, 998.2, E870.0, E849.7, 31201-50, 31051-50, 31020-50
c. 478.19, 473.8, 31267-50, 31288-50, 31254-50, 69990
d. 473.8, 471.8, 998.11, 998.2, E870.0, E849.7, 31090-50, 69990

9.73. A patient with bilateral partial vocal cord paralysis requires removal of the arytenoid cartilage to improve breathing. Following a temporary tracheostomy, a topical anesthetic is applied to the oral cavity, pharynx, and larynx, and the laryngoscope with operating microscope is inserted. After adequate visualization is established, the arytenoid cartilage is exposed by excision of the mucosa overlying it. The procedure is performed in the outpatient surgery center of the hospital. Which diagnosis and procedure code(s) is going to be reported for this procedure?

a. 478.33, 31561, 31600
b. 478.30, 31560
c. 478.33, 31561
d. 478.33, 31560, 69990

9.74. A 54-year-old male patient with bronchial carcinoma, right lower lobe, has an obstructed bronchus in the right lower lobe of the lung. The pulmonologist views the airway using a bronchoscope introduced through the oral airway following administration of conscious sedation. Thirty minutes of moderate sedation services were performed. The obstruction is identified with the assistance of fluoroscopic guidance. A laser probe is introduced through the bronchoscope to eradicate the obstruction and relieve the stenosis. The procedure was performed in the physician's clinic/surgery center. What codes are reported for this outpatient ambulatory surgery service?

a. 162.5, 31641, 99143
b. 162.5, 31641, 76001
c. 239.1, 31640, 99143-51
d. 239.1, 31641, 99143, 76001

9.75. A patient is scheduled for a transbronchial needle aspiration biopsy with fluoroscopic guidance for a lung mass. Following the administration of conscious sedation by the anesthetist, the patient experiences a run of atrial fibrillation, and the physician elects to terminate the procedure before the biopsy is obtained. The procedure is done in the hospital same-day surgery department.

Which of the following shows correct code assignment?

a. 239.1, V64.1, 31629, 76000
b. 786.6, 427.31, 31629-52
c. 786.6, 427.31, V64.1, 31628-53
d. 786.6, 427.31, V64.1, 31629-53

9.76. This patient was admitted to have a thoracoscopic lobectomy performed. The patient has a malignant neoplasm of the left lower lobe. Because of extensive pleural effusion, I was unable to complete the endoscopic procedure. We converted to an open technique, and a successful lobectomy was performed. The patient tolerated the procedure well. What are the correct procedure codes?

a. 32480, 32663-53
b. 32663, 32480
c. 32480
d. 32484, 32663-52

Trauma and Poisoning

9.77. An adult patient sustained second- and third-degree burns of the abdomen after knocking a pan of boiling water off the stove. The burn size was documented as greater than 10 percent of the total body surface area. Due to the associated pain, local anesthesia including IM Demerol was administered. The wound was debrided, and a sterile dressing was applied. The patient was transferred to a burn unit for further treatment.

What are the correct CPT and ICD-9-CM code assignments for this procedure as reported and billed by the emergency department physician, who performed a detailed medical history, performed an expanded problem-focused physical examination to rule out other injuries, and rendered moderately complex medical decision making before undertaking the burn care?

a. 99283-25, 16030, 942.33, 948.10, E924.0
b. 16030, 942.33, 948.00, E924.0
c. 99284, 16025, 942.23, 942.33, E924.0
d. 16000, 948.10, E924.0

9.78. A motorcyclist is brought into the emergency department after a motorcycle accident. The ED physician confirms an open tibia (proximal) fracture and performs extensive debridement of gravel, glass, and other matter, down to and including part of the muscle, at the site of the fracture in preparation for surgery. The orthopedic surgeon then takes the patient to surgery to perform the reduction of the fracture, and the patient is subsequently admitted to the hospital.

In addition to the evaluation and management service, what is the correct code assignment for the ED physician's services?

a. 27535, 11011-51; 823.10, E819.2
b. 11043; 823.12, E819.2
c. 11011; 823.10, E819.2
d. 27535, 11043-51; 823.90, E819.2

9.79. A 35-year-old patient was a passenger on a motorcycle involved in an accident and sustained three severely broken ribs and a fractured femur. Chest x-ray showed a 45 percent collapse of the left lung and air in the pleural space.

The patient complained of increasing shortness of breath and was cyanotic. A chest tube was inserted into the third intercostal space by the ED physician. Subsequent chest x-ray showed marked improvement, to only 5 percent collapse. The patient was thoroughly evaluated by the emergency department physician for possible internal injuries. The emergency department physician documented a comprehensive history, physical examination, and complex medical decision making. Final diagnosis was tension pneumothorax; fractured femur, midshaft; and multiple rib fractures. The patient was taken to surgery by the on-call orthopedic surgeon to care for the fractured femur sustained in the accident.

Which of the following is the correct code set for reporting the ED physician's services?

a. 512.0, 821.01, 807.03, E819.3; 99284-25, 32020
b. 860.0, 821.01, 807.03, E819.3; 99285-25, 32020
c. 860.0, 821.00, 807.09, E819.3; 99285, 32002
d. 512.0, 821.00, 807.09, E819.3; 99284, 32002

9.80. In the same accident as above, the 23-year-old driver of the motorcycle, who was not wearing a helmet, was brought into the ED, unresponsive, with tachypnea and tachycardia. The diagnosis was a severe head injury with multiple skull fractures. Dr. Smith, following intubation with an 8 mm endotracheal tube, placed a percutaneous nontunneled centrally inserted central venous line. History was unobtainable from the patient. The patient was hand-bagged by Dr. Smith for approximately 20 minutes until the neurosurgeon arrived and assumed care of the patient.

Which of the following code sets would be reported by Dr. Smith?

a. 803.06, E819.2, 99291, 36556
b. 803.46, E819.3, 99291, 31500
c. 803.33, E819.2, 99285, 31500, 36556-51
d. 803.46, E819.2, 99285, 31500, 36556-51

9.81. A patient arrived in the ED in full cardiopulmonary arrest, following a gunshot wound to the chest. He was intubated, and large-bore IVs of lactated Ringer's solution were started in each arm. A STAT type and cross-match was ordered, along with 6 units of PRBCs. Dr. Jones, a private trauma surgeon, was on call and was present in the ED when the patient arrived. The patient's chest was opened, and cardiac massage was begun. Despite all efforts at resuscitation, the patient expired of massive blood loss after approximately 85 minutes in the ED.

What CPT codes will be reported by Dr. Jones?

a. 99291, 99292, 32160, 31500
b. 99291, 99292, 32160
c. 99291, 99292, 31500-51
d. 99291, 32160, 31500

9.82.   A surgeon performs an evacuation of an epidural hematoma. The physician incises the scalp and peels it away from the area to be drilled. After drilling a burr hole in the cranium and identifying the hematoma via CT scan, the hematoma is decompressed and bleeding is controlled. The hematoma is located outside the dura, just under the periosteum. The scalp is repositioned and sutured into place. The patient tolerates the procedure well and is sent to recovery.

What is the correct code set for reporting this procedure?

a. 61154; 852.40
b. 61108; 853.00
c. 61156; 852.40
d. 61156; 853.00

Part IV

Coding Challenge

Chapter 10

Coding Challenge: Nonacute Settings; ICD-10-CM and ICD-10-PCS Code Sets

Note: Even though the specific cases are divided by setting, most of the information pertaining to the diagnosis is applicable to most settings. If you practice or apply codes in a particular type of setting, you may find additional information in other sections of this publication that may be pertinent to you.

Every effort has been made to follow current recognized coding guidelines and principles, as well as nationally recognized reporting guidelines. The material presented may differ from some health plan requirements for reporting. The ICD-9-CM codes used are effective through September 30, 2007, and the HCPCS (CPT and HCPCS Level II) codes are in effect through December 31, 2006. The current standard transactions and code sets named in HIPAA have been utilized, which require ICD-9-CM Volume III procedure codes for inpatients.

Instructions:

Assign all applicable ICD-9-CM codes appropriate for the setting for the case studies presented. Some of the cases provide multiple-choice answers, and the reader must select the appropriate code set. In other instances, the reader is expected to assign codes without any prompts.

The scenarios are based on selected excerpts from health records without reproducing the entire health record. However, in practice, the coding professional should have access to the entire health record. Health records are analyzed and codes are selected only with the physician's complete and appropriate documentation available. According to coding guidelines, codes are not assigned without physician documentation.

The objective of the cases and scenarios reproduced in this publication is to provide practice in assigning correct codes, not necessarily to emulate actual health record analysis. For example, the reader may be asked to assign codes based only on an operative report or discharge summary. Labeled excerpts are used as source documentation for coding skill practice.

Home Health

10.1. A patient is being followed for postoperative care after surgery for bleeding gastric ulcer. What code would be assigned in M0230?

   a. V-code for aftercare of surgery
   b. Bleeding gastric ulcer
   c. Traumatic wound of abdomen
   d. None of the above

10.2. This 85-year-old female lives alone. She recently was in the hospital with aspiration pneumonia. There are infiltrates still present on the chest x-ray, and home health care is focused on the treatment of the pneumonia. She also has type II diabetes mellitus. She had partial colectomy last year for acute diverticulitis. What diagnosis would be reported in M0240?

   a. Aspiration pneumonia
   b. Diverticulitis
   c. Diabetes mellitus
   d. Acute diverticulitis and diabetes mellitus

10.3. This patient had colon resection because of carcinoma of the transverse colon. He has skilled nursing services for management of surgical wound, which has a surgical drain not scheduled to be removed for several days. He lives alone and has right hemiplegia after a stroke. What code is reported in M0230?

   a. 438.20
   b. 153.1
   c. V58.42
   d. V58.31

10.4. A 72-year-old female patient recently had rectal resection for rectal cancer. She is scheduled for radiation and chemo treatments. HH will provide visits four times per week to teach colostomy care and assess compliance with medication. What coding is the best?

   a. M0230: V58.42; M0240: 154.1, V55.3
   b. M0230: V55.3; M0240: 154.1, V58.42
   c. M0230: 154.1; M0240: V55.3, V58.42
   d. M0230: V55.3; M0240: V10.06, V58.42

10.5. What code is assigned for a patient who had prostate cancer two years ago? He underwent a proctectomy and received chemotherapy. He has had no treatment in the last year. How is the cancer reported in M0240?

   a. 185
   b. V10.46
   c. V16.42
   d. The status of the cancer would not be reported.

10.6. This 80-year-old female patient recently had cholecystectomy for chronic cholecystitis and cholelithiasis. She developed postoperative infection and is being seen for monitoring of antibiotics, vital signs, and observation of the wound, with frequent surgical wound dressing changes. What code is assigned in M0230?

    a. 998.59
    b. V58.31
    c. 879.2
    d. 574.10

10.7. Patient is status post total hip replacement secondary to localized osteoarthritis and was experiencing problems with ambulation and gait following hip surgery. The patient was discharged with home health services twice weekly. Home care was ordered for wound care. The patient also received physical therapy for gait training and strengthening to increase the patient's ability to ambulate. How should this encounter be coded? **Note:** Include codes for M0230, M0240, and M0245 (if applicable).

_____

10.8. The patient is a 75-year-old male with chronic stasis ulcer of the leg, but he also has two diabetic toe ulcers at this time. Patient has chronic lower extremity edema, CHF, HTN. He has daily caregivers through the Medicaid program. The nurse is seeing him four times per week to change leg dressings (using Polymem® and covering with stretch bandage), monitor/adjust medications, teach medication management, teach caregivers to provide low sodium diet, and keep leg elevated. The nurse hopes to teach a neighbor to change the dressing at least once per week. Physical therapy is ordered every other week for exercise, transfer training, and gait training. Patient ambulates minimally, only with close assist and walker. He needs assistance with all ADLs. What codes are assigned? **Note:** Include codes for M0230, M0240, and M0245 (if applicable). _____

10.9. A 69-year-old right-handed woman is discharged from the hospital four days after a left modified radical mastectomy for breast cancer. Her only medications are oral tamoxifen and pain medications. She is scheduled to begin chemotherapy in the next two weeks. Skilled nursing is prescribed for management of the surgical wound including dressing changes. The surgical drain is not scheduled to be removed for several days. The patient lives alone and has residual dysfunction of her right arm due to monoplegia after a stroke. The nurse will also supervise the patient's performance of the exercises ordered to improve her shoulder range of motion on the affected side and to monitor for the development of lymphedema in her arm. What codes are assigned? **Note:** Include codes for M0230, M0240, and M0245 (if applicable). _____

10.10. Section I of the *Official Coding Guidelines for Coding and Reporting* must be followed for:

a. Hospital inpatients
b. Physician services
c. Home health agencies
d. All of the above

10.11. A 74-year-old patient was discharged from the hospital after undergoing a surgical amputation of the right foot due to diabetic osteomyelitis. The patient has type 2 diabetes. She was admitted to home health care for wound care consisting of assessment for signs and symptoms of a wound infection, instructing patient and patient's husband on wound care, and surgical wound dressing changes. She will also receive physical therapy to improve her gait. What codes are assigned? **Note:** Include codes for MO230, MO240, and MO245 (if applicable). _____

10.12. An 89-year-old male fell in his home, sustaining a right hip fracture. An open reduction with internal fixation was performed six days ago. The patient was discharged home, where his daughter now cares for him. The patient is non-weight-bearing on right lower extremity but can perform supervised pivot transfers with contact guard assist in and out of bed. The physician orders the agency to provide physical therapy for gait training and exercise three times per week for five weeks. What codes are assigned? **Note:** Include codes for MO230, MO240, and MO245 (if applicable). _____

10.13. What code(s) is/are assigned for a patient receiving home care after a kidney transplant?

a. V58.44
b. V58.44, V42.0
c. 585.6
d. V42.0

ICD-10-CM and ICD-10-PCS

Introduction: HIM professionals across the country will lead the transition from ICD-9-CM to ICD-10-CM and ICD-10-PCS. In preparation, they need to take steps to become experts on how ICD-10-CM and ICD-10-PCS differ from ICD-9-CM. Coding professionals will need to become proficient in coding with the ICD-10 systems. The following exercises are designed to increase your familiarity with ICD-10-CM and ICD-10-PCS.

Selected sections of the code sets are included with the exercises where possible. Current drafts of the ICD-10-CM index and tabular volumes are available on the Web site for the National Center for Health Statistics (NCHS). You may download the volumes at www.cdc.gov/nchs/about/otheract/icd9/abticd10.htm

The current draft of the ICD-10-PCS coding system and training manual is available on the Web site for the Centers for Medicare and Medicaid Services (CMS). You may access this information at www.cms.hhs.gov/paymentsystems/icd9/icd10.asp?

ICD-10-CM

10.14. Which of the following statements is false concerning code I46.9, Cardiac arrest, cause unspecified?

    a. It is considered a nonspecific principal diagnosis.

    b. It can only be assigned as a principal diagnosis if the patient is discharged or expires within 24 hours of admission and no determination is made as to the cause of the cardiac arrest.

    c. It should never be used as a principal diagnosis if attempts were made to resuscitate the patient, even if they failed.

    d. It should not be used as a secondary diagnosis unless the cause of the event cannot be determined.

10.15. Which of the following conditions is not represented by a code from the J44 category?

    a. Asthma with chronic obstructive pulmonary disease

    b. Chronic bronchitis with emphysema

    c. Chronic emphysematous bronchitis

    d. Emphysema

10.16. Unlike ICD-9-CM, ICD-10-CM uses the same coding guidelines for all practice settings.

    a. True

    b. False

10.17. What would be the appropriate ICD-10-CM code for acute gangrenous cholecystitis?

    a. K81.0

    b. K81.2

    c. K80.13

    d. K81.12

10.18. Assign the appropriate ICD-10-CM diagnosis code(s) for cataract due to hypoparathyroidism.

    a. E88.9, H28

    b. H28

    c. E20.9, H28

    d. H28, E20.9

10.19. Assign the appropriate ICD-10-CM diagnosis code(s) for aspiration pneumonia due to inhalation of food.

    a. J15.9

    b. J69.0

    c. J18.9

    d. J69.1

ICD-10-PCS

10.20. ICD-10-PCS is based on a seven-character alphanumeric code. The meanings of each individual character changes according to the needs of the clinical section.

a. True
b. False

10.21. Recall that the first character of an ICD-10-PCS code specifies the section within ICD-10-PCS. Using the list of ICD-10-PCS sections provided below, identify the first character that would be assigned to the following procedures.

Sections of ICD-10-PCS

0   Medical and Surgical
1   Obstetrics
2   Placement
3   Administration
4   Measurement and Monitoring
5   Imaging
6   Nuclear Medicine
7   Radiation Oncology
8   Osteopathic
9   Physical Rehabilitation and Diagnostic Audiology
B   Extracorporeal Assistance and Performance
C   Extracorporeal Therapies
D   Laboratory
F   Mental Health
G   Chiropractic
H   Miscellaneous
J   Substance Abuse Treatment

a. _____ Cranioplasty

b. _____ Cholecystectomy

c. _____ Gait Training

d. _____ Computerized Tomography, Spine

10.22. Using the list of ICD-10-PCS root operations provided below, identify the root operation used to describe each of the following procedures.

ICD-10-PCS Medical and Surgical Root Operations

0	Alternation	H	Insertion
1	Bypass	J	Inspection
2	Change	K	Map
3	Control	L	Occlusion
4	Creation	M	Reattachment
5	Destruction	N	Release
6	Detachment	P	Removal
7	Dilation	Q	Repair
8	Division	R	Replacement
9	Drainage	S	Reposition
B	Excision	T	Resection
C	Extirpation	V	Restriction
D	Extraction	W	Revision
F	Fragmentation	X	Transfer
G	Fusion	Y	Transplantation

a. _____ Kidney Transplant

b. _____ Appendectomy

c. _____ Diagnostic Bronchoscopy

d. _____ Lithotripsy, Bladder Stone

10.23. Match the approach term with the correct definition:

ICD-10-PCS Character-Approach

0   Open

9   Open with Cardiopulmonary Bypass

1   Open Intraluminal

3   Percutaneous

C   Open with Temporary Shunt

4   Percutaneous Endoscopic

Definition:

a. ____ Entry, by puncture or minor incision, of instrumentation through the skin or mucous membrane and any other body layers necessary to reach the site of the operation.

b. ____ Cutting through the skin or mucous membrane and any other body layers necessary to expose the site of the operation with the use of cardiopulmonary bypass during a portion of the procedure.

c. ____ Cutting through the skin or mucous membrane and any other body layers necessary to expose the body site of the operation.

d. ____ Cutting through the skin or mucous membrane and any other body layers necessary to expose the site of the operation with use of a temporary shunt during a portion of the procedure.

    e. ___ Cutting through the skin or mucous membrane and any other body layers necessary to expose a tubular body part, and introduction of instrumentation into the lumen to reach the site of the operation.

    f. ___ Entry, by puncture or minor incision, of instrumentation through the skin or mucous membrane and any other body layers necessary to reach and visualize the site of the operation.

10.24. Using the definitions listed in item 10.23 above, match the following:

Procedure	Approach
a. ___Total abdominal hysterectomy	1. Open Intraluminal
b. ___Needle biopsy of the pancreas	2. Open
c. ___Common bile duct exploration	3. Percutaneous Endoscopic
d. ___Arthroscopy	4. Percutaneous

10.25. What is the correct ICD-10-PCS code for complete removal of the appendix performed laparoscopically? _____

ICD-10-CM/PCS Application Exercise

10.26. You are a coding professional at General Medical Center. One of your responsibilities includes responding to requests for coded data. Facility data in the registry has been coded in ICD-10-CM and ICD-10-PCS for two years. Prior to that, data was coded in ICD-9-CM. You receive requests for data that spans the most recent five years for the following cases. How will you find all applicable cases in the registry for these two requests?

    a. Request for cases with an initial acute myocardial infarction of the anterior wall: _____

    _____

    b. Request for cases with exploration of the common bile duct during an open cholecystectomy: _____

    _____

CPT Modifiers

10.27. Dr. Raddy, staff radiologist, interprets a chest x-ray that was obtained in the hospital radiology department. Dr. Raddy is contracted with the hospital to read radiographs. The equipment and staff are owned and/or employed by the hospital. What modifier, if any, should Dr. Raddy report with the chest x-ray code?

    a. No modifier is necessary because Dr. Raddy interpreted the x-ray under contract with the hospital. The hospital will bill the global and pay Dr. Raddy from the reimbursement.

    b. Modifier -26, Professional component

    c. Modifier -TC, Technical component

    d. Modifier -59

10.28. Tiny Patti Sue Smith, 15 days old, currently weighs 1652 grams. She is taken to the operating room for small bowel resection for necrotizing enterocolitis, a frequent complication of prematurity. The remaining portions of the small bowel were anastomosed end-to-end. CPT code 44120 reports a small bowel resection with anastomosis. Is a modifier necessary, and if so, which modifier?

    a. No modifier is needed for the surgery; although the anesthesiologist might need a modifier.

    b. Modifier -63 is reported because the baby weighs less than 4 kg and thus is a higher surgical risk than a larger neonate.

    c. No modifier is needed because code 44120 already applies to neonates who are very low weight.

    d. A modifier is optional and may or may not be assigned depending upon the departmental coding guidelines.

10.29. A patient is seen in the emergency department because of hyperkalemia due to an inadvertent overdose of his potassium medication. Over the course of the next 6 hours he receives infusions, and his potassium is measured three times. What is the appropriate modifier to report with the second and third potassium determinations?

    a. Modifier -59, to show that these were not duplicate charges, but indeed separate incidents.

    b. No modifier is necessary for repeat laboratory tests, only for repeat surgical procedures.

    c. Modifier -91

    d. Modifier -91 and -59 should be reported for the second and third determinations.

10.30. A patient who was high on PCP stabbed himself in the chest, causing a pneumothorax. He was seen in the emergency department, and Dr. Jones inserted a chest tube. The patient continued under the influence of the PCP and about an hour later, despite soft restraints, managed to free himself and pull out his chest tube. Dr. Jones reinserted the chest tube via a fresh incision. What modifier should be reported on each procedure?

    a. Modifier -76, Repeat procedure by the same physician, should be reported for each chest tube insertion.

    b. Modifier -76 should be reported with the second procedure, no modifier on the first procedure.

    c. Modifier -59 should be reported with the second procedure, no modifier with the first procedure.

    d. Either modifier -59 or -76 may be reported on the first and second procedure.

10.31. A patient underwent gallbladder removal by Dr. Pitts on 4/1. On 4/16, he developed right lower quadrant abdominal pain and evaluation was strongly suggestive of acute appendicitis. Dr. Pitt performed an exploratory laparotomy and appendectomy for an acutely inflamed appendix. What modifier, if any, should be reported with the appendectomy code?

a. No modifier is needed because the ICD-9-CM diagnosis code and the CPT procedure code clearly identify that this was a procedure not related to the cholecystectomy.
b. Modifier -79, Unrelated procedure or service by the same physician during the postoperative period, should be reported with the appendectomy code.
c. Modifier -78, Return to the operating room for a related procedure during the postoperative period, should be reported with the appendectomy code.
d. Modifier -58, Staged or related procedure or service by the same physician during the postoperative period.

HCPCS Level II Modifiers

10.32. A patient is brought to the emergency department of Community Hospital following a motor vehicle accident. He appears to have an avulsion of the aortic root and is rushed to the operating room where repair is attempted. The patient expires on the operating room table just as the surgery is being completed and before he can be admitted to the hospital. The CPT code for repair of avulsion of the aortic root is designated as an "inpatient only" code under the outpatient prospective payment system (OPPS). Is there a modifier that the hospital can report to obtain reimbursement for this procedure when performed as an outpatient?

a. No, if an "inpatient only" procedure is performed on an outpatient basis, the hospital cannot obtain reimbursement under any circumstances.
b. Modifier -CA, Procedure payable only in the inpatient setting when performed emergently on an outpatient who expires prior to admission, may be appended to the CPT procedure code.
c. Modifier -ST, Related to trauma or injury, may be appended and a 50 percent reimbursement will be available to the hospital.
d. Modifier -SC, Medically necessary service or supply, may be appended and a 25 percent reimbursement will be available to the hospital.

10.33. A patient undergoes a bunionectomy on the big toe of the right foot. What modifier is appended to report the location of this procedure?

a. No modifier. By definition, bunionectomy is performed on the big toe.
b. Modifier -T5
c. Modifier -RT
d. Modifier -TA

10.34. A hospice patient, under hospice care for terminal COPD, falls out of bed and fractures his wrist. He is taken to the emergency department at the local hospital and has cast application for the nondisplaced fracture. What modifier is reported to show that these services are not related to the patient's hospice-qualifying condition?

a. Modifier -GW
b. Modifier -AT
c. Modifier -GZ
d. Modifier -SC

10.35. HCPCS Level II modifiers can be used with which of the following code sets?

    a. CPT codes

    b. HCPCS Level II codes

    c. ICD-9-CM Volume III codes

    d. Both a and b

10.36. Modifiers -G1 through -G5, which report the levels of URR (Urea Reduction Ratio) in the blood, are reported with codes for _____ and measure the efficacy of this modality.

    a. Laboratory tests

    b. Dialysis codes

    c. Coronary artery interventional procedures

    d. Oxygen therapy

10.37. Match the HCPCS Level II modifier in column 2 with its application in column 1.

Column 1	Column 2
1. The patient was pronounced dead after the ambulance was called. Ambulance company is entitled to reimbursement.	a. -KA
2. Left hand, fourth digit	b. -SG
3. The beneficiary has been informed of rent/purchase option and has decided to rent the item.	c. -GH
4. Service furnished in an ambulatory surgery center	d. -QY
5. Left circumflex coronary artery	e. -E4
6. Monitored anesthesia care	f. -QL
7. Diagnostic mammogram converted from screening mammogram same day	g. -F3
8. Add-on option or accessory for wheelchair	h. -QS
9. Lower right eyelid	i. -BR
10. Medical supervision of one CRNA by an anesthesiologist	j. -LC

LTAC Coding

10.38. Patient Julie Jones suffers a massive intracerebral hemorrhage due to right basilar artery bleed. She is admitted to City Acute Hospital where she remains for eight days undergoing acute care and regulation of anticoagulation.

Following her acute hospital stay, she is transferred to City LTAC for continued management. Treatment at CLTAC will focus on continued management and intensive physical, occupational, and speech-language therapy for rehabilitation from the following sequelae of her intracranial bleed:

Left (dominant sided) hemiplegia involving her upper and lower extremities

Expressive aphasia

Severe dysphagia with impaired swallowing and risk for aspiration

Assign the admission diagnoses that CLTAC will report.

a. 433.00, 438.21, 438.11, 438.82
b. V57.89, 438.21, 438.11, 438.82
c. V58.9, 438.21, 438.11, 438.82
d. V57.2, V57.3, V57.89

10.39. The patient developed buttock and heel decubiti following an extended stay in the acute hospital. He has had resolution of the underlying acute condition that occasioned his admission there and is transferred to the LTAC for treatment of the decubitus ulcers. While in the LTAC, he undergoes nonexcisional debridement of the decubiti. He also has underlying diabetes without documented complications and COPD. Assign the appropriate ICD-9-CM diagnoses and procedural codes for this admission.

a. 707.05, 707.07, 250.00, 496, 86.28
b. V57.89, 707.05, 707.07, 250.00, 496, 86.28
c. 707.05, 707.07, 86.28
d. 707.05, 707.07, 86.22

10.40. This patient is admitted for pulmonary rehabilitation in a setting of advanced COPD. She also has ASHD and type II diabetes mellitus with peripheral neuropathy. She has been ventilator-dependent at the local acute hospital but was weaned from the ventilator prior to transfer to the LTAC. Which are the principal diagnosis and secondary diagnoses that the LTAC will report for her stay?

a. 496, 414.00, 250.60, 337.1
b. V57.0, 496
c. V57.89, 496, 414.00, 250.60, 337.1
d. V57.89

10.41. This patient underwent an above-knee amputation of her left leg for severe vascular trauma with transaction of the posterior tibial artery just below the level of the knee and loss of viability of the distal leg, following a motor vehicle accident. She has had continued stump infections and healing has not occurred, now four weeks post amputation. She is transferred to the long-term acute hospital for management of the stump infection, eventual rehabilitation, and possible prosthetic fitting. What is the principal diagnosis that the LTAC should report for this admission?

a. V57.89
b. V52.1
c. 904.53
d. 997.62

Outpatient Rehabilitation Cases

10.42. Physician Order

Diagnosis: Congenital CP, scoliosis, bilateral congenital dislocated hips

Treatment Goals: Increase in ADLs, strengthening

Therapy Provided:

PT: ROM exercises, strengthening, stretching

OT: ADLs, upper extremity strengthening/ROM

What are the correct diagnosis codes for this outpatient therapy visit? (Procedure codes are captured via the chargemaster.)

_____

10.43. Physician Order

PT to evaluate and treat neck pain

Therapy Provided:

PT: Evaluation and treatment in the weight room

What are the correct diagnosis codes for this outpatient therapy visit? (Procedure codes are captured via the chargemaster.) _____

Inpatient Rehabilitation Cases

10.44. History and Physical for Inpatient Case

Purpose of Consultation: Physical medicine and rehabilitation evaluation at the request of Dr. Brown; status posttrochanteric femoral nailing of left IT fracture on May 19 with touch weight-bearing restrictions.

History of Present Illness: Joe is now a 52-year-old male with history of mental retardation. He resides at home with parents whom I believe are near their 70s. Joe apparently fell in the home setting and sustained a left intertrochanteric femur fracture and was admitted to Regional Hospital on May 16. He was evaluated by Dr. Smith and then operated on 5/19 with trochanteric femoral nailing, Synthes® type, placed by Dr. Brown.

The patient has been followed by Dr. Smith secondary to difficulties with prior arrhythmia and A Fib flutter with him having been on Coumadin chronically to this admission. His INR today is 2.7, his platelets are 283,000, and his hemoglobin preoperative on 5/16 was 15.6 g/dl. His hemoglobin on 5/22 was 13.2 g/dl.

Chemistries of today, 5/25, are sodium 138, potassium 4.3, chloride 99, CO_2 31, BUN 20, creatinine 0.8, glucose 105, magnesium low at 1.4.

He has been working with a physical therapist and has been very slow to progress until significantly improving and tolerating activities and instructions yesterday on 5/24. At that time, he was able with touch to non-weight-bearing on the left lower limb with walker ambulate 15 to 20 feet to the doorway and back with contact-guard assist. He is tall in stature at 6′2″. His admission weight was recorded at 119.3 kg, weight today is 138.5 kg with there being a discrepancy likely in his admission weight recording. Pain scores have ranged from a 1–2 of 10 today. He has noted some cramping and tightness in his calf; although nontender. He has been working on stretching this out. His medications are as per MAR. He currently remains on telemetry.

Past Medical History:
1. As above, notable for mental retardation and living with parents. He lives in a trilevel home which he describes as having no stairs to enter the main floor or second level. He lives in the lower level with stair access and frequently is at the upper or higher level. Please refer to the occupational therapy evaluation of tub and difficulties with transfers therein.
2. History of A Fib flutter as above
3. History of gastroesophageal reflux
4. History of chronic Coumadin

Allergies: No known drug allergies

Current Medications: Per MAR, as above

Family History: Noncontributory

Social History: As per above. His care is monitored by his parents. His father has stated that he needs to be more mobile and able to care for himself before returning home. He has been very concerned about his disposition at this time. There is a history of tobacco use having stopped some 10 years ago. He has a bridge prosthesis dentally. He wears glasses for vision and has had a history of night terrors. He is disabled. He is single. His primary care physician is Dr. Allen Smith.

Review of Systems: As per admission H&P of Dr. Brown, as well as ER evaluation of Dr. Canter. See also Dr. Smith evaluation and ongoing care. He has recommended telemetry until discharged from Regional Hospital.

Physical Examination: Admission height: 6′2″

Admission Weight: As above I believe is in error at 119.3.

Most Recent Weights: These have been in the 130 to 140 kg. range. Today is 138.5.

Vital Signs: BP 133/73, afebrile at 97.6, heart rate in the mid 70s.

General: He is alert and conversant. He is sitting up in a chair. He is reading a magazine. He has his lenses in place. He is able to demonstrate functional range of the shoulders and upper extremities and denies any aggravation or irritation with use of the walker for the touch or non-weight-bearing on the left. He does have a saline lock. He has significant ecchymotic change about the left posterior elbow and forearm; this is nontender. He is able to demonstrate good strength, and this limits symmetric reflexes.

Lungs: Clear to auscultation

Cardiovascular: Regular rate and rhythm without A Fib at this time

Abdomen: Soft, normoactive bowel sounds

GU: He is voiding spontaneously.

Extremities: Lower lungs demonstrate +1 reflexes, left knee jerk does evoke some left hip discomfort. He is able to ankle plantar flex, somewhat pain-inhibited on the left. There is no distal swelling. He has TED hose in place, knee high. He is able to follow instructions.

Assessment:	1. Status post fall with left intertrochanteric femur fracture on 5/16 in the home setting
	2. Status post 5/19 ORIF with trochanteric femoral nailing
	3. Touch weight-bearing limitations, left lower extremity
	4. History of arrhythmia and A Fib flutter; on chronic Coumadin
	5. Gastroesophageal reflux disorder
	6. Mental retardation, mild; living with parents
	7. Pain issues
	8. Slow progress but now improving and tolerating therapies per my discussion with his physical therapist

Plan/Comment: I had the pleasure of evaluating Joe today. He appears to be a good candidate for rehab intervention to maximize his functional status so that he can return home with his parents. We will anticipate his admission therein on 5/28 if he continues to progress as well.

Discharge Summary

Date of Admission:	5/28/2005
Date of Discharge:	6/21/05
Discharging Diagnoses:	1. Status post fall with left intertrochanteric femur fracture 5/16/05, in home setting
	2. Status post open reduction and internal fixation with intertrochanteric femoral nailing 5/19/05, by Dr. Brown, with touch weight-bearing restrictions left lower limb
	3. History of arrhythmia and atrial fibrillation flutter, on Coumadin chronically
	4. Gastroesophageal reflux disorder
	5. Postoperative pain issues
	6. Mild cognitive issues, chronic
	7. Mobility and self-care deficits

History of Present Illness: The patient is a 52-year-old Caucasian male. He has a history of some mild mental retardation and resides with his parents who are in their 70s.

His primary physician is Dr. Smith, and he is being followed by Dr. Brown in current hospitalization since being admitted on 5/16/05, at Regional Hospital.

The patient was evaluated by myself in consultation on 5/25/05, for rehabilitation needs with him coming to the Rehabilitation Hospital on 5/28/05. Please refer to my consultation of 5/25/05, for specifics.

Hospital Course: The patient was brought to Rehabilitation Hospital for comprehensive therapy programming. He and his parents were in agreement with this.

He is a large Caucasian male who is pleasant and cooperative. He has had problems with pain limitations and some swelling in the left leg. He has remained on Coumadin and was on this chronically before. He has been followed by cardiology and is scheduled to see Dr. Smith in follow-up on 6/22/05, at 11:15 a.m. He remains on Coumadin, which is followed by his primary physician with him to have further pro time/INR on 6/23/05, Thursday.

His physical mobility has continued to progress. He has been maintaining touch weight bearing much better with contact guard assist for gait using front-wheeled walker for 50-feet distances × 2. He has been able to perform total hip arthroplasty exercise program and is independent in 10 repetitions of each.

He has been followed for lymphedema of the left lower limb and has been issued Juzo® garments, and his parents were instructed by the physical therapist on his day of discharge on how to don and doff these garments.

With self-care skills, his upper extremities remained with 4/5 strength and active range of motion. Sensation was intact. Somewhat slower on the right side than the left side for 9-Hole-Peg coordination: 38 seconds right, 24 seconds left. Sitting balance was good. Endurance was within functional limits. He has some mild problems with cognition in terms of problem solving and judgment. Visual perceptive skills were felt to be good using his lenses. FIM-level scores were improved by two levels for all tasks except for toileting, which improved from a 3 to a 4. He is independent in feeding and dressing. Dressing lower extremities FIM level 5, grooming 6, toileting 4, showering 5. Discharge equipment includes commode.

Medications at Discharge:

1. Fentanyl patch 25 mcg per hour with this having been decreased the day prior to discharge from 50 mcg to 25 mcg with him noting no substantial change in pain levels. He is provided with refill for five patches or 15 days with these to be changed every 72 hours with it to then be discontinued.
2. He has also been using oral medications for pain relief, using Percocet (oxycodone /acetaminophen) 5/325 with 10,100 provided for one to two p.o. every 4 to 6 hours p.r.n. No refills.
3. Coumadin 3 mg daily currently with two-week supply issued on 6/21/05.
4. Durable medical equipment includes:

   Front-wheeled walker with large fixed wheels

   Bedside commode

   Rental wheelchair, 20-inches wide. This gentleman is 6'2" or 6'3" in height and weighs 116 kg secondary to left hip fracture and mobility defects with limited weight bearing.
5. Ferrous sulfate 650 mg p.o. b.i.d. with meals
6. He has been on Prevacid but will resume his previous proton pump inhibitor at home for which he has a prescription. His home PPI is Aciphex®.
7. He is on Betapace® 160 mg p.o. b.i.d.
8. Lanoxin 0.25 mg p.o. every evening
9. Cardizem CD 120 mg p.o. daily
10. He may use over-the-counter stool softeners as needed.

Discharge Instructions:

1. He is to wear his Juzo stockings to the left leg, being placed initially on in the morning, removed at bedtime.
2. Fall precautions should be in place.
3. Patient and family chose Regional Hospital Home Health Care for ongoing home health PT, OT, visiting nurse, and aid, with his parents involved in all care decisions.

His prognosis is fair for continued compliance and ongoing follow-ups.

a. What are the correct diagnosis codes for reporting on the UB-92?
_____

b. What are the correct diagnosis codes for the Patient Assessment Instrument (IRF-PAI)? _____

10.45. Neurology Rehabilitation H&P for Inpatient Case

Date of Consultation: 4/10/05

Introduction: Rehabilitation consultation is requested to evaluate this 30-year-old man who was injured in a motorcycle accident on 4/3. At that time, he was thrown from his bike and apparently sustained a transient loss of consciousness consistent with concussion. He also apparently had quadriparesis at the scene. He was transported to Regional Hospital where he was ultimately found to have, I believe, a significant hyperflexion injury without major fracture dislocation. He did not require emergency stabilization surgery.

He was clinically and radiographically diagnosed with a cervical spinal cord contusion. This was most prominent at the C3–C4 level. There was some initial respiratory impairment, and he was transiently placed on a ventilator. He has since been extubated.

The patient's clinical course has been consistent with a central type of spinal cord contusion such that he has had paralysis of his arms and paresis of the legs. The sensory deficits follow similarly. Patient is now being considered for eventual transfer to the Rehab Hospital.

Current Medications:

1. Insulin by sliding scale
2. Bacitracin
3. Dulcolax®, p.r.n.
4. Decadron, 4 mg q. 6 h. and eventually will be tapered according to protocol
5. Lovenox, 90 mg subcutaneously q.12 h.
6. Prevacid, 30 mg p.o. b.i.d.
7. Claritin, 10 mg p.o. daily
8. Senokot®, 8.6 mg p.o. b.i.d.
9. Tylenol, p.r.n.
10. Benadryl®, 25 mg p.o. q. 6 h. p.r.n.
11. Ativan, 0.5 mg was used 1 time only
12. Percocet, 5/325, 1 to 2 hours p.o. q. 4 to 6 h. p.r.n.
13. Ambien®, p.r.n.
14. Zofran®, p.r.n.

Allergies: He has no known medication allergies but has a history of intolerance to morphine and to Motrin. These tend to cause significant itching. He is having some mild itching with his Percocet, but this is relieved with Benadryl.

Past Medical History: He has a torn anterior cruciate ligament on one of his knees.

Review of Systems: Prior to admission, the patient has had no fever, chills, sweats, weight loss. No change in his vision. No ear, nose, or throat complaints. No chest pains or palpitations. No shortness of breath, coughing, or wheezing. No nausea, vomiting, diarrhea, constipation. No bladder or kidney dysfunction. No bone or joint problems outside of the anterior cruciate tear. No skin lesions such as rash. No mental illness. No other neurologic problems. No diabetes, thyroid disease, blood or bleeding problems, swollen lymph nodes, allergic or asthmatic problems.

Family History: Parents are in good health. No neurologic problems.

Social History: He is divorced. Lives in Watson. He is a corrections officer for County Jail. Parents live in Plainsville. He has two children; however they do not reside with him.

General Exam: Appearance: The appearance is that of a well-developed, athletic-appearing young man who is laying on his back. He has a rigid cervical collar in place. The rigid collar is not to be removed.

Vital signs: His temp reached a maximum of 100.3°F but is now down to 99°F. Blood pressure 121/68, pulse is at 72. Respirations 18.

General: He appears normocephalic. The left arm is swollen and wrapped with an ACE type wrap. No obvious head trauma.

Heart: Is beating at a regular rate and rhythm without murmur. Carotid pulsations cannot be examined at this time. Peripheral pulses cannot easily be examined at this time.

Neurological Exam: He is a bit sleepy. He has received some narcotics and Benadryl. He arouses easily to voice. He is oriented to place and person and thought the date was 4/17. His recent and remote memory is grossly intact; although he has some amnesia for the accident when he was rendered unconscious. His attention span and concentration is grossly normal. Receptive expressive language normal. Fund of knowledge appropriate. His pupils are equal, round, and reactive to light. Funduscopic exam is benign. Visual fields are intact. Visual acuity is grossly normal. Eye movements are intact. Facial sensation, corneal responses, muscles of mastication are normal. Facial movement symmetrical and normal. Hearing intact. Tongue and palate move normally. The sternocleidomastoid is not examined at this time due to the rigid collar. Trapezius testing was not attempted because of his immobilized neck.

He has complete plegia of the upper extremities bilaterally. In the legs, he does have some leg extension, hip extension and thigh adduction with abduction. He has some ability to extend the legs bilaterally. There is a limited ability to lift the heels off the bed. There is virtual absence of foot dorsiflexion bilaterally; however, there is a weak plantar flexion response bilaterally. Muscle tone slightly increased in the legs. Babinski responses were not attempted. The muscle stretch reflexes are absent in the upper extremities and hyperactive at the knees and ankles. Sensation grossly intact to light touch and temperature in the legs bilaterally. There is anesthesia of the arms bilaterally and reduced sensation of the lower abdomen. The chest sensation and upper shoulders have essentially normal light touch sensation.

Coordination cannot be attempted. Patient obviously not ambulatory at this time.

Lab Studies: Most recent lab studies of note: Glucose is 137, BUN is at 23, creatinine 1.1. Sodium is at 136. The other chemistry parameters are normal. White count is elevated at 12,100, hemoglobin normal at 15.

Imaging Studies: Are most pertinent for the MRI scans. The MRI is most noteworthy for the abnormal signal within the spinal cord, primarily at the C3–C4 disk space level. An additional small area of signal abnormality noted at the C5–C6 disk level. The abnormality within the spinal cord is consistent with spinal cord edema and contusion. There is an additional abnormality in the soft tissues with interspinous ligamentous edema at C3–C4, and C5–C6. Patient coincidentally also has relatively small spinal canal which appears to be on a congenital basis.

Assessment: Thirty-year-old man with spinal cord injury without significant fracture but is associated with severe cervical spinal cord contusion, primarily at the C3–C4 disk level. Clinically, patient has a "central cord" syndrome with paralysis of his arms and paresis of the legs.

Plan: Patient should be an excellent candidate for comprehensive rehabilitation.

We will follow along and facilitate transfer when needed.

Interim Discharge Summary for Inpatient Rehab Case

Discharge Diagnosis:
1. Cervical instability with plans for cervical fusion and stabilization procedure by Dr. Johnson, neurosurgery
2. Status post motor vehicle accident with cervical trauma and cord myelopathy
3. Quadriparesis and central cord syndrome
4. Neurogenic bowel and neurogenic bladder
5. Dysesthetic pain and numbness
6. Mobility and self-care deficits

John is a 30-year-old, Caucasian male who was involved in motor vehicle trauma with subsequent spinal injury and quadriparesis. Please refer to admission H&P for details. He was admitted in transfer from Regional Hospital for comprehensive rehabilitation programming given his quadriparesis. He has been undergoing spinal recovery program with comprehensive therapies and intervention to include neuropsychology.

He has remained somewhat unrealistic and has deferred on much of the spinal education efforts that have been offered to him. He is returning on 5/13/05, to Regional Hospital for cervical stabilization procedure, with Dr. Johnson planning a C3 through C6 anterior cervical diskectomy and fusion.

He has had significant motor recovery from his initial presentation, with his lower extremity strength now +3/5 at the hip extensors and knee extensors. Quadriceps +3/5 bilaterally. Knee flexors, hamstrings, were 2/5. Ankle dorsiflexion +1/5. Plantar flexion 3/5. Spasticity and tone does interfere with gait patterning and does limit his ability to progress, with him needing assistance. Bed mobility is rolling with minimal assist to his stronger right side. Sliding board transfers to bed and chair were with moderate assistance of 1. Supine to sit was with moderate to maximum assist of 1. Gait with ARJO Walker with heavy truncal support is 75 feet with moderate assistance of 1, knee brace on the right, and AFO on the right. Steps and stairs have not yet been attempted.

In terms of self-care skills, the patient remains essentially dependent; although he is beginning to show almost antigravity strength being –2 to +2 in the upper limbs with some flicker of hand movement. Palmer grasp on the right 3 pounds and left 1 pound. He continues to have a greater degree of sensation proximally than distally; although deep pressure is intact. Light touch is impaired. He is unable to complete a 9-Hole Peg Test and is unable to functionally use the hands bilaterally. Visual perceptive skills are intact.

Medications as per MARS.

Plans are for return within 72 hours to the Rehabilitation Hospital if medically stable to resume acute rehabilitation program.

Plan: Disposition is home with support of family and possible spinal cord attendant program via state services. Equipment needs are still to be determined. The patient remains optimistic.

a. What are the correct diagnosis codes for reporting on the UB-92?
_____

b. What are the correct diagnosis codes for the Patient Assessment Instrument (IRF-PAI)? _____

10.46. Interim History and Physical for Inpatient Case

Subjective: This is an interim history and physical for a 73-year-old woman who, unfortunately, sustained an acute right hemisphere ischemic stroke on 03/30/05. The patient was actually in preadmission at Regional Hospital where she was planning to undergo an orthopedic procedure when she developed acute left hemiparesis. She was transported immediately to the emergency department. It was determined that she had an acute ischemic stroke and received TPA. Despite the TPA; however, the patient was left with severe residual deficits in the form of left hemineglect, left facial weakness, left arm plegia, left leg paresis, and inability to walk. In the course of her workup, she was found to have atrial fibrillation but no significant stenosis of the internal carotid arteries. She was determined to be a suitable candidate for chronic Coumadin therapy.

The patient was fairly stable neurologically; although she had chronic debilitation prior to her admission. This was related to multiple medical problems, but she was ambulatory, I believe, with a walker. Because of her severe deficits, the patient is now being transferred to the Rehabilitation Hospital for complete rehabilitation program.

The patient has quite a number of comorbid medical problems. These include atrial fibrillation, diabetes mellitus, morbid obesity, hyperlipidemia, and degenerative arthritis to include a particular problem with her hip, which was being considered for replacement.

At the time of transfer, she has a temperature of 97.8°F, pulse 108, respirations 20, and blood pressure 134/93. She is awake, alert, and oriented. Her speech is fluent. Her eyes tend to gaze to the right. There is left facial droop consistent with central-type facial weakness. There is left upper extremity plegia, left neglect, and left lower extremity paresis. She is unable to walk.

Assessment:
1. Right hemisphere ischemic infarction with severe residual deficits
2. There are quite a number of complicating comorbid problems, which are likely going to aggravate her stroke deficit. In particular, these include degenerative arthritis, diabetes, heart disease, and chronic mobility problems.

Plan:
1. Transfer to the Rehabilitation Hospital
2. Physical therapy, occupational therapy, speech therapy, and therapeutic recreation
3. Primary goals of therapy will be to improve her ability to ambulate and take care of herself with regard to independence of ADLs.
4. It is anticipated the patient will require three to four weeks of inpatient rehabilitation.
5. It is anticipated disposition would be to home with the care of family, if possible.

Rehab Hospital Discharge Summary for Inpatient Rehab

Date of Admission: 4/7/05

Date of Discharge: 5/10/05

Admission Diagnosis: Right hemisphere infarction with severe residual deficits

Secondary or Comorbid Conditions:
1. Degenerative arthritis
2. Diabetes
3. Coronary artery disease
4. Chronic mobility problems

Discharge Diagnoses:
1. Right hemisphere infarction with severe residual deficits
2. Degenerative arthritis
3. Diabetes
4. Coronary artery disease
5. Chronic mobility problems

History of Present Illness: Patient is a 73-year-old female who sustained a right hemisphere infarction on 3/30/05. Patient apparently was in the process of undergoing preadmit for orthopedic procedure when she developed acute left hemiparesis. She was transferred to the emergency room. She received TPA. However, she was left with severe left deficits in the form of left hemineglect, left facial weakness, left arm plegia, left leg paresis, and an inability to walk.

In the course of her workup, she was found to have atrial fibrillation. It was felt she was a suitable candidate for chronic Coumadin. Patient was stabilized in the Regional Hospital setting, and it was felt that she would be an appropriate rehabilitation candidate. Her examination at the transfer to the Rehabilitation

Hospital showed her general medical exam to be stable. Neurologically, she was awake, alert, and oriented on mental status, and her speech was fluent. The cranial nerves showed a right gaze preference with a left facial droop that was central in nature. There was left upper extremity plegia and left neglect and left lower extremity paresis, and the patient was unable to walk.

During the course of her rehab stay, the patient did undergo some lab workup. This consisted of a series of PT and INR values. Initial PT/INR from 4/8/05, showed PT of 24.0 with an INR of 2.2. Prior to discharge on 5/01/05, the PT was 26.7 with an INR of 2.5. The patient did undergo some limited metabolic profiles including one from 4/22/05, showing elevated glucose of 143 with a sodium low at 123, chloride low at 88. Uric acid was 6.2. The osmolality was 0.273. On repeat metabolic profile from 4/23/05, showed an elevated glucose of 126 with a sodium low at 123, and a low chloride at 88. On 4/26/05, glucose was 131. Sodium was 127, chloride 92. On 5/5/05, patient had a sodium checked and it was at 130 it had improved to 134. Patient had a series of Glucometer® checks done throughout the course of her rehabilitation stay. These appeared to have remained fairly consistently elevated with values at times up near 190 but no values were noted below grossly 120.

During the course of her rehabilitation stay, she underwent some radiographic imaging including a swallowing study from 4/8/05, which showed some delay in oral phase of swallowing, likely the result of sensory issues. She had a right hip x-ray from 4/10/05, showing relatively severe arthritic involvement of the right hip. Right shoulder x-ray from 4/10/05, showed a degenerative change with history of previous surgery. A CT of the right shoulder from 4/19/05, showed previous surgery with screws in the proximal right humerus. There were arthritic changes with subluxation of the humeral head superiorly, suggesting a chronic degenerative rotator cuff tear.

During the course of her rehabilitation stay, the patient was seen by the various therapy services. This included speech therapy who felt that she had swallowing trouble and was to undergo dysphagia management techniques and diet texture modification and full supervision with p.o. She had speech trouble and was to undergo oromotor exercises. She had communication and language deficits and was to undergo standard speech therapy protocol assessment. She had memory trouble and was to undergo assessment, and she was to be 79 percent accurate with auditory and visual memory exercises. The occupational therapy team felt she had decreased independence with ADLs, and she was to be seen three to five times per week to be educated in ADL techniques and in AE. She had decreased use of the left lower extremity and was to be seen for education and weight-bearing techniques and self-range of motion. She had decreased independence with functional transfers and was to be educated in safety with functional transfers. She had decreased independence with leisure participation and was to be seen for education in leisure exploration. Therapeutic recreation felt she had decreased leisure participation due to hospitalization and was to be provided an opportunity for successful leisure involvement in activity of choice. The physical therapy team felt that she had dependence with transfers and was to undergo transfer training. She had decreased lower extremity strength and was to undergo strengthening exercise. She had dependence with stand and gait and was to undergo standing and gait training.

Rehab Hospital Course: Patient was admitted for an aggressive inpatient rehabilitation stay. The patient was able to participate with rehabilitation efforts and did make slow but steady progress throughout the course of her rehabilitation stay. She was followed along by internal medicine during her stay, and various medical issues were addressed in that regard. Patient had no major setbacks during the course of her stay. She was seen by Dr. Benson for a chronic rotator cuff tear and physical therapy was recommended. The patient's hyponatremia gradually improved throughout the course of her rehabilitation stay.

By 5/10/05, it was felt that patient had optimized her rehabilitation hospital benefits. As of that date, the various therapy services noted as follows: Occupational therapy felt that the patient had met some but not all of her goals due to inconsistency and poor attention to task. Physical therapy felt that the patient had met almost all of her goals except goal 1 of bed mobility and also her standing goal as she still needed moderate assistance. Therapeutic recreation felt that she had met her established goals with recommendations to continue with social and leisure interest and community involvement. Speech therapy felt she had improved.

On 5/10/05, the patient was discharged home with outpatient physical therapy, occupational therapy, speech therapy, and nursing. She was on a diabetic, pureed food, full-supervision diet and was to be encouraged to eat a consistent diet. Her activity was as tolerated, and she was not to drive. She was transfer with 2 on a sliding board, and she was to continue with her knee-high T.E.D. hose. She was to get a PT/INR on 5/11/05. She was to check her blood sugar before breakfast and evening meals. She was to have a drop-arm shower and transport in a commode. She was to get a hospital bed with rails and a slide board.

Discharge Medications:

1. Baby aspirin daily
2. Lemon juice b.i.d. to t.i.d.
3. Over-the-counter stool softeners
4. Novolin® R insulin subcu b.i.d. on a sliding-scale basis
5. Sinemet® 25/100 at bedtime for restless legs
6. Coreg 6.25 mg b.i.d.
7. Klonopin 0.5 mg at bedtime
8. Lanoxin 0.125 mg daily
9. Kaopectate® 240 mg b.i.d.
10. Zetia® 5 mg b.i.d.
11. Neurontin® 600 mg b.i.d. and then 900 mg at 10 p.m.
12. Prevacid 30 mg b.i.d.
13. Levothyroxine 100 mcg at bedtime
14. Cozaar® 100 mg at 8 a.m.
15. Magnesium oxide 400 mg at 8 a.m.
16. Glucophage 1000 mg b.i.d., 500 mg at noon
17. Singulair® 10 mg at 10 p.m.
18. Actos 45 mg at 8 a.m.
19. Zoloft 50 mg b.i.d.
20. Zocor® 80 mg at 6 p.m.
21. Coumadin 1 mg at 4 p.m.

a. What are the correct diagnosis codes for reporting on the UB-92?

_____

b. What are the correct diagnosis codes for the Patient Assessment Instrument (IRF-PAI)? _____

SNF Cases

10.47. The patient was admitted to the acute hospital with a pathological fracture of the left femur due to underlying metastatic cancer from the breast (resected years ago). She underwent percutaneous fixation in the hospital. She had been largely nonambulatory prior to the injury, and remains so. She is admitted to the skilled nursing facility for continued healing of the fracture and for general conditioning. Assign the appropriate diagnosis codes for the skilled facility to report.

a. V54.25, 198.5, V10.3
b. 733.14, 198.5, V10.3
c. V57.89, 733.14, 198.5, V10.3
d. V54.15, 821.00

10.48. This patient had been residing at home until an episode of pneumonia resulted in his hospitalization. While there, it was determined that he really was not able to remain in his home on his own due to rapidly advancing Alzheimer's dementia and episodes where he tried to wander away from the hospital. He was transferred to the skilled nursing facility because of this condition; although no specific therapy was ordered. The pneumonia had completely resolved in the acute hospital, and no further treatment was needed in the skilled nursing facility. The patient does have underlying COPD, hypertension, and ASHD that require daily medication. Assign the appropriate diagnosis for this long-term admission.

a. 486, 496, 401.9, 414.00
b. 331.0, 294.11
c. 331.0, 294.11, 496, 401.9, 414.00
d. V57.89, 331.0, 294.11, 496, 401.9, 414.00

10.49. This patient underwent a subtotal colectomy in the acute hospital for resection of a carcinoma of the transverse colon. She was left significantly weak and debilitated following her surgery and was admitted to the skilled nursing facility for conditioning. The surgery appears to have been successful in eradicating the malignancy, and she was receiving no chemotherapy or radiation therapy for it at the time of her transfer. Assign the appropriate codes for the skilled nursing facility to report for this admission.

a. V58.75, 780.79, V10.05
b. V58.75, 997.99, 780.79, V10.05
c. V10.05, 780.79
d. V58.75, 780.79, 153.1

References

American Hospital Association. 1985–2005. *Coding Clinic for ICD-9-CM*. Chicago: American Hospital Association.

American Medical Association. 2006. *Current Procedural Terminology (CPT)*. Chicago: American Medical Association.

American Medical Association. 1992–2006. *CPT Assistant*. Chicago: American Medical Association.

Hazelwood, Anita, and Carol Venable. 2006. *ICD-9-CM Diagnostic Coding and Reimbursement for Physician Services*. Chicago: American Health Information Management Association.

ICD-9-CM Professional for Hospitals: Volumes 1, 2, and 3. 2006. Salt Lake City, UT: Ingenix.

Kuehn, Lynn. 2006. *CPT/HCPCS Coding and Reimbursement for Physician Services*. Chicago: American Health Information Management Association.

Schraffenberger, Lou Ann. 2007. *Basic ICD-9-CM Coding*. Chicago: American Health Information Management Association.

Smith, Gail. 2006. *Basic CPT/HCPCS Coding*. Chicago: American Health Information Management Association.

Appendix A

Certification Competencies

To ensure that its members meet professional standards of excellence, AHIMA issues credentials in health information management, coding, and healthcare privacy and security. Members earn credentials through a combination of education and experience and, finally, performance on national certification exams. Following their initial certification, AHIMA members must maintain their credentials and, thereby, the highest level of competency for their employers and consumers through rigorous continuing education requirements.

This appendix contains tables that link each exercise to the AHIMA certifications and competencies to which it pertains. Linkages for the following three certifications (Certified Coding Associate, Certified Coding Specialist, and Certified Coding Specialist—Physician-based) are detailed herein, and are detailed by certification and also by question number. Additional information, including certification candidate handbooks, is available online from www.ahima.org/certification/

Certified Coding Associate (CCA)

The Certified Coding Associate (CCA) is the entry-level certification for coders without any related job experience. CCA holders distinguish themselves from noncredentialed coders and those who hold credentials from other organizations that do not require the higher level of expertise necessary to earn AHIMA certification. The CCA should be viewed as the starting point for a career as a coder. The CCS and/or CCS-P exams demonstrate the mastery level skills that the CCA would strive for to advance his or her career.

CCA Competencies

Domain I: Health Records and Data Content

1. Collect and maintain health data.
2. Analyze health records to ensure that documentation supports the patient's diagnosis and procedures, reflects progress, clinical findings, and discharge status.
3. Request patient-specific documentation from other sources (such as ancillary departments, physicians offices, and the like).
4. Apply clinical vocabularies and terminologies used in the organization's health information systems.

Domain II: Health Information Requirements and Standards

1. Evaluate the accuracy and completeness of the patient record as defined by organizational policy and external regulations and standards.
2. Monitor compliance with organization-wide health record documentation guidelines.
3. Report compliance findings according to organizational policy.
4. Assist in preparing the organization for accreditation, licensing, and/or certification surveys.

Domain III: Clinical Classification Systems

1. Utilize electronic applications to support clinical classification and coding (such as encoders).
2. Assign secondary diagnosis procedure codes using ICD-9-CM official coding guidelines:
    a. Assign principal diagnosis (Inpatient) or first listed diagnosis (Outpatient).
    b. Assign secondary diagnosis(es), including complications and comorbidities (CC).
    c. Assign principal and secondary procedure(s).
3. Assign procedure codes using CPT coding guidelines.
4. Assign appropriate HCPCS codes.
5. Identify discrepancies between coded data and supporting documentation.
6. Consult reference materials to facilitate code assignment.

Domain IV: Reimbursement Methodologies

1. Validate the data collected for appropriate reimbursement:
    a. Validate Diagnosis Related Groups (DRGs).
    b. Validate Ambulatory Payment Classifications (APCs).
2. Comply with the National Correct Coding Initiative.
3. Verify the National and Local Coverage Determinations (NCD/LCD) for medical necessity.

Domain V: Information and Communication Technologies

1. Use personal computer to ensure data collection, storage, analysis, and reporting of information.
2. Use common software applications (such as word processing, spreadsheets, e-mail, and the like) in the execution of work processes.
3. Use specialized software in the completion of HIM processes.

Domain VI: Privacy, Confidentiality, Legal, and Ethical Issues

1. Apply policies and procedures for access and disclosure of personal health information.
2. Release patient-specific data to authorized individuals.
3. Apply ethical standards of practice.
4. Recognize and report privacy issues/problems.
5. Protect data integrity and validity using software or hardware technology.

Certified Coding Associate (CCA) Competencies

CCA Exam Competency	CCA Exam Level	Question Number	CCA Exam Competency	CCA Exam Level	Question Number
III.2.a	Application	10.13	III.2.a	Application	1.57
III.2.a	Application	1.5	III.2.a	Application	1.58
III.2.a	Application	1.16	III.2.a	Application	1.60
III.2.a	Application	1.17	III.2.a	Application	1.61
III.2.a	Application	1.18	III.2.a	Application	1.62
III.2.a	Application	1.20	III.2.a	Application	1.63
III.2.a	Application	1.21	III.2.a	Application	1.64
III.2.a	Application	1.22	III.2.a	Application	1.65
III.2.a	Application	1.23	III.2.a	Application	1.67
III.2.a	Application	1.24	III.2.a	Application	1.68
III.2.a	Application	1.25	III.2.a	Application	1.69
III.2.a	Application	1.26	III.2.a	Application	1.71
III.2.a	Application	1.27	III.2.a	Application	1.72
III.2.a	Application	1.28	III.2.a	Application	1.73
III.2.a	Application	1.29	III.2.a	Application	1.74
III.2.a	Application	1.30	III.2.a	Application	1.75
III.2.a	Application	1.31	III.2.a	Application	1.76
III.2.a	Application	1.32	III.2.a	Application	1.78
III.2.a	Application	1.33	III.2.a	Application	1.79
III.2.a	Application	1.34	III.2.a	Application	1.80
III.2.a	Application	1.35	III.2.a	Application	1.82
III.2.a	Application	1.36	III.2.a	Application	1.84
III.2.a	Application	1.37	III.2.a	Application	1.85
III.2.a	Application	1.38	III.2.a	Application	1.86
III.2.a	Application	1.39	III.2.a	Application	1.87
III.2.a	Application	1.40	III.2.a	Application	1.88
III.2.a	Application	1.41	III.2.a	Application	1.89
III.2.a	Application	1.42	III.2.a	Application	1.90
III.2.a	Application	1.43	III.2.a	Application	1.91
III.2.a	Application	1.44	III.2.a	Application	1.92
III.2.a	Application	1.45	III.2.a	Application	1.93
III.2.a	Application	1.46	III.2.a	Application	1.94
III.2.a	Application	1.47	III.2.a	Application	1.95
III.2.a	Application	1.51	III.2.a	Application	1.97
III.2.a	Application	1.52	III.2.a	Application	1.98
III.2.a	Recall	1.53	III.2.a	Application	1.99
III.2.a	Application	1.54	III.2.a	Application	1.100
III.2.a	Application	1.55	III.2.a	Application	1.102
III.2.a	Application	1.56	III.2.a	Application	1.104

CCA Exam Competency	CCA Exam Level	Question Number	CCA Exam Competency	CCA Exam Level	Question Number
III.2.a	Application	1.105	III.2.a	Application	1.151
III.2.a	Application	1.106	III.2.a	Application	1.152
III.2.a	Application	1.107	III.2.a	Application	1.153
III.2.a	Application	1.108	III.2.a	Application	1.154
III.2.a	Application	1.109	III.2.a	Application	1.155
III.2.a	Application	1.110	III.2.a	Application	1.156
III.2.a	Application	1.111	III.2.a	Application	1.157
III.2.a	Application	1.112	III.2.a	Application	1.158
III.2.a	Application	1.113	III.2.a	Application	1.159
III.2.a	Application	1.114	III.2.a	Application	1.160
III.2.a	Application	1.115	III.2.a	Application	1.161
III.2.a	Application	1.116	III.2.a	Application	1.162
III.2.a	Application	1.117	III.2.a	Application	1.163
III.2.a	Application	1.119	III.2.a	Application	1.164
III.2.a	Application	1.120	III.2.a	Application	1.165
III.2.a	Application	1.121	III.2.a	Application	1.166
III.2.a	Application	1.122	III.2.a	Application	1.167
III.2.a	Application	1.123	III.2.a	Application	1.168
III.2.a	Application	1.125	III.2.a	Application	1.169
III.2.a	Application	1.126	III.2.a	Application	1.170
III.2.a	Application	1.128	III.2.a	Application	1.171
III.2.a	Application	1.129	III.2.a	Application	1.172
III.2.a	Application	1.130	III.2.a	Application	1.173
III.2.a	Application	1.131	III.2.a	Application	1.174
III.2.a	Application	1.132	III.2.a	Application	1.175
III.2.a	Application	1.133	III.2.a	Application	1.176
III.2.a	Application	1.134	III.2.a	Application	1.177
III.2.a	Application	1.135	III.2.a	Application	1.178
III.2.a	Application	1.136	III.2.a	Application	1.179
III.2.a	Application	1.138	III.2.a	Application	1.180
III.2.a	Application	1.139	III.2.a	Application	1.181
III.2.a	Application	1.141	III.2.a	Application	1.182
III.2.a	Application	1.143	III.2.a	Application	1.183
III.2.a	Application	1.144	III.2.a	Application	1.184
III.2.a	Application	1.145	III.2.a	Application	1.185
III.2.a	Application	1.146	III.2.a	Application	1.186
III.2.a	Application	1.147	III.2.a	Application	1.187
III.2.a	Application	1.148	III.2.a	Application	1.188
III.2.a	Application	1.149	III.2.a	Application	1.189
III.2.a	Application	1.150	III.2.a	Application	1.190

CCA Exam Competency	CCA Exam Level	Question Number	CCA Exam Competency	CCA Exam Level	Question Number
III.2.a	Application	1.191	III.2.a	Application	1.239
III.2.a	Application	1.192	III.2.a	Application	1.240
III.2.a	Application	1.193	III.2.a	Application	1.241
III.2.a	Application	1.194	III.2.a	Application	1.242
III.2.a	Application	1.195	III.2.a	Application	1.243
III.2.a	Application	1.196	III.2.a	Application	1.244
III.2.a	Application	1.197	III.2.a	Application	1.245
III.2.a	Application	1.198	III.2.a	Application	1.246
III.2.a	Application	1.199	III.2.a	Application	1.247
III.2.a	Application	1.200	III.2.a	Application	1.248
III.2.a	Application	1.201	III.2.a	Recall	1.249
III.2.a	Application	1.202	III.2.a	Application	1.250
III.2.a	Application	1.203	III.2.a	Application	1.251
III.2.a	Application	1.204	III.2.a	Application	1.252
III.2.a	Application	1.206	III.2.a	Application	1.253
III.2.a	Application	1.207	III.2.a	Application	1.254
III.2.a	Application	1.208	III.2.a	Application	1.255
III.2.a	Application	1.209	III.2.a	Application	1.256
III.2.a	Application	1.210	III.2.a	Application	1.257
III.2.a	Application	1.211	III.2.a	Application	1.258
III.2.a	Application	1.212	III.2.a	Application	1.259
III.2.a	Application	1.213	III.2.a	Application	1.260
III.2.a	Application	1.214	III.2.a	Application	1.261
III.2.a	Application	1.215	III.2.a	Application	1.262
III.2.a	Application	1.216	III.2.a	Application	1.263
III.2.a	Application	1.217	III.2.a	Application	1.264
III.2.a	Application	1.218	III.2.a	Application	1.265
III.2.a	Application	1.221	III.2.a	Application	1.266
III.2.a	Application	1.222	III.2.a	Application	1.267
III.2.a	Application	1.223	III.2.a	Application	1.268
III.2.a	Application	1.224	III.2.a	Application	1.269
III.2.a	Application	1.225	III.2.a	Application	1.270
III.2.a	Application	1.226	III.2.a	Application	1.271
III.2.a	Application	1.227	III.2.a	Application	1.272
III.2.a	Application	1.228	III.2.a	Application	1.273
III.2.a	Application	1.229	III.2.a	Application	1.274
III.2.a	Application	1.233	III.2.a	Application	1.275
III.2.a	Application	1.236	III.2.a	Application	1.276
III.2.a	Application	1.237	III.2.a	Application	1.277
III.2.a	Application	1.238	III.2.a	Application	1.278

CCA Exam Competency	CCA Exam Level	Question Number	CCA Exam Competency	CCA Exam Level	Question Number
III.2.a	Application	1.279	III.2.a	Application	1.319
III.2.a	Application	1.280	III.2.a	Application	1.320
III.2.a	Application	1.281	III.2.a	Application	1.321
III.2.a	Application	1.282	III.2.a	Application	1.322
III.2.a	Application	1.283	III.2.a	Application	1.323
III.2.a	Application	1.284	III.2.a	Application	1.324
III.2.a	Application	1.285	III.2.a	Application	1.325
III.2.a	Application	1.286	III.2.a	Application	1.326
III.2.a	Application	1.287	III.2.a	Application	1.327
III.2.a	Application	1.288	III.2.a	Application	1.328
III.2.a	Application	1.289	III.2.a	Application	1.329
III.2.a	Application	1.290	III.2.a	Application	1.330
III.2.a	Application	1.291	III.2.a	Application	1.331
III.2.a	Application	1.292	III.2.a	Application	1.332
III.2.a	Application	1.293	III.2.a	Application	1.333
III.2.a	Application	1.294	III.2.a	Application	1.334
III.2.a	Application	1.295	III.2.a	Application	1.335
III.2.a	Application	1.296	III.2.a	Application	1.336
III.2.a	Application	1.297	III.2.a	Application	1.337
III.2.a	Application	1.298	III.2.a	Application	1.338
III.2.a	Application	1.299	III.2.a	Application	1.339
III.2.a	Application	1.300	III.2.a	Application	1.340
III.2.a	Application	1.301	III.2.a	Application	1.341
III.2.a	Application	1.302	III.2.a	Application	1.342
III.2.a	Application	1.303	III.2.a	Application	1.343
III.2.a	Application	1.304	III.2.a	Application	1.344
III.2.a	Application	1.305	III.2.a	Application	1.345
III.2.a	Application	1.306	III.2.a	Application	1.346
III.2.a	Application	1.307	III.2.a	Application	1.347
III.2.a	Application	1.308	III.2.a	Application	1.348
III.2.a	Application	1.309	III.2.a	Application	1.349
III.2.a	Application	1.310	III.2.a	Application	1.350
III.2.a	Application	1.311	III.2.a	Application	1.351
III.2.a	Application	1.312	III.2.a	Application	1.352
III.2.a	Application	1.313	III.2.a	Application	1.353
III.2.a	Application	1.314	III.2.a	Application	1.354
III.2.a	Application	1.315	III.2.a	Application	1.355
III.2.a	Application	1.316	III.2.a	Application	1.356
III.2.a	Application	1.317	III.2.a	Application	1.357
III.2.a	Application	1.318	III.2.a	Application	1.358

CCA Exam Competency	CCA Exam Level	Question Number	CCA Exam Competency	CCA Exam Level	Question Number
III.2.a	Application	1.359	III.2.a	Application	5.37
III.2.a	Application	1.360	III.2.a	Application	5.38
III.2.a	Application	1.361	III.2.a	Application	5.66
III.2.a	Application	1.362	III.2.a	Application	5.80
III.2.a	Application	1.363	III.2.a	Application	6.14
III.2.a	Application	1.364	III.2.a	Application	6.31
III.2.a	Application	1.365	III.2.a	Application	6.52
III.2.a	Application	1.366	III.2.a	Application	6.82
III.2.a	Application	1.367	III.2.a	Application	6.87
III.2.a	Application	1.368	III.2.a	Recall	10.1
III.2.a	Application	1.369	III.2.a	Recall	10.2
III.2.a	Application	1.370	III.2.a	Application	10.3
III.2.a	Application	1.371	III.2.a	Application	10.4
III.2.a	Application	1.372	III.2.a	Application	10.5
III.2.a	Application	1.373	III.2.a	Application	10.6
III.2.a	Application	1.374	III.2.a	Application	10.7
III.2.a	Application	1.375	III.2.a	Application	10.8
III.2.a	Application	1.401	III.2.a	Application	10.9
III.2.a	Recall	1.402	III.2.a	Application	10.11
III.2.a	Recall	1.404	III.2.a	Application	10.12
III.2.a	Recall	1.405	III.2.a	Application	10.41
III.2.a	Application	1.406	III.2.a,b	Application	4.5
III.2.a	Recall	1.408	III.2.a,b	Application	4.6
III.2.a	Recall	1.409	III.2.a,b	Application	4.10
III.2.a	Recall	1.410	III.2.a,b	Application	4.12
III.2.a	Recall	1.411	III.2.a,b	Application	4.13
III.2.a	Recall	1.415	III.2.a,b	Application	4.19
III.2.a	Recall	1.421	III.2.a,b	Application	4.23
III.2.a	Recall	1.422	III.2.a,b	Application	4.24
III.2.a	Application	4.1	III.2.a,b	Application	4.25
III.2.a	Application	4.14	III.2.a,b	Application	4.27
III.2.a	Application	4.35	III.2.a,b	Application	4.30
III.2.a	Application	4.49	III.2.a,b	Application	4.33
III.2.a	Application	4.77	III.2.a,b	Application	4.34
III.2.a	Application	4.85	III.2.a,b	Application	4.37
III.2.a	Application	4.87	III.2.a,b	Application	4.38
III.2.a	Application	5.10	III.2.a,b	Application	4.39
III.2.a	Application	5.23	III.2.a,b	Application	4.40
III.2.a	Application	5.35	III.2.a,b	Application	4.41
III.2.a	Application	5.36	III.2.a,b	Application	4.42

CCA Exam Competency	CCA Exam Level	Question Number	CCA Exam Competency	CCA Exam Level	Question Number
III.2.a,b	Application	4.43	III.2.a,b	Analysis	7.20
III.2.a,b	Application	4.50	III.2.a,b	Analysis	7.23
III.2.a,b	Application	4.58	III.2.a,b	Analysis	7.24
III.2.a,b	Application	4.60	III.2.a,b	Analysis	7.27
III.2.a,b	Application	4.61	III.2.a,b	Analysis	7.32
III.2.a,b	Application	4.72	III.2.a,b	Analysis	7.36
III.2.a,b	Application	4.74	III.2.a,b	Analysis	7.38
III.2.a,b	Application	4.75	III.2.a,b	Analysis	7.45
III.2.a,b	Application	4.78	III.2.a,b	Analysis	7.50
III.2.a,b	Application	4.79	III.2.a,b	Analysis	7.52
III.2.a,b	Application	4.88	III.2.a,b	Analysis	7.53
III.2.a,b	Application	4.93	III.2.a,b	Analysis	7.54
III.2.a,b	Application	4.94	III.2.a,b	Analysis	7.55
III.2.a,b	Application	5.5	III.2.a,b	Analysis	8.3
III.2.a,b	Application	5.20	III.2.a,b	Application	8.4
III.2.a,b	Application	5.21	III.2.a,b	Application	8.10
III.2.a,b	Application	5.22	III.2.a,b	Analysis	8.16
III.2.a,b	Application	5.46	III.2.a,b	Analysis	8.17
III.2.a,b	Application	5.49	III.2.a,b	Analysis	9.5
III.2.a,b	Application	5.50	III.2.a,b	Application	9.7
III.2.a,b	Application	5.72	III.2.a,b	Application	9.10
III.2.a,b	Application	5.75	III.2.a,b	Analysis	9.26
III.2.a,b	Application	6.8	III.2.a,b	Analysis	9.27
III.2.a,b	Application	6.11	III.2.a,b	Analysis	9.28
III.2.a,b	Application	6.13	III.2.a,b	Analysis	9.50
III.2.a,b	Application	6.33	III.2.a,b	Application	10.38
III.2.a,b	Application	6.34	III.2.a,b	Application	10.39
III.2.a,b	Application	6.35	III.2.a,b	Application	10.40
III.2.a,b	Application	6.36	III.2.a,b	Application	10.42
III.2.a,b	Application	6.53	III.2.a,b	Application	10.43
III.2.a,b	Application	6.69	III.2.a,b	Application	10.44
III.2.a,b	Application	6.83	III.2.a,b	Application	10.45
III.2.a,b	Application	6.88	III.2.a,b	Application	10.46
III.2.a,b	Application	6.90	III.2.a,b	Application	10.47
III.2.a,b	Application	6.91	III.2.a,b	Application	10.48
III.2.a,b	Application	6.92	III.2.a,b	Application	10.49
III.2.a,b	Application	6.94	III.2.a,b,c	Application	4.2
III.2.a,b	Analysis	7.1	III.2.a,b,c	Application	4.3
III.2.a,b	Analysis	7.4	III.2.a,b,c	Application	4.4
III.2.a,b	Analysis	7.15	III.2.a,b,c	Application	4.7

CCA Exam Competency	CCA Exam Level	Question Number	CCA Exam Competency	CCA Exam Level	Question Number
III.2.a,b,c	Application	4.8	III.2.a,b,c	Analysis	7.2
III.2.a,b,c	Application	4.9	III.2.a,b,c	Analysis	7.3
III.2.a,b,c	Application	4.11	III.2.a,b,c	Analysis	7.9
III.2.a,b,c	Application	4.16	III.2.a,b,c	Analysis	7.10
III.2.a,b,c	Application	4.17	III.2.a,b,c	Analysis	7.11
III.2.a,b,c	Application	4.18	III.2.a,b,c	Analysis	7.12
III.2.a,b,c	Application	4.20	III.2.a,b,c	Analysis	7.13
III.2.a,b,c	Application	4.21	III.2.a,b,c	Analysis	7.14
III.2.a,b,c	Application	4.22	III.2.a,b,c	Analysis	7.16
III.2.a,b,c	Application	4.26	III.2.a,b,c	Analysis	7.17
III.2.a,b,c	Application	4.28	III.2.a,b,c	Analysis	7.18
III.2.a,b,c	Application	4.31	III.2.a,b,c	Analysis	7.19
III.2.a,b,c	Application	4.32	III.2.a,b,c	Analysis	7.21
III.2.a,b,c	Application	4.36	III.2.a,b,c	Analysis	7.22
III.2.a,b,c	Application	4.44	III.2.a,b,c	Analysis	7.25
III.2.a,b,c	Application	4.45	III.2.a,b,c	Analysis	7.26
III.2.a,b,c	Application	4.46	III.2.a,b,c	Analysis	7.28
III.2.a,b,c	Application	4.48	III.2.a,b,c	Analysis	7.29
III.2.a,b,c	Application	4.52	III.2.a,b,c	Analysis	7.30
III.2.a,b,c	Application	4.54	III.2.a,b,c	Analysis	7.31
III.2.a,b,c	Application	4.55	III.2.a,b,c	Analysis	7.33
III.2.a,b,c	Application	4.59	III.2.a,b,c	Analysis	7.34
III.2.a,b,c	Application	4.62	III.2.a,b,c	Analysis	7.35
III.2.a,b,c	Application	4.63	III.2.a,b,c	Analysis	7.37
III.2.a,b,c	Application	4.64	III.2.a,b,c	Analysis	7.39
III.2.a,b,c	Application	4.65	III.2.a,b,c	Analysis	7.41
III.2.a,b,c	Application	4.67	III.2.a,b,c	Analysis	7.42
III.2.a,b,c	Application	4.69	III.2.a,b,c	Analysis	7.43
III.2.a,b,c	Application	4.71	III.2.a,b,c	Analysis	7.44
III.2.a,b,c	Application	4.73	III.2.a,b,c	Analysis	7.46
III.2.a,b,c	Application	4.82	III.2.a,b,c	Analysis	7.47
III.2.a,b,c	Application	4.83	III.2.a,b,c	Analysis	7.48
III.2.a,b,c	Application	4.84	III.2.a,b,c	Analysis	7.49
III.2.a,b,c	Application	4.86	III.2.a,b,c	Analysis	7.51
III.2.a,b,c	Application	4.89	III.2.a,b,c	Analysis	7.56
III.2.a,b,c	Application	4.90	III.2.a,b,c	Analysis	7.57
III.2.a,b,c	Application	4.91	III.2.a,b,c	Analysis	7.58
III.2.a,b,c	Application	4.92	III.2.a,b/III.3	Application	5.4
III.2.a,b,c	Application	4.95	III.2.a,b/III.3	Application	5.9
III.2.a,b,c	Application	4.97	III.2.a,b/III.3	Application	5.14

CCA Exam Competency	CCA Exam Level	Question Number	CCA Exam Competency	CCA Exam Level	Question Number
III.2.a,b/III.3	Application	5.16	III.2.a,b/III.3	Analysis	8.7
III.2.a,b/III.3	Application	5.18	III.2.a,b/III.3	Analysis	8.12
III.2.a,b/III.3	Application	5.25	III.2.a,b/III.3	Application	8.13
III.2.a,b/III.3	Application	5.30	III.2.a,b/III.3	Analysis	8.14
III.2.a,b/III.3	Application	5.31	III.2.a,b/III.3	Analysis	8.15
III.2.a,b/III.3	Application	5.51	III.2.a,b/III.3	Analysis	8.18
III.2.a,b/III.3	Application	5.54	III.2.a,b/III.3	Analysis	8.19
III.2.a,b/III.3	Application	5.57	III.2.a,b/III.3	Analysis	8.20
III.2.a,b/III.3	Application	5.59	III.2.a,b/III.3	Analysis	8.21
III.2.a,b/III.3	Application	5.60	III.2.a,b/III.3	Analysis	8.22
III.2.a,b/III.3	Application	5.64	III.2.a,b/III.3	Analysis	8.23
III.2.a,b/III.3	Application	5.71	III.2.a,b/III.3	Analysis	8.25
III.2.a,b/III.3	Application	5.81	III.2.a,b/III.3	Analysis	8.27
III.2.a,b/III.3	Application	5.83	III.2.a,b/III.3	Application	8.28
III.2.a,b/III.3	Application	5.84	III.2.a,b/III.3	Analysis	8.29
III.2.a,b/III.3	Application	5.86	III.2.a,b/III.3	Analysis	8.30
III.2.a,b/III.3	Application	5.87	III.2.a,b/III.3	Analysis	8.31
III.2.a,b/III.3	Application	6.2	III.2.a,b/III.3	Analysis	8.32
III.2.a,b/III.3	Application	6.5	III.2.a,b/III.3	Analysis	8.33
III.2.a,b/III.3	Application	6.12	III.2.a,b/III.3	Analysis	8.34
III.2.a,b/III.3	Application	6.15	III.2.a,b/III.3	Analysis	8.35
III.2.a,b/III.3	Application	6.16	III.2.a,b/III.3	Analysis	8.36
III.2.a,b/III.3	Application	6.17	III.2.a,b/III.3	Application	8.37
III.2.a,b/III.3	Application	6.22	III.2.a,b/III.3	Analysis	8.39
III.2.a,b/III.3	Application	6.28	III.2.a,b/III.3	Analysis	8.41
III.2.a,b/III.3	Application	6.32	III.2.a,b/III.3	Analysis	8.44
III.2.a,b/III.3	Application	6.38	III.2.a,b/III.3	Analysis	8.45
III.2.a,b/III.3	Application	6.40	III.2.a,b/III.3	Application	8.47
III.2.a,b/III.3	Application	6.45	III.2.a,b/III.3	Analysis	8.48
III.2.a,b/III.3	Application	6.55	III.2.a,b/III.3	Analysis	8.49
III.2.a,b/III.3	Application	6.57	III.2.a,b/III.3	Analysis	8.50
III.2.a,b/III.3	Application	6.58	III.2.a,b/III.3	Analysis	8.51
III.2.a,b/III.3	Application	6.61	III.2.a,b/III.3	Analysis	8.52
III.2.a,b/III.3	Application	6.62	III.2.a,b/III.3	Analysis	8.53
III.2.a,b/III.3	Application	6.64	III.2.a,b/III.3	Application	8.54
III.2.a,b/III.3	Application	6.70	III.2.a,b/III.3	Analysis	8.55
III.2.a,b/III.3	Application	6.84	III.2.a,b/III.3	Analysis	9.2
III.2.a,b/III.3	Application	8.1	III.2.a,b/III.3	Analysis	9.6
III.2.a,b/III.3	Application	8.5	III.2.a,b/III.3	Application	9.8
III.2.a,b/III.3	Application	8.6	III.2.a,b/III.3	Analysis	9.9

CCA Exam Competency	CCA Exam Level	Question Number	CCA Exam Competency	CCA Exam Level	Question Number
III.2.a,b/III.3	Analysis	9.14	III.2.a,b/III.3/III.4	Analysis	8.2
III.2.a,b/III.3	Analysis	9.15	III.2.a,b/III.3/III.4	Analysis	9.34
III.2.a,b/III.3	Analysis	9.16	III.2.a,b/III.3/III.4	Analysis	9.62
III.2.a,b/III.3	Analysis	9.23	III.2.a,b/III.3/III.4	Analysis	9.67
III.2.a,b/III.3	Analysis	9.30	III.2.a,c	Application	4.29
III.2.a,b/III.3	Analysis	9.33	III.2.a,c	Application	4.47
III.2.a,b/III.3	Analysis	9.35	III.2.a,c	Application	4.51
III.2.a,b/III.3	Analysis	9.36	III.2.a,c	Application	4.53
III.2.a,b/III.3	Analysis	9.39	III.2.a,c	Application	4.66
III.2.a,b/III.3	Analysis	9.40	III.2.a,c	Application	4.68
III.2.a,b/III.3	Analysis	9.41	III.2.a,c	Application	4.70
III.2.a,b/III.3	Analysis	9.42	III.2.a,c	Application	4.76
III.2.a,b/III.3	Analysis	9.44	III.2.a,c	Application	4.80
III.2.a,b/III.3	Analysis	9.46	III.2.a,c	Application	4.81
III.2.a,b/III.3	Analysis	9.47	III.2.a,c	Application	4.96
III.2.a,b/III.3	Analysis	9.48	III.2.a,c	Analysis	7.40
III.2.a,b/III.3	Analysis	9.49	III.2.a,b	Application	1.137
III.2.a,b/III.3	Analysis	9.52	III.2.a,b	Recall	1.423
III.2.a,b/III.3	Analysis	9.53	III.2.a,b	Application	1.118
III.2.a,b/III.3	Analysis	9.54	III.2.a/III.3	Application	5.1
III.2.a,b/III.3	Analysis	9.55	III.2.a/III.3	Application	5.2
III.2.a,b/III.3	Analysis	9.56	III.2.a/III.3	Application	5.3
III.2.a,b/III.3	Analysis	9.57	III.2.a/III.3	Application	5.6
III.2.a,b/III.3	Application	9.58	III.2.a/III.3	Application	5.7
III.2.a,b/III.3	Analysis	9.60	III.2.a/III.3	Application	5.8
III.2.a,b/III.3	Analysis	9.63	III.2.a/III.3	Application	5.12
III.2.a,b/III.3	Analysis	9.66	III.2.a/III.3	Application	5.13
III.2.a,b/III.3	Analysis	9.68	III.2.a/III.3	Application	5.15
III.2.a,b/III.3	Analysis	9.69	III.2.a/III.3	Application	5.17
III.2.a,b/III.3	Analysis	9.70	III.2.a/III.3	Application	5.24
III.2.a,b/III.3	Analysis	9.72	III.2.a/III.3	Application	5.26
III.2.a,b/III.3	Application	9.75	III.2.a/III.3	Application	5.27
III.2.a,b/III.3	Analysis	9.77	III.2.a/III.3	Application	5.28
III.2.a,b/III.3	Analysis	9.78	III.2.a/III.3	Application	5.29
III.2.a,b/III.3	Analysis	9.79	III.2.a/III.3	Application	5.32
III.2.a,b/III.3	Analysis	9.80	III.2.a/III.3	Application	5.33
III.2.a,b/III.3/III.4	Application	5.41	III.2.a/III.3	Application	5.39
III.2.a,b/III.3/III.4	Application	5.53	III.2.a/III.3	Application	5.40
III.2.a,b/III.3/III.4	Application	5.61	III.2.a/III.3	Application	5.42
III.2.a,b/III.3/III.4	Application	5.62	III.2.a/III.3	Application	5.44

CCA Exam Competency	CCA Exam Level	Question Number	CCA Exam Competency	CCA Exam Level	Question Number
III.2.a/III.3	Application	5.47	III.2.a/III.3	Application	6.73
III.2.a/III.3	Application	5.52	III.2.a/III.3	Application	6.74
III.2.a/III.3	Application	5.55	III.2.a/III.3	Application	6.76
III.2.a/III.3	Application	5.58	III.2.a/III.3	Application	6.77
III.2.a/III.3	Application	5.63	III.2.a/III.3	Application	6.78
III.2.a/III.3	Application	5.65	III.2.a/III.3	Application	6.79
III.2.a/III.3	Application	5.68	III.2.a/III.3	Application	6.80
III.2.a/III.3	Application	5.69	III.2.a/III.3	Application	6.81
III.2.a/III.3	Application	5.70	III.2.a/III.3	Application	6.85
III.2.a/III.3	Application	5.73	III.2.a/III.3	Application	6.86
III.2.a/III.3	Application	5.74	III.2.a/III.3	Analysis	8.11
III.2.a/III.3	Application	5.76	III.2.a/III.3	Analysis	8.24
III.2.a/III.3	Application	5.77	III.2.a/III.3	Analysis	8.26
III.2.a/III.3	Application	5.78	III.2.a/III.3	Analysis	8.38
III.2.a/III.3	Application	5.79	III.2.a/III.3	Application	8.40
III.2.a/III.3	Application	5.82	III.2.a/III.3	Application	8.42
III.2.a/III.3	Application	5.85	III.2.a/III.3	Analysis	8.46
III.2.a/III.3	Application	6.3	III.2.a/III.3	Analysis	9.1
III.2.a/III.3	Application	6.6	III.2.a/III.3	Analysis	9.3
III.2.a/III.3	Application	6.7	III.2.a/III.3	Analysis	9.4
III.2.a/III.3	Application	6.19	III.2.a/III.3	Application	9.17
III.2.a/III.3	Application	6.21	III.2.a/III.3	Analysis	9.18
III.2.a/III.3	Application	6.25	III.2.a/III.3	Analysis	9.29
III.2.a/III.3	Application	6.27	III.2.a/III.3	Analysis	9.31
III.2.a/III.3	Application	6.37	III.2.a/III.3	Analysis	9.32
III.2.a/III.3	Application	6.39	III.2.a/III.3	Analysis	9.38
III.2.a/III.3	Application	6.41	III.2.a/III.3	Analysis	9.45
III.2.a/III.3	Application	6.42	III.2.a/III.3	Analysis	9.51
III.2.a/III.3	Application	6.43	III.2.a/III.3	Analysis	9.64
III.2.a/III.3	Application	6.44	III.2.a/III.3	Analysis	9.71
III.2.a/III.3	Application	6.46	III.2.a/III.3	Analysis	9.73
III.2.a/III.3	Application	6.47	III.2.a/III.3	Application	9.74
III.2.a/III.3	Application	6.51	III.2.a/III.3	Application	9.82
III.2.a/III.3	Application	6.54	III.2.a/III.3/III.4	Application	6.60
III.2.a/III.3	Application	6.56	III.2.c	Application	1.376
III.2.a/III.3	Application	6.59	III.2.c	Application	1.377
III.2.a/III.3	Application	6.63	III.2.c	Application	1.378
III.2.a/III.3	Application	6.67	III.2.c	Application	1.379
III.2.a/III.3	Application	6.68	III.2.c	Application	1.380
III.2.a/III.3	Application	6.71	III.2.c	Application	1.381

CCA Exam Competency	CCA Exam Level	Question Number	CCA Exam Competency	CCA Exam Level	Question Number
III.2.c	Application	1.382	III.3	Application	2.54
III.2.c	Application	1.383	III.3	Application	2.55
III.2.c	Application	1.384	III.3	Application	2.56
III.2.c	Application	1.385	III.3	Application	2.57
III.2.c	Application	1.386	III.3	Application	2.58
III.2.c	Application	1.387	III.3	Application	2.59
III.2.c	Application	1.388	III.3	Application	2.60
III.2.c	Application	1.389	III.3	Application	2.61
III.2.c	Application	1.390	III.3	Application	2.62
III.2.c	Application	1.391	III.3	Application	2.63
III.2.c	Application	1.392	III.3	Application	2.69
III.2.c	Application	1.393	III.3	Application	2.72
III.2.c	Application	1.394	III.3	Application	2.73
III.2.c	Application	1.395	III.3	Application	2.74
III.2.c	Application	1.396	III.3	Application	2.75
III.2.c	Application	1.397	III.3	Application	2.76
III.2.c	Application	1.398	III.3	Application	2.77
III.2.c	Application	1.399	III.3	Application	2.78
III.2.c	Application	1.400	III.3	Application	2.79
III.2.c	Recall	1.420	III.3	Application	2.80
III.2.c	Application	4.15	III.3	Application	2.81
III.2.c	Application	4.56	III.3	Application	2.83
III.2.c	Application	4.57	III.3	Application	2.85
III.2.c	Analysis	7.5	III.3	Application	2.86
III.2.c	Analysis	7.6	III.3	Application	2.89
III.2.c	Analysis	7.7	III.3	Application	2.93
III.2.c	Analysis	7.8	III.3	Application	2.94
III.3	Application	2.23	III.3	Application	2.95
III.3	Application	2.25	III.3	Application	2.96
III.3	Application	2.26	III.3	Application	2.97
III.3	Application	2.27	III.3	Application	2.98
III.3	Application	2.35	III.3	Application	2.99
III.3	Application	2.37	III.3	Application	2.100
III.3	Application	2.47	III.3	Application	2.101
III.3	Application	2.48	III.3	Application	2.102
III.3	Application	2.49	III.3	Application	2.104
III.3	Application	2.50	III.3	Application	2.105
III.3	Application	2.51	III.3	Application	2.106
III.3	Application	2.52	III.3	Application	2.107
III.3	Application	2.53	III.3	Application	2.108

CCA Exam Competency	CCA Exam Level	Question Number	CCA Exam Competency	CCA Exam Level	Question Number
III.3	Application	2.109	III.3	Application	2.155
III.3	Application	2.111	III.3	Application	2.156
III.3	Application	2.112	III.3	Application	2.158
III.3	Application	2.113	III.3	Application	2.159
III.3	Application	2.114	III.3	Application	2.161
III.3	Application	2.115	III.3	Application	2.162
III.3	Application	2.116	III.3	Application	2.163
III.3	Application	2.117	III.3	Application	2.164
III.3	Application	2.118	III.3	Application	2.165
III.3	Application	2.119	III.3	Application	2.166
III.3	Application	2.120	III.3	Application	2.167
III.3	Application	2.121	III.3	Application	2.168
III.3	Application	2.122	III.3	Application	2.169
III.3	Application	2.123	III.3	Application	2.170
III.3	Application	2.124	III.3	Application	2.171
III.3	Application	2.125	III.3	Application	2.172
III.3	Application	2.127	III.3	Application	2.173
III.3	Application	2.128	III.3	Application	2.174
III.3	Application	2.129	III.3	Application	2.175
III.3	Application	2.133	III.3	Application	2.176
III.3	Application	2.134	III.3	Application	2.177
III.3	Application	2.136	III.3	Application	2.178
III.3	Application	2.137	III.3	Application	2.179
III.3	Application	2.138	III.3	Application	2.180
III.3	Application	2.139	III.3	Application	2.181
III.3	Application	2.140	III.3	Application	2.182
III.3	Application	2.141	III.3	Application	2.183
III.3	Application	2.142	III.3	Application	2.184
III.3	Application	2.143	III.3	Application	2.185
III.3	Application	2.144	III.3	Application	2.186
III.3	Application	2.145	III.3	Application	2.187
III.3	Application	2.146	III.3	Application	2.188
III.3	Application	2.147	III.3	Application	2.189
III.3	Application	2.148	III.3	Application	2.190
III.3	Application	2.149	III.3	Application	2.191
III.3	Application	2.150	III.3	Application	2.192
III.3	Application	2.151	III.3	Application	2.193
III.3	Application	2.152	III.3	Application	2.194
III.3	Application	2.153	III.3	Application	2.195
III.3	Application	2.154	III.3	Application	2.196

CCA Exam Competency	CCA Exam Level	Question Number	CCA Exam Competency	CCA Exam Level	Question Number
III.3	Application	2.197	III.3	Application	2.237
III.3	Application	2.198	III.3	Application	2.238
III.3	Application	2.199	III.3	Application	2.239
III.3	Application	2.200	III.3	Application	2.240
III.3	Application	2.201	III.3	Application	2.241
III.3	Application	2.202	III.3	Application	2.242
III.3	Application	2.203	III.3	Application	2.243
III.3	Application	2.204	III.3	Application	2.244
III.3	Application	2.205	III.3	Application	2.245
III.3	Application	2.206	III.3	Application	2.246
III.3	Application	2.207	III.3	Application	2.247
III.3	Application	2.208	III.3	Application	2.248
III.3	Application	2.209	III.3	Application	2.249
III.3	Application	2.210	III.3	Application	2.250
III.3	Application	2.211	III.3	Application	2.251
III.3	Application	2.212	III.3	Application	2.252
III.3	Application	2.213	III.3	Application	2.253
III.3	Application	2.214	III.3	Application	2.254
III.3	Application	2.215	III.3	Application	2.255
III.3	Application	2.216	III.3	Application	2.256
III.3	Application	2.217	III.3	Application	2.257
III.3	Application	2.218	III.3	Application	2.258
III.3	Application	2.219	III.3	Application	2.259
III.3	Application	2.220	III.3	Application	2.260
III.3	Application	2.221	III.3	Application	2.261
III.3	Application	2.222	III.3	Application	2.262
III.3	Application	2.223	III.3	Application	2.263
III.3	Application	2.224	III.3	Application	2.264
III.3	Application	2.225	III.3	Application	2.265
III.3	Application	2.226	III.3	Application	2.266
III.3	Application	2.227	III.3	Application	2.267
III.3	Application	2.228	III.3	Application	2.268
III.3	Application	2.229	III.3	Application	2.269
III.3	Application	2.230	III.3	Application	2.270
III.3	Application	2.231	III.3	Application	2.271
III.3	Application	2.232	III.3	Application	2.272
III.3	Application	2.233	III.3	Application	2.273
III.3	Application	2.234	III.3	Application	2.274
III.3	Application	2.235	III.3	Application	2.275
III.3	Application	2.236	III.3	Application	2.276

CCA Exam Competency	CCA Exam Level	Question Number	CCA Exam Competency	CCA Exam Level	Question Number
III.3	Application	2.277	III.3	Application	2.321
III.3	Application	2.278	III.3	Application	2.322
III.3	Application	2.279	III.3	Application	2.323
III.3	Application	2.280	III.3	Application	2.324
III.3	Application	2.281	III.3	Application	2.325
III.3	Application	2.282	III.3	Application	2.326
III.3	Application	2.283	III.3	Application	2.327
III.3	Application	2.284	III.3	Application	2.328
III.3	Application	2.285	III.3	Application	2.329
III.3	Application	2.286	III.3	Application	2.330
III.3	Application	2.287	III.3	Application	2.331
III.3	Application	2.288	III.3	Application	2.332
III.3	Application	2.289	III.3	Application	2.333
III.3	Application	2.290	III.3	Application	2.334
III.3	Application	2.291	III.3	Application	2.335
III.3	Application	2.293	III.3	Application	2.336
III.3	Application	2.294	III.3	Application	2.338
III.3	Application	2.295	III.3	Application	2.340
III.3	Application	2.296	III.3	Application	2.342
III.3	Application	2.297	III.3	Application	2.344
III.3	Application	2.298	III.3	Application	2.345
III.3	Application	2.299	III.3	Application	2.346
III.3	Application	2.300	III.3	Application	2.347
III.3	Application	2.301	III.3	Application	2.348
III.3	Application	2.302	III.3	Application	2.349
III.3	Application	2.303	III.3	Application	2.350
III.3	Application	2.304	III.3	Application	2.351
III.3	Application	2.305	III.3	Application	2.352
III.3	Application	2.306	III.3	Application	2.353
III.3	Application	2.307	III.3	Application	2.354
III.3	Application	2.308	III.3	Application	2.355
III.3	Application	2.309	III.3	Application	2.356
III.3	Application	2.310	III.3	Application	2.357
III.3	Application	2.311	III.3	Application	2.358
III.3	Application	2.312	III.3	Application	2.359
III.3	Application	2.314	III.3	Application	2.360
III.3	Application	2.317	III.3	Application	2.361
III.3	Application	2.318	III.3	Application	2.366
III.3	Application	2.319	III.3	Application	2.368
III.3	Application	2.320	III.3	Application	2.373

CCA Exam Competency	CCA Exam Level	Question Number	CCA Exam Competency	CCA Exam Level	Question Number
III.3	Application	2.385	III.3	Application	5.11
III.3	Application	2.386	III.3	Application	5.19
III.3	Application	2.387	III.3	Application	5.34
III.3	Application	2.388	III.3	Application	5.43
III.3	Application	2.390	III.3	Application	5.45
III.3	Application	2.391	III.3	Application	5.48
III.3	Application	2.392	III.3	Application	5.67
III.3	Application	2.393	III.3	Application	6.1
III.3	Application	2.394	III.3	Application	6.4
III.3	Application	2.396	III.3	Application	6.9
III.3	Application	2.397	III.3	Application	6.10
III.3	Application	2.398	III.3	Application	6.18
III.3	Application	2.399	III.3	Application	6.20
III.3	Application	2.400	III.3	Application	6.23
III.3	Application	2.401	III.3	Application	6.24
III.3	Application	2.402	III.3	Application	6.26
III.3	Application	2.403	III.3	Application	6.29
III.3	Application	2.404	III.3	Application	6.30
III.3	Application	2.405	III.3	Application	6.48
III.3	Application	2.406	III.3	Application	6.49
III.3	Application	2.407	III.3	Application	6.50
III.3	Application	2.408	III.3	Application	6.65
III.3	Application	2.409	III.3	Application	6.72
III.3	Application	2.410	III.3	Application	6.75
III.3	Application	2.411	III.3	Application	6.89
III.3	Application	2.412	III.3	Application	6.93
III.3	Application	2.413	III.3	Application	8.9
III.3	Application	2.414	III.3	Analysis	8.43
III.3	Application	2.415	III.3	Application	9.11
III.3	Application	2.416	III.3	Application	9.12
III.3	Application	2.417	III.3	Application	9.13
III.3	Application	2.418	III.3	Application	9.19
III.3	Application	2.419	III.3	Application	9.20
III.3	Application	2.420	III.3	Application	9.21
III.3	Application	2.421	III.3	Analysis	9.22
III.3	Application	2.422	III.3	Analysis	9.24
III.3	Application	2.423	III.3	Analysis	9.25
III.3	Application	2.424	III.3	Application	9.37
III.3	Application	2.425	III.3	Application	9.43
III.3	Application	2.426	III.3	Application	9.59

CCA Exam Competency	CCA Exam Level	Question Number	CCA Exam Competency	CCA Exam Level	Question Number
III.3	Analysis	9.61	III.4	Application	3.30
III.3	Analysis	9.65	III.4	Application	3.31
III.3	Analysis	9.76	III.4	Application	3.32
III.3	Application	9.81	III.4	Application	3.33
III.3	Application	10.27	III.4	Application	3.34
III.3	Application	10.28	III.4	Application	3.35
III.3	Application	10.29	III.4	Application	3.36
III.3	Application	10.30	III.4	Application	3.37
III.3	Application	10.31	III.4	Application	3.38
III.3/III.4	Application	6.66	III.4	Application	3.39
III.3/III.4	Application	8.8	III.4	Application	3.40
III.4	Recall	3.1	III.4	Application	3.41
III.4	Application	3.2	III.4	Application	3.42
III.4	Application	3.3	III.4	Application	3.43
III.4	Application	3.4	III.4	Application	3.44
III.4	Application	3.5	III.4	Application	3.45
III.4	Application	3.6	III.4	Application	3.46
III.4	Application	3.7	III.4	Application	3.47
III.4	Application	3.8	III.4	Application	3.48
III.4	Application	3.9	III.4	Application	3.49
III.4	Application	3.10	III.4	Application	3.50
III.4	Application	3.11	III.4	Application	10.32
III.4	Application	3.12	III.4	Application	10.33
III.4	Application	3.13	III.4	Application	10.34
III.4	Application	3.14	III.4	Recall	10.35
III.4	Application	3.15	III.4	Recall	10.36
III.4	Application	3.16	III.4	Recall	10.37
III.4	Application	3.17	III.6	Recall	2.29
III.4	Application	3.18	III.6	Recall	1.1
III.4	Application	3.19	III.6	Recall	1.2
III.4	Application	3.20	III.6	Recall	1.3
III.4	Application	3.21	III.6	Recall	1.4
III.4	Application	3.22	III.6	Recall	1.6
III.4	Application	3.23	III.6	Recall	1.7
III.4	Recall	3.24	III.6	Recall	1.8
III.4	Application	3.25	III.6	Recall	1.9
III.4	Application	3.26	III.6	Recall	1.10
III.4	Recall	3.27	III.6	Recall	1.11
III.4	Application	3.28	III.6	Recall	1.12
III.4	Application	3.29	III.6	Recall	1.13

CCA Exam Competency	CCA Exam Level	Question Number	CCA Exam Competency	CCA Exam Level	Question Number
III.6	Recall	1.14	III.6	Recall	2.2
III.6	Recall	1.15	III.6	Recall	2.3
III.6	Application	1.19	III.6	Recall	2.4
III.6	Recall	1.48	III.6	Recall	2.5
III.6	Application	1.49	III.6	Recall	2.6
III.6	Recall	1.50	III.6	Recall	2.7
III.6	Application	1.59	III.6	Recall	2.8
III.6	Recall	1.66	III.6	Recall	2.9
III.6	Application	1.70	III.6	Recall	2.10
III.6	Recall	1.77	III.6	Recall	2.11
III.6	Recall	1.81	III.6	Recall	2.12
III.6	Recall	1.83	III.6	Recall	2.13
III.6	Recall	1.96	III.6	Recall	2.14
III.6	Recall	1.101	III.6	Recall	2.15
III.6	Recall	1.103	III.6	Recall	2.16
III.6	Recall	1.124	III.6	Recall	2.17
III.6	Recall	1.127	III.6	Recall	2.18
III.6	Recall	1.140	III.6	Recall	2.19
III.6	Recall	1.142	III.6	Recall	2.20
III.6	Recall	1.205	III.6	Recall	2.21
III.6	Recall	1.219	III.6	Recall	2.22
III.6	Recall	1.220	III.6	Recall	2.24
III.6	Recall	1.230	III.6	Recall	2.28
III.6	Recall	1.231	III.6	Recall	2.30
III.6	Recall	1.232	III.6	Recall	2.31
III.6	Recall	1.234	III.6	Recall	2.32
III.6	Recall	1.235	III.6	Recall	2.33
III.6	Recall	1.403	III.6	Recall	2.34
III.6	Recall	1.407	III.6	Recall	2.36
III.6	Recall	1.412	III.6	Recall	2.38
III.6	Recall	1.413	III.6	Recall	2.39
III.6	Recall	1.414	III.6	Recall	2.40
III.6	Recall	1.416	III.6	Recall	2.41
III.6	Recall	1.417	III.6	Recall	2.42
III.6	Recall	1.418	III.6	Recall	2.43
III.6	Recall	1.419	III.6	Recall	2.44
III.6	Recall	1.424	III.6	Recall	2.45
III.6	Recall	1.425	III.6	Recall	2.46
III.6	Recall	1.426	III.6	Recall	2.64
III.6	Recall	2.1	III.6	Recall	2.65

CCA Exam Competency	CCA Exam Level	Question Number	CCA Exam Competency	CCA Exam Level	Question Number
III.6	Recall	2.66	III.6	Application	2.367
III.6	Recall	2.67	III.6	Application	2.369
III.6	Recall	2.68	III.6	Application	2.370
III.6	Recall	2.70	III.6	Recall	2.371
III.6	Recall	2.71	III.6	Application	2.372
III.6	Recall	2.82	III.6	Application	2.374
III.6	Recall	2.84	III.6	Application	2.375
III.6	Recall	2.87	III.6	Application	2.376
III.6	Recall	2.88	III.6	Application	2.377
III.6	Recall	2.90	III.6	Application	2.378
III.6	Recall	2.91	III.6	Application	2.379
III.6	Recall	2.92	III.6	Application	2.380
III.6	Recall	2.103	III.6	Application	2.381
III.6	Recall	2.110	III.6	Recall	2.382
III.6	Recall	2.126	III.6	Recall	2.383
III.6	Recall	2.130	III.6	Recall	2.384
III.6	Recall	2.131	III.6	Recall	2.389
III.6	Recall	2.132	III.6	Recall	2.395
III.6	Recall	2.135	III.6	Application	5.56
III.6	Recall	2.157	III.6	Recall	10.10
III.6	Recall	2.160	N/A	ICD-10	10.14
III.6	Recall	2.292	N/A	ICD-10	10.15
III.6	Recall	2.313	N/A	ICD-10	10.16
III.6	Recall	2.315	N/A	ICD-10	10.17
III.6	Recall	2.316	N/A	ICD-10	10.18
III.6	Recall	2.337	N/A	ICD-10	10.19
III.6	Recall	2.339	N/A	ICD-10	10.20
III.6	Recall	2.341	N/A	ICD-10	10.21
III.6	Recall	2.343	N/A	ICD-10	10.22
III.6	Application	2.362	N/A	ICD-10	10.23
III.6	Application	2.363	N/A	ICD-10	10.24
III.6	Recall	2.364	N/A	ICD-10	10.25
III.6	Application	2.365	N/A	ICD-10	10.26

Certified Coding Specialist (CCS)

Certified Coding Specialists are professionals skilled in classifying medical data from patient records, generally in the hospital setting. These coding practitioners review patients' records and assign numeric codes for each diagnosis and procedure. To perform this task, they must possess expertise in the ICD-9-CM coding system and the surgery section within the CPT coding system. In addition, the CCS is knowledgeable about medical terminology, disease processes, and pharmacology.

Hospitals or medical providers report coded data to insurance companies or the government, in the case of Medicare and Medicaid recipients, for reimbursement of their expenses. Researchers and public health officials also use coded medical data to monitor patterns and explore new interventions. Coding accuracy is thus highly important to healthcare organizations because of its impact on revenues and describing health outcomes. Accordingly, the CCS credential demonstrates tested data quality and integrity skills in a coding practitioner. The CCS certification exam assesses mastery or proficiency in coding rather than entry-level skills.

CCS Coding Competencies

Domain I. Health Information Documentation

1. Interpret health record documentation using knowledge of anatomy, physiology, clinical disease processes, pharmacology, and medical terminology to identify codable diagnoses and/or procedures.
2. Determine when additional clinical information is needed to assign the diagnosis and/or procedure code(s).
3. Consult with physicians and other healthcare providers to obtain further clinical information to assist with code assignment.
4. Consult reference materials to facilitate code assignment.
5. Identify patient encounter type to assign codes (such as inpatient versus outpatient).
6. Identify the etiology and manifestation(s) of clinical conditions.

Domain II. Diagnostic Coding Guidelines

1. Select the diagnoses that require coding according to current coding and reporting requirements for inpatient services.
2. Select the diagnoses that require coding according to current coding and reporting requirements for hospital-based outpatient services.
3. Interpret conventions, formats, instructional notations, tables, and definitions of the classification system to select diagnoses, conditions, problems, or other reasons for the encounter that require coding.
4. Sequence diagnoses and other reasons for encounter according to notations and conventions of the classification system and standard data set definitions [such as Uniform Hospital Discharge Data Set (UHDDS)].
5. Determine if signs, symptoms, or manifestations require separate code assignments.
6. Determine if the diagnostic statement provided by the healthcare provider does not allow for more specific code assignment (such as fourth or fifth digit).
7. Recognize when the classification system does not provide a precise code for the condition documented (such as residual categories and/or nonclassified syndromes).

8. Assign supplementary code(s) to indicate reasons for the healthcare encounter other than illness or injury.
9. Assign supplementary code(s) to indicate factors other than illness or injury that influence the patient's health status.
10. Assign supplementary code(s) to indicate the external cause of an injury, adverse effect, or poisoning.

Domain III. Procedural Coding Guidelines

1. Select the procedures that require coding according to current coding and reporting requirements for inpatient services.
2. Select the procedures that require coding according to current coding and reporting requirements for hospital-based outpatient services.
3. Interpret conventions, formats, instructional notations, and definitions of the classification system and/or nomenclature to select procedures/services that require coding.
4. Sequence procedures according to notations and conventions of the classification system/ nomenclature and standard data set definitions (such as UHDDS).
5. Determine if more than one code is necessary to fully describe the procedure/service performed.
6. Determine if the procedural statement provided by the healthcare provider does not allow for a more specific code assignment.
7. Recognize when the classification system/nomenclature does not provide a precise code for the procedure/service.

Domain IV. Regulatory Guidelines and Reporting Requirements for Inpatient Hospitalizations

1. Select the principal diagnosis, principal procedure, complications and comorbid conditions, and other significant procedures that require coding according to UHDDS definitions and official coding guidelines.
2. Evaluate the effect of code selection on DRG assignment.
3. Verify DRG assignment based on Prospective Payment System (PPS) definitions.

Domain V. Regulatory Guidelines and Reporting Requirements for Hospital-based Outpatient Services

1. Apply guidelines for bundling and unbundling codes.
2. Apply outpatient PPS reporting requirements:
   a. Modifiers
   b. CPT versus HCPCS II
   c. Medical necessity (for example, linking diagnosis to procedure/service)
   d. Evaluation and Management code assignment
3. Select the reason for encounter, pertinent secondary conditions, primary procedure, and other significant procedures that require coding.
4. Verify APC assignment based on OPPS definitions.

Domain VI. Data Quality

1. Assess the quality of coding from an array of data (such as reports).
2. Educate physicians and staff regarding reimbursement methodologies and documentation rules and regulations related to coding.

3. Participate in the development of institutional coding policies to ensure compliance with official coding rules and guidelines.
4. Analyze health record documentation for quality and completeness of coding (such as inclusion or exclusion of codes).
5. Review health record documentation to substantiate claims processing and appeals (such as codes, discharge disposition, patient type, charge codes).
6. Analyze edits from the Correct Coding Initiative (CCI) and Outpatient Code Editor (OCE).

Domain VII. Data Management

1. Manage accounts (such as unbilled, denied, suspended).
2. Recognize UB-92 data elements.
3. Identify Charge Description Master (CDM) issues (such as revenue codes, units of service, CPT/HCPCS, text descriptions, modifiers).
4. Identify accounts subject to the 72-hour rule.
5. Identify hospital-based outpatient accounts subject to the "to/from" dates of service edits.
6. Identify cases needed for health record reviews (such as committee, clinical pertinence, research).
7. Analyze case mix index data.

Certified Coding Specialist (CCS) Competencies

CCS Exam Competency	CCS Exam Level	Question Number	CCS Exam Competency	CCS Exam Level	Question Number
I.1	Recall	1.8	I.1/II.1/III.1	Analysis	7.38
I.1	Recall	1.48	I.1/III.2	Analysis	8.19
I.1	Recall	1.59	I.1/IV.1	Analysis	7.43
I.1	Recall	1.101	I.1/IV.1/III.5	Analysis	7.13
I.1	Recall	1.103	I.2	Recall	1.406
I.1	Application	1.142	I.3	Recall	2.144
I.1	Application	1.208	I.3/II.3	Analysis	7.21
I.1	Recall	1.235	I.3/IV.1	Analysis	7.58
I.1	Recall	1.403	I.3/IV.1/II.6	Analysis	7.16
I.1	Recall	1.416	II.1	Recall	1.4
I.1	Recall	1.424	II.1	Recall	1.6
I.1	Recall	1.425	II.1	Application	1.139
I.1	Recall	1.426	II.1	Application	1.221
I.1	Recall	2.96	II.1	Application	1.222
I.1	Recall	2.116	II.1	Application	1.224
I.1/I.3	Analysis	7.18	II.1	Application	1.227
I.1/I.4	Application	5.56	II.1	Application	1.228
I.1/II.1	Analysis	7.24	II.1	Application	1.229
I.1/II.1	Analysis	7.33	II.1	Application	1.294
I.1/II.1/III.1	Analysis	7.11	II.1	Application	1.336
I.1/II.1/III.1	Analysis	7.12	II.1	Application	1.337

CCS Exam Competency	CCS Exam Level	Question Number	CCS Exam Competency	CCS Exam Level	Question Number
II.1	Application	1.338	II.1	Application	10.44
II.1	Application	1.339	II.1	Application	10.45
II.1	Application	1.340	II.1	Application	10.46
II.1	Application	1.341	II.1	Application	10.47
II.1	Application	1.342	II.1	Application	10.48
II.1	Application	1.343	II.1	Application	10.49
II.1	Application	1.344	II.1/II.10	Application	4.72
II.1	Application	1.345	II.1/II.10	Application	4.91
II.1	Application	1.346	II.1/II.10	Application	4.92
II.1	Application	1.347	II.1/II.10	Application	4.93
II.1	Application	1.348	II.1/II.10	Application	4.95
II.1	Application	1.349	II.1/II.10	Application	4.97
II.1	Application	1.350	II.1/II.10	Analysis	7.2
II.1	Application	1.351	II.1/II.10	Analysis	7.55
II.1	Application	1.352	II.1/II.2	Application	1.16
II.1	Application	1.353	II.1/II.2	Application	1.17
II.1	Application	1.354	II.1/II.2	Application	1.18
II.1	Application	1.355	II.1/II.2	Application	1.19
II.1	Application	4.9	II.1/II.2	Application	1.20
II.1	Application	4.11	II.1/II.2	Application	1.21
II.1	Application	4.12	II.1/II.2	Application	1.22
II.1	Application	4.20	II.1/II.2	Application	1.23
II.1	Application	4.21	II.1/II.2	Application	1.24
II.1	Application	4.22	II.1/II.2	Application	1.25
II.1	Application	4.34	II.1/II.2	Application	1.26
II.1	Application	4.35	II.1/II.2	Application	1.27
II.1	Application	4.60	II.1/II.2	Application	1.28
II.1	Application	4.62	II.1/II.2	Application	1.29
II.1	Application	4.67	II.1/II.2	Application	1.30
II.1	Application	4.71	II.1/II.2	Application	1.31
II.1	Application	4.79	II.1/II.2	Application	1.32
II.1	Application	4.81	II.1/II.2	Application	1.33
II.1	Application	4.83	II.1/II.2	Application	1.34
II.1	Application	4.84	II.1/II.2	Application	1.35
II.1	Application	4.88	II.1/II.2	Application	1.36
II.1	Analysis	7.51	II.1/II.2	Application	1.37
II.1	Application	10.38	II.1/II.2	Application	1.40
II.1	Application	10.39	II.1/II.2	Application	1.41
II.1	Application	10.40	II.1/II.2	Application	1.42
II.1	Application	10.43	II.1/II.2	Application	1.43

CCS Exam Competency	CCS Exam Level	Question Number	CCS Exam Competency	CCS Exam Level	Question Number
II.1/II.2	Application	1.44	II.1/II.2	Application	1.91
II.1/II.2	Application	1.45	II.1/II.2	Application	1.92
II.1/II.2	Application	1.46	II.1/II.2	Application	1.93
II.1/II.2	Application	1.47	II.1/II.2	Application	1.94
II.1/II.2	Application	1.49	II.1/II.2	Application	1.95
II.1/II.2	Application	1.50	II.1/II.2	Application	1.97
II.1/II.2	Application	1.51	II.1/II.2	Application	1.98
II.1/II.2	Application	1.52	II.1/II.2	Application	1.99
II.1/II.2	Application	1.54	II.1/II.2	Application	1.100
II.1/II.2	Application	1.55	II.1/II.2	Application	1.102
II.1/II.2	Application	1.56	II.1/II.2	Application	1.104
II.1/II.2	Application	1.57	II.1/II.2	Application	1.105
II.1/II.2	Application	1.58	II.1/II.2	Application	1.106
II.1/II.2	Application	1.60	II.1/II.2	Application	1.107
II.1/II.2	Application	1.61	II.1/II.2	Application	1.108
II.1/II.2	Application	1.62	II.1/II.2	Application	1.109
II.1/II.2	Application	1.63	II.1/II.2	Application	1.110
II.1/II.2	Application	1.64	II.1/II.2	Application	1.111
II.1/II.2	Application	1.65	II.1/II.2	Application	1.112
II.1/II.2	Application	1.67	II.1/II.2	Application	1.113
II.1/II.2	Application	1.68	II.1/II.2	Application	1.114
II.1/II.2	Application	1.69	II.1/II.2	Application	1.115
II.1/II.2	Application	1.70	II.1/II.2	Application	1.116
II.1/II.2	Application	1.71	II.1/II.2	Application	1.117
II.1/II.2	Application	1.72	II.1/II.2	Application	1.119
II.1/II.2	Application	1.73	II.1/II.2	Application	1.120
II.1/II.2	Application	1.74	II.1/II.2	Application	1.121
II.1/II.2	Application	1.75	II.1/II.2	Application	1.122
II.1/II.2	Application	1.76	II.1/II.2	Application	1.123
II.1/II.2	Application	1.78	II.1/II.2	Application	1.125
II.1/II.2	Application	1.79	II.1/II.2	Application	1.126
II.1/II.2	Application	1.80	II.1/II.2	Application	1.128
II.1/II.2	Application	1.82	II.1/II.2	Application	1.129
II.1/II.2	Application	1.84	II.1/II.2	Application	1.130
II.1/II.2	Application	1.85	II.1/II.2	Application	1.131
II.1/II.2	Application	1.86	II.1/II.2	Application	1.132
II.1/II.2	Application	1.87	II.1/II.2	Application	1.133
II.1/II.2	Application	1.88	II.1/II.2	Application	1.134
II.1/II.2	Application	1.89	II.1/II.2	Application	1.135
II.1/II.2	Application	1.90	II.1/II.2	Application	1.136

CCS Exam Competency	CCS Exam Level	Question Number	CCS Exam Competency	CCS Exam Level	Question Number
II.1/II.2	Application	1.137	II.1/II.2	Application	1.180
II.1/II.2	Application	1.138	II.1/II.2	Application	1.181
II.1/II.2	Application	1.141	II.1/II.2	Application	1.182
II.1/II.2	Application	1.143	II.1/II.2	Application	1.183
II.1/II.2	Application	1.144	II.1/II.2	Application	1.184
II.1/II.2	Application	1.145	II.1/II.2	Application	1.185
II.1/II.2	Application	1.146	II.1/II.2	Application	1.186
II.1/II.2	Application	1.147	II.1/II.2	Application	1.187
II.1/II.2	Application	1.148	II.1/II.2	Application	1.188
II.1/II.2	Application	1.149	II.1/II.2	Application	1.189
II.1/II.2	Application	1.150	II.1/II.2	Application	1.190
II.1/II.2	Application	1.151	II.1/II.2	Application	1.191
II.1/II.2	Application	1.152	II.1/II.2	Application	1.192
II.1/II.2	Application	1.153	II.1/II.2	Application	1.193
II.1/II.2	Application	1.154	II.1/II.2	Application	1.194
II.1/II.2	Application	1.155	II.1/II.2	Application	1.195
II.1/II.2	Application	1.156	II.1/II.2	Application	1.196
II.1/II.2	Application	1.157	II.1/II.2	Application	1.197
II.1/II.2	Application	1.158	II.1/II.2	Application	1.198
II.1/II.2	Application	1.159	II.1/II.2	Application	1.199
II.1/II.2	Application	1.160	II.1/II.2	Application	1.200
II.1/II.2	Application	1.161	II.1/II.2	Application	1.201
II.1/II.2	Application	1.162	II.1/II.2	Application	1.202
II.1/II.2	Application	1.163	II.1/II.2	Application	1.203
II.1/II.2	Application	1.164	II.1/II.2	Application	1.204
II.1/II.2	Application	1.165	II.1/II.2	Application	1.206
II.1/II.2	Application	1.166	II.1/II.2	Application	1.207
II.1/II.2	Application	1.167	II.1/II.2	Application	1.209
II.1/II.2	Application	1.168	II.1/II.2	Application	1.210
II.1/II.2	Application	1.169	II.1/II.2	Application	1.211
II.1/II.2	Application	1.170	II.1/II.2	Application	1.212
II.1/II.2	Application	1.171	II.1/II.2	Application	1.213
II.1/II.2	Application	1.172	II.1/II.2	Application	1.214
II.1/II.2	Application	1.173	II.1/II.2	Application	1.215
II.1/II.2	Application	1.174	II.1/II.2	Application	1.216
II.1/II.2	Application	1.175	II.1/II.2	Application	1.217
II.1/II.2	Application	1.176	II.1/II.2	Application	1.218
II.1/II.2	Application	1.177	II.1/II.2	Application	1.223
II.1/II.2	Application	1.178	II.1/II.2	Application	1.225
II.1/II.2	Application	1.179	II.1/II.2	Application	1.226

CCS Exam Competency	CCS Exam Level	Question Number	CCS Exam Competency	CCS Exam Level	Question Number
II.1/II.2	Application	1.233	II.1/II.2	Application	1.276
II.1/II.2	Application	1.236	II.1/II.2	Application	1.277
II.1/II.2	Application	1.237	II.1/II.2	Application	1.278
II.1/II.2	Application	1.238	II.1/II.2	Application	1.279
II.1/II.2	Application	1.239	II.1/II.2	Application	1.280
II.1/II.2	Application	1.240	II.1/II.2	Application	1.281
II.1/II.2	Application	1.241	II.1/II.2	Application	1.282
II.1/II.2	Application	1.242	II.1/II.2	Application	1.283
II.1/II.2	Application	1.243	II.1/II.2	Application	1.284
II.1/II.2	Application	1.244	II.1/II.2	Application	1.285
II.1/II.2	Application	1.245	II.1/II.2	Application	1.286
II.1/II.2	Application	1.246	II.1/II.2	Application	1.287
II.1/II.2	Application	1.247	II.1/II.2	Application	1.288
II.1/II.2	Application	1.248	II.1/II.2	Application	1.289
II.1/II.2	Application	1.250	II.1/II.2	Application	1.290
II.1/II.2	Application	1.251	II.1/II.2	Application	1.291
II.1/II.2	Application	1.252	II.1/II.2	Application	1.292
II.1/II.2	Application	1.253	II.1/II.2	Application	1.293
II.1/II.2	Application	1.254	II.1/II.2	Application	1.295
II.1/II.2	Application	1.255	II.1/II.2	Application	1.296
II.1/II.2	Application	1.256	II.1/II.2	Application	1.297
II.1/II.2	Application	1.257	II.1/II.2	Application	1.298
II.1/II.2	Application	1.258	II.1/II.2	Application	1.299
II.1/II.2	Application	1.259	II.1/II.2	Application	1.300
II.1/II.2	Application	1.260	II.1/II.2	Application	1.301
II.1/II.2	Application	1.261	II.1/II.2	Application	1.302
II.1/II.2	Application	1.262	II.1/II.2	Application	1.303
II.1/II.2	Application	1.263	II.1/II.2	Application	1.304
II.1/II.2	Application	1.264	II.1/II.2	Application	1.305
II.1/II.2	Application	1.265	II.1/II.2	Application	1.306
II.1/II.2	Application	1.266	II.1/II.2	Application	1.307
II.1/II.2	Application	1.267	II.1/II.2	Application	1.308
II.1/II.2	Application	1.268	II.1/II.2	Application	1.309
II.1/II.2	Application	1.269	II.1/II.2	Application	1.310
II.1/II.2	Application	1.270	II.1/II.2	Application	1.311
II.1/II.2	Application	1.271	II.1/II.2	Application	1.312
II.1/II.2	Application	1.272	II.1/II.2	Application	1.313
II.1/II.2	Application	1.273	II.1/II.2	Application	1.314
II.1/II.2	Application	1.274	II.1/II.2	Application	1.315
II.1/II.2	Application	1.275	II.1/II.2	Application	1.316

CCS Exam Competency	CCS Exam Level	Question Number	CCS Exam Competency	CCS Exam Level	Question Number
II.1/II.2	Application	1.317	II.1/II.2	Application	1.397
II.1/II.2	Application	1.318	II.1/II.2	Application	1.398
II.1/II.2	Application	1.319	II.1/II.2	Application	1.399
II.1/II.2	Application	1.320	II.1/II.2	Application	1.400
II.1/II.2	Application	1.321	II.1/II.4	Analysis	7.4
II.1/II.2	Application	1.322	II.1/II.4	Analysis	7.52
II.1/II.2	Application	1.323	II.1/II.4	Analysis	7.53
II.1/II.2	Application	1.324	II.1/II.4	Analysis	7.54
II.1/II.2	Application	1.325	II.1/II.6	Analysis	7.3
II.1/II.2	Application	1.326	II.1/II.8	Analysis	7.1
II.1/II.2	Application	1.327	II.1/II.9	Analysis	7.32
II.1/II.2	Application	1.328	II.1/III.1	Application	4.15
II.1/II.2	Application	1.329	II.1/III.1	Application	4.16
II.1/II.2	Application	1.330	II.1/III.1	Application	4.17
II.1/II.2	Application	1.331	II.1/III.1	Application	4.18
II.1/II.2	Application	1.332	II.1/III.1	Application	4.19
II.1/II.2	Application	1.333	II.1/III.1	Application	4.29
II.1/II.2	Application	1.334	II.1/III.1	Application	4.36
II.1/II.2	Application	1.335	II.1/III.1	Application	4.37
II.1/II.2	Application	1.376	II.1/III.1	Application	4.38
II.1/II.2	Application	1.377	II.1/III.1	Application	4.39
II.1/II.2	Application	1.378	II.1/III.1	Application	4.40
II.1/II.2	Application	1.379	II.1/III.1	Application	4.41
II.1/II.2	Application	1.380	II.1/III.1	Application	4.42
II.1/II.2	Application	1.381	II.1/III.1	Application	4.43
II.1/II.2	Application	1.382	II.1/III.1	Application	4.46
II.1/II.2	Application	1.383	II.1/III.1	Application	4.47
II.1/II.2	Application	1.384	II.1/III.1	Application	4.48
II.1/II.2	Application	1.385	II.1/III.1	Application	4.50
II.1/II.2	Application	1.386	II.1/III.1	Application	4.59
II.1/II.2	Application	1.387	II.1/III.1	Application	4.61
II.1/II.2	Application	1.388	II.1/III.1	Application	4.63
II.1/II.2	Application	1.389	II.1/III.1	Application	4.64
II.1/II.2	Application	1.390	II.1/III.1	Application	4.66
II.1/II.2	Application	1.391	II.1/III.1	Application	4.69
II.1/II.2	Application	1.392	II.1/III.1	Application	4.73
II.1/II.2	Application	1.393	II.1/III.1	Application	4.74
II.1/II.2	Application	1.394	II.1/III.1	Application	4.89
II.1/II.2	Application	1.395	II.1/III.1	Application	4.90
II.1/II.2	Application	1.396	II.1/III.1	Application	4.94

CCS Exam Competency	CCS Exam Level	Question Number	CCS Exam Competency	CCS Exam Level	Question Number
II.1/III.1	Application	4.96	II.2/III.2	Application	5.12
II.1/III.1	Analysis	7.9	II.2/III.2	Application	5.13
II.1/III.1	Analysis	7.10	II.2/III.2	Application	5.16
II.1/III.1	Analysis	7.14	II.2/III.2	Application	5.24
II.1/III.1	Analysis	7.15	II.2/III.2	Application	5.25
II.1/III.1	Analysis	7.19	II.2/III.2	Application	5.26
II.1/III.1	Analysis	7.25	II.2/III.2	Application	5.27
II.1/III.1	Analysis	7.29	II.2/III.2	Application	5.28
II.1/III.1	Analysis	7.31	II.2/III.2	Application	5.29
II.1/III.1	Analysis	7.48	II.2/III.2	Application	5.31
II.1/III.1/II.10	Application	4.49	II.2/III.2	Application	5.42
II.1/III.1/II.10	Application	4.55	II.2/III.2	Application	5.43
II.1/III.2	Application	5.4	II.2/III.2	Application	5.44
II.1/III.2	Application	5.87	II.2/III.2	Application	5.47
II.1/III.5	Application	4.25	II.2/III.2	Application	5.48
II.1/III.5	Application	4.26	II.2/III.2	Application	5.49
II.1/III.5	Application	4.56	II.2/III.2	Application	5.55
II.1/V.4	Analysis	8.2	II.2/III.2	Application	5.61
II.2	Application	1.5	II.2/III.2	Application	5.62
II.2	Application	5.22	II.2/III.2	Application	5.64
II.2	Application	5.23	II.2/III.2	Application	5.69
II.2	Application	5.46	II.2/III.2	Application	5.70
II.2	Application	5.50	II.2/III.2	Application	5.76
II.2	Application	5.66	II.2/III.2	Application	5.77
II.2	Application	10.41	II.2/III.2	Application	5.78
II.2	Application	10.42	II.2/III.2	Application	5.79
II.2/II.10	Application	8.4	II.2/III.2	Application	5.85
II.2/II.10/III.2	Application	5.51	II.2/III.2	Application	8.6
II.2/II.10/III.2	Application	5.54	II.2/III.2	Analysis	8.7
II.2/II.10/III.2	Application	5.83	II.2/III.2	Analysis	8.11
II.2/II.10/III.2	Application	5.84	II.2/III.2	Analysis	8.18
II.2/II.10/III.3	Application	5.53	II.2/III.2	Analysis	8.21
II.2/II.10/V.2.a	Analysis	8.55	II.2/III.2	Analysis	8.22
II.2/II.3	Application	8.5	II.2/III.2	Analysis	8.23
II.2/II.9/III.2	Analysis	8.39	II.2/III.2	Application	8.28
II.2/III.2	Application	5.1	II.2/III.2	Analysis	8.30
II.2/III.2	Application	5.3	II.2/III.2	Analysis	8.35
II.2/III.2	Application	5.7	II.2/III.2	Analysis	8.36
II.2/III.2	Application	5.8	II.2/III.2	Application	8.37
II.2/III.2	Application	5.9	II.2/III.2	Application	8.40

CCS Exam Competency	CCS Exam Level	Question Number		CCS Exam Competency	CCS Exam Level	Question Number
II.2/III.2	Analysis	8.41		II.2/V.2.b	Analysis	8.45
II.2/III.2	Application	8.47		II.2/V.2.b	Analysis	8.51
II.2/III.2	Analysis	8.50		II.2/V.4	Analysis	8.12
II.2/III.2	Analysis	8.52		II.3	Recall	1.1
II.2/III.2	Application	8.54		II.3	Recall	1.2
II.2/III.3	Application	5.40		II.3	Recall	1.7
II.2/III.3	Application	5.41		II.3	Recall	1.10
II.2/III.3	Application	8.42		II.3	Recall	1.11
II.2/III.3	Analysis	8.48		II.3	Recall	1.12
II.2/III.3	Analysis	8.49		II.3	Recall	1.13
II.2/III.5	Application	5.2		II.3	Recall	1.14
II.2/III.5	Application	5.15		II.3	Recall	1.15
II.2/III.5	Application	5.17		II.3	Recall	1.38
II.2/III.5	Application	5.39		II.3	Recall	1.53
II.2/III.5	Application	5.52		II.3	Recall	1.66
II.2/III.5	Application	5.58		II.3	Recall	1.77
II.2/III.5	Application	5.63		II.3	Recall	1.81
II.2/V.1	Analysis	8.24		II.3	Recall	1.83
II.2/V.1	Analysis	8.29		II.3	Recall	1.96
II.2/V.1	Analysis	8.32		II.3	Application	1.118
II.2/V.1/V.2.a	Analysis	8.31		II.3	Recall	1.124
II.2/V.2.a	Application	5.6		II.3	Recall	1.127
II.2/V.2.a	Application	5.59		II.3	Recall	1.140
II.2/V.2.a	Application	5.71		II.3	Recall	1.219
II.2/V.2.a	Application	5.73		II.3	Recall	1.220
II.2/V.2.a	Application	5.74		II.3	Recall	1.230
II.2/V.2.a	Application	5.82		II.3	Recall	1.231
II.2/V.2.a	Application	5.86		II.3	Recall	1.232
II.2/V.2.a	Application	8.13		II.3	Recall	1.234
II.2/V.2.a	Analysis	8.14		II.3	Recall	1.402
II.2/V.2.a	Analysis	8.15		II.3	Recall	1.407
II.2/V.2.a	Analysis	8.33		II.3	Recall	1.410
II.2/V.2.a	Analysis	8.34		II.3	Recall	1.412
II.2/V.2.a	Analysis	8.38		II.3	Recall	1.413
II.2/V.2.a	Analysis	8.44		II.3	Recall	1.414
II.2/V.2.a	Analysis	8.46		II.3	Recall	1.417
II.2/V.2.a	Analysis	8.53		II.3	Recall	1.418
II.2/V.2.b	Application	5.14		II.3	Application	4.1
II.2/V.2.b	Analysis	8.26		II.3	Application	4.2
II.2/V.2.b	Analysis	8.27		II.3	Application	4.5

CCS Exam Competency	CCS Exam Level	Question Number
II.3	Application	4.24
II.3	Application	4.30
II.3	Application	4.32
II.3	Application	4.33
II.3	Application	4.44
II.3	Application	4.45
II.3	Application	4.68
II.3	Application	4.76
II.3	Application	4.77
II.3	Application	4.78
II.3	Application	4.80
II.3	Application	4.87
II.3	Application	5.10
II.3	Application	5.20
II.3	Application	5.21
II.3	Analysis	7.39
II.3	Analysis	7.46
II.3	Analysis	7.47
II.3	Analysis	8.3
II.3	Analysis	8.16
II.3/II.10	Analysis	7.56
II.3/III.1	Analysis	7.20
II.3/III.1	Analysis	7.40
II.3/III.1	Analysis	7.44
II.3/III.2	Application	5.68
II.3/III.3	Application	4.14
II.3/III.3	Analysis	7.41
II.3/III.3	Analysis	7.42
II.3/III.5	Application	5.60
II.4	Recall	1.205
II.4	Recall	1.249
II.4	Application	1.401
II.4	Application	4.31
II.4	Application	4.53
II.4	Application	4.65
II.4	Application	4.82
II.4/II.10	Application	4.85
II.4/II.10	Application	4.86
II.4/II.10	Analysis	7.28
II.4/III.1	Application	4.23

CCS Exam Competency	CCS Exam Level	Question Number
II.4/III.1	Analysis	7.17
II.4/III.4	Analysis	7.50
II.4/IV.1	Recall	1.3
II.4/IV.1	Recall	1.404
II.4/IV.1	Recall	1.405
II.4/IV.1	Recall	1.408
II.4/IV.1	Recall	1.409
II.4/IV.1	Recall	1.411
II.4/IV.1	Recall	1.415
II.4/IV.1	Application	1.421
II.4/IV.1	Application	1.422
II.4/V.2.b	Analysis	8.25
II.5	Recall	1.423
II.5	Application	4.27
II.5	Application	4.54
II.5	Application	4.70
II.5	Application	5.5
II.5	Application	5.35
II.5	Application	5.36
II.5	Application	5.37
II.5	Application	5.38
II.5	Application	5.72
II.5	Application	5.75
II.5	Application	5.80
II.5	Analysis	7.23
II.5	Application	8.10
II.5/II.10	Analysis	7.37
II.5/III.1	Application	4.13
II.5/III.1	Application	4.28
II.5/III.1	Application	4.58
II.5/III.2	Application	5.33
II.5/III.2	Application	5.81
II.5/III.2	Application	8.1
II.6	Application	4.75
II.6/III.1	Analysis	7.57
II.6/III.2	Application	5.30
II.6/III.5	Application	5.32
II.6/V.2.a	Application	5.65
II.8	Application	1.39
II.8/II.9	Application	1.356

CCS Exam Competency	CCS Exam Level	Question Number	CCS Exam Competency	CCS Exam Level	Question Number
II.8/II.9	Application	1.357	III.2	Application	2.52
II.8/II.9	Application	1.358	III.2	Application	2.53
II.8/II.9	Application	1.359	III.2	Application	2.54
II.8/II.9	Application	1.360	III.2	Application	2.55
II.8/II.9	Application	1.361	III.2	Application	2.58
II.8/II.9	Application	1.362	III.2	Application	2.61
II.8/II.9	Application	1.363	III.2	Application	2.62
II.8/II.9	Application	1.364	III.2	Application	2.63
II.8/II.9	Application	1.365	III.2	Application	2.64
II.8/II.9	Application	1.366	III.2	Application	2.65
II.8/II.9	Application	1.367	III.2	Application	2.66
II.8/II.9	Application	1.368	III.2	Application	2.67
II.8/II.9	Application	1.369	III.2	Application	2.68
II.8/II.9	Application	1.370	III.2	Application	2.69
II.8/II.9	Application	1.371	III.2	Application	2.70
II.8/II.9	Application	1.372	III.2	Application	2.71
II.8/II.9	Application	1.373	III.2	Application	2.72
II.8/II.9	Application	1.374	III.2	Application	2.74
II.8/II.9	Application	1.375	III.2	Application	2.75
II.9	Application	4.52	III.2	Application	2.79
II.9/III.2	Application	5.57	III.2	Application	2.80
III.1	Analysis	7.5	III.2	Application	2.81
III.1	Analysis	7.8	III.2	Application	2.82
III.1/II.1	Application	4.4	III.2	Application	2.83
III.1/II.2	Application	4.3	III.2	Application	2.84
III.1/III.2	Recall	1.419	III.2	Application	2.85
III.1/III.5	Analysis	7.6	III.2	Application	2.86
III.1/III.5	Analysis	7.7	III.2	Application	2.87
III.2	Application	2.40	III.2	Application	2.88
III.2	Application	2.41	III.2	Recall	2.89
III.2	Application	2.42	III.2	Application	2.90
III.2	Application	2.43	III.2	Application	2.91
III.2	Application	2.44	III.2	Application	2.92
III.2	Application	2.45	III.2	Application	2.93
III.2	Application	2.46	III.2	Application	2.94
III.2	Application	2.47	III.2	Application	2.95
III.2	Application	2.48	III.2	Application	2.97
III.2	Application	2.49	III.2	Application	2.98
III.2	Application	2.50	III.2	Application	2.99
III.2	Application	2.51	III.2	Application	2.100

CCS Exam Competency	CCS Exam Level	Question Number	CCS Exam Competency	CCS Exam Level	Question Number
III.2	Application	2.101	III.2	Application	2.146
III.2	Application	2.102	III.2	Application	2.147
III.2	Application	2.103	III.2	Application	2.148
III.2	Application	2.104	III.2	Application	2.149
III.2	Application	2.105	III.2	Application	2.150
III.2	Application	2.106	III.2	Application	2.151
III.2	Application	2.107	III.2	Application	2.152
III.2	Application	2.108	III.2	Application	2.153
III.2	Application	2.109	III.2	Application	2.154
III.2	Application	2.110	III.2	Application	2.155
III.2	Application	2.111	III.2	Application	2.156
III.2	Application	2.113	III.2	Application	2.157
III.2	Application	2.114	III.2	Application	2.158
III.2	Application	2.115	III.2	Application	2.159
III.2	Application	2.117	III.2	Application	2.160
III.2	Application	2.118	III.2	Application	2.161
III.2	Application	2.120	III.2	Application	2.162
III.2	Application	2.121	III.2	Application	2.163
III.2	Application	2.122	III.2	Application	2.164
III.2	Application	2.123	III.2	Application	2.165
III.2	Application	2.124	III.2	Application	2.166
III.2	Application	2.125	III.2	Application	2.167
III.2	Application	2.126	III.2	Application	2.168
III.2	Application	2.127	III.2	Application	2.169
III.2	Application	2.128	III.2	Application	2.170
III.2	Application	2.129	III.2	Application	2.171
III.2	Application	2.130	III.2	Application	2.172
III.2	Application	2.131	III.2	Application	2.173
III.2	Application	2.132	III.2	Application	2.174
III.2	Application	2.133	III.2	Application	2.175
III.2	Application	2.134	III.2	Application	2.176
III.2	Application	2.135	III.2	Application	2.177
III.2	Application	2.136	III.2	Application	2.178
III.2	Application	2.137	III.2	Application	2.179
III.2	Application	2.138	III.2	Application	2.180
III.2	Application	2.139	III.2	Application	2.181
III.2	Application	2.140	III.2	Application	2.182
III.2	Application	2.142	III.2	Application	2.183
III.2	Application	2.143	III.2	Application	2.184
III.2	Application	2.145	III.2	Application	2.185

CCS Exam Competency	CCS Exam Level	Question Number	CCS Exam Competency	CCS Exam Level	Question Number
III.2	Application	2.186	III.2	Application	2.226
III.2	Application	2.187	III.2	Application	2.227
III.2	Application	2.188	III.2	Application	2.228
III.2	Application	2.189	III.2	Application	2.229
III.2	Application	2.190	III.2	Application	2.230
III.2	Application	2.191	III.2	Application	2.231
III.2	Application	2.192	III.2	Application	2.232
III.2	Application	2.193	III.2	Application	2.233
III.2	Application	2.194	III.2	Application	2.234
III.2	Application	2.195	III.2	Application	2.235
III.2	Application	2.196	III.2	Application	2.236
III.2	Application	2.197	III.2	Application	2.237
III.2	Application	2.198	III.2	Application	2.238
III.2	Application	2.199	III.2	Application	2.239
III.2	Application	2.200	III.2	Application	2.240
III.2	Application	2.201	III.2	Application	2.241
III.2	Application	2.202	III.2	Application	2.242
III.2	Application	2.203	III.2	Application	2.243
III.2	Application	2.204	III.2	Application	2.244
III.2	Application	2.205	III.2	Application	2.245
III.2	Application	2.206	III.2	Application	2.246
III.2	Application	2.207	III.2	Application	2.247
III.2	Application	2.208	III.2	Application	2.248
III.2	Application	2.209	III.2	Application	2.249
III.2	Application	2.210	III.2	Application	2.250
III.2	Application	2.211	III.2	Application	2.251
III.2	Application	2.212	III.2	Application	2.252
III.2	Application	2.213	III.2	Application	2.253
III.2	Application	2.214	III.2	Application	2.254
III.2	Application	2.215	III.2	Application	2.255
III.2	Application	2.216	III.2	Application	2.256
III.2	Application	2.217	III.2	Application	2.257
III.2	Application	2.218	III.2	Application	2.258
III.2	Application	2.219	III.2	Application	2.259
III.2	Application	2.220	III.2	Application	2.260
III.2	Application	2.221	III.2	Application	2.261
III.2	Application	2.222	III.2	Application	2.262
III.2	Application	2.223	III.2	Application	2.263
III.2	Application	2.224	III.2	Application	2.264
III.2	Application	2.225	III.2	Application	2.265

CCS Exam Competency	CCS Exam Level	Question Number	CCS Exam Competency	CCS Exam Level	Question Number
III.2	Application	2.266	III.2	Application	2.306
III.2	Application	2.267	III.2	Application	2.307
III.2	Application	2.268	III.2	Application	2.308
III.2	Application	2.269	III.2	Application	2.309
III.2	Application	2.270	III.2	Application	2.310
III.2	Application	2.271	III.2	Application	2.311
III.2	Application	2.272	III.2	Application	2.312
III.2	Application	2.273	III.2	Application	2.313
III.2	Application	2.274	III.2	Application	2.314
III.2	Application	2.275	III.2	Application	2.315
III.2	Application	2.276	III.2	Application	2.316
III.2	Application	2.277	III.2	Application	2.318
III.2	Application	2.278	III.2	Application	2.319
III.2	Application	2.279	III.2	Application	2.320
III.2	Application	2.280	III.2	Application	2.321
III.2	Application	2.281	III.2	Application	2.322
III.2	Application	2.282	III.2	Application	2.323
III.2	Application	2.283	III.2	Application	2.324
III.2	Application	2.284	III.2	Application	2.325
III.2	Application	2.285	III.2	Application	2.326
III.2	Application	2.286	III.2	Application	2.327
III.2	Application	2.287	III.2	Application	2.328
III.2	Application	2.288	III.2	Application	2.329
III.2	Application	2.289	III.2	Application	2.330
III.2	Application	2.290	III.2	Application	2.331
III.2	Application	2.291	III.2	Application	2.332
III.2	Application	2.292	III.2	Application	2.333
III.2	Application	2.293	III.2	Application	2.334
III.2	Application	2.294	III.2	Application	2.335
III.2	Application	2.295	III.2	Application	2.359
III.2	Application	2.296	III.2	Application	2.360
III.2	Application	2.297	III.2	Application	2.361
III.2	Application	2.298	III.2	Application	2.362
III.2	Application	2.299	III.2	Application	2.364
III.2	Application	2.300	III.2	Application	2.365
III.2	Application	2.301	III.2	Application	2.366
III.2	Application	2.302	III.2	Application	2.367
III.2	Application	2.303	III.2	Application	2.368
III.2	Application	2.304	III.2	Application	2.370
III.2	Application	2.305	III.2	Application	2.371

CCS Exam Competency	CCS Exam Level	Question Number	CCS Exam Competency	CCS Exam Level	Question Number
III.2	Application	2.372	III.2	Application	2.412
III.2	Application	2.373	III.2	Application	2.413
III.2	Application	2.374	III.2	Application	2.414
III.2	Application	2.375	III.2	Application	2.415
III.2	Application	2.376	III.2	Application	2.416
III.2	Application	2.377	III.2	Application	2.417
III.2	Application	2.378	III.2	Application	2.418
III.2	Application	2.379	III.2	Application	2.419
III.2	Application	2.380	III.2	Application	2.420
III.2	Application	2.381	III.2	Application	2.421
III.2	Application	2.382	III.2	Application	2.422
III.2	Application	2.383	III.2	Application	2.423
III.2	Application	2.384	III.2	Application	2.424
III.2	Application	2.385	III.2	Application	2.425
III.2	Application	2.386	III.2	Application	2.426
III.2	Application	2.387	III.2	Application	3.2
III.2	Application	2.388	III.2	Application	3.3
III.2	Application	2.389	III.2	Application	3.4
III.2	Application	2.390	III.2	Application	3.5
III.2	Application	2.391	III.2	Application	3.6
III.2	Application	2.392	III.2	Application	3.7
III.2	Application	2.393	III.2	Application	3.8
III.2	Application	2.394	III.2	Application	3.9
III.2	Application	2.395	III.2	Application	3.10
III.2	Application	2.396	III.2	Application	3.11
III.2	Application	2.397	III.2	Application	3.12
III.2	Application	2.398	III.2	Application	3.13
III.2	Application	2.399	III.2	Application	3.14
III.2	Application	2.400	III.2	Application	3.15
III.2	Application	2.401	III.2	Application	3.16
III.2	Application	2.402	III.2	Application	3.17
III.2	Application	2.403	III.2	Application	3.18
III.2	Application	2.404	III.2	Application	3.19
III.2	Application	2.405	III.2	Application	3.20
III.2	Application	2.406	III.2	Application	3.23
III.2	Application	2.407	III.2	Application	3.25
III.2	Application	2.408	III.2	Application	3.28
III.2	Application	2.409	III.2	Application	3.29
III.2	Application	2.410	III.2	Application	3.30
III.2	Application	2.411	III.2	Application	3.31

CCS Exam Competency	CCS Exam Level	Question Number	CCS Exam Competency	CCS Exam Level	Question Number
III.2	Application	3.32	III.3	Recall	2.14
III.2	Application	3.33	III.3	Recall	2.15
III.2	Application	3.34	III.3	Recall	2.16
III.2	Application	3.35	III.3	Recall	2.17
III.2	Application	3.36	III.3	Recall	2.18
III.2	Application	3.37	III.3	Recall	2.19
III.2	Application	3.38	III.3	Recall	2.20
III.2	Application	3.39	III.3	Recall	2.21
III.2	Application	3.40	III.3	Recall	2.22
III.2	Application	3.41	III.3	Recall	2.23
III.2	Application	3.42	III.3	Recall	2.24
III.2	Application	3.43	III.3	Recall	2.25
III.2	Application	3.44	III.3	Recall	2.26
III.2	Application	3.45	III.3	Recall	2.27
III.2	Application	3.46	III.3	Recall	2.28
III.2	Application	3.47	III.3	Recall	2.29
III.2	Application	3.48	III.3	Recall	2.30
III.2	Application	3.49	III.3	Recall	2.31
III.2	Application	3.50	III.3	Recall	2.32
III.2	Application	5.11	III.3	Recall	2.33
III.2	Application	5.19	III.3	Recall	2.34
III.2	Application	5.34	III.3	Recall	2.35
III.2	Application	5.45	III.3	Recall	2.36
III.2	Application	5.67	III.3	Recall	2.37
III.2	Application	8.8	III.3	Recall	2.38
III.2	Application	8.9	III.3	Recall	2.39
III.2/II.5	Application	4.6	III.3	Recall	2.56
III.3	Recall	2.1	III.3	Recall	2.57
III.3	Recall	2.2	III.3	Recall	2.59
III.3	Recall	2.3	III.3	Recall	2.60
III.3	Recall	2.4	III.3	Recall	2.73
III.3	Recall	2.5	III.3	Recall	2.76
III.3	Recall	2.6	III.3	Recall	2.77
III.3	Recall	2.7	III.3	Recall	2.78
III.3	Recall	2.8	III.3	Recall	2.119
III.3	Recall	2.9	III.3	Recall	2.141
III.3	Recall	2.10	III.3	Recall	2.317
III.3	Recall	2.11	III.3	Recall	2.356
III.3	Recall	2.12	III.3	Recall	2.357
III.3	Recall	2.13	III.3	Recall	2.358

CCS Exam Competency	CCS Exam Level	Question Number	CCS Exam Competency	CCS Exam Level	Question Number
III.3	Recall	2.363	N/A	N/A	6.5
III.3	Recall	2.369	N/A	N/A	6.6
III.3	Recall	3.1	N/A	N/A	6.7
III.5	Recall	2.112	N/A	N/A	6.8
III.5	Analysis	8.43	N/A	N/A	6.9
IV.1	Application	4.7	N/A	N/A	6.10
IV.1	Application	4.8	N/A	N/A	6.11
IV.1	Application	4.51	N/A	N/A	6.12
IV.1	Application	4.57	N/A	N/A	6.13
IV.1	Analysis	7.22	N/A	N/A	6.14
IV.1	Analysis	7.26	N/A	N/A	6.15
IV.1	Analysis	7.27	N/A	N/A	6.16
IV.1	Analysis	7.30	N/A	N/A	6.17
IV.1	Analysis	7.35	N/A	N/A	6.18
IV.1	Analysis	7.36	N/A	N/A	6.19
IV.1	Analysis	7.45	N/A	N/A	6.20
IV.1	Analysis	7.49	N/A	N/A	6.21
IV.1/II.3	Analysis	7.34	N/A	N/A	6.22
IV.1/III.4	Recall	1.420	N/A	N/A	6.23
IV.21/II.1	Application	4.10	N/A	N/A	6.24
N/A	N/A	2.336	N/A	N/A	6.25
N/A	N/A	2.339	N/A	N/A	6.26
N/A	N/A	2.341	N/A	N/A	6.27
N/A	N/A	2.345	N/A	N/A	6.28
N/A	N/A	2.347	N/A	N/A	6.29
N/A	N/A	2.348	N/A	N/A	6.30
N/A	N/A	2.349	N/A	N/A	6.31
N/A	N/A	2.352	N/A	N/A	6.32
N/A	N/A	2.353	N/A	N/A	6.33
N/A	N/A	2.354	N/A	N/A	6.34
N/A	N/A	2.355	N/A	N/A	6.35
N/A	N/A	3.21	N/A	N/A	6.36
N/A	N/A	3.22	N/A	N/A	6.37
N/A	N/A	3.24	N/A	N/A	6.38
N/A	N/A	3.26	N/A	N/A	6.39
N/A	N/A	3.27	N/A	N/A	6.40
N/A	N/A	6.1	N/A	N/A	6.41
N/A	N/A	6.2	N/A	N/A	6.42
N/A	N/A	6.3	N/A	N/A	6.43
N/A	N/A	6.4	N/A	N/A	6.44

CCS Exam Competency	CCS Exam Level	Question Number	CCS Exam Competency	CCS Exam Level	Question Number
N/A	N/A	6.45	N/A	N/A	6.85
N/A	N/A	6.46	N/A	N/A	6.86
N/A	N/A	6.47	N/A	N/A	6.87
N/A	N/A	6.48	N/A	N/A	6.88
N/A	N/A	6.49	N/A	N/A	6.89
N/A	N/A	6.50	N/A	N/A	6.90
N/A	N/A	6.51	N/A	N/A	6.91
N/A	N/A	6.52	N/A	N/A	6.92
N/A	N/A	6.53	N/A	N/A	6.93
N/A	N/A	6.54	N/A	N/A	6.94
N/A	N/A	6.55	N/A	N/A	9.1
N/A	N/A	6.56	N/A	N/A	9.2
N/A	N/A	6.57	N/A	N/A	9.3
N/A	N/A	6.58	N/A	N/A	9.4
N/A	N/A	6.59	N/A	N/A	9.5
N/A	N/A	6.60	N/A	N/A	9.6
N/A	N/A	6.61	N/A	N/A	9.7
N/A	N/A	6.62	N/A	N/A	9.8
N/A	N/A	6.63	N/A	N/A	9.9
N/A	N/A	6.64	N/A	N/A	9.10
N/A	N/A	6.65	N/A	N/A	9.11
N/A	N/A	6.66	N/A	N/A	9.12
N/A	N/A	6.67	N/A	N/A	9.13
N/A	N/A	6.68	N/A	N/A	9.14
N/A	N/A	6.69	N/A	N/A	9.15
N/A	N/A	6.70	N/A	N/A	9.16
N/A	N/A	6.71	N/A	N/A	9.17
N/A	N/A	6.72	N/A	N/A	9.18
N/A	N/A	6.73	N/A	N/A	9.19
N/A	N/A	6.74	N/A	N/A	9.20
N/A	N/A	6.75	N/A	N/A	9.21
N/A	N/A	6.76	N/A	N/A	9.22
N/A	N/A	6.77	N/A	N/A	9.23
N/A	N/A	6.78	N/A	N/A	9.24
N/A	N/A	6.79	N/A	N/A	9.25
N/A	N/A	6.80	N/A	N/A	9.26
N/A	N/A	6.81	N/A	N/A	9.27
N/A	N/A	6.82	N/A	N/A	9.28
N/A	N/A	6.83	N/A	N/A	9.29
N/A	N/A	6.84	N/A	N/A	9.30

CCS Exam Competency	CCS Exam Level	Question Number	CCS Exam Competency	CCS Exam Level	Question Number
N/A	N/A	9.31	N/A	N/A	9.71
N/A	N/A	9.32	N/A	N/A	9.72
N/A	N/A	9.33	N/A	N/A	9.73
N/A	N/A	9.34	N/A	N/A	9.74
N/A	N/A	9.35	N/A	N/A	9.75
N/A	N/A	9.36	N/A	N/A	9.76
N/A	N/A	9.37	N/A	N/A	9.77
N/A	N/A	9.38	N/A	N/A	9.78
N/A	N/A	9.39	N/A	N/A	9.79
N/A	N/A	9.40	N/A	N/A	9.80
N/A	N/A	9.41	N/A	N/A	9.81
N/A	N/A	9.42	N/A	N/A	9.82
N/A	N/A	9.43	N/A	Home Health	10.1
N/A	N/A	9.44	N/A	Home Health	10.2
N/A	N/A	9.45	N/A	Home Health	10.3
N/A	N/A	9.46	N/A	Home Health	10.4
N/A	N/A	9.47	N/A	Home Health	10.5
N/A	N/A	9.48	N/A	Home Health	10.6
N/A	N/A	9.49	N/A	Home Health	10.7
N/A	N/A	9.50	N/A	Home Health	10.8
N/A	N/A	9.51	N/A	Home Health	10.9
N/A	N/A	9.52	N/A	Home Health	10.10
N/A	N/A	9.53	N/A	Home Health	10.11
N/A	N/A	9.54	N/A	Home Health	10.12
N/A	N/A	9.55	N/A	Home Health	10.13
N/A	N/A	9.56	N/A	ICD-10	10.14
N/A	N/A	9.57	N/A	ICD-10	10.15
N/A	N/A	9.58	N/A	ICD-10	10.16
N/A	N/A	9.59	N/A	ICD-10	10.17
N/A	N/A	9.60	N/A	ICD-10	10.18
N/A	N/A	9.61	N/A	ICD-10	10.19
N/A	N/A	9.62	N/A	ICD-10	10.20
N/A	N/A	9.63	N/A	ICD-10	10.21
N/A	N/A	9.64	N/A	ICD-10	10.22
N/A	N/A	9.65	N/A	ICD-10	10.23
N/A	N/A	9.66	N/A	ICD-10	10.24
N/A	N/A	9.67	N/A	ICD-10	10.25
N/A	N/A	9.68	N/A	ICD-10	10.26
N/A	N/A	9.69	V.2.a	Recall	2.337
N/A	N/A	9.70	V.2.a	Recall	2.338

CCS Exam Competency	CCS Exam Level	Question Number
V.2.a	Recall	2.342
V.2.a	Recall	2.344
V.2.a	Recall	2.346
V.2.a	Recall	2.350
V.2.a	Recall	2.351
V.2.a	Application	10.27
V.2.a	Application	10.28
V.2.a	Application	10.29
V.2.a	Application	10.30
V.2.a	Application	10.31
V.2.a	Application	10.32

CCS Exam Competency	CCS Exam Level	Question Number
V.2.a	Application	10.33
V.2.a	Application	10.34
V.2.a	Recall	10.35
V.2.a	Recall	10.36
V.2.a	Recall	10.37
V.2.a/III.2	Application	2.340
V.2.a/III.2	Application	2.343
V.3	Application	5.18
V.3	Analysis	8.17
V.3/V.1	Analysis	8.20
VI.3	Recall	1.9

Certified Coding Specialist—Physician-based (CCS-P)

The CCS-P is a coding practitioner with expertise in physician-based settings such as physician offices, group practices, multispecialty clinics, or specialty centers. This coding practitioner reviews patients' records and assigns numeric codes for each diagnosis and procedure. To perform this task, the individual must possess in-depth knowledge of the CPT coding system and familiarity with the ICD-9-CM and HCPCS Level II coding systems. The CCS-P is also expert in health information documentation, data integrity, and quality. Because patients' coded data is submitted to insurance companies or the government for expense reimbursement, the CCS-P plays a critical role in the health provider's business operation. The CCS-P certification exam assesses mastery or proficiency in coding rather than entry-level skills.

CCS-P Coding Competencies

Domain I. Health Information Documentation

1. Interpret health record documentation to identify diagnoses and conditions for code assignment.
2. Interpret health record documentation to identify procedures or services for code assignment.
3. Determine if sufficient clinical information is available to assign one or more diagnosis codes.
4. Determine if sufficient clinical information is available to assign one or more procedure or service codes.
5. Consult with physicians or other healthcare providers when additional information is needed for coding and/or to clarify conflicting or ambiguous information.
6. Consult reference materials to facilitate code assignment.
7. Identify the etiology and manifestation(s) of clinical conditions.

Domain II. CODING 5 7 13 25

1. Assign ICD-9-CM code by applying "Diagnostic Coding and Reporting Guidelines for Outpatient Services (Hospital-based and Physician Office)."
2. Interpret ICD-9-CM conventions, formats, instructional notations, tables, and definitions to select diagnoses, conditions, problems, or other reasons for the encounter that require coding.
3. Interpret CPT and HCPCS II guidelines, format, and instructional notes to select services, procedures, and supplies that require coding.
4. Assign CPT code(s) for procedures and/or services rendered during the encounter.
5. Assign codes to identify Evaluation and Management (E/M) services.
6. Recognize if an unlisted code must be assigned.
7. Exclude from coding those procedures that are component parts of other reported procedure codes.
8. Code for the professional vs. technical component when applicable.
9. Assign HCPCS II codes.
10. Append modifiers to procedure or service codes when applicable.

Domain III. Reimbursement Methods and Regulatory Guidelines

1. Apply global surgical package concept to surgical procedures.
2. Apply bundling and unbundling guidelines (such as National Correct Coding Initiative [NCCI]).

3. Interpret health record documentation to identify diagnoses and conditions for code assignment.
4. Apply reimbursement methods for billing or reporting (such as OIG, CMS [HCFA], Federal Register).
5. Link diagnosis code to the associated procedure code for billing or reporting.
6. Evaluate payer remittance or payment (such as EOB, EOMB) reports for reimbursement and/or denials.
7. Interpret Local Medical Review Policies (LMRP) or payer policies to determine coverage.
8. Process claim denials and/or appeals.

Domain IV. Data Quality

1. Validate assigned diagnosis and procedure codes supported by health record documentation.
2. Validate assigned Evaluation and Management codes based on health record documentation using the E/M guidelines.
3. Assess the quality of coding and billing using routinely generated reports.
4. Verify that the data on the claim form correctly reflect the services provided.
5. Verify that the data on the claim form correctly reflect the conditions managed or treated during the encounter.
6. Validate the accuracy of the required data elements on the claim form.
7. Conduct coding and billing audits for compliance and trending.
8. Determine educational needs for physicians and staff on reimbursement and documentation rules and regulations related to coding.
9. Participate in the development of coding and billing policies and procedures for reporting professional services.
10. Evaluate payer remittance or payment (such as EOB, EOMB) reports for data quality.

Certified Coding Specialist—Physician-based (CCS-P) Competencies

CCS-P Exam Competency	CCS-P Exam Level	Question Number	CCS-P Exam Competency	CCS-P Exam Level	Question Number
I.1	Recall	1.48	I.2/I.6	Application	5.56
I.1	Recall	1.59	I.3	Recall	1.6
I.1	Recall	1.101	I.3/II.7	Application	5.32
I.1	Recall	1.103	I.5	Recall	2.144
I.1	Application	1.142	II.1	Application	1.16
I.1	Application	1.208	II.1	Application	1.17
I.1	Recall	1.235	II.1	Application	1.18
I.1	Recall	1.403	II.1	Application	1.19
I.1	Recall	1.406	II.1	Application	1.20
I.1	Recall	1.416	II.1	Application	1.21
I.1	Recall	1.424	II.1	Application	1.22
I.1	Recall	1.425	II.1	Application	1.23
I.1	Recall	1.426	II.1	Application	1.24
I.2	Recall	2.96	II.1	Application	1.25
I.2	Recall	2.116	II.1	Application	1.26

CCS-P Exam Competency	CCS-P Exam Level	Question Number	CCS-P Exam Competency	CCS-P Exam Level	Question Number
II.1	Application	1.27	II.1	Application	1.73
II.1	Application	1.28	II.1	Application	1.74
II.1	Application	1.29	II.1	Application	1.75
II.1	Application	1.30	II.1	Application	1.76
II.1	Application	1.31	II.1	Application	1.78
II.1	Application	1.32	II.1	Application	1.79
II.1	Application	1.33	II.1	Application	1.80
II.1	Application	1.34	II.1	Application	1.82
II.1	Application	1.35	II.1	Application	1.84
II.1	Application	1.36	II.1	Application	1.85
II.1	Application	1.37	II.1	Application	1.86
II.1	Application	1.40	II.1	Application	1.87
II.1	Application	1.41	II.1	Application	1.88
II.1	Application	1.42	II.1	Application	1.89
II.1	Application	1.43	II.1	Application	1.90
II.1	Application	1.44	II.1	Application	1.91
II.1	Application	1.45	II.1	Application	1.92
II.1	Application	1.46	II.1	Application	1.93
II.1	Application	1.47	II.1	Application	1.94
II.1	Application	1.49	II.1	Application	1.95
II.1	Application	1.50	II.1	Application	1.97
II.1	Application	1.51	II.1	Application	1.98
II.1	Application	1.52	II.1	Application	1.99
II.1	Application	1.54	II.1	Application	1.100
II.1	Application	1.55	II.1	Application	1.102
II.1	Application	1.56	II.1	Application	1.104
II.1	Application	1.57	II.1	Application	1.105
II.1	Application	1.58	II.1	Application	1.106
II.1	Application	1.60	II.1	Application	1.107
II.1	Application	1.61	II.1	Application	1.108
II.1	Application	1.62	II.1	Application	1.109
II.1	Application	1.63	II.1	Application	1.110
II.1	Application	1.64	II.1	Application	1.111
II.1	Application	1.65	II.1	Application	1.112
II.1	Application	1.67	II.1	Application	1.113
II.1	Application	1.68	II.1	Application	1.114
II.1	Application	1.69	II.1	Application	1.115
II.1	Application	1.70	II.1	Application	1.116
II.1	Application	1.71	II.1	Application	1.117
II.1	Application	1.72	II.1	Application	1.119

CCS-P Exam Competency	CCS-P Exam Level	Question Number	CCS-P Exam Competency	CCS-P Exam Level	Question Number
II.1	Application	1.120	II.1	Application	1.164
II.1	Application	1.121	II.1	Application	1.165
II.1	Application	1.122	II.1	Application	1.166
II.1	Application	1.123	II.1	Application	1.167
II.1	Application	1.125	II.1	Application	1.168
II.1	Application	1.126	II.1	Application	1.169
II.1	Application	1.128	II.1	Application	1.170
II.1	Application	1.129	II.1	Application	1.171
II.1	Application	1.130	II.1	Application	1.172
II.1	Application	1.131	II.1	Application	1.173
II.1	Application	1.132	II.1	Application	1.174
II.1	Application	1.133	II.1	Application	1.175
II.1	Application	1.134	II.1	Application	1.176
II.1	Application	1.135	II.1	Application	1.177
II.1	Application	1.136	II.1	Application	1.178
II.1	Application	1.137	II.1	Application	1.179
II.1	Application	1.138	II.1	Application	1.180
II.1	Application	1.139	II.1	Application	1.181
II.1	Application	1.141	II.1	Application	1.182
II.1	Application	1.143	II.1	Application	1.183
II.1	Application	1.144	II.1	Application	1.184
II.1	Application	1.145	II.1	Application	1.185
II.1	Application	1.146	II.1	Application	1.186
II.1	Application	1.147	II.1	Application	1.187
II.1	Application	1.148	II.1	Application	1.188
II.1	Application	1.149	II.1	Application	1.189
II.1	Application	1.150	II.1	Application	1.190
II.1	Application	1.151	II.1	Application	1.191
II.1	Application	1.152	II.1	Application	1.192
II.1	Application	1.153	II.1	Application	1.193
II.1	Application	1.154	II.1	Application	1.194
II.1	Application	1.155	II.1	Application	1.195
II.1	Application	1.156	II.1	Application	1.196
II.1	Application	1.157	II.1	Application	1.197
II.1	Application	1.158	II.1	Application	1.198
II.1	Application	1.159	II.1	Application	1.199
II.1	Application	1.160	II.1	Application	1.200
II.1	Application	1.161	II.1	Application	1.201
II.1	Application	1.162	II.1	Application	1.202
II.1	Application	1.163	II.1	Application	1.203

CCS-P Exam Competency	CCS-P Exam Level	Question Number	CCS-P Exam Competency	CCS-P Exam Level	Question Number
II.1	Application	1.204	II.1	Application	1.253
II.1	Recall	1.205	II.1	Application	1.254
II.1	Application	1.206	II.1	Application	1.255
II.1	Application	1.207	II.1	Application	1.256
II.1	Application	1.209	II.1	Application	1.257
II.1	Application	1.210	II.1	Application	1.258
II.1	Application	1.211	II.1	Application	1.259
II.1	Application	1.212	II.1	Application	1.260
II.1	Application	1.213	II.1	Application	1.261
II.1	Application	1.214	II.1	Application	1.262
II.1	Application	1.215	II.1	Application	1.263
II.1	Application	1.216	II.1	Application	1.264
II.1	Application	1.217	II.1	Application	1.265
II.1	Application	1.218	II.1	Application	1.266
II.1	Application	1.221	II.1	Application	1.267
II.1	Application	1.222	II.1	Application	1.268
II.1	Application	1.223	II.1	Application	1.269
II.1	Application	1.224	II.1	Application	1.270
II.1	Application	1.225	II.1	Application	1.271
II.1	Application	1.226	II.1	Application	1.272
II.1	Application	1.227	II.1	Application	1.273
II.1	Application	1.228	II.1	Application	1.274
II.1	Application	1.229	II.1	Application	1.275
II.1	Application	1.233	II.1	Application	1.276
II.1	Application	1.236	II.1	Application	1.277
II.1	Application	1.237	II.1	Application	1.278
II.1	Application	1.238	II.1	Application	1.279
II.1	Application	1.239	II.1	Application	1.280
II.1	Application	1.240	II.1	Application	1.281
II.1	Application	1.241	II.1	Application	1.282
II.1	Application	1.242	II.1	Application	1.283
II.1	Application	1.243	II.1	Application	1.284
II.1	Application	1.244	II.1	Application	1.285
II.1	Application	1.245	II.1	Application	1.286
II.1	Application	1.246	II.1	Application	1.287
II.1	Application	1.247	II.1	Application	1.288
II.1	Application	1.248	II.1	Application	1.289
II.1	Application	1.250	II.1	Application	1.290
II.1	Application	1.251	II.1	Application	1.291
II.1	Application	1.252	II.1	Application	1.292

CCS-P Exam Competency	CCS-P Exam Level	Question Number	CCS-P Exam Competency	CCS-P Exam Level	Question Number
II.1	Application	1.293	II.1	Application	1.334
II.1	Application	1.295	II.1	Application	1.335
II.1	Application	1.296	II.1	Application	1.336
II.1	Application	1.297	II.1	Application	1.337
II.1	Application	1.298	II.1	Application	1.338
II.1	Application	1.299	II.1	Application	1.339
II.1	Application	1.300	II.1	Application	1.340
II.1	Application	1.301	II.1	Application	1.341
II.1	Application	1.302	II.1	Application	1.342
II.1	Application	1.303	II.1	Application	1.343
II.1	Application	1.304	II.1	Application	1.344
II.1	Application	1.305	II.1	Application	1.345
II.1	Application	1.306	II.1	Application	1.346
II.1	Application	1.307	II.1	Application	1.347
II.1	Application	1.308	II.1	Application	1.348
II.1	Application	1.309	II.1	Application	1.349
II.1	Application	1.310	II.1	Application	1.350
II.1	Application	1.311	II.1	Application	1.351
II.1	Application	1.312	II.1	Application	1.352
II.1	Application	1.313	II.1	Application	1.353
II.1	Application	1.314	II.1	Application	1.354
II.1	Application	1.315	II.1	Application	1.355
II.1	Application	1.316	II.1	Application	1.356
II.1	Application	1.317	II.1	Application	1.357
II.1	Application	1.318	II.1	Application	1.358
II.1	Application	1.319	II.1	Application	1.359
II.1	Application	1.320	II.1	Application	1.360
II.1	Application	1.321	II.1	Application	1.361
II.1	Application	1.322	II.1	Application	1.362
II.1	Application	1.323	II.1	Application	1.363
II.1	Application	1.324	II.1	Application	1.364
II.1	Application	1.325	II.1	Application	1.365
II.1	Application	1.326	II.1	Application	1.366
II.1	Application	1.327	II.1	Application	1.367
II.1	Application	1.328	II.1	Application	1.368
II.1	Application	1.329	II.1	Application	1.369
II.1	Application	1.330	II.1	Application	1.370
II.1	Application	1.331	II.1	Application	1.371
II.1	Application	1.332	II.1	Application	1.372
II.1	Application	1.333	II.1	Application	1.373

CCS-P Exam Competency	CCS-P Exam Level	Question Number	CCS-P Exam Competency	CCS-P Exam Level	Question Number
II.1	Application	1.374	II.1	Application	6.11
II.1	Application	1.375	II.1	Application	6.13
II.1	Application	1.401	II.1	Application	6.14
II.1	Recall	1.404	II.1	Application	6.28
II.1	Recall	1.405	II.1	Application	6.29
II.1	Recall	1.411	II.1	Application	6.30
II.1	Recall	1.415	II.1	Application	6.31
II.1	Recall	2.336	II.1	Application	6.45
II.1	Recall	2.337	II.1	Application	6.61
II.1	Recall	2.338	II.1	Application	6.74
II.1	Recall	2.339	II.1	Application	6.75
II.1	Recall	2.341	II.1	Application	6.79
II.1	Recall	2.342	II.1	Application	6.80
II.1	Recall	2.344	II.1	Application	6.81
II.1	Recall	2.345	II.1	Application	6.82
II.1	Recall	2.346	II.1	Application	6.83
II.1	Recall	2.348	II.1	Application	6.85
II.1	Recall	2.349	II.1	Application	6.87
II.1	Recall	2.350	II.1	Application	6.88
II.1	Recall	2.351	II.1	Application	6.90
II.1	Recall	2.352	II.1	Application	6.91
II.1	Recall	2.353	II.1	Application	6.92
II.1	Recall	2.354	II.1	Application	6.94
II.1	Recall	2.355	II.1	Analysis	8.3
II.1	Recall	3.21	II.1	Application	8.4
II.1	Recall	3.22	II.1	Application	8.10
II.1	Application	5.5	II.1	Analysis	8.17
II.1	Application	5.22	II.1	Application	9.5
II.1	Application	5.23	II.1	Application	9.7
II.1	Application	5.35	II.1	Analysis	9.26
II.1	Application	5.36	II.1	Analysis	9.27
II.1	Application	5.37	II.1	Analysis	9.28
II.1	Application	5.38	II.1	Application	9.49
II.1	Application	5.46	II.1	Application	10.27
II.1	Application	5.50	II.1	Application	10.28
II.1	Application	5.66	II.1	Application	10.29
II.1	Application	5.72	II.1	Application	10.30
II.1	Application	5.75	II.1	Application	10.31
II.1	Application	5.80	II.1	Application	10.32
II.1	Application	6.8	II.1	Application	10.33

CCS-P Exam Competency	CCS-P Exam Level	Question Number	CCS-P Exam Competency	CCS-P Exam Level	Question Number
II.1	Application	10.34	II.1/II.3	Application	5.53
II.1	Recall	10.35	II.1/II.3	Application	5.87
II.1	Recall	10.36	II.1/II.3	Application	6.48
II.1	Recall	10.37	II.1/II.3	Application	6.72
II.1	Application	10.41	II.1/II.3	Analysis	8.7
II.1	Application	10.42	II.1/II.3	Analysis	8.21
II.1/II.10	Application	5.59	II.1/II.3	Analysis	8.29
II.1/II.10	Application	5.65	II.1/II.3	Application	8.37
II.1/II.10	Application	5.71	II.1/II.3	Application	8.42
II.1/II.10	Application	5.73	II.1/II.3	Analysis	8.48
II.1/II.10	Application	5.74	II.1/II.3	Analysis	8.49
II.1/II.10	Application	5.82	II.1/II.3	Analysis	9.36
II.1/II.10	Application	5.86	II.1/II.3	Analysis	9.38
II.1/II.10	Application	6.3	II.1/II.3	Analysis	9.44
II.1/II.10	Application	6.4	II.1/II.3	Analysis	9.54
II.1/II.10	Application	6.5	II.1/II.3	Application	9.59
II.1/II.10	Application	6.20	II.1/II.3	Application	9.69
II.1/II.10	Application	6.21	II.1/II.3	Application	9.72
II.1/II.10	Application	6.34	II.1/II.3	Analysis	9.73
II.1/II.10	Application	6.47	II.1/II.3	Application	9.74
II.1/II.10	Application	6.59	II.1/II.3	Application	9.77
II.1/II.10	Application	6.60	II.1/II.4	Application	5.1
II.1/II.10	Application	6.64	II.1/II.4	Application	5.3
II.1/II.10	Application	6.65	II.1/II.4	Application	5.4
II.1/II.10	Application	8.13	II.1/II.4	Application	5.7
II.1/II.10	Analysis	8.33	II.1/II.4	Application	5.8
II.1/II.10	Analysis	8.34	II.1/II.4	Application	5.12
II.1/II.10	Analysis	8.38	II.1/II.4	Application	5.13
II.1/II.10	Analysis	8.44	II.1/II.4	Application	5.16
II.1/II.10	Analysis	8.46	II.1/II.4	Application	5.24
II.1/II.10	Analysis	8.51	II.1/II.4	Application	5.25
II.1/II.10	Analysis	8.53	II.1/II.4	Application	5.26
II.1/II.10	Analysis	9.1	II.1/II.4	Application	5.27
II.1/II.10	Analysis	9.3	II.1/II.4	Application	5.28
II.1/II.10	Analysis	9.30	II.1/II.4	Application	5.29
II.1/II.10	Analysis	9.67	II.1/II.4	Application	5.30
II.1/II.10/II.4	Analysis	8.55	II.1/II.4	Application	5.31
II.1/II.10/III.2	Analysis	8.31	II.1/II.4	Application	5.33
II.1/II.10/III.4	Analysis	8.14	II.1/II.4	Application	5.39
II.1/II.3	Application	5.9	II.1/II.4	Application	5.42

CCS-P Exam Competency	CCS-P Exam Level	Question Number	CCS-P Exam Competency	CCS-P Exam Level	Question Number
II.1/II.4	Application	5.47	II.1/II.4	Application	6.54
II.1/II.4	Application	5.48	II.1/II.4	Application	6.55
II.1/II.4	Application	5.49	II.1/II.4	Application	6.56
II.1/II.4	Application	5.51	II.1/II.4	Application	6.62
II.1/II.4	Application	5.54	II.1/II.4	Application	6.63
II.1/II.4	Application	5.55	II.1/II.4	Application	6.69
II.1/II.4	Application	5.57	II.1/II.4	Application	6.73
II.1/II.4	Application	5.62	II.1/II.4	Application	6.76
II.1/II.4	Application	5.64	II.1/II.4	Application	6.77
II.1/II.4	Application	5.69	II.1/II.4	Application	6.78
II.1/II.4	Application	5.70	II.1/II.4	Application	6.86
II.1/II.4	Application	5.76	II.1/II.4	Application	8.6
II.1/II.4	Application	5.77	II.1/II.4	Analysis	8.11
II.1/II.4	Application	5.78	II.1/II.4	Analysis	8.22
II.1/II.4	Application	5.79	II.1/II.4	Analysis	8.23
II.1/II.4	Application	5.81	II.1/II.4	Application	8.28
II.1/II.4	Application	5.83	II.1/II.4	Analysis	8.35
II.1/II.4	Application	5.84	II.1/II.4	Analysis	8.36
II.1/II.4	Application	5.85	II.1/II.4	Analysis	8.39
II.1/II.4	Application	6.2	II.1/II.4	Application	8.40
II.1/II.4	Application	6.6	II.1/II.4	Analysis	8.41
II.1/II.4	Application	6.7	II.1/II.4	Application	8.47
II.1/II.4	Application	6.12	II.1/II.4	Application	8.52
II.1/II.4	Application	6.15	II.1/II.4	Application	8.54
II.1/II.4	Application	6.16	II.1/II.4	Application	9.4
II.1/II.4	Application	6.17	II.1/II.4	Application	9.8
II.1/II.4	Application	6.18	II.1/II.4	Analysis	9.9
II.1/II.4	Application	6.19	II.1/II.4	Analysis	9.18
II.1/II.4	Application	6.32	II.1/II.4	Analysis	9.29
II.1/II.4	Application	6.33	II.1/II.4	Analysis	9.35
II.1/II.4	Application	6.35	II.1/II.4	Application	9.39
II.1/II.4	Application	6.36	II.1/II.4	Analysis	9.41
II.1/II.4	Application	6.38	II.1/II.4	Analysis	9.45
II.1/II.4	Application	6.40	II.1/II.4	Analysis	9.48
II.1/II.4	Application	6.41	II.1/II.4	Analysis	9.51
II.1/II.4	Application	6.42	II.1/II.4	Application	9.56
II.1/II.4	Application	6.44	II.1/II.4	Application	9.62
II.1/II.4	Application	6.49	II.1/II.4	Application	9.64
II.1/II.4	Application	6.50	II.1/II.4	Application	9.66
II.1/II.4	Application	6.53	II.1/II.4	Analysis	9.68

CCS-P Exam Competency	CCS-P Exam Level	Question Number	CCS-P Exam Competency	CCS-P Exam Level	Question Number
II.1/II.4	Application	9.70	II.1/II.5/II.9	Application	5.40
II.1/II.4	Application	9.81	II.1/II.5/II.9	Application	5.41
II.1/II.4	Application	9.82	II.1/II.5/II.9	Application	6.52
II.1/II.4/II.10	Application	5.6	II.1/II.5/II.9	Analysis	9.34
II.1/II.4/II.10	Application	5.43	II.1/II.5/II.9	Application	9.61
II.1/II.4/II.10	Application	5.44	II.1/II.7	Application	5.2
II.1/II.4/II.10	Analysis	9.15	II.1/II.7	Application	5.15
II.1/II.4/II.10	Analysis	9.16	II.1/II.7	Application	5.17
II.1/II.4/II.10	Application	9.17	II.1/II.7	Application	5.52
II.1/II.4/II.10	Analysis	9.46	II.1/II.7	Application	5.58
II.1/II.4/II.10	Analysis	9.71	II.1/II.7	Application	5.60
II.1/II.4/II.10	Analysis	9.76	II.1/II.7	Application	5.63
II.1/II.4/II.5	Application	6.70	II.1/II.8	Application	5.14
II.1/II.4/II.5	Application	6.71	II.1/II.8	Application	8.5
II.1/II.4/II.5	Analysis	9.2	II.1/II.8	Analysis	9.33
II.1/II.4/II.5/II.9	Analysis	9.65	II.1/II.9	Application	5.61
II.1/II.4/II.9	Analysis	9.52	II.1/III.2	Analysis	8.24
II.1/II.5	Application	6.24	II.1/III.2	Analysis	8.32
II.1/II.5	Application	6.25	II.1/III.2	Analysis	9.31
II.1/II.5	Application	6.26	II.1/III.2	Application	9.32
II.1/II.5	Application	6.27	II.1/III.2	Analysis	9.50
II.1/II.5	Application	6.37	II.1/III.2/II.10	Analysis	8.26
II.1/II.5	Application	6.39	II.10/II.4	Application	2.340
II.1/II.5	Application	6.51	II.10/II.4	Application	2.343
II.1/II.5	Application	6.66	II.10/II.4	Application	2.347
II.1/II.5	Application	6.68	II.10/III.2	Analysis	8.12
II.1/II.5	Analysis	8.25	II.2	Recall	1.1
II.1/II.5	Analysis	8.27	II.2	Recall	1.2
II.1/II.5	Analysis	8.30	II.2	Recall	1.4
II.1/II.5	Analysis	8.45	II.2	Application	1.5
II.1/II.5	Analysis	9.6	II.2	Recall	1.8
II.1/II.5	Analysis	9.23	II.2	Recall	1.9
II.1/II.5	Analysis	9.40	II.2	Recall	1.10
II.1/II.5	Analysis	9.42	II.2	Recall	1.11
II.1/II.5	Analysis	9.57	II.2	Recall	1.12
II.1/II.5	Analysis	9.78	II.2	Recall	1.13
II.1/II.5/II.10	Analysis	9.14	II.2	Recall	1.14
II.1/II.5/II.10	Analysis	9.47	II.2	Recall	1.15
II.1/II.5/II.10	Analysis	9.53	II.2	Recall	1.53
II.1/II.5/II.10	Analysis	9.55	II.2	Recall	1.66

CCS-P Exam Competency	CCS-P Exam Level	Question Number	CCS-P Exam Competency	CCS-P Exam Level	Question Number
II.2	Recall	1.77	II.3	Recall	2.6
II.2	Recall	1.81	II.3	Recall	2.7
II.2	Recall	1.83	II.3	Recall	2.8
II.2	Recall	1.96	II.3	Recall	2.9
II.2	Application	1.118	II.3	Recall	2.10
II.2	Recall	1.124	II.3	Recall	2.11
II.2	Recall	1.127	II.3	Recall	2.12
II.2	Recall	1.140	II.3	Recall	2.13
II.2	Recall	1.219	II.3	Recall	2.14
II.2	Recall	1.220	II.3	Recall	2.15
II.2	Recall	1.230	II.3	Recall	2.16
II.2	Recall	1.231	II.3	Recall	2.17
II.2	Recall	1.232	II.3	Recall	2.18
II.2	Recall	1.234	II.3	Recall	2.19
II.2	Recall	1.249	II.3	Recall	2.20
II.2	Recall	1.402	II.3	Recall	2.21
II.2	Recall	1.407	II.3	Recall	2.22
II.2	Recall	1.410	II.3	Recall	2.23
II.2	Recall	1.412	II.3	Recall	2.24
II.2	Recall	1.413	II.3	Recall	2.25
II.2	Recall	1.414	II.3	Recall	2.26
II.2	Recall	1.417	II.3	Recall	2.27
II.2	Recall	1.418	II.3	Recall	2.28
II.2	Application	5.10	II.3	Recall	2.29
II.2	Application	5.20	II.3	Recall	2.30
II.2	Application	5.21	II.3	Recall	2.31
II.2	Application	6.46	II.3	Recall	2.32
II.2	Application	6.57	II.3	Recall	2.33
II.2	Analysis	8.16	II.3	Recall	2.34
II.2	Application	9.10	II.3	Recall	2.35
II.2/II.10	Analysis	8.15	II.3	Recall	2.36
II.2/II.3	Application	8.1	II.3	Recall	2.37
II.2/II.4	Application	5.68	II.3	Recall	2.38
II.2/II.4	Analysis	8.18	II.3	Recall	2.39
II.2/III.2	Analysis	8.50	II.3	Recall	2.56
II.3	Recall	2.1	II.3	Recall	2.57
II.3	Recall	2.2	II.3	Recall	2.59
II.3	Recall	2.3	II.3	Recall	2.60
II.3	Recall	2.4	II.3	Recall	2.73
II.3	Recall	2.5	II.3	Recall	2.76

CCS-P Exam Competency	CCS-P Exam Level	Question Number	CCS-P Exam Competency	CCS-P Exam Level	Question Number
II.3	Recall	2.77	II.4	Application	2.64
II.3	Recall	2.78	II.4	Application	2.65
II.3	Recall	2.89	II.4	Application	2.66
II.3	Recall	2.119	II.4	Application	2.67
II.3	Recall	2.141	II.4	Application	2.68
II.3	Recall	2.317	II.4	Application	2.69
II.3	Recall	2.356	II.4	Application	2.70
II.3	Recall	2.357	II.4	Application	2.71
II.3	Recall	2.358	II.4	Application	2.72
II.3	Recall	2.363	II.4	Application	2.74
II.3	Recall	2.369	II.4	Application	2.75
II.3	Recall	3.1	II.4	Application	2.79
II.3	Recall	3.24	II.4	Application	2.80
II.3	Recall	3.27	II.4	Application	2.81
II.3	Application	6.84	II.4	Application	2.82
II.3	Application	9.37	II.4	Application	2.83
II.3	Application	9.43	II.4	Application	2.84
II.3	Application	9.75	II.4	Application	2.85
II.3	Analysis	9.80	II.4	Application	2.86
II.3/II.4	Application	6.22	II.4	Application	2.87
II.4	Application	2.40	II.4	Application	2.88
II.4	Application	2.41	II.4	Application	2.90
II.4	Application	2.42	II.4	Application	2.91
II.4	Application	2.43	II.4	Application	2.92
II.4	Application	2.44	II.4	Application	2.93
II.4	Application	2.45	II.4	Application	2.94
II.4	Application	2.46	II.4	Application	2.95
II.4	Application	2.47	II.4	Application	2.97
II.4	Application	2.48	II.4	Application	2.98
II.4	Application	2.49	II.4	Application	2.99
II.4	Application	2.50	II.4	Application	2.100
II.4	Application	2.51	II.4	Application	2.101
II.4	Application	2.52	II.4	Application	2.102
II.4	Application	2.53	II.4	Application	2.103
II.4	Application	2.54	II.4	Application	2.104
II.4	Application	2.55	II.4	Application	2.105
II.4	Application	2.58	II.4	Application	2.106
II.4	Application	2.61	II.4	Application	2.107
II.4	Application	2.62	II.4	Application	2.108
II.4	Application	2.63	II.4	Application	2.109

CCS-P Exam Competency	CCS-P Exam Level	Question Number	CCS-P Exam Competency	CCS-P Exam Level	Question Number
II.4	Application	2.110	II.4	Application	2.155
II.4	Application	2.111	II.4	Application	2.156
II.4	Application	2.113	II.4	Application	2.157
II.4	Application	2.114	II.4	Application	2.158
II.4	Application	2.115	II.4	Application	2.159
II.4	Application	2.117	II.4	Application	2.160
II.4	Application	2.118	II.4	Application	2.161
II.4	Application	2.120	II.4	Application	2.162
II.4	Application	2.121	II.4	Application	2.163
II.4	Application	2.122	II.4	Application	2.164
II.4	Application	2.123	II.4	Application	2.165
II.4	Application	2.124	II.4	Application	2.166
II.4	Application	2.125	II.4	Application	2.167
II.4	Application	2.126	II.4	Application	2.168
II.4	Application	2.127	II.4	Application	2.169
II.4	Application	2.128	II.4	Application	2.170
II.4	Application	2.129	II.4	Application	2.171
II.4	Application	2.130	II.4	Application	2.172
II.4	Application	2.131	II.4	Application	2.173
II.4	Application	2.132	II.4	Application	2.174
II.4	Application	2.133	II.4	Application	2.175
II.4	Application	2.134	II.4	Application	2.176
II.4	Application	2.135	II.4	Application	2.177
II.4	Application	2.136	II.4	Application	2.178
II.4	Application	2.137	II.4	Application	2.179
II.4	Application	2.138	II.4	Application	2.180
II.4	Application	2.139	II.4	Application	2.181
II.4	Application	2.140	II.4	Application	2.182
II.4	Application	2.142	II.4	Application	2.183
II.4	Application	2.143	II.4	Application	2.184
II.4	Application	2.145	II.4	Application	2.185
II.4	Application	2.146	II.4	Application	2.186
II.4	Application	2.147	II.4	Application	2.187
II.4	Application	2.148	II.4	Application	2.188
II.4	Application	2.149	II.4	Application	2.189
II.4	Application	2.150	II.4	Application	2.190
II.4	Application	2.151	II.4	Application	2.191
II.4	Application	2.152	II.4	Application	2.192
II.4	Application	2.153	II.4	Application	2.193
II.4	Application	2.154	II.4	Application	2.194

CCS-P Exam Competency	CCS-P Exam Level	Question Number	CCS-P Exam Competency	CCS-P Exam Level	Question Number
II.4	Application	2.195	II.4	Application	2.235
II.4	Application	2.196	II.4	Application	2.236
II.4	Application	2.197	II.4	Application	2.237
II.4	Application	2.198	II.4	Application	2.238
II.4	Application	2.199	II.4	Application	2.239
II.4	Application	2.200	II.4	Application	2.240
II.4	Application	2.201	II.4	Application	2.241
II.4	Application	2.202	II.4	Application	2.242
II.4	Application	2.203	II.4	Application	2.243
II.4	Application	2.204	II.4	Application	2.244
II.4	Application	2.205	II.4	Application	2.245
II.4	Application	2.206	II.4	Application	2.246
II.4	Application	2.207	II.4	Application	2.247
II.4	Application	2.208	II.4	Application	2.248
II.4	Application	2.209	II.4	Application	2.249
II.4	Application	2.210	II.4	Application	2.250
II.4	Application	2.211	II.4	Application	2.251
II.4	Application	2.212	II.4	Application	2.252
II.4	Application	2.213	II.4	Application	2.253
II.4	Application	2.214	II.4	Application	2.254
II.4	Application	2.215	II.4	Application	2.255
II.4	Application	2.216	II.4	Application	2.256
II.4	Application	2.217	II.4	Application	2.257
II.4	Application	2.218	II.4	Application	2.258
II.4	Application	2.219	II.4	Application	2.259
II.4	Application	2.220	II.4	Application	2.260
II.4	Application	2.221	II.4	Application	2.261
II.4	Application	2.222	II.4	Application	2.262
II.4	Application	2.223	II.4	Application	2.263
II.4	Application	2.224	II.4	Application	2.264
II.4	Application	2.225	II.4	Application	2.265
II.4	Application	2.226	II.4	Application	2.266
II.4	Application	2.227	II.4	Application	2.267
II.4	Application	2.228	II.4	Application	2.268
II.4	Application	2.229	II.4	Application	2.269
II.4	Application	2.230	II.4	Application	2.270
II.4	Application	2.231	II.4	Application	2.271
II.4	Application	2.232	II.4	Application	2.272
II.4	Application	2.233	II.4	Application	2.273
II.4	Application	2.234	II.4	Application	2.274

CCS-P Exam Competency	CCS-P Exam Level	Question Number	CCS-P Exam Competency	CCS-P Exam Level	Question Number
II.4	Application	2.275	II.4	Application	2.315
II.4	Application	2.276	II.4	Application	2.316
II.4	Application	2.277	II.4	Application	2.318
II.4	Application	2.278	II.4	Application	2.319
II.4	Application	2.279	II.4	Application	2.320
II.4	Application	2.280	II.4	Application	2.321
II.4	Application	2.281	II.4	Application	2.322
II.4	Application	2.282	II.4	Application	2.323
II.4	Application	2.283	II.4	Application	2.324
II.4	Application	2.284	II.4	Application	2.325
II.4	Application	2.285	II.4	Application	2.326
II.4	Application	2.286	II.4	Application	2.327
II.4	Application	2.287	II.4	Application	2.328
II.4	Application	2.288	II.4	Application	2.329
II.4	Application	2.289	II.4	Application	2.330
II.4	Application	2.290	II.4	Application	2.331
II.4	Application	2.291	II.4	Application	2.332
II.4	Application	2.292	II.4	Application	2.333
II.4	Application	2.293	II.4	Application	2.334
II.4	Application	2.294	II.4	Application	2.335
II.4	Application	2.295	II.4	Application	2.359
II.4	Application	2.296	II.4	Application	2.360
II.4	Application	2.297	II.4	Application	2.361
II.4	Application	2.298	II.4	Application	2.362
II.4	Application	2.299	II.4	Application	2.364
II.4	Application	2.300	II.4	Application	2.365
II.4	Application	2.301	II.4	Application	2.366
II.4	Application	2.302	II.4	Application	2.367
II.4	Application	2.303	II.4	Application	2.368
II.4	Application	2.304	II.4	Application	2.370
II.4	Application	2.305	II.4	Application	2.371
II.4	Application	2.306	II.4	Application	2.372
II.4	Application	2.307	II.4	Application	2.373
II.4	Application	2.308	II.4	Application	2.374
II.4	Application	2.309	II.4	Application	2.375
II.4	Application	2.310	II.4	Application	2.376
II.4	Application	2.311	II.4	Application	2.377
II.4	Application	2.312	II.4	Application	2.378
II.4	Application	2.313	II.4	Application	2.379
II.4	Application	2.314	II.4	Application	2.380

CCS-P Exam Competency	CCS-P Exam Level	Question Number	CCS-P Exam Competency	CCS-P Exam Level	Question Number
II.4	Application	2.381	II.4	Application	2.421
II.4	Application	2.382	II.4	Application	2.422
II.4	Application	2.383	II.4	Application	2.423
II.4	Application	2.384	II.4	Application	2.424
II.4	Application	2.385	II.4	Application	2.425
II.4	Application	2.386	II.4	Application	2.426
II.4	Application	2.387	II.4	Application	3.28
II.4	Application	2.388	II.4	Application	3.29
II.4	Application	2.389	II.4	Application	3.30
II.4	Application	2.390	II.4	Application	3.31
II.4	Application	2.391	II.4	Application	3.32
II.4	Application	2.392	II.4	Application	3.33
II.4	Application	2.393	II.4	Application	3.34
II.4	Application	2.394	II.4	Application	3.35
II.4	Application	2.395	II.4	Application	3.36
II.4	Application	2.396	II.4	Application	3.37
II.4	Application	2.397	II.4	Application	3.38
II.4	Application	2.398	II.4	Application	3.39
II.4	Application	2.399	II.4	Application	3.40
II.4	Application	2.400	II.4	Application	3.41
II.4	Application	2.401	II.4	Application	3.42
II.4	Application	2.402	II.4	Application	3.43
II.4	Application	2.403	II.4	Application	3.44
II.4	Application	2.404	II.4	Application	3.45
II.4	Application	2.405	II.4	Application	3.46
II.4	Application	2.406	II.4	Application	3.47
II.4	Application	2.407	II.4	Application	3.48
II.4	Application	2.408	II.4	Application	3.49
II.4	Application	2.409	II.4	Application	3.50
II.4	Application	2.410	II.4	Application	5.11
II.4	Application	2.411	II.4	Application	5.19
II.4	Application	2.412	II.4	Application	5.34
II.4	Application	2.413	II.4	Application	5.45
II.4	Application	2.414	II.4	Application	5.67
II.4	Application	2.415	II.4	Application	6.1
II.4	Application	2.416	II.4	Application	6.89
II.4	Application	2.417	II.4	Application	6.93
II.4	Application	2.418	II.4	Application	8.9
II.4	Application	2.419	II.4	Application	9.11
II.4	Application	2.420	II.4	Application	9.12

CCS-P Exam Competency	CCS-P Exam Level	Question Number		CCS-P Exam Competency	CCS-P Exam Level	Question Number
II.4	Application	9.13		II.9	Application	3.23
II.4	Application	9.58		II.9	Application	3.25
II.4/II.5	Application	6.43		II.9	Application	3.26
II.4/II.9	Application	6.58		III.3	Application	5.18
II.4/II.9	Application	6.67		III.3/II.4	Analysis	8.19
II.4/II.9	Application	8.8		III.3/III.2	Analysis	8.20
II.4/V.2.b	Analysis	8.2		IV.9	Recall	1.7
II.5	Application	6.9		N/A	N/A	1.3
II.5	Application	6.10		N/A	N/A	1.38
II.5	Application	6.23		N/A	N/A	1.39
II.5	Application	9.19		N/A	N/A	1.294
II.5	Application	9.20		N/A	N/A	1.376
II.5	Application	9.21		N/A	N/A	1.377
II.5	Analysis	9.22		N/A	N/A	1.378
II.5	Analysis	9.24		N/A	N/A	1.379
II.5	Analysis	9.25		N/A	N/A	1.380
II.5	Analysis	9.60		N/A	N/A	1.381
II.5	Application	9.63		N/A	N/A	1.382
II.5	Analysis	9.79		N/A	N/A	1.383
II.7	Recall	2.112		N/A	N/A	1.384
II.7	Analysis	8.43		N/A	N/A	1.385
II.9	Application	3.2		N/A	N/A	1.386
II.9	Application	3.3		N/A	N/A	1.387
II.9	Application	3.4		N/A	N/A	1.388
II.9	Application	3.5		N/A	N/A	1.389
II.9	Application	3.6		N/A	N/A	1.390
II.9	Application	3.7		N/A	N/A	1.391
II.9	Application	3.8		N/A	N/A	1.392
II.9	Application	3.9		N/A	N/A	1.393
II.9	Application	3.10		N/A	N/A	1.394
II.9	Application	3.11		N/A	N/A	1.395
II.9	Application	3.12		N/A	N/A	1.396
II.9	Application	3.13		N/A	N/A	1.397
II.9	Application	3.14		N/A	N/A	1.398
II.9	Application	3.15		N/A	N/A	1.399
II.9	Application	3.16		N/A	N/A	1.400
II.9	Application	3.17		N/A	Recall	1.408
II.9	Application	3.18		N/A	Recall	1.409
II.9	Application	3.19		N/A	N/A	1.419
II.9	Application	3.20		N/A	N/A	1.420

CCS-P Exam Competency	CCS-P Exam Level	Question Number	CCS-P Exam Competency	CCS-P Exam Level	Question Number
N/A	N/A	1.421	N/A	N/A	4.38
N/A	N/A	1.422	N/A	N/A	4.39
N/A	N/A	1.423	N/A	N/A	4.40
N/A	N/A	4.1	N/A	N/A	4.41
N/A	N/A	4.2	N/A	N/A	4.42
N/A	N/A	4.3	N/A	N/A	4.43
N/A	N/A	4.4	N/A	N/A	4.44
N/A	N/A	4.5	N/A	N/A	4.45
N/A	N/A	4.6	N/A	N/A	4.46
N/A	N/A	4.7	N/A	N/A	4.47
N/A	N/A	4.8	N/A	N/A	4.48
N/A	N/A	4.9	N/A	N/A	4.49
N/A	N/A	4.10	N/A	N/A	4.50
N/A	N/A	4.11	N/A	N/A	4.51
N/A	N/A	4.12	N/A	N/A	4.52
N/A	N/A	4.13	N/A	N/A	4.53
N/A	N/A	4.14	N/A	N/A	4.54
N/A	N/A	4.15	N/A	N/A	4.55
N/A	N/A	4.16	N/A	N/A	4.56
N/A	N/A	4.17	N/A	N/A	4.57
N/A	N/A	4.18	N/A	N/A	4.58
N/A	N/A	4.19	N/A	N/A	4.59
N/A	N/A	4.20	N/A	N/A	4.60
N/A	N/A	4.21	N/A	N/A	4.61
N/A	N/A	4.22	N/A	N/A	4.62
N/A	N/A	4.23	N/A	N/A	4.63
N/A	N/A	4.24	N/A	N/A	4.64
N/A	N/A	4.25	N/A	N/A	4.65
N/A	N/A	4.26	N/A	N/A	4.66
N/A	N/A	4.27	N/A	N/A	4.67
N/A	N/A	4.28	N/A	N/A	4.68
N/A	N/A	4.29	N/A	N/A	4.69
N/A	N/A	4.30	N/A	N/A	4.70
N/A	N/A	4.31	N/A	N/A	4.71
N/A	N/A	4.32	N/A	N/A	4.72
N/A	N/A	4.33	N/A	N/A	4.73
N/A	N/A	4.34	N/A	N/A	4.74
N/A	N/A	4.35	N/A	N/A	4.75
N/A	N/A	4.36	N/A	N/A	4.76
N/A	N/A	4.37	N/A	N/A	4.77

CCS-P Exam Competency	CCS-P Exam Level	Question Number	CCS-P Exam Competency	CCS-P Exam Level	Question Number
N/A	N/A	4.78	N/A	N/A	7.21
N/A	N/A	4.79	N/A	N/A	7.22
N/A	N/A	4.80	N/A	N/A	7.23
N/A	N/A	4.81	N/A	N/A	7.24
N/A	N/A	4.82	N/A	N/A	7.25
N/A	N/A	4.83	N/A	N/A	7.26
N/A	N/A	4.84	N/A	N/A	7.27
N/A	N/A	4.85	N/A	N/A	7.28
N/A	N/A	4.86	N/A	N/A	7.29
N/A	N/A	4.87	N/A	N/A	7.30
N/A	N/A	4.88	N/A	N/A	7.31
N/A	N/A	4.89	N/A	N/A	7.32
N/A	N/A	4.90	N/A	N/A	7.33
N/A	N/A	4.91	N/A	N/A	7.34
N/A	N/A	4.92	N/A	N/A	7.35
N/A	N/A	4.93	N/A	N/A	7.36
N/A	N/A	4.94	N/A	N/A	7.37
N/A	N/A	4.95	N/A	N/A	7.38
N/A	N/A	4.96	N/A	N/A	7.39
N/A	N/A	4.97	N/A	N/A	7.40
N/A	N/A	7.1	N/A	N/A	7.41
N/A	N/A	7.2	N/A	N/A	7.42
N/A	N/A	7.3	N/A	N/A	7.43
N/A	N/A	7.4	N/A	N/A	7.44
N/A	N/A	7.5	N/A	N/A	7.45
N/A	N/A	7.6	N/A	N/A	7.46
N/A	N/A	7.7	N/A	N/A	7.47
N/A	N/A	7.8	N/A	N/A	7.48
N/A	N/A	7.9	N/A	N/A	7.49
N/A	N/A	7.10	N/A	N/A	7.50
N/A	N/A	7.11	N/A	N/A	7.51
N/A	N/A	7.12	N/A	N/A	7.52
N/A	N/A	7.13	N/A	N/A	7.53
N/A	N/A	7.14	N/A	N/A	7.54
N/A	N/A	7.15	N/A	N/A	7.55
N/A	N/A	7.16	N/A	N/A	7.56
N/A	N/A	7.17	N/A	N/A	7.57
N/A	N/A	7.18	N/A	N/A	7.58
N/A	N/A	7.19	N/A	Home Health	10.1
N/A	N/A	7.20	N/A	Home Health	10.2

CCS-P Exam Competency	CCS-P Exam Level	Question Number	CCS-P Exam Competency	CCS-P Exam Level	Question Number
N/A	Home Health	10.3	N/A	ICD-10	10.20
N/A	Home Health	10.4	N/A	ICD-10	10.21
N/A	Home Health	10.5	N/A	ICD-10	10.22
N/A	Home Health	10.6	N/A	ICD-10	10.23
N/A	Home Health	10.7	N/A	ICD-10	10.24
N/A	Home Health	10.8	N/A	ICD-10	10.25
N/A	Home Health	10.9	N/A	ICD-10	10.26
N/A	Home Health	10.10	N/A	N/A	10.38
N/A	Home Health	10.11	N/A	N/A	10.39
N/A	Home Health	10.12	N/A	N/A	10.40
N/A	Home Health	10.13	N/A	N/A	10.43
N/A	ICD-10	10.14	N/A	N/A	10.44
N/A	ICD-10	10.15	N/A	N/A	10.45
N/A	ICD-10	10.16	N/A	N/A	10.46
N/A	ICD-10	10.17	N/A	N/A	10.47
N/A	ICD-10	10.18	N/A	N/A	10.48
N/A	ICD-10	10.19	N/A	N/A	10.49

Question Number Index to Competencies

Chapter 1

Question	CCA Exam Competency	CCA Exam Level	CCS Exam Competency	CCS Exam Level	CCS-P Exam Competency	CCS-P Exam Level
1.1	III.6	Recall	II.3	Recall	II.2	Recall
1.2	III.6	Recall	II.3	Recall	II.2	Recall
1.3	III.6	Recall	II.4/IV.1	Recall	N/A	N/A
1.4	III.6	Recall	II.1	Recall	II.2	Recall
1.5	III.2.a	Application	II.2	Application	II.2	Application
1.6	III.6	Recall	II.1	Recall	I.3	Recall
1.7	III.6	Recall	II.3	Recall	IV.9	Recall
1.8	III.6	Recall	I.1	Recall	II.2	Recall
1.9	III.6	Recall	VI.3	Recall	II.2	Recall
1.10	III.6	Recall	II.3	Recall	II.2	Recall
1.11	III.6	Recall	II.3	Recall	II.2	Recall
1.12	III.6	Recall	II.3	Recall	II.2	Recall
1.13	III.6	Recall	II.3	Recall	II.2	Recall
1.14	III.6	Recall	II.3	Recall	II.2	Recall
1.15	III.6	Recall	II.3	Recall	II.2	Recall
1.16	III.2.a	Application	II.1/II.2	Application	II.1	Application
1.17	III.2.a	Application	II.1/II.2	Application	II.1	Application
1.18	III.2.a	Application	II.1/II.2	Application	II.1	Application
1.19	III.6	Application	II.1/II.2	Application	II.1	Application
1.20	III.2.a	Application	II.1/II.2	Application	II.1	Application
1.21	III.2.a	Application	II.1/II.2	Application	II.1	Application
1.22	III.2.a	Application	II.1/II.2	Application	II.1	Application
1.23	III.2.a	Application	II.1/II.2	Application	II.1	Application
1.24	III.2.a	Application	II.1/II.2	Application	II.1	Application
1.25	III.2.a	Application	II.1/II.2	Application	II.1	Application
1.26	III.2.a	Application	II.1/II.2	Application	II.1	Application
1.27	III.2.a	Application	II.1/II.2	Application	II.1	Application
1.28	III.2.a	Application	II.1/II.2	Application	II.1	Application
1.29	III.2.a	Application	II.1/II.2	Application	II.1	Application
1.30	III.2.a	Application	II.1/II.2	Application	II.1	Application
1.31	III.2.a	Application	II.1/II.2	Application	II.1	Application
1.32	III.2.a	Application	II.1/II.2	Application	II.1	Application
1.33	III.2.a	Application	II.1/II.2	Application	II.1	Application
1.34	III.2.a	Application	II.1/II.2	Application	II.1	Application
1.35	III.2.a	Application	II.1/II.2	Application	II.1	Application
1.36	III.2.a	Application	II.1/II.2	Application	II.1	Application
1.37	III.2.a	Application	II.1/II.2	Application	II.1	Application
1.38	III.2.a	Application	II.3	Recall	N/A	N/A

Question	CCA Exam Competency	CCA Exam Level	CCS Exam Competency	CCS Exam Level	CCS-P Exam Competency	CCS-P Exam Level
1.39	III.2.a	Application	II.8	Application	N/A	N/A
1.40	III.2.a	Application	II.1/II.2	Application	II.1	Application
1.41	III.2.a	Application	II.1/II.2	Application	II.1	Application
1.42	III.2.a	Application	II.1/II.2	Application	II.1	Application
1.43	III.2.a	Application	II.1/II.2	Application	II.1	Application
1.44	III.2.a	Application	II.1/II.2	Application	II.1	Application
1.45	III.2.a	Application	II.1/II.2	Application	II.1	Application
1.46	III.2.a	Application	II.1/II.2	Application	II.1	Application
1.47	III.2.a	Application	II.1/II.2	Application	II.1	Application
1.48	III.6	Recall	I.1	Recall	I.1	Recall
1.49	III.6	Application	II.1/II.2	Application	II.1	Application
1.50	III.6	Recall	II.1/II.2	Application	II.1	Application
1.51	III.2.a	Application	II.1/II.2	Application	II.1	Application
1.52	III.2.a	Application	II.1/II.2	Application	II.1	Application
1.53	III.2.a	Recall	II.3	Recall	II.2	Recall
1.54	III.2.a	Application	II.1/II.2	Application	II.1	Application
1.55	III.2.a	Application	II.1/II.2	Application	II.1	Application
1.56	III.2.a	Application	II.1/II.2	Application	II.1	Application
1.57	III.2.a	Application	II.1/II.2	Application	II.1	Application
1.58	III.2.a	Application	II.1/II.2	Application	II.1	Application
1.59	III.6	Application	I.1	Recall	I.1	Recall
1.60	III.2.a	Application	II.1/II.2	Application	II.1	Application
1.61	III.2.a	Application	II.1/II.2	Application	II.1	Application
1.62	III.2.a	Application	II.1/II.2	Application	II.1	Application
1.63	III.2.a	Application	II.1/II.2	Application	II.1	Application
1.64	III.2.a	Application	II.1/II.2	Application	II.1	Application
1.65	III.2.a	Application	II.1/II.2	Application	II.1	Application
1.66	III.6	Recall	II.3	Recall	II.2	Recall
1.67	III.2.a	Application	II.1/II.2	Application	II.1	Application
1.68	III.2.a	Application	II.1/II.2	Application	II.1	Application
1.69	III.2.a	Application	II.1/II.2	Application	II.1	Application
1.70	III.6	Application	II.1/II.2	Application	II.1	Application
1.71	III.2.a	Application	II.1/II.2	Application	II.1	Application
1.72	III.2.a	Application	II.1/II.2	Application	II.1	Application
1.73	III.2.a	Application	II.1/II.2	Application	II.1	Application
1.74	III.2.a	Application	II.1/II.2	Application	II.1	Application
1.75	III.2.a	Application	II.1/II.2	Application	II.1	Application
1.76	III.2.a	Application	II.1/II.2	Application	II.1	Application
1.77	III.6	Recall	II.3	Recall	II.2	Recall
1.78	III.2.a	Application	II.1/II.2	Application	II.1	Application

Question	CCA Exam Competency	CCA Exam Level	CCS Exam Competency	CCS Exam Level	CCS-P Exam Competency	CCS-P Exam Level
1.79	III.2.a	Application	II.1/II.2	Application	II.1	Application
1.80	III.2.a	Application	II.1/II.2	Application	II.1	Application
1.81	III.6	Recall	II.3	Recall	II.2	Recall
1.82	III.2.a	Application	II.1/II.2	Application	II.1	Application
1.83	III.6	Recall	II.3	Recall	II.2	Recall
1.84	III.2.a	Application	II.1/II.2	Application	II.1	Application
1.85	III.2.a	Application	II.1/II.2	Application	II.1	Application
1.86	III.2.a	Application	II.1/II.2	Application	II.1	Application
1.87	III.2.a	Application	II.1/II.2	Application	II.1	Application
1.88	III.2.a	Application	II.1/II.2	Application	II.1	Application
1.89	III.2.a	Application	II.1/II.2	Application	II.1	Application
1.90	III.2.a	Application	II.1/II.2	Application	II.1	Application
1.91	III.2.a	Application	II.1/II.2	Application	II.1	Application
1.92	III.2.a	Application	II.1/II.2	Application	II.1	Application
1.93	III.2.a	Application	II.1/II.2	Application	II.1	Application
1.94	III.2.a	Application	II.1/II.2	Application	II.1	Application
1.95	III.2.a	Application	II.1/II.2	Application	II.1	Application
1.96	III.6	Recall	II.3	Recall	II.2	Recall
1.97	III.2.a	Application	II.1/II.2	Application	II.1	Application
1.98	III.2.a	Application	II.1/II.2	Application	II.1	Application
1.99	III.2.a	Application	II.1/II.2	Application	II.1	Application
1.100	III.2.a	Application	II.1/II.2	Application	II.1	Application
1.101	III.6	Recall	I.1	Recall	I.1	Recall
1.102	III.2.a	Application	II.1/II.2	Application	II.1	Application
1.103	III.6	Recall	I.1	Recall	I.1	Recall
1.104	III.2.a	Application	II.1/II.2	Application	II.1	Application
1.105	III.2.a	Application	II.1/II.2	Application	II.1	Application
1.106	III.2.a	Application	II.1/II.2	Application	II.1	Application
1.107	III.2.a	Application	II.1/II.2	Application	II.1	Application
1.108	III.2.a	Application	II.1/II.2	Application	II.1	Application
1.109	III.2.a	Application	II.1/II.2	Application	II.1	Application
1.110	III.2.a	Application	II.1/II.2	Application	II.1	Application
1.111	III.2.a	Application	II.1/II.2	Application	II.1	Application
1.112	III.2.a	Application	II.1/II.2	Application	II.1	Application
1.113	III.2.a	Application	II.1/II.2	Application	II.1	Application
1.114	III.2.a	Application	II.1/II.2	Application	II.1	Application
1.115	III.2.a	Application	II.1/II.2	Application	II.1	Application
1.116	III.2.a	Application	II.1/II.2	Application	II.1	Application
1.117	III.2.a	Application	II.1/II.2	Application	II.1	Application
1.118	III.2.a, b	Application	II.3	Application	II.2	Application

Question	CCA Exam Competency	CCA Exam Level	CCS Exam Competency	CCS Exam Level	CCS-P Exam Competency	CCS-P Exam Level
1.119	III.2.a	Application	II.1/II.2	Application	II.1	Application
1.120	III.2.a	Application	II.1/II.2	Application	II.1	Application
1.121	III.2.a	Application	II.1/II.2	Application	II.1	Application
1.122	III.2.a	Application	II.1/II.2	Application	II.1	Application
1.123	III.2.a	Application	II.1/II.2	Application	II.1	Application
1.124	III.6	Recall	II.3	Recall	II.2	Recall
1.125	III.2.a	Application	II.1/II.2	Application	II.1	Application
1.126	III.2.a	Application	II.1/II.2	Application	II.1	Application
1.127	III.6	Recall	II.3	Recall	II.2	Recall
1.128	III.2.a	Application	II.1/II.2	Application	II.1	Application
1.129	III.2.a	Application	II.1/II.2	Application	II.1	Application
1.130	III.2.a	Application	II.1/II.2	Application	II.1	Application
1.131	III.2.a	Application	II.1/II.2	Application	II.1	Application
1.132	III.2.a	Application	II.1/II.2	Application	II.1	Application
1.133	III.2.a	Application	II.1/II.2	Application	II.1	Application
1.134	III.2.a	Application	II.1/II.2	Application	II.1	Application
1.135	III.2.a	Application	II.1/II.2	Application	II.1	Application
1.136	III.2.a	Application	II.1/II.2	Application	II.1	Application
1.137	III.2.a/III.2.b	Application	II.1/II.2	Application	II.1	Application
1.138	III.2.a	Application	II.1/II.2	Application	II.1	Application
1.139	III.2.a	Application	II.1	Application	II.1	Application
1.140	III.6	Recall	II.3	Recall	II.2	Recall
1.141	III.2.a	Application	II.1/II.2	Application	II.1	Application
1.142	III.6	Recall	I.1	Application	I.1	Application
1.143	III.2.a	Application	II.1/II.2	Application	II.1	Application
1.144	III.2.a	Application	II.1/II.2	Application	II.1	Application
1.145	III.2.a	Application	II.1/II.2	Application	II.1	Application
1.146	III.2.a	Application	II.1/II.2	Application	II.1	Application
1.147	III.2.a	Application	II.1/II.2	Application	II.1	Application
1.148	III.2.a	Application	II.1/II.2	Application	II.1	Application
1.149	III.2.a	Application	II.1/II.2	Application	II.1	Application
1.150	III.2.a	Application	II.1/II.2	Application	II.1	Application
1.151	III.2.a	Application	II.1/II.2	Application	II.1	Application
1.152	III.2.a	Application	II.1/II.2	Application	II.1	Application
1.153	III.2.a	Application	II.1/II.2	Application	II.1	Application
1.154	III.2.a	Application	II.1/II.2	Application	II.1	Application
1.155	III.2.a	Application	II.1/II.2	Application	II.1	Application
1.156	III.2.a	Application	II.1/II.2	Application	II.1	Application
1.157	III.2.a	Application	II.1/II.2	Application	II.1	Application
1.158	III.2.a	Application	II.1/II.2	Application	II.1	Application

Question	CCA Exam Competency	CCA Exam Level	CCS Exam Competency	CCS Exam Level	CCS-P Exam Competency	CCS-P Exam Level
1.159	III.2.a	Application	II.1/II.2	Application	II.1	Application
1.160	III.2.a	Application	II.1/II.2	Application	II.1	Application
1.161	III.2.a	Application	II.1/II.2	Application	II.1	Application
1.162	III.2.a	Application	II.1/II.2	Application	II.1	Application
1.163	III.2.a	Application	II.1/II.2	Application	II.1	Application
1.164	III.2.a	Application	II.1/II.2	Application	II.1	Application
1.165	III.2.a	Application	II.1/II.2	Application	II.1	Application
1.166	III.2.a	Application	II.1/II.2	Application	II.1	Application
1.167	III.2.a	Application	II.1/II.2	Application	II.1	Application
1.168	III.2.a	Application	II.1/II.2	Application	II.1	Application
1.169	III.2.a	Application	II.1/II.2	Application	II.1	Application
1.170	III.2.a	Application	II.1/II.2	Application	II.1	Application
1.171	III.2.a	Application	II.1/II.2	Application	II.1	Application
1.172	III.2.a	Application	II.1/II.2	Application	II.1	Application
1.173	III.2.a	Application	II.1/II.2	Application	II.1	Application
1.174	III.2.a	Application	II.1/II.2	Application	II.1	Application
1.175	III.2.a	Application	II.1/II.2	Application	II.1	Application
1.176	III.2.a	Application	II.1/II.2	Application	II.1	Application
1.177	III.2.a	Application	II.1/II.2	Application	II.1	Application
1.178	III.2.a	Application	II.1/II.2	Application	II.1	Application
1.179	III.2.a	Application	II.1/II.2	Application	II.1	Application
1.180	III.2.a	Application	II.1/II.2	Application	II.1	Application
1.181	III.2.a	Application	II.1/II.2	Application	II.1	Application
1.182	III.2.a	Application	II.1/II.2	Application	II.1	Application
1.183	III.2.a	Application	II.1/II.2	Application	II.1	Application
1.184	III.2.a	Application	II.1/II.2	Application	II.1	Application
1.185	III.2.a	Application	II.1/II.2	Application	II.1	Application
1.186	III.2.a	Application	II.1/II.2	Application	II.1	Application
1.187	III.2.a	Application	II.1/II.2	Application	II.1	Application
1.188	III.2.a	Application	II.1/II.2	Application	II.1	Application
1.189	III.2.a	Application	II.1/II.2	Application	II.1	Application
1.190	III.2.a	Application	II.1/II.2	Application	II.1	Application
1.191	III.2.a	Application	II.1/II.2	Application	II.1	Application
1.192	III.2.a	Application	II.1/II.2	Application	II.1	Application
1.193	III.2.a	Application	II.1/II.2	Application	II.1	Application
1.194	III.2.a	Application	II.1/II.2	Application	II.1	Application
1.195	III.2.a	Application	II.1/II.2	Application	II.1	Application
1.196	III.2.a	Application	II.1/II.2	Application	II.1	Application
1.197	III.2.a	Application	II.1/II.2	Application	II.1	Application
1.198	III.2.a	Application	II.1/II.2	Application	II.1	Application

Question	CCA Exam Competency	CCA Exam Level	CCS Exam Competency	CCS Exam Level	CCS-P Exam Competency	CCS-P Exam Level
1.199	III.2.a	Application	II.1/II.2	Application	II.1	Application
1.200	III.2.a	Application	II.1/II.2	Application	II.1	Application
1.201	III.2.a	Application	II.1/II.2	Application	II.1	Application
1.202	III.2.a	Application	II.1/II.2	Application	II.1	Application
1.203	III.2.a	Application	II.1/II.2	Application	II.1	Application
1.204	III.2.a	Application	II.1/II.2	Application	II.1	Application
1.205	III.6	Recall	II.4	Recall	II.1	Recall
1.206	III.2.a	Application	II.1/II.2	Application	II.1	Application
1.207	III.2.a	Application	II.1/II.2	Application	II.1	Application
1.208	III.2.a	Application	I.1	Application	I.1	Application
1.209	III.2.a	Application	II.1/II.2	Application	II.1	Application
1.210	III.2.a	Application	II.1/II.2	Application	II.1	Application
1.211	III.2.a	Application	II.1/II.2	Application	II.1	Application
1.212	III.2.a	Application	II.1/II.2	Application	II.1	Application
1.213	III.2.a	Application	II.1/II.2	Application	II.1	Application
1.214	III.2.a	Application	II.1/II.2	Application	II.1	Application
1.215	III.2.a	Application	II.1/II.2	Application	II.1	Application
1.216	III.2.a	Application	II.1/II.2	Application	II.1	Application
1.217	III.2.a	Application	II.1/II.2	Application	II.1	Application
1.218	III.2.a	Application	II.1/II.2	Application	II.1	Application
1.219	III.6	Recall	II.3	Recall	II.2	Recall
1.220	III.6	Recall	II.3	Recall	II.2	Recall
1.221	III.2.a	Application	II.1	Application	II.1	Application
1.222	III.2.a	Application	II.1	Application	II.1	Application
1.223	III.2.a	Application	II.1/II.2	Application	II.1	Application
1.224	III.2.a	Application	II.1	Application	II.1	Application
1.225	III.2.a	Application	II.1/II.2	Application	II.1	Application
1.226	III.2.a	Application	II.1/II.2	Application	II.1	Application
1.227	III.2.a	Application	II.1	Application	II.1	Application
1.228	III.2.a	Application	II.1	Application	II.1	Application
1.229	III.2.a	Application	II.1	Application	II.1	Application
1.230	III.6	Recall	II.3	Recall	II.2	Recall
1.231	III.6	Recall	II.3	Recall	II.2	Recall
1.232	III.6	Recall	II.3	Recall	II.2	Recall
1.233	III.2.a	Application	II.1/II.2	Application	II.1	Application
1.234	III.6	Recall	II.3	Recall	II.2	Recall
1.235	III.6	Recall	I.1	Recall	I.1	Recall
1.236	III.2.a	Application	II.1/II.2	Application	II.1	Application
1.237	III.2.a	Application	II.1/II.2	Application	II.1	Application
1.238	III.2.a	Application	II.1/II.2	Application	II.1	Application

Question	CCA Exam Competency	CCA Exam Level	CCS Exam Competency	CCS Exam Level	CCS-P Exam Competency	CCS-P Exam Level
1.239	III.2.a	Application	II.1/II.2	Application	II.1	Application
1.240	III.2.a	Application	II.1/II.2	Application	II.1	Application
1.241	III.2.a	Application	II.1/II.2	Application	II.1	Application
1.242	III.2.a	Application	II.1/II.2	Application	II.1	Application
1.243	III.2.a	Application	II.1/II.2	Application	II.1	Application
1.244	III.2.a	Application	II.1/II.2	Application	II.1	Application
1.245	III.2.a	Application	II.1/II.2	Application	II.1	Application
1.246	III.2.a	Application	II.1/II.2	Application	II.1	Application
1.247	III.2.a	Application	II.1/II.2	Application	II.1	Application
1.248	III.2.a	Application	II.1/II.2	Application	II.1	Application
1.249	III.2.a	Recall	II.4	Recall	II.2	Recall
1.250	III.2.a	Application	II.1/II.2	Application	II.1	Application
1.251	III.2.a	Application	II.1/II.2	Application	II.1	Application
1.252	III.2.a	Application	II.1/II.2	Application	II.1	Application
1.253	III.2.a	Application	II.1/II.2	Application	II.1	Application
1.254	III.2.a	Application	II.1/II.2	Application	II.1	Application
1.255	III.2.a	Application	II.1/II.2	Application	II.1	Application
1.256	III.2.a	Application	II.1/II.2	Application	II.1	Application
1.257	III.2.a	Application	II.1/II.2	Application	II.1	Application
1.258	III.2.a	Application	II.1/II.2	Application	II.1	Application
1.259	III.2.a	Application	II.1/II.2	Application	II.1	Application
1.260	III.2.a	Application	II.1/II.2	Application	II.1	Application
1.261	III.2.a	Application	II.1/II.2	Application	II.1	Application
1.262	III.2.a	Application	II.1/II.2	Application	II.1	Application
1.263	III.2.a	Application	II.1/II.2	Application	II.1	Application
1.264	III.2.a	Application	II.1/II.2	Application	II.1	Application
1.265	III.2.a	Application	II.1/II.2	Application	II.1	Application
1.266	III.2.a	Application	II.1/II.2	Application	II.1	Application
1.267	III.2.a	Application	II.1/II.2	Application	II.1	Application
1.268	III.2.a	Application	II.1/II.2	Application	II.1	Application
1.269	III.2.a	Application	II.1/II.2	Application	II.1	Application
1.270	III.2.a	Application	II.1/II.2	Application	II.1	Application
1.271	III.2.a	Application	II.1/II.2	Application	II.1	Application
1.272	III.2.a	Application	II.1/II.2	Application	II.1	Application
1.273	III.2.a	Application	II.1/II.2	Application	II.1	Application
1.274	III.2.a	Application	II.1/II.2	Application	II.1	Application
1.275	III.2.a	Application	II.1/II.2	Application	II.1	Application
1.276	III.2.a	Application	II.1/II.2	Application	II.1	Application
1.277	III.2.a	Application	II.1/II.2	Application	II.1	Application
1.278	III.2.a	Application	II.1/II.2	Application	II.1	Application

Question	CCA Exam Competency	CCA Exam Level	CCS Exam Competency	CCS Exam Level	CCS-P Exam Competency	CCS-P Exam Level
1.279	III.2.a	Application	II.1/II.2	Application	II.1	Application
1.280	III.2.a	Application	II.1/II.2	Application	II.1	Application
1.281	III.2.a	Application	II.1/II.2	Application	II.1	Application
1.282	III.2.a	Application	II.1/II.2	Application	II.1	Application
1.283	III.2.a	Application	II.1/II.2	Application	II.1	Application
1.284	III.2.a	Application	II.1/II.2	Application	II.1	Application
1.285	III.2.a	Application	II.1/II.2	Application	II.1	Application
1.286	III.2.a	Application	II.1/II.2	Application	II.1	Application
1.287	III.2.a	Application	II.1/II.2	Application	II.1	Application
1.288	III.2.a	Application	II.1/II.2	Application	II.1	Application
1.289	III.2.a	Application	II.1/II.2	Application	II.1	Application
1.290	III.2.a	Application	II.1/II.2	Application	II.1	Application
1.291	III.2.a	Application	II.1/II.2	Application	II.1	Application
1.292	III.2.a	Application	II.1/II.2	Application	II.1	Application
1.293	III.2.a	Application	II.1/II.2	Application	II.1	Application
1.294	III.2.a	Application	II.1	Application	N/A	N/A
1.295	III.2.a	Application	II.1/II.2	Application	II.1	Application
1.296	III.2.a	Application	II.1/II.2	Application	II.1	Application
1.297	III.2.a	Application	II.1/II.2	Application	II.1	Application
1.298	III.2.a	Application	II.1/II.2	Application	II.1	Application
1.299	III.2.a	Application	II.1/II.2	Application	II.1	Application
1.300	III.2.a	Application	II.1/II.2	Application	II.1	Application
1.301	III.2.a	Application	II.1/II.2	Application	II.1	Application
1.302	III.2.a	Application	II.1/II.2	Application	II.1	Application
1.303	III.2.a	Application	II.1/II.2	Application	II.1	Application
1.304	III.2.a	Application	II.1/II.2	Application	II.1	Application
1.305	III.2.a	Application	II.1/II.2	Application	II.1	Application
1.306	III.2.a	Application	II.1/II.2	Application	II.1	Application
1.307	III.2.a	Application	II.1/II.2	Application	II.1	Application
1.308	III.2.a	Application	II.1/II.2	Application	II.1	Application
1.309	III.2.a	Application	II.1/II.2	Application	II.1	Application
1.310	III.2.a	Application	II.1/II.2	Application	II.1	Application
1.311	III.2.a	Application	II.1/II.2	Application	II.1	Application
1.312	III.2.a	Application	II.1/II.2	Application	II.1	Application
1.313	III.2.a	Application	II.1/II.2	Application	II.1	Application
1.314	III.2.a	Application	II.1/II.2	Application	II.1	Application
1.315	III.2.a	Application	II.1/II.2	Application	II.1	Application
1.316	III.2.a	Application	II.1/II.2	Application	II.1	Application
1.317	III.2.a	Application	II.1/II.2	Application	II.1	Application
1.318	III.2.a	Application	II.1/II.2	Application	II.1	Application

Question	CCA Exam Competency	CCA Exam Level	CCS Exam Competency	CCS Exam Level	CCS-P Exam Competency	CCS-P Exam Level
1.319	III.2.a	Application	II.1/II.2	Application	II.1	Application
1.320	III.2.a	Application	II.1/II.2	Application	II.1	Application
1.321	III.2.a	Application	II.1/II.2	Application	II.1	Application
1.322	III.2.a	Application	II.1/II.2	Application	II.1	Application
1.323	III.2.a	Application	II.1/II.2	Application	II.1	Application
1.324	III.2.a	Application	II.1/II.2	Application	II.1	Application
1.325	III.2.a	Application	II.1/II.2	Application	II.1	Application
1.326	III.2.a	Application	II.1/II.2	Application	II.1	Application
1.327	III.2.a	Application	II.1/II.2	Application	II.1	Application
1.328	III.2.a	Application	II.1/II.2	Application	II.1	Application
1.329	III.2.a	Application	II.1/II.2	Application	II.1	Application
1.330	III.2.a	Application	II.1/II.2	Application	II.1	Application
1.331	III.2.a	Application	II.1/II.2	Application	II.1	Application
1.332	III.2.a	Application	II.1/II.2	Application	II.1	Application
1.333	III.2.a	Application	II.1/II.2	Application	II.1	Application
1.334	III.2.a	Application	II.1/II.2	Application	II.1	Application
1.335	III.2.a	Application	II.1/II.2	Application	II.1	Application
1.336	III.2.a	Application	II.1	Application	II.1	Application
1.337	III.2.a	Application	II.1	Application	II.1	Application
1.338	III.2.a	Application	II.1	Application	II.1	Application
1.339	III.2.a	Application	II.1	Application	II.1	Application
1.340	III.2.a	Application	II.1	Application	II.1	Application
1.341	III.2.a	Application	II.1	Application	II.1	Application
1.342	III.2.a	Application	II.1	Application	II.1	Application
1.343	III.2.a	Application	II.1	Application	II.1	Application
1.344	III.2.a	Application	II.1	Application	II.1	Application
1.345	III.2.a	Application	II.1	Application	II.1	Application
1.346	III.2.a	Application	II.1	Application	II.1	Application
1.347	III.2.a	Application	II.1	Application	II.1	Application
1.348	III.2.a	Application	II.1	Application	II.1	Application
1.349	III.2.a	Application	II.1	Application	II.1	Application
1.350	III.2.a	Application	II.1	Application	II.1	Application
1.351	III.2.a	Application	II.1	Application	II.1	Application
1.352	III.2.a	Application	II.1	Application	II.1	Application
1.353	III.2.a	Application	II.1	Application	II.1	Application
1.354	III.2.a	Application	II.1	Application	II.1	Application
1.355	III.2.a	Application	II.1	Application	II.1	Application
1.356	III.2.a	Application	II.8/II.9	Application	II.1	Application
1.357	III.2.a	Application	II.8/II.9	Application	II.1	Application
1.358	III.2.a	Application	II.8/II.9	Application	II.1	Application

Question	CCA Exam Competency	CCA Exam Level	CCS Exam Competency	CCS Exam Level	CCS-P Exam Competency	CCS-P Exam Level
1.359	III.2.a	Application	II.8/II.9	Application	II.1	Application
1.360	III.2.a	Application	II.8/II.9	Application	II.1	Application
1.361	III.2.a	Application	II.8/II.9	Application	II.1	Application
1.362	III.2.a	Application	II.8/II.9	Application	II.1	Application
1.363	III.2.a	Application	II.8/II.9	Application	II.1	Application
1.364	III.2.a	Application	II.8/II.9	Application	II.1	Application
1.365	III.2.a	Application	II.8/II.9	Application	II.1	Application
1.366	III.2.a	Application	II.8/II.9	Application	II.1	Application
1.367	III.2.a	Application	II.8/II.9	Application	II.1	Application
1.368	III.2.a	Application	II.8/II.9	Application	II.1	Application
1.369	III.2.a	Application	II.8/II.9	Application	II.1	Application
1.370	III.2.a	Application	II.8/II.9	Application	II.1	Application
1.371	III.2.a	Application	II.8/II.9	Application	II.1	Application
1.372	III.2.a	Application	II.8/II.9	Application	II.1	Application
1.373	III.2.a	Application	II.8/II.9	Application	II.1	Application
1.374	III.2.a	Application	II.8/II.9	Application	II.1	Application
1.375	III.2.a	Application	II.8/II.9	Application	II.1	Application
1.376	III.2.c	Application	II.1/II.2	Application	N/A	N/A
1.377	III.2.c	Application	II.1/II.2	Application	N/A	N/A
1.378	III.2.c	Application	II.1/II.2	Application	N/A	N/A
1.379	III.2.c	Application	II.1/II.2	Application	N/A	N/A
1.380	III.2.c	Application	II.1/II.2	Application	N/A	N/A
1.381	III.2.c	Application	II.1/II.2	Application	N/A	N/A
1.382	III.2.c	Application	II.1/II.2	Application	N/A	N/A
1.383	III.2.c	Application	II.1/II.2	Application	N/A	N/A
1.384	III.2.c	Application	II.1/II.2	Application	N/A	N/A
1.385	III.2.c	Application	II.1/II.2	Application	N/A	N/A
1.386	III.2.c	Application	II.1/II.2	Application	N/A	N/A
1.387	III.2.c	Application	II.1/II.2	Application	N/A	N/A
1.388	III.2.c	Application	II.1/II.2	Application	N/A	N/A
1.389	III.2.c	Application	II.1/II.2	Application	N/A	N/A
1.390	III.2.c	Application	II.1/II.2	Application	N/A	N/A
1.391	III.2.c	Application	II.1/II.2	Application	N/A	N/A
1.392	III.2.c	Application	II.1/II.2	Application	N/A	N/A
1.393	III.2.c	Application	II.1/II.2	Application	N/A	N/A
1.394	III.2.c	Application	II.1/II.2	Application	N/A	N/A
1.395	III.2.c	Application	II.1/II.2	Application	N/A	N/A
1.396	III.2.c	Application	II.1/II.2	Application	N/A	N/A
1.397	III.2.c	Application	II.1/II.2	Application	N/A	N/A
1.398	III.2.c	Application	II.1/II.2	Application	N/A	N/A

Question	CCA Exam Competency	CCA Exam Level	CCS Exam Competency	CCS Exam Level	CCS-P Exam Competency	CCS-P Exam Level
1.399	III.2.c	Application	II.1/II.2	Application	N/A	N/A
1.400	III.2.c	Application	II.1/II.2	Application	N/A	N/A
1.401	III.2.a	Application	II.4	Application	II.1	Application
1.402	III.2.a	Recall	II.3	Recall	II.2	Recall
1.403	III.6	Recall	I.1	Recall	I.1	Recall
1.404	III.2.a	Recall	II.4/IV.1	Recall	II.1	Recall
1.405	III.2.a	Recall	II.4/IV.1	Recall	II.1	Recall
1.406	III.2.a	Application	I.2	Recall	I.1	Recall
1.407	III.6	Recall	II.3	Recall	II.2	Recall
1.408	III.2.a	Recall	II.4/IV.1	Recall	N/A	Recall
1.409	III.2.a	Recall	II.4/IV.1	Recall	N/A	Recall
1.410	III.2.a	Recall	II.3	Recall	II.2	Recall
1.411	III.2.a	Recall	II.4/IV.1	Recall	II.1	Recall
1.412	III.6	Recall	II.3	Recall	II.2	Recall
1.413	III.6	Recall	II.3	Recall	II.2	Recall
1.414	III.6	Recall	II.3	Recall	II.2	Recall
1.415	III.2.a	Recall	II.4/IV.1	Recall	II.1	Recall
1.416	III.6	Recall	I.1	Recall	I.1	Recall
1.417	III.6	Recall	II.3	Recall	II.2	Recall
1.418	III.6	Recall	II.3	Recall	II.2	Recall
1.419	III.6	Recall	III.1/III.2	Recall	N/A	N/A
1.420	III.2.c	Recall	IV.1/III.4	Recall	N/A	N/A
1.421	III.2.a	Recall	II.4/IV.1	Application	N/A	N/A
1.422	III.2.a	Recall	II.4/IV.1	Application	N/A	N/A
1.423	III.2.a/III.2.b	Recall	II.5	Recall	N/A	N/A
1.424	III.6	Recall	I.1	Recall	I.1	Recall
1.425	III.6	Recall	I.1	Recall	I.1	Recall
1.426	III.6	Recall	1.1	Recall	1.1	Recall

Chapter 2

Question	CCA Exam Competency	CCA Exam Level	CCS Exam Competency	CCS Exam Level	CCS-P Exam Competency	CCS-P Exam Level
2.1	III.6	Recall	III.3	Recall	II.3	Recall
2.2	III.6	Recall	III.3	Recall	II.3	Recall
2.3	III.6	Recall	III.3	Recall	II.3	Recall
2.4	III.6	Recall	III.3	Recall	II.3	Recall
2.5	III.6	Recall	III.3	Recall	II.3	Recall
2.6	III.6	Recall	III.3	Recall	II.3	Recall
2.7	III.6	Recall	III.3	Recall	II.3	Recall
2.8	III.6	Recall	III.3	Recall	II.3	Recall
2.9	III.6	Recall	III.3	Recall	II.3	Recall
2.10	III.6	Recall	III.3	Recall	II.3	Recall
2.11	III.6	Recall	III.3	Recall	II.3	Recall
2.12	III.6	Recall	III.3	Recall	II.3	Recall
2.13	III.6	Recall	III.3	Recall	II.3	Recall
2.14	III.6	Recall	III.3	Recall	II.3	Recall
2.15	III.6	Recall	III.3	Recall	II.3	Recall
2.16	III.6	Recall	III.3	Recall	II.3	Recall
2.17	III.6	Recall	III.3	Recall	II.3	Recall
2.18	III.6	Recall	III.3	Recall	II.3	Recall
2.19	III.6	Recall	III.3	Recall	II.3	Recall
2.20	III.6	Recall	III.3	Recall	II.3	Recall
2.21	III.6	Recall	III.3	Recall	II.3	Recall
2.22	III.6	Recall	III.3	Recall	II.3	Recall
2.23	III.3	Application	III.3	Recall	II.3	Recall
2.24	III.6	Recall	III.3	Recall	II.3	Recall
2.25	III.3	Application	III.3	Recall	II.3	Recall
2.26	III.3	Application	III.3	Recall	II.3	Recall
2.27	III.3	Application	III.3	Recall	II.3	Recall
2.28	III.6	Recall	III.3	Recall	II.3	Recall
2.29	III.6	Recall	III.3	Recall	II.3	Recall
2.30	III.6	Recall	III.3	Recall	II.3	Recall
2.31	III.6	Recall	III.3	Recall	II.3	Recall
2.32	III.6	Recall	III.3	Recall	II.3	Recall
2.33	III.6	Recall	III.3	Recall	II.3	Recall
2.34	III.6	Recall	III.3	Recall	II.3	Recall
2.35	III.3	Application	III.3	Recall	II.3	Recall
2.36	III.6	Recall	III.3	Recall	II.3	Recall
2.37	III.3	Application	III.3	Recall	II.3	Recall
2.38	III.6	Recall	III.3	Recall	II.3	Recall
2.39	III.6	Recall	III.3	Recall	II.3	Recall

Question	CCA Exam Competency	CCA Exam Level	CCS Exam Competency	CCS Exam Level	CCS-P Exam Competency	CCS-P Exam Level
2.40	III.6	Recall	III.2	Application	II.4	Application
2.41	III.6	Recall	III.2	Application	II.4	Application
2.42	III.6	Recall	III.2	Application	II.4	Application
2.43	III.6	Recall	III.2	Application	II.4	Application
2.44	III.6	Recall	III.2	Application	II.4	Application
2.45	III.6	Recall	III.2	Application	II.4	Application
2.46	III.6	Recall	III.2	Application	II.4	Application
2.47	III.3	Application	III.2	Application	II.4	Application
2.48	III.3	Application	III.2	Application	II.4	Application
2.49	III.3	Application	III.2	Application	II.4	Application
2.50	III.3	Application	III.2	Application	II.4	Application
2.51	III.3	Application	III.2	Application	II.4	Application
2.52	III.3	Application	III.2	Application	II.4	Application
2.53	III.3	Application	III.2	Application	II.4	Application
2.54	III.3	Application	III.2	Application	II.4	Application
2.55	III.3	Application	III.2	Application	II.4	Application
2.56	III.3	Application	III.3	Recall	II.3	Recall
2.57	III.3	Application	III.3	Recall	II.3	Recall
2.58	III.3	Application	III.2	Application	II.4	Application
2.59	III.3	Application	III.3	Recall	II.3	Recall
2.60	III.3	Application	III.3	Recall	II.3	Recall
2.61	III.3	Application	III.2	Application	II.4	Application
2.62	III.3	Application	III.2	Application	II.4	Application
2.63	III.3	Application	III.2	Application	II.4	Application
2.64	III.6	Recall	III.2	Application	II.4	Application
2.65	III.6	Recall	III.2	Application	II.4	Application
2.66	III.6	Recall	III.2	Application	II.4	Application
2.67	III.6	Recall	III.2	Application	II.4	Application
2.68	III.6	Recall	III.2	Application	II.4	Application
2.69	III.3	Application	III.2	Application	II.4	Application
2.70	III.6	Recall	III.2	Application	II.4	Application
2.71	III.6	Recall	III.2	Application	II.4	Application
2.72	III.3	Application	III.2	Application	II.4	Application
2.73	III.3	Application	III.3	Recall	II.3	Recall
2.74	III.3	Application	III.2	Application	II.4	Application
2.75	III.3	Application	III.2	Application	II.4	Application
2.76	III.3	Application	III.3	Recall	II.3	Recall
2.77	III.3	Application	III.3	Recall	II.3	Recall
2.78	III.3	Application	III.3	Recall	II.3	Recall
2.79	III.3	Application	III.2	Application	II.4	Application

Question	CCA Exam Competency	CCA Exam Level	CCS Exam Competency	CCS Exam Level	CCS-P Exam Competency	CCS-P Exam Level
2.80	III.3	Application	III.2	Application	II.4	Application
2.81	III.3	Application	III.2	Application	II.4	Application
2.82	III.6	Recall	III.2	Application	II.4	Application
2.83	III.3	Application	III.2	Application	II.4	Application
2.84	III.6	Recall	III.2	Application	II.4	Application
2.85	III.3	Application	III.2	Application	II.4	Application
2.86	III.3	Application	III.2	Application	II.4	Application
2.87	III.6	Recall	III.2	Application	II.4	Application
2.88	III.6	Recall	III.2	Application	II.4	Application
2.89	III.3	Application	III.2	Recall	II.3	Recall
2.90	III.6	Recall	III.2	Application	II.4	Application
2.91	III.6	Recall	III.2	Application	II.4	Application
2.92	III.6	Recall	III.2	Application	II.4	Application
2.93	III.3	Application	III.2	Application	II.4	Application
2.94	III.3	Application	III.2	Application	II.4	Application
2.95	III.3	Application	III.2	Application	II.4	Application
2.96	III.3	Application	I.1	Recall	I.2	Recall
2.97	III.3	Application	III.2	Application	II.4	Application
2.98	III.3	Application	III.2	Application	II.4	Application
2.99	III.3	Application	III.2	Application	II.4	Application
2.100	III.3	Application	III.2	Application	II.4	Application
2.101	III.3	Application	III.2	Application	II.4	Application
2.102	III.3	Application	III.2	Application	II.4	Application
2.103	III.6	Recall	III.2	Application	II.4	Application
2.104	III.3	Application	III.2	Application	II.4	Application
2.105	III.3	Application	III.2	Application	II.4	Application
2.106	III.3	Application	III.2	Application	II.4	Application
2.107	III.3	Application	III.2	Application	II.4	Application
2.108	III.3	Application	III.2	Application	II.4	Application
2.109	III.3	Application	III.2	Application	II.4	Application
2.110	III.6	Recall	III.2	Application	II.4	Application
2.111	III.3	Application	III.2	Application	II.4	Application
2.112	III.3	Application	III.5	Recall	II.7	Recall
2.113	III.3	Application	III.2	Application	II.4	Application
2.114	III.3	Application	III.2	Application	II.4	Application
2.115	III.3	Application	III.2	Application	II.4	Application
2.116	III.3	Application	I.1	Recall	I.2	Recall
2.117	III.3	Application	III.2	Application	II.4	Application
2.118	III.3	Application	III.2	Application	II.4	Application
2.119	III.3	Application	III.3	Recall	II.3	Recall

Question	CCA Exam Competency	CCA Exam Level	CCS Exam Competency	CCS Exam Level	CCS-P Exam Competency	CCS-P Exam Level
2.120	III.3	Application	III.2	Application	II.4	Application
2.121	III.3	Application	III.2	Application	II.4	Application
2.122	III.3	Application	III.2	Application	II.4	Application
2.123	III.3	Application	III.2	Application	II.4	Application
2.124	III.3	Application	III.2	Application	II.4	Application
2.125	III.3	Application	III.2	Application	II.4	Application
2.126	III.6	Recall	III.2	Application	II.4	Application
2.127	III.3	Application	III.2	Application	II.4	Application
2.128	III.3	Application	III.2	Application	II.4	Application
2.129	III.3	Application	III.2	Application	II.4	Application
2.130	III.6	Recall	III.2	Application	II.4	Application
2.131	III.6	Recall	III.2	Application	II.4	Application
2.132	III.6	Recall	III.2	Application	II.4	Application
2.133	III.3	Application	III.2	Application	II.4	Application
2.134	III.3	Application	III.2	Application	II.4	Application
2.135	III.6	Recall	III.2	Application	II.4	Application
2.136	III.3	Application	III.2	Application	II.4	Application
2.137	III.3	Application	III.2	Application	II.4	Application
2.138	III.3	Application	III.2	Application	II.4	Application
2.139	III.3	Application	III.2	Application	II.4	Application
2.140	III.3	Application	III.2	Application	II.4	Application
2.141	III.3	Application	III.3	Recall	II.3	Recall
2.142	III.3	Application	III.2	Application	II.4	Application
2.143	III.3	Application	III.2	Application	II.4	Application
2.144	III.3	Application	I.3	Recall	I.5	Recall
2.145	III.3	Application	III.2	Application	II.4	Application
2.146	III.3	Application	III.2	Application	II.4	Application
2.147	III.3	Application	III.2	Application	II.4	Application
2.148	III.3	Application	III.2	Application	II.4	Application
2.149	III.3	Application	III.2	Application	II.4	Application
2.150	III.3	Application	III.2	Application	II.4	Application
2.151	III.3	Application	III.2	Application	II.4	Application
2.152	III.3	Application	III.2	Application	II.4	Application
2.153	III.3	Application	III.2	Application	II.4	Application
2.154	III.3	Application	III.2	Application	II.4	Application
2.155	III.3	Application	III.2	Application	II.4	Application
2.156	III.3	Application	III.2	Application	II.4	Application
2.157	III.6	Recall	III.2	Application	II.4	Application
2.158	III.3	Application	III.2	Application	II.4	Application
2.159	III.3	Application	III.2	Application	II.4	Application

Question	CCA Exam Competency	CCA Exam Level	CCS Exam Competency	CCS Exam Level	CCS-P Exam Competency	CCS-P Exam Level
2.160	III.6	Recall	III.2	Application	II.4	Application
2.161	III.3	Application	III.2	Application	II.4	Application
2.162	III.3	Application	III.2	Application	II.4	Application
2.163	III.3	Application	III.2	Application	II.4	Application
2.164	III.3	Application	III.2	Application	II.4	Application
2.165	III.3	Application	III.2	Application	II.4	Application
2.166	III.3	Application	III.2	Application	II.4	Application
2.167	III.3	Application	III.2	Application	II.4	Application
2.168	III.3	Application	III.2	Application	II.4	Application
2.169	III.3	Application	III.2	Application	II.4	Application
2.170	III.3	Application	III.2	Application	II.4	Application
2.171	III.3	Application	III.2	Application	II.4	Application
2.172	III.3	Application	III.2	Application	II.4	Application
2.173	III.3	Application	III.2	Application	II.4	Application
2.174	III.3	Application	III.2	Application	II.4	Application
2.175	III.3	Application	III.2	Application	II.4	Application
2.176	III.3	Application	III.2	Application	II.4	Application
2.177	III.3	Application	III.2	Application	II.4	Application
2.178	III.3	Application	III.2	Application	II.4	Application
2.179	III.3	Application	III.2	Application	II.4	Application
2.180	III.3	Application	III.2	Application	II.4	Application
2.181	III.3	Application	III.2	Application	II.4	Application
2.182	III.3	Application	III.2	Application	II.4	Application
2.183	III.3	Application	III.2	Application	II.4	Application
2.184	III.3	Application	III.2	Application	II.4	Application
2.185	III.3	Application	III.2	Application	II.4	Application
2.186	III.3	Application	III.2	Application	II.4	Application
2.187	III.3	Application	III.2	Application	II.4	Application
2.188	III.3	Application	III.2	Application	II.4	Application
2.189	III.3	Application	III.2	Application	II.4	Application
2.190	III.3	Application	III.2	Application	II.4	Application
2.191	III.3	Application	III.2	Application	II.4	Application
2.192	III.3	Application	III.2	Application	II.4	Application
2.193	III.3	Application	III.2	Application	II.4	Application
2.194	III.3	Application	III.2	Application	II.4	Application
2.195	III.3	Application	III.2	Application	II.4	Application
2.196	III.3	Application	III.2	Application	II.4	Application
2.197	III.3	Application	III.2	Application	II.4	Application
2.198	III.3	Application	III.2	Application	II.4	Application
2.199	III.3	Application	III.2	Application	II.4	Application

Question	CCA Exam Competency	CCA Exam Level	CCS Exam Competency	CCS Exam Level	CCS-P Exam Competency	CCS-P Exam Level
2.200	III.3	Application	III.2	Application	II.4	Application
2.201	III.3	Application	III.2	Application	II.4	Application
2.202	III.3	Application	III.2	Application	II.4	Application
2.203	III.3	Application	III.2	Application	II.4	Application
2.204	III.3	Application	III.2	Application	II.4	Application
2.205	III.3	Application	III.2	Application	II.4	Application
2.206	III.3	Application	III.2	Application	II.4	Application
2.207	III.3	Application	III.2	Application	II.4	Application
2.208	III.3	Application	III.2	Application	II.4	Application
2.209	III.3	Application	III.2	Application	II.4	Application
2.210	III.3	Application	III.2	Application	II.4	Application
2.211	III.3	Application	III.2	Application	II.4	Application
2.212	III.3	Application	III.2	Application	II.4	Application
2.213	III.3	Application	III.2	Application	II.4	Application
2.214	III.3	Application	III.2	Application	II.4	Application
2.215	III.3	Application	III.2	Application	II.4	Application
2.216	III.3	Application	III.2	Application	II.4	Application
2.217	III.3	Application	III.2	Application	II.4	Application
2.218	III.3	Application	III.2	Application	II.4	Application
2.219	III.3	Application	III.2	Application	II.4	Application
2.220	III.3	Application	III.2	Application	II.4	Application
2.221	III.3	Application	III.2	Application	II.4	Application
2.222	III.3	Application	III.2	Application	II.4	Application
2.223	III.3	Application	III.2	Application	II.4	Application
2.224	III.3	Application	III.2	Application	II.4	Application
2.225	III.3	Application	III.2	Application	II.4	Application
2.226	III.3	Application	III.2	Application	II.4	Application
2.227	III.3	Application	III.2	Application	II.4	Application
2.228	III.3	Application	III.2	Application	II.4	Application
2.229	III.3	Application	III.2	Application	II.4	Application
2.230	III.3	Application	III.2	Application	II.4	Application
2.231	III.3	Application	III.2	Application	II.4	Application
2.232	III.3	Application	III.2	Application	II.4	Application
2.233	III.3	Application	III.2	Application	II.4	Application
2.234	III.3	Application	III.2	Application	II.4	Application
2.235	III.3	Application	III.2	Application	II.4	Application
2.236	III.3	Application	III.2	Application	II.4	Application
2.237	III.3	Application	III.2	Application	II.4	Application
2.238	III.3	Application	III.2	Application	II.4	Application
2.239	III.3	Application	III.2	Application	II.4	Application

Question	CCA Exam Competency	CCA Exam Level	CCS Exam Competency	CCS Exam Level	CCS-P Exam Competency	CCS-P Exam Level
2.240	III.3	Application	III.2	Application	II.4	Application
2.241	III.3	Application	III.2	Application	II.4	Application
2.242	III.3	Application	III.2	Application	II.4	Application
2.243	III.3	Application	III.2	Application	II.4	Application
2.244	III.3	Application	III.2	Application	II.4	Application
2.245	III.3	Application	III.2	Application	II.4	Application
2.246	III.3	Application	III.2	Application	II.4	Application
2.247	III.3	Application	III.2	Application	II.4	Application
2.248	III.3	Application	III.2	Application	II.4	Application
2.249	III.3	Application	III.2	Application	II.4	Application
2.250	III.3	Application	III.2	Application	II.4	Application
2.251	III.3	Application	III.2	Application	II.4	Application
2.252	III.3	Application	III.2	Application	II.4	Application
2.253	III.3	Application	III.2	Application	II.4	Application
2.254	III.3	Application	III.2	Application	II.4	Application
2.255	III.3	Application	III.2	Application	II.4	Application
2.256	III.3	Application	III.2	Application	II.4	Application
2.257	III.3	Application	III.2	Application	II.4	Application
2.258	III.3	Application	III.2	Application	II.4	Application
2.259	III.3	Application	III.2	Application	II.4	Application
2.260	III.3	Application	III.2	Application	II.4	Application
2.261	III.3	Application	III.2	Application	II.4	Application
2.262	III.3	Application	III.2	Application	II.4	Application
2.263	III.3	Application	III.2	Application	II.4	Application
2.264	III.3	Application	III.2	Application	II.4	Application
2.265	III.3	Application	III.2	Application	II.4	Application
2.266	III.3	Application	III.2	Application	II.4	Application
2.267	III.3	Application	III.2	Application	II.4	Application
2.268	III.3	Application	III.2	Application	II.4	Application
2.269	III.3	Application	III.2	Application	II.4	Application
2.270	III.3	Application	III.2	Application	II.4	Application
2.271	III.3	Application	III.2	Application	II.4	Application
2.272	III.3	Application	III.2	Application	II.4	Application
2.273	III.3	Application	III.2	Application	II.4	Application
2.274	III.3	Application	III.2	Application	II.4	Application
2.275	III.3	Application	III.2	Application	II.4	Application
2.276	III.3	Application	III.2	Application	II.4	Application
2.277	III.3	Application	III.2	Application	II.4	Application
2.278	III.3	Application	III.2	Application	II.4	Application
2.279	III.3	Application	III.2	Application	II.4	Application

Question	CCA Exam Competency	CCA Exam Level	CCS Exam Competency	CCS Exam Level	CCS-P Exam Competency	CCS-P Exam Level
2.280	III.3	Application	III.2	Application	II.4	Application
2.281	III.3	Application	III.2	Application	II.4	Application
2.282	III.3	Application	III.2	Application	II.4	Application
2.283	III.3	Application	III.2	Application	II.4	Application
2.284	III.3	Application	III.2	Application	II.4	Application
2.285	III.3	Application	III.2	Application	II.4	Application
2.286	III.3	Application	III.2	Application	II.4	Application
2.287	III.3	Application	III.2	Application	II.4	Application
2.288	III.3	Application	III.2	Application	II.4	Application
2.289	III.3	Application	III.2	Application	II.4	Application
2.290	III.3	Application	III.2	Application	II.4	Application
2.291	III.3	Application	III.2	Application	II.4	Application
2.292	III.6	Recall	III.2	Application	II.4	Application
2.293	III.3	Application	III.2	Application	II.4	Application
2.294	III.3	Application	III.2	Application	II.4	Application
2.295	III.3	Application	III.2	Application	II.4	Application
2.296	III.3	Application	III.2	Application	II.4	Application
2.297	III.3	Application	III.2	Application	II.4	Application
2.298	III.3	Application	III.2	Application	II.4	Application
2.299	III.3	Application	III.2	Application	II.4	Application
2.300	III.3	Application	III.2	Application	II.4	Application
2.301	III.3	Application	III.2	Application	II.4	Application
2.302	III.3	Application	III.2	Application	II.4	Application
2.303	III.3	Application	III.2	Application	II.4	Application
2.304	III.3	Application	III.2	Application	II.4	Application
2.305	III.3	Application	III.2	Application	II.4	Application
2.306	III.3	Application	III.2	Application	II.4	Application
2.307	III.3	Application	III.2	Application	II.4	Application
2.308	III.3	Application	III.2	Application	II.4	Application
2.309	III.3	Application	III.2	Application	II.4	Application
2.310	III.3	Application	III.2	Application	II.4	Application
2.311	III.3	Application	III.2	Application	II.4	Application
2.312	III.3	Application	III.2	Application	II.4	Application
2.313	III.6	Recall	III.2	Application	II.4	Application
2.314	III.3	Application	III.2	Application	II.4	Application
2.315	III.6	Recall	III.2	Application	II.4	Application
2.316	III.6	Recall	III.2	Application	II.4	Application
2.317	III.3	Application	III.3	Recall	II.3	Recall
2.318	III.3	Application	III.2	Application	II.4	Application
2.319	III.3	Application	III.2	Application	II.4	Application

Question	CCA Exam Competency	CCA Exam Level	CCS Exam Competency	CCS Exam Level	CCS-P Exam Competency	CCS-P Exam Level
2.320	III.3	Application	III.2	Application	II.4	Application
2.321	III.3	Application	III.2	Application	II.4	Application
2.322	III.3	Application	III.2	Application	II.4	Application
2.323	III.3	Application	III.2	Application	II.4	Application
2.324	III.3	Application	III.2	Application	II.4	Application
2.325	III.3	Application	III.2	Application	II.4	Application
2.326	III.3	Application	III.2	Application	II.4	Application
2.327	III.3	Application	III.2	Application	II.4	Application
2.328	III.3	Application	III.2	Application	II.4	Application
2.329	III.3	Application	III.2	Application	II.4	Application
2.330	III.3	Application	III.2	Application	II.4	Application
2.331	III.3	Application	III.2	Application	II.4	Application
2.332	III.3	Application	III.2	Application	II.4	Application
2.333	III.3	Application	III.2	Application	II.4	Application
2.334	III.3	Application	III.2	Application	II.4	Application
2.335	III.3	Application	III.2	Application	II.4	Application
2.336	III.3	Application	N/A	N/A	II.1	Recall
2.337	III.6	Recall	V.2.a	Recall	II.1	Recall
2.338	III.3	Application	V.2.a	Recall	II.1	Recall
2.339	III.6	Recall	N/A	N/A	II.1	Recall
2.340	III.3	Application	V.2.a/III.2	Application	II.10/II.4	Application
2.341	III.6	Recall	N/A	N/A	II.1	Recall
2.342	III.3	Application	V.2.a	Recall	II.1	Recall
2.343	III.6	Recall	V.2.a/III.2	Application	II.10/II.4	Application
2.344	III.3	Application	V.2.a	Recall	II.1	Recall
2.345	III.3	Application	N/A	N/A	II.1	Recall
2.346	III.3	Application	V.2.a	Recall	II.1	Recall
2.347	III.3	Application	N/A	N/A	II.10/II.4	Application
2.348	III.3	Application	N/A	N/A	II.1	Recall
2.349	III.3	Application	N/A	N/A	II.1	Recall
2.350	III.3	Application	V.2.a	Recall	II.1	Recall
2.351	III.3	Application	V.2.a	Recall	II.1	Recall
2.352	III.3	Application	N/A	N/A	II.1	Recall
2.353	III.3	Application	N/A	N/A	II.1	Recall
2.354	III.3	Application	N/A	N/A	II.1	Recall
2.355	III.3	Application	N/A	N/A	II.1	Recall
2.356	III.3	Application	III.3	Recall	II.3	Recall
2.357	III.3	Application	III.3	Recall	II.3	Recall
2.358	III.3	Application	III.3	Recall	II.3	Recall
2.359	III.3	Application	III.2	Application	II.4	Application

Question	CCA Exam Competency	CCA Exam Level	CCS Exam Competency	CCS Exam Level	CCS-P Exam Competency	CCS-P Exam Level
2.360	III.3	Application	III.2	Application	II.4	Application
2.361	III.3	Application	III.2	Application	II.4	Application
2.362	III.6	Application	III.2	Application	II.4	Application
2.363	III.6	Application	III.3	Recall	II.3	Recall
2.364	III.6	Recall	III.2	Application	II.4	Application
2.365	III.6	Application	III.2	Application	II.4	Application
2.366	III.3	Application	III.2	Application	II.4	Application
2.367	III.6	Application	III.2	Application	II.4	Application
2.368	III.3	Application	III.2	Application	II.4	Application
2.369	III.6	Application	III.3	Recall	II.3	Recall
2.370	III.6	Application	III.2	Application	II.4	Application
2.371	III.6	Recall	III.2	Application	II.4	Application
2.372	III.6	Application	III.2	Application	II.4	Application
2.373	III.3	Application	III.2	Application	II.4	Application
2.374	III.6	Application	III.2	Application	II.4	Application
2.375	III.6	Application	III.2	Application	II.4	Application
2.376	III.6	Application	III.2	Application	II.4	Application
2.377	III.6	Application	III.2	Application	II.4	Application
2.378	III.6	Application	III.2	Application	II.4	Application
2.379	III.6	Application	III.2	Application	II.4	Application
2.380	III.6	Application	III.2	Application	II.4	Application
2.381	III.6	Application	III.2	Application	II.4	Application
2.382	III.6	Recall	III.2	Application	II.4	Application
2.383	III.6	Recall	III.2	Application	II.4	Application
2.384	III.6	Recall	III.2	Application	II.4	Application
2.385	III.3	Application	III.2	Application	II.4	Application
2.386	III.3	Application	III.2	Application	II.4	Application
2.387	III.3	Application	III.2	Application	II.4	Application
2.388	III.3	Application	III.2	Application	II.4	Application
2.389	III.6	Recall	III.2	Application	II.4	Application
2.390	III.3	Application	III.2	Application	II.4	Application
2.391	III.3	Application	III.2	Application	II.4	Application
2.392	III.3	Application	III.2	Application	II.4	Application
2.393	III.3	Application	III.2	Application	II.4	Application
2.394	III.3	Application	III.2	Application	II.4	Application
2.395	III.6	Recall	III.2	Application	II.4	Application
2.396	III.3	Application	III.2	Application	II.4	Application
2.397	III.3	Application	III.2	Application	II.4	Application
2.398	III.3	Application	III.2	Application	II.4	Application
2.399	III.3	Application	III.2	Application	II.4	Application

Question	CCA Exam Competency	CCA Exam Level	CCS Exam Competency	CCS Exam Level	CCS-P Exam Competency	CCS-P Exam Level
2.400	III.3	Application	III.2	Application	II.4	Application
2.401	III.3	Application	III.2	Application	II.4	Application
2.402	III.3	Application	III.2	Application	II.4	Application
2.403	III.3	Application	III.2	Application	II.4	Application
2.404	III.3	Application	III.2	Application	II.4	Application
2.405	III.3	Application	III.2	Application	II.4	Application
2.406	III.3	Application	III.2	Application	II.4	Application
2.407	III.3	Application	III.2	Application	II.4	Application
2.408	III.3	Application	III.2	Application	II.4	Application
2.409	III.3	Application	III.2	Application	II.4	Application
2.410	III.3	Application	III.2	Application	II.4	Application
2.411	III.3	Application	III.2	Application	II.4	Application
2.412	III.3	Application	III.2	Application	II.4	Application
2.413	III.3	Application	III.2	Application	II.4	Application
2.414	III.3	Application	III.2	Application	II.4	Application
2.415	III.3	Application	III.2	Application	II.4	Application
2.416	III.3	Application	III.2	Application	II.4	Application
2.417	III.3	Application	III.2	Application	II.4	Application
2.418	III.3	Application	III.2	Application	II.4	Application
2.419	III.3	Application	III.2	Application	II.4	Application
2.420	III.3	Application	III.2	Application	II.4	Application
2.421	III.3	Application	III.2	Application	II.4	Application
2.422	III.3	Application	III.2	Application	II.4	Application
2.423	III.3	Application	III.2	Application	II.4	Application
2.424	III.3	Application	III.2	Application	II.4	Application
2.425	III.3	Application	III.2	Application	II.4	Application
2.426	III.3	Application	III.2	Application	II.4	Application

Chapter 3

Question	CCA Exam Competency	CCA Exam Level	CCS Exam Competency	CCS Exam Level	CCS-P Exam Competency	CCS-P Exam Level
3.1	III.4	Recall	III.3	Recall	II.3	Recall
3.2	III.4	Application	III.2	Application	II.9	Application
3.3	III.4	Application	III.2	Application	II.9	Application
3.4	III.4	Application	III.2	Application	II.9	Application
3.5	III.4	Application	III.2	Application	II.9	Application
3.6	III.4	Application	III.2	Application	II.9	Application
3.7	III.4	Application	III.2	Application	II.9	Application
3.8	III.4	Application	III.2	Application	II.9	Application
3.9	III.4	Application	III.2	Application	II.9	Application
3.10	III.4	Application	III.2	Application	II.9	Application
3.11	III.4	Application	III.2	Application	II.9	Application
3.12	III.4	Application	III.2	Application	II.9	Application
3.13	III.4	Application	III.2	Application	II.9	Application
3.14	III.4	Application	III.2	Application	II.9	Application
3.15	III.4	Application	III.2	Application	II.9	Application
3.16	III.4	Application	III.2	Application	II.9	Application
3.17	III.4	Application	III.2	Application	II.9	Application
3.18	III.4	Application	III.2	Application	II.9	Application
3.19	III.4	Application	III.2	Application	II.9	Application
3.20	III.4	Application	III.2	Application	II.9	Application
3.21	III.4	Application	N/A	N/A	II.1	Recall
3.22	III.4	Application	N/A	N/A	II.1	Recall
3.23	III.4	Application	III.2	Application	II.9	Application
3.24	III.4	Recall	N/A	N/A	II.3	Recall
3.25	III.4	Application	III.2	Application	II.9	Application
3.26	III.4	Application	N/A	N/A	II.9	Application
3.27	III.4	Recall	N/A	N/A	II.3	Recall
3.28	III.4	Application	III.2	Application	II.4	Application
3.29	III.4	Application	III.2	Application	II.4	Application
3.30	III.4	Application	III.2	Application	II.4	Application
3.31	III.4	Application	III.2	Application	II.4	Application
3.32	III.4	Application	III.2	Application	II.4	Application
3.33	III.4	Application	III.2	Application	II.4	Application
3.34	III.4	Application	III.2	Application	II.4	Application
3.35	III.4	Application	III.2	Application	II.4	Application
3.36	III.4	Application	III.2	Application	II.4	Application
3.37	III.4	Application	III.2	Application	II.4	Application
3.38	III.4	Application	III.2	Application	II.4	Application
3.39	III.4	Application	III.2	Application	II.4	Application

Question	CCA Exam Competency	CCA Exam Level	CCS Exam Competency	CCS Exam Level	CCS-P Exam Competency	CCS-P Exam Level
3.40	III.4	Application	III.2	Application	II.4	Application
3.41	III.4	Application	III.2	Application	II.4	Application
3.42	III.4	Application	III.2	Application	II.4	Application
3.43	III.4	Application	III.2	Application	II.4	Application
3.44	III.4	Application	III.2	Application	II.4	Application
3.45	III.4	Application	III.2	Application	II.4	Application
3.46	III.4	Application	III.2	Application	II.4	Application
3.47	III.4	Application	III.2	Application	II.4	Application
3.48	III.4	Application	III.2	Application	II.4	Application
3.49	III.4	Application	III.2	Application	II.4	Application
3.50	III.4	Application	III.2	Application	II.4	Application

Chapter 4

Question	CCA Exam Competency	CCA Exam Level	CCS Exam Competency	CCS Exam Level	CCS-P Exam Competency	CCS-P Exam Level
4.1	III.2.a	Application	II.3	Application	N/A	N/A
4.2	III.2.a,b,c	Application	II.3	Application	N/A	N/A
4.3	III.2.a,b,c	Application	III.1/II.2	Application	N/A	N/A
4.4	III.2.a,b,c	Application	III.1/II.1	Application	N/A	N/A
4.5	III.2.a,b	Application	II.3	Application	N/A	N/A
4.6	III.2.a,b	Application	III.2/II.5	Application	N/A	N/A
4.7	III.2.a,b,c	Application	IV.1	Application	N/A	N/A
4.8	III.2.a,b,c	Application	IV.1	Application	N/A	N/A
4.9	III.2.a,b,c	Application	II.1	Application	N/A	N/A
4.10	III.2.a,b	Application	IV.21/II.1	Application	N/A	N/A
4.11	III.2.a,b,c	Application	II.1	Application	N/A	N/A
4.12	III.2.a,b	Application	II.1	Application	N/A	N/A
4.13	III.2.a,b	Application	II.5/III.1	Application	N/A	N/A
4.14	III.2.a	Application	II.3/III.3	Application	N/A	N/A
4.15	III.2.c	Application	II.1/III.1	Application	N/A	N/A
4.16	III.2.a,b,c	Application	II.1/III.1	Application	N/A	N/A
4.17	III.2.a,b,c	Application	II.1/III.1	Application	N/A	N/A
4.18	III.2.a,b,c	Application	II.1/III.1	Application	N/A	N/A
4.19	III.2.a,b	Application	II.1/III.1	Application	N/A	N/A
4.20	III.2.a,b,c	Application	II.1	Application	N/A	N/A
4.21	III.2.a,b,c	Application	II.1	Application	N/A	N/A
4.22	III.2.a,b,c	Application	II.1	Application	N/A	N/A
4.23	III.2.a,b	Application	II.4/III.1	Application	N/A	N/A
4.24	III.2.a,b	Application	II.3	Application	N/A	N/A
4.25	III.2.a,b	Application	II.1/III.5	Application	N/A	N/A
4.26	III.2.a,b,c	Application	II.1/III.5	Application	N/A	N/A
4.27	III.2.a,b	Application	II.5	Application	N/A	N/A
4.28	III.2.a,b,c	Application	II.5/III.1	Application	N/A	N/A
4.29	III.2.a,c	Application	II.1/III.1	Application	N/A	N/A
4.30	III.2.a,b	Application	II.3	Application	N/A	N/A
4.31	III.2.a,b,c	Application	II.4	Application	N/A	N/A
4.32	III.2.a,b,c	Application	II.3	Application	N/A	N/A
4.33	III.2.a,b	Application	II.3	Application	N/A	N/A
4.34	III.2.a,b	Application	II.1	Application	N/A	N/A
4.35	III.2.a	Application	II.1	Application	N/A	N/A
4.36	III.2.a,b,c	Application	II.1/III.1	Application	N/A	N/A
4.37	III.2.a,b	Application	II.1/III.1	Application	N/A	N/A
4.38	III.2.a,b	Application	II.1/III.1	Application	N/A	N/A
4.39	III.2.a,b	Application	II.1/III.1	Application	N/A	N/A

Question	CCA Exam Competency	CCA Exam Level	CCS Exam Competency	CCS Exam Level	CCS-P Exam Competency	CCS-P Exam Level
4.40	III.2.a,b	Application	II.1/III.1	Application	N/A	N/A
4.41	III.2.a,b	Application	II.1/III.1	Application	N/A	N/A
4.42	III.2.a,b	Application	II.1/III.1	Application	N/A	N/A
4.43	III.2.a,b	Application	II.1/III.1	Application	N/A	N/A
4.44	III.2.a,b,c	Application	II.3	Application	N/A	N/A
4.45	III.2.a,b,c	Application	II.3	Application	N/A	N/A
4.46	III.2.a,b,c	Application	II.1/III.1	Application	N/A	N/A
4.47	III.2.a,c	Application	II.1/III.1	Application	N/A	N/A
4.48	III.2.a,b,c	Application	II.1/III.1	Application	N/A	N/A
4.49	III.2.a	Application	II.1/III.1/II.10	Application	N/A	N/A
4.50	III.2.a,b	Application	II.1/III.1	Application	N/A	N/A
4.51	III.2.a,c	Application	IV.1	Application	N/A	N/A
4.52	III.2.a,b,c	Application	II.9	Application	N/A	N/A
4.53	III.2.a,c	Application	II.4	Application	N/A	N/A
4.54	III.2.a,b,c	Application	II.5	Application	N/A	N/A
4.55	III.2.a,b,c	Application	II.1/III.1/II.10	Application	N/A	N/A
4.56	III.2.c	Application	II.1/III.5	Application	N/A	N/A
4.57	III.2.c	Application	IV.1	Application	N/A	N/A
4.58	III.2.a,b	Application	II.5/III.1	Application	N/A	N/A
4.59	III.2.a,b,c	Application	II.1/III.1	Application	N/A	N/A
4.60	III.2.a,b	Application	II.1	Application	N/A	N/A
4.61	III.2.a,b	Application	II.1/III.1	Application	N/A	N/A
4.62	III.2.a,b,c	Application	II.1	Application	N/A	N/A
4.63	III.2.a,b,c	Application	II.1/III.1	Application	N/A	N/A
4.64	III.2.a,b,c	Application	II.1/III.1	Application	N/A	N/A
4.65	III.2.a,b,c	Application	II.4	Application	N/A	N/A
4.66	III.2.a,c	Application	II.1/III.1	Application	N/A	N/A
4.67	III.2.a,b,c	Application	II.1	Application	N/A	N/A
4.68	III.2.a,c	Application	II.3	Application	N/A	N/A
4.69	III.2.a,b,c	Application	II.1/III.1	Application	N/A	N/A
4.70	III.2.a,c	Application	II.5	Application	N/A	N/A
4.71	III.2.a,b,c	Application	II.1	Application	N/A	N/A
4.72	III.2.a,b	Application	II.1/II.10	Application	N/A	N/A
4.73	III.2.a,b,c	Application	II.1/III.1	Application	N/A	N/A
4.74	III.2.a,b	Application	II.1/III.1	Application	N/A	N/A
4.75	III.2.a,b	Application	II.6	Application	N/A	N/A
4.76	III.2.a,c	Application	II.3	Application	N/A	N/A
4.77	III.2.a	Application	II.3	Application	N/A	N/A
4.78	III.2.a,b	Application	II.3	Application	N/A	N/A
4.79	III.2.a,b	Application	II.1	Application	N/A	N/A

Question	CCA Exam Competency	CCA Exam Level	CCS Exam Competency	CCS Exam Level	CCS-P Exam Competency	CCS-P Exam Level
4.80	III.2.a,c	Application	II.3	Application	N/A	N/A
4.81	III.2.a,c	Application	II.1	Application	N/A	N/A
4.82	III.2.a,b,c	Application	II.4	Application	N/A	N/A
4.83	III.2.a,b,c	Application	II.1	Application	N/A	N/A
4.84	III.2.a,b,c	Application	II.1	Application	N/A	N/A
4.85	III.2.a	Application	II.4/II.10	Application	N/A	N/A
4.86	III.2.a,b,c	Application	II.4/II.10	Application	N/A	N/A
4.87	III.2.a	Application	II.3	Application	N/A	N/A
4.88	III.2.a,b	Application	II.1	Application	N/A	N/A
4.89	III.2.a,b,c	Application	II.1/III.1	Application	N/A	N/A
4.90	III.2.a,b,c	Application	II.1/III.1	Application	N/A	N/A
4.91	III.2.a,b,c	Application	II.1/II.10	Application	N/A	N/A
4.92	III.2.a,b,c	Application	II.1/II.10	Application	N/A	N/A
4.93	III.2.a,b	Application	II.1/II.10	Application	N/A	N/A
4.94	III.2.a,b	Application	II.1/III.1	Application	N/A	N/A
4.95	III.2.a,b,c	Application	II.1/II.10	Application	N/A	N/A
4.96	III.2.a,c	Application	II.1/III.1	Application	N/A	N/A
4.97	III.2.a,b,c	Application	II.1/II.10	Application	N/A	N/A

Chapter 5

Question	CCA Exam Competency	CCA Exam Level	CCS Exam Competency	CCS Exam Level	CCS-P Exam Competency	CCS-P Exam Level
5.1	III.2.a/III.3	Application	II.2/III.2	Application	II.1/II.4	Application
5.2	III.2.a/III.3	Application	II.2/III.5	Application	II.1/II.7	Application
5.3	III.2.a/III.3	Application	II.2/III.2	Application	II.1/II.4	Application
5.4	III.2.a,b/III.3	Application	II.1/III.2	Application	II.1/II.4	Application
5.5	III.2.a,b	Application	II.5	Application	II.1	Application
5.6	III.2.a/III.3	Application	II.2/V.2.a	Application	II.1/II.4/II.10	Application
5.7	III.2.a/III.3	Application	II.2/III.2	Application	II.1/II.4	Application
5.8	III.2.a/III.3	Application	II.2/III.2	Application	II.1/II.4	Application
5.9	III.2.a,b/III.3	Application	II.2/III.2	Application	II.1/II.3	Application
5.10	III.2.a	Application	II.3	Application	II.2	Application
5.11	III.3	Application	III.2	Application	II.4	Application
5.12	III.2.a/III.3	Application	II.2/III.2	Application	II.1/II.4	Application
5.13	III.2.a/III.3	Application	II.2/III.2	Application	II.1/II.4	Application
5.14	III.2.a,b/III.3	Application	II.2/V.2.b	Application	II.1/II.8	Application
5.15	III.2.a/III.3	Application	II.2/III.5	Application	II.1/II.7	Application
5.16	III.2.a,b/III.3	Application	II.2/III.2	Application	II.1/II.4	Application
5.17	III.2.a/III.3	Application	II.2/III.5	Application	II.1/II.7	Application
5.18	III.2.a,b/III.3	Application	V.3	Application	III.3	Application
5.19	III.3	Application	III.2	Application	II.4	Application
5.20	III.2.a,b	Application	II.3	Application	II.2	Application
5.21	III.2.a,b	Application	II.3	Application	II.2	Application
5.22	III.2.a,b	Application	II.2	Application	II.1	Application
5.23	III.2.a	Application	II.2	Application	II.1	Application
5.24	III.2.a/III.3	Application	II.2/III.2	Application	II.1/II.4	Application
5.25	III.2.a,b/III.3	Application	II.2/III.2	Application	II.1/II.4	Application
5.26	III.2.a/III.3	Application	II.2/III.2	Application	II.1/II.4	Application
5.27	III.2.a/III.3	Application	II.2/III.2	Application	II.1/II.4	Application
5.28	III.2.a/III.3	Application	II.2/III.2	Application	II.1/II.4	Application
5.29	III.2.a/III.3	Application	II.2/III.2	Application	II.1/II.4	Application
5.30	III.2.a,b/III.3	Application	II.6/III.2	Application	II.1/II.4	Application
5.31	III.2.a,b/III.3	Application	II.2/III.2	Application	II.1/II.4	Application
5.32	III.2.a/III.3	Application	II.6/III.5	Application	I.3/II.7	Application
5.33	III.2.a/III.3	Application	II.5/III.2	Application	II.1/II.4	Application
5.34	III.3	Application	III.2	Application	II.4	Application
5.35	III.2.a	Application	II.5	Application	II.1	Application
5.36	III.2.a	Application	II.5	Application	II.1	Application
5.37	III.2.a	Application	II.5	Application	II.1	Application
5.38	III.2.a	Application	II.5	Application	II.1	Application
5.39	III.2.a/III.3	Application	II.2/III.5	Application	II.1/II.4	Application
5.40	III.2.a/III.3	Application	II.2/III.3	Application	II.1/II.5/II.9	Application

Question	CCA Exam Competency	CCA Exam Level	CCS Exam Competency	CCS Exam Level	CCS-P Exam Competency	CCS-P Exam Level
5.41	III.2.a,b/III.3/III.4	Application	II.2/III.3	Application	II.1/II.5/II.9	Application
5.42	III.2.a/III.3	Application	II.2/III.2	Application	II.1/II.4	Application
5.43	III.3	Application	II.2/III.2	Application	II.1/II.4/II.10	Application
5.44	III.2.a/III.3	Application	II.2/III.2	Application	II.1/II.4/II.10	Application
5.45	III.3	Application	III.2	Application	II.4	Application
5.46	III.2.a,b	Application	II.2	Application	II.1	Application
5.47	III.2.a/III.3	Application	II.2/III.2	Application	II.1/II.4	Application
5.48	III.3	Application	II.2/III.2	Application	II.1/II.4	Application
5.49	III.2.a,b	Application	II.2/III.2	Application	II.1/II.4	Application
5.50	III.2.a,b	Application	II.2	Application	II.1	Application
5.51	III.2.a,b/III.3	Application	II.2/II.10/III.2	Application	II.1/II.4	Application
5.52	III.2.a/III.3	Application	II.2/III.5	Application	II.1/II.7	Application
5.53	III.2.a,b/III.3/III.4	Application	II.2/II.10/III.3	Application	II.1/II.3	Application
5.54	III.2.a,b/III.3	Application	II.2/II.10/III.2	Application	II.1/II.4	Application
5.55	III.2.a/III.3	Application	II.2/III.2	Application	II.1/II.4	Application
5.56	III.6	Application	I.1/I.4	Application	I.2/I.6	Application
5.57	III.2.a,b/III.3	Application	II.9/III.2	Application	II.1/II.4	Application
5.58	III.2.a/III.3	Application	II.2/III.5	Application	II.1/II.7	Application
5.59	III.2.a,b/III.3	Application	II.2/V.2.a	Application	II.1/II.10	Application
5.60	III.2.a,b/III.3	Application	II.3/III.5	Application	II.1/II.7	Application
5.61	III.2.a,b/III.3/III.4	Application	II.2/III.2	Application	II.1/II.9	Application
5.62	III.2.a,b/III.3/III.4	Application	II.2/III.2	Application	II.1/II.4	Application
5.63	III.2.a/III.3	Application	II.2/III.5	Application	II.1/II.7	Application
5.64	III.2.a,b/III.3	Application	II.2/III.2	Application	II.1/II.4	Application
5.65	III.2.a/III.3	Application	II.6/V.2.a	Application	II.1/II.10	Application
5.66	III.2.a	Application	II.2	Application	II.1	Application
5.67	III.3	Application	III.2	Application	II.4	Application
5.68	III.2.a/III.3	Application	II.3/III.2	Application	II.2/II.4	Application
5.69	III.2.a/III.3	Application	II.2/III.2	Application	II.1/II.4	Application
5.70	III.2.a/III.3	Application	II.2/III.2	Application	II.1/II.4	Application
5.71	III.2.a,b/III.3	Application	II.2/V.2.a	Application	II.1/II.10	Application
5.72	III.2.a,b	Application	II.5	Application	II.1	Application
5.73	III.2.a/III.3	Application	II.2/V.2.a	Application	II.1/II.10	Application
5.74	III.2.a/III.3	Application	II.2/V.2.a	Application	II.1/II.10	Application
5.75	III.2.a,b	Application	II.5	Application	II.1	Application
5.76	III.2.a/III.3	Application	II.2/III.2	Application	II.1/II.4	Application
5.77	III.2.a/III.3	Application	II.2/III.2	Application	II.1/II.4	Application
5.78	III.2.a/III.3	Application	II.2/III.2	Application	II.1/II.4	Application
5.79	III.2.a/III.3	Application	II.2/III.2	Application	II.1/II.4	Application
5.80	III.2.a	Application	II.5	Application	II.1	Application

Question	CCA Exam Competency	CCA Exam Level	CCS Exam Competency	CCS Exam Level	CCS-P Exam Competency	CCS-P Exam Level
5.81	III.2.a,b/III.3	Application	II.5/III.2	Application	II.1/II.4	Application
5.82	III.2.a/III.3	Application	II.2/V.2.a	Application	II.1/II.10	Application
5.83	III.2.a,b/III.3	Application	II.2/II.10/III.2	Application	II.1/II.4	Application
5.84	III.2.a,b/III.3	Application	II.2/II.10/III.2	Application	II.1/II.4	Application
5.85	III.2.a/III.3	Application	II.2/III.2	Application	II.1/II.4	Application
5.86	III.2.a,b/III.3	Application	II.2/V.2.a	Application	II.1/II.10	Application
5.87	III.2.a,b/III.3	Application	II.1/III.2	Application	II.1/II.3	Application

Chapter 6

Question	CCA Exam Competency	CCA Exam Level	CCS Exam Competency	CCS Exam Level	CCS-P Exam Competency	CCS-P Exam Level
6.1	III.3	Application	N/A	N/A	II.4	Application
6.2	III.2.a,b/III.3	Application	N/A	N/A	II.1/II.4	Application
6.3	III.2.a/III.3	Application	N/A	N/A	II.1/II.10	Application
6.4	III.3	Application	N/A	N/A	II.1/II.10	Application
6.5	III.2.a,b/III.3	Application	N/A	N/A	II.1/II.10	Application
6.6	III.2.a/III.3	Application	N/A	N/A	II.1/II.4	Application
6.7	III.2.a/III.3	Application	N/A	N/A	II.1/II.4	Application
6.8	III.2.a,b	Application	N/A	N/A	II.1	Application
6.9	III.3	Application	N/A	N/A	II.5	Application
6.10	III.3	Application	N/A	N/A	II.5	Application
6.11	III.2.a,b	Application	N/A	N/A	II.1	Application
6.12	III.2.a,b/III.3	Application	N/A	N/A	II.1/II.4	Application
6.13	III.2.a,b	Application	N/A	N/A	II.1	Application
6.14	III.2.a	Application	N/A	N/A	II.1	Application
6.15	III.2.a,b/III.3	Application	N/A	N/A	II.1/II.4	Application
6.16	III.2.a,b/III.3	Application	N/A	N/A	II.1/II.4	Application
6.17	III.2.a,b/III.3	Application	N/A	N/A	II.1/II.4	Application
6.18	III.3	Application	N/A	N/A	II.1/II.4	Application
6.19	III.2.a/III.3	Application	N/A	N/A	II.1/II.4	Application
6.20	III.3	Application	N/A	N/A	II.1/II.10	Application
6.21	III.2.a/III.3	Application	N/A	N/A	II.1/II.10	Application
6.22	III.2.a,b/III.3	Application	N/A	N/A	II.3/II.4	Application
6.23	III.3	Application	N/A	N/A	II.5	Application
6.24	III.3	Application	N/A	N/A	II.1/II.5	Application
6.25	III.2.a/III.3	Application	N/A	N/A	II.1/II.5	Application
6.26	III.3	Application	N/A	N/A	II.1/II.5	Application
6.27	III.2.a/III.3	Application	N/A	N/A	II.1/II.5	Application
6.28	III.2.a,b/III.3	Application	N/A	N/A	II.1	Application
6.29	III.3	Application	N/A	N/A	II.1	Application
6.30	III.3	Application	N/A	N/A	II.1	Application
6.31	III.2.a	Application	N/A	N/A	II.1	Application
6.32	III.2.a,b/III.3	Application	N/A	N/A	II.1/II.4	Application
6.33	III.2.a,b	Application	N/A	N/A	II.1/II.4	Application
6.34	III.2.a,b	Application	N/A	N/A	II.1/II.10	Application
6.35	III.2.a,b	Application	N/A	N/A	II.1/II.4	Application
6.36	III.2.a,b	Application	N/A	N/A	II.1/II.4	Application
6.37	III.2.a/III.3	Application	N/A	N/A	II.1/II.5	Application
6.38	III.2.a,b/III.3	Application	N/A	N/A	II.1/II.4	Application
6.39	III.2.a/III.3	Application	N/A	N/A	II.1/II.5	Application
6.40	III.2.a,b/III.3	Application	N/A	N/A	II.1/II.4	Application

Question	CCA Exam Competency	CCA Exam Level	CCS Exam Competency	CCS Exam Level	CCS-P Exam Competency	CCS-P Exam Level
6.41	III.2.a/III.3	Application	N/A	N/A	II.1/II.4	Application
6.42	III.2.a/III.3	Application	N/A	N/A	II.1/II.4	Application
6.43	III.2.a/III.3	Application	N/A	N/A	II.4/II.5	Application
6.44	III.2.a/III.3	Application	N/A	N/A	II.1/II.4	Application
6.45	III.2.a,b/III.3	Application	N/A	N/A	II.1	Application
6.46	III.2.a/III.3	Application	N/A	N/A	II.2	Application
6.47	III.2.a/III.3	Application	N/A	N/A	II.1/II.10	Application
6.48	III.3	Application	N/A	N/A	II.1/II.3	Application
6.49	III.3	Application	N/A	N/A	II.1/II.4	Application
6.50	III.3	Application	N/A	N/A	II.1/II.4	Application
6.51	III.2.a/III.3	Application	N/A	N/A	II.1/II.5	Application
6.52	III.2.a	Application	N/A	N/A	II.1/II.5/II.9	Application
6.53	III.2.a,b	Application	N/A	N/A	II.1/II.4	Application
6.54	III.2.a/III.3	Application	N/A	N/A	II.1/II.4	Application
6.55	III.2.a,b/III.3	Application	N/A	N/A	II.1/II.4	Application
6.56	III.2.a/III.3	Application	N/A	N/A	II.1/II.4	Application
6.57	III.2.a,b/III.3	Application	N/A	N/A	II.2	Application
6.58	III.2.a,b/III.3	Application	N/A	N/A	II.4/II.9	Application
6.59	III.2.a/III.3	Application	N/A	N/A	II.1/II.10	Application
6.60	III.2.a/III.3/III.4	Application	N/A	N/A	II.1/II.10	Application
6.61	III.2.a,b/III.3	Application	N/A	N/A	II.1	Application
6.62	III.2.a,b/III.3	Application	N/A	N/A	II.1/II.4	Application
6.63	III.2.a/III.3	Application	N/A	N/A	II.1/II.4	Application
6.64	III.2.a,b/III.3	Application	N/A	N/A	II.1/II.10	Application
6.65	III.3	Application	N/A	N/A	II.1/II.10	Application
6.66	III.3/III.4	Application	N/A	N/A	II.1/II.5	Application
6.67	III.2.a/III.3	Application	N/A	N/A	II.4/II.9	Application
6.68	III.2.a/III.3	Application	N/A	N/A	II.1/II.5	Application
6.69	III.2.a,b	Application	N/A	N/A	II.1/II.4	Application
6.70	III.2.a,b/III.3	Application	N/A	N/A	II.1/II.4/II.5	Application
6.71	III.2.a/III.3	Application	N/A	N/A	II.1/II.4/II.5	Application
6.72	III.3	Application	N/A	N/A	II.1/II.3	Application
6.73	III.2.a/III.3	Application	N/A	N/A	II.1/II.4	Application
6.74	III.2.a/III.3	Application	N/A	N/A	II.1	Application
6.75	III.3	Application	N/A	N/A	II.1	Application
6.76	III.2.a/III.3	Application	N/A	N/A	II.1/II.4	Application
6.77	III.2.a/III.3	Application	N/A	N/A	II.1/II.4	Application
6.78	III.2.a/III.3	Application	N/A	N/A	II.1/II.4	Application
6.79	III.2.a/III.3	Application	N/A	N/A	II.1	Application
6.80	III.2.a/III.3	Application	N/A	N/A	II.1	Application

Question	CCA Exam Competency	CCA Exam Level	CCS Exam Competency	CCS Exam Level	CCS-P Exam Competency	CCS-P Exam Level
6.81	III.2.a/III.3	Application	N/A	N/A	II.1	Application
6.82	III.2.a	Application	N/A	N/A	II.1	Application
6.83	III.2.a,b	Application	N/A	N/A	II.1	Application
6.84	III.2.a,b/III.3	Application	N/A	N/A	II.3	Application
6.85	III.2.a/III.3	Application	N/A	N/A	II.1	Application
6.86	III.2.a/III.3	Application	N/A	N/A	II.1/II.4	Application
6.87	III.2.a	Application	N/A	N/A	II.1	Application
6.88	III.2.a,b	Application	N/A	N/A	II.1	Application
6.89	III.3	Application	N/A	N/A	II.4	Application
6.90	III.2.a,b	Application	N/A	N/A	II.1	Application
6.91	III.2.a,b	Application	N/A	N/A	II.1	Application
6.92	III.2.a,b	Application	N/A	N/A	II.1	Application
6.93	III.3	Application	N/A	N/A	II.4	Application
6.94	III.2.a,b	Application	N/A	N/A	II.1	Application

Chapter 7

Question	CCA Exam Competency	CCA Exam Level	CCS Exam Competency	CCS Exam Level	CCS-P Exam Competency	CCS-P Exam Level
7.1	III.2.a,b	Analysis	II.1/II.8	Analysis	N/A	N/A
7.2	III.2.a,b,c	Analysis	II.1/II.10	Analysis	N/A	N/A
7.3	III.2.a,b,c	Analysis	II.1/II.6	Analysis	N/A	N/A
7.4	III.2.a,b	Analysis	II.1/II.4	Analysis	N/A	N/A
7.5	III.2.c	Analysis	III.1	Analysis	N/A	N/A
7.6	III.2.c	Analysis	III.1/III.5	Analysis	N/A	N/A
7.7	III.2.c	Analysis	III.1/III.5	Analysis	N/A	N/A
7.8	III.2.c	Analysis	III.1	Analysis	N/A	N/A
7.9	III.2.a,b,c	Analysis	II.1/III.1	Analysis	N/A	N/A
7.10	III.2.a,b,c	Analysis	II.1/III.1	Analysis	N/A	N/A
7.11	III.2.a,b,c	Analysis	I.1/II.1/III.1	Analysis	N/A	N/A
7.12	III.2.a,b,c	Analysis	I.1/II.1/III.1	Analysis	N/A	N/A
7.13	III.2.a,b,c	Analysis	I.1/IV.1/III.5	Analysis	N/A	N/A
7.14	III.2.a,b,c	Analysis	II.1/III.1	Analysis	N/A	N/A
7.15	III.2.a,b	Analysis	II.1/III.1	Analysis	N/A	N/A
7.16	III.2.a,b,c	Analysis	I.3/IV.1/II.6	Analysis	N/A	N/A
7.17	III.2.a,b,c	Analysis	II.4/III.1	Analysis	N/A	N/A
7.18	III.2.a,b,c	Analysis	I.1/I.3	Analysis	N/A	N/A
7.19	III.2.a,b,c	Analysis	II.1/III.1	Analysis	N/A	N/A
7.20	III.2.a,b	Analysis	II.3/III.1	Analysis	N/A	N/A
7.21	III.2.a,b,c	Analysis	I.3/II.3	Analysis	N/A	N/A
7.22	III.2.a,b,c	Analysis	IV.1	Analysis	N/A	N/A
7.23	III.2.a,b	Analysis	II.5	Analysis	N/A	N/A
7.24	III.2.a,b	Analysis	I.1/II.1	Analysis	N/A	N/A
7.25	III.2.a,b,c	Analysis	II.1/III.1	Analysis	N/A	N/A
7.26	III.2.a,b,c	Analysis	IV.1	Analysis	N/A	N/A
7.27	III.2.a,b	Analysis	IV.1	Analysis	N/A	N/A
7.28	III.2.a,b,c	Analysis	II.4/II.10	Analysis	N/A	N/A
7.29	III.2.a,b,c	Analysis	II.1/III.1	Analysis	N/A	N/A
7.30	III.2.a,b,c	Analysis	IV.1	Analysis	N/A	N/A
7.31	III.2.a,b,c	Analysis	II.1/III.1	Analysis	N/A	N/A
7.32	III.2.a,b	Analysis	II.1/II.9	Analysis	N/A	N/A
7.33	III.2.a,b,c	Analysis	I.1/II.1	Analysis	N/A	N/A
7.34	III.2.a,b,c	Analysis	IV.1/II.3	Analysis	N/A	N/A
7.35	III.2.a,b,c	Analysis	IV.1	Analysis	N/A	N/A
7.36	III.2.a,b	Analysis	IV.1	Analysis	N/A	N/A
7.37	III.2.a,b,c	Analysis	II.5/II.10	Analysis	N/A	N/A
7.38	III.2.a,b	Analysis	I.1/II.1/III.1	Analysis	N/A	N/A
7.39	III.2.a,b,c	Analysis	II.3	Analysis	N/A	N/A
7.40	III.2.a,c	Analysis	II.3/III.1	Analysis	N/A	N/A

Question	CCA Exam Competency	CCA Exam Level	CCS Exam Competency	CCS Exam Level	CCS-P Exam Competency	CCS-P Exam Level
7.41	III.2.a,b,c	Analysis	II.3/III.3	Analysis	N/A	N/A
7.42	III.2.a,b,c	Analysis	II.3/III.3	Analysis	N/A	N/A
7.43	III.2.a,b,c	Analysis	I.1/IV.1	Analysis	N/A	N/A
7.44	III.2.a,b,c	Analysis	II.3/III.1	Analysis	N/A	N/A
7.45	III.2.a,b	Analysis	IV.1	Analysis	N/A	N/A
7.46	III.2.a,b,c	Analysis	II.3	Analysis	N/A	N/A
7.47	III.2.a,b,c	Analysis	II.3	Analysis	N/A	N/A
7.48	III.2.a,b,c	Analysis	II.1/III.1	Analysis	N/A	N/A
7.49	III.2.a,b,c	Analysis	IV.1	Analysis	N/A	N/A
7.50	III.2.a,b	Analysis	II.4/III.4	Analysis	N/A	N/A
7.51	III.2.a,b,c	Analysis	II.1	Analysis	N/A	N/A
7.52	III.2.a,b	Analysis	II.1/II.4	Analysis	N/A	N/A
7.53	III.2.a,b	Analysis	II.1/II.4	Analysis	N/A	N/A
7.54	III.2.a,b	Analysis	II.1/II.4	Analysis	N/A	N/A
7.55	III.2.a,b	Analysis	II.1/II.10	Analysis	N/A	N/A
7.56	III.2.a,b,c	Analysis	II.3/II.10	Analysis	N/A	N/A
7.57	III.2.a,b,c	Analysis	II.6/III.1	Analysis	N/A	N/A
7.58	III.2.a,b,c	Analysis	I.3/IV.1	Analysis	N/A	N/A

Chapter 8

Question	CCA Exam Competency	CCA Exam Level	CCS Exam Competency	CCS Exam Level	CCS-P Exam Competency	CCS-P Exam Level
8.1	III.2.a,b/III.3	Application	II.5/III.2	Application	II.2/II.3	Application
8.2	III.2.a,b/III.3/III.4	Analysis	II.1/V.4	Analysis	II.4/V.2.b	Analysis
8.3	III.2.a,b	Analysis	II.3	Analysis	II.1	Analysis
8.4	III.2.a,b	Application	II.2/II.10	Application	II.1	Application
8.5	III.2.a,b/III.3	Application	II.2/II.3	Application	II.1/II.8	Application
8.6	III.2.a,b/III.3	Application	II.2/III.2	Application	II.1/II.4	Application
8.7	III.2.a,b/III.3	Analysis	II.2/III.2	Analysis	II.1/II.3	Analysis
8.8	III.3/III.4	Application	III.2	Application	II.4/II.9	Application
8.9	III.3	Application	III.2	Application	II.4	Application
8.10	III.2.a,b	Application	II.5	Application	II.1	Application
8.11	III.2.a/III.3	Analysis	II.2/III.2	Analysis	II.1/II.4	Analysis
8.12	III.2.a,b/III.3	Analysis	II.2/V.4	Analysis	II.10/III.2	Analysis
8.13	III.2.a,b/III.3	Application	II.2/V.2.a	Application	II.1/II.10	Application
8.14	III.2.a,b/III.3	Analysis	II.2/V.2.a	Analysis	II.1/II.10/III.4	Analysis
8.15	III.2.a,b/III.3	Analysis	II.2/V.2.a	Analysis	II.2/II.10	Analysis
8.16	III.2.a,b	Analysis	II.3	Analysis	II.2	Analysis
8.17	III.2.a,b	Analysis	V.3	Analysis	II.1	Analysis
8.18	III.2.a,b/III.3	Analysis	II.2/III.2	Analysis	II.2/II.4	Analysis
8.19	III.2.a,b/III.3	Analysis	I.1/III.2	Analysis	III.3/II.4	Analysis
8.20	III.2.a,b/III.3	Analysis	V.3/V.1	Analysis	III.3/III.2	Analysis
8.21	III.2.a,b/III.3	Analysis	II.2/III.2	Analysis	II.1/II.3	Analysis
8.22	III.2.a,b/III.3	Analysis	II.2/III.2	Analysis	II.1/II.4	Analysis
8.23	III.2.a,b/III.3	Analysis	II.2/III.2	Analysis	II.1/II.4	Analysis
8.24	III.2.a/III.3	Analysis	II.2/V.1	Analysis	II.1/III.2	Analysis
8.25	III.2.a,b/III.3	Analysis	II.4/V.2.b	Analysis	II.1/II.5	Analysis
8.26	III.2.a/III.3	Analysis	II.2/V.2.b	Analysis	II.1/III.2/II.10	Analysis
8.27	III.2.a,b/III.3	Analysis	II.2/V.2.b	Analysis	II.1/II.5	Analysis
8.28	III.2.a,b/III.3	Application	II.2/III.2	Application	II.1/II.4	Application
8.29	III.2.a,b/III.3	Analysis	II.2/V.1	Analysis	II.1/II.3	Analysis
8.30	III.2.a,b/III.3	Analysis	II.2/III.2	Analysis	II.1/II.5	Analysis
8.31	III.2.a,b/III.3	Analysis	II.2/V.1/V.2.a	Analysis	II.1/II.10/III.2	Analysis
8.32	III.2.a,b/III.3	Analysis	II.2/V.1	Analysis	II.1/III.2	Analysis
8.33	III.2.a,b/III.3	Analysis	II.2/V.2.a	Analysis	II.1/II.10	Analysis
8.34	III.2.a,b/III.3	Analysis	II.2/V.2.a	Analysis	II.1/II.10	Analysis
8.35	III.2.a,b/III.3	Analysis	II.2/III.2	Analysis	II.1/II.4	Analysis
8.36	III.2.a,b/III.3	Analysis	II.2/III.2	Analysis	II.1/II.4	Analysis
8.37	III.2.a,b/III.3	Application	II.2/III.2	Application	II.1/II.3	Application
8.38	III.2.a/III.3	Analysis	II.2/V.2.a	Analysis	II.1/II.10	Analysis
8.39	III.2.a,b/III.3	Analysis	II.2/II.9/III.2	Analysis	II.1/II.4	Analysis
8.40	III.2.a/III.3	Application	II.2/III.2	Application	II.1/II.4	Application

Question	CCA Exam Competency	CCA Exam Level	CCS Exam Competency	CCS Exam Level	CCS-P Exam Competency	CCS-P Exam Level
8.41	III.2.a,b/III.3	Analysis	II.2/III.2	Analysis	II.1/II.4	Analysis
8.42	III.2.a/III.3	Application	II.2/III.3	Application	II.1/II.3	Application
8.43	III.3	Analysis	III.5	Analysis	II.7	Analysis
8.44	III.2.a,b/III.3	Analysis	II.2/V.2.a	Analysis	II.1/II.10	Analysis
8.45	III.2.a,b/III.3	Analysis	II.2/V.2.b	Analysis	II.1/II.5	Analysis
8.46	III.2.a/III.3	Analysis	II.2/V.2.a	Analysis	II.1/II.10	Analysis
8.47	III.2.a,b/III.3	Application	II.2/III.2	Application	II.1/II.4	Application
8.48	III.2.a,b/III.3	Analysis	II.2/III.3	Analysis	II.1/II.3	Analysis
8.49	III.2.a,b/III.3	Analysis	II.2/III.3	Analysis	II.1/II.3	Analysis
8.50	III.2.a,b/III.3	Analysis	II.2/III.2	Analysis	II.2/III.2	Analysis
8.51	III.2.a,b/III.3	Analysis	II.2/V.2.b	Analysis	II.1/II.10	Analysis
8.52	III.2.a,b/III.3	Analysis	II.2/III.2	Analysis	II.1/II.4	Application
8.53	III.2.a,b/III.3	Analysis	II.2/V.2.a	Analysis	II.1/II.10	Analysis
8.54	III.2.a,b/III.3	Application	II.2/III.2	Application	II.1/II.4	Application
8.55	III.2.a,b/III.3	Analysis	II.2/II.10/V.2.a	Analysis	II.1/II.10/II.4	Analysis

Chapter 9

Question	CCA Exam Competency	CCA Exam Level	CCS Exam Competency	CCS Exam Level	CCS-P Exam Competency	CCS-P Exam Level
9.1	III.2.a/III.3	Analysis	N/A	N/A	II.1/II.10	Analysis
9.2	III.2.a,b/III.3	Analysis	N/A	N/A	II.1/II.4/II.5	Analysis
9.3	III.2.a/III.3	Analysis	N/A	N/A	II.1/II.10	Analysis
9.4	III.2.a/III.3	Analysis	N/A	N/A	II.1/II.4	Application
9.5	III.2.a,b	Analysis	N/A	N/A	II.1	Application
9.6	III.2.a,b/III.3	Analysis	N/A	N/A	II.1/II.5	Analysis
9.7	III.2.a,b	Application	N/A	N/A	II.1	Application
9.8	III.2.a,b/III.3	Application	N/A	N/A	II.1/II.4	Application
9.9	III.2.a,b/III.3	Analysis	N/A	N/A	II.1/II.4	Analysis
9.10	III.2.a,b	Application	N/A	N/A	II.2	Application
9.11	III.3	Application	N/A	N/A	II.4	Application
9.12	III.3	Application	N/A	N/A	II.4	Application
9.13	III.3	Application	N/A	N/A	II.4	Application
9.14	III.2.a,b/III.3	Analysis	N/A	N/A	II.1/II.5/II.10	Analysis
9.15	III.2.a,b/III.3	Analysis	N/A	N/A	II.1/II.4/II.10	Analysis
9.16	III.2.a,b/III.3	Analysis	N/A	N/A	II.1/II.4/II.10	Analysis
9.17	III.2.a/III.3	Application	N/A	N/A	II.1/II.4/II.10	Application
9.18	III.2.a/III.3	Analysis	N/A	N/A	II.1/II.4	Analysis
9.19	III.3	Application	N/A	N/A	II.5	Application
9.20	III.3	Application	N/A	N/A	II.5	Application
9.21	III.3	Application	N/A	N/A	II.5	Application
9.22	III.3	Analysis	N/A	N/A	II.5	Analysis
9.23	III.2.a,b/III.3	Analysis	N/A	N/A	II.1/II.5	Analysis
9.24	III.3	Analysis	N/A	N/A	II.5	Analysis
9.25	III.3	Analysis	N/A	N/A	II.5	Analysis
9.26	III.2.a,b	Analysis	N/A	N/A	II.1	Analysis
9.27	III.2.a,b	Analysis	N/A	N/A	II.1	Analysis
9.28	III.2.a,b	Analysis	N/A	N/A	II.1	Analysis
9.29	III.2.a/III.3	Analysis	N/A	N/A	II.1/II.4	Analysis
9.30	III.2.a,b/III.3	Analysis	N/A	N/A	II.1/II.10	Analysis
9.31	III.2.a/III.3	Analysis	N/A	N/A	II.1/III.2	Analysis
9.32	III.2.a/III.3	Analysis	N/A	N/A	II.1/III.2	Application
9.33	III.2.a,b/III.3	Analysis	N/A	N/A	II.1/II.8	Analysis
9.34	III.2.a,b/III.3/III.4	Analysis	N/A	N/A	II.1/II.5/II.9	Analysis
9.35	III.2.a,b/III.3	Analysis	N/A	N/A	II.1/II.4	Analysis
9.36	III.2.a,b/III.3	Analysis	N/A	N/A	II.1/II.3	Analysis
9.37	III.3	Application	N/A	N/A	II.3	Application
9.38	III.2.a/III.3	Analysis	N/A	N/A	II.1/II.3	Analysis
9.39	III.2.a,b/III.3	Analysis	N/A	N/A	II.1/II.4	Application
9.40	III.2.a,b/III.3	Analysis	N/A	N/A	II.1/II.5	Analysis

Question	CCA Exam Competency	CCA Exam Level	CCS Exam Competency	CCS Exam Level	CCS-P Exam Competency	CCS-P Exam Level
9.41	III.2.a,b/III.3	Analysis	N/A	N/A	II.1/II.4	Analysis
9.42	III.2.a,b/III.3	Analysis	N/A	N/A	II.1/II.5	Analysis
9.43	III.3	Application	N/A	N/A	II.3	Application
9.44	III.2.a,b/III.3	Analysis	N/A	N/A	II.1/II.3	Analysis
9.45	III.2.a/III.3	Analysis	N/A	N/A	II.1/II.4	Analysis
9.46	III.2.a,b/III.3	Analysis	N/A	N/A	II.1/II.4/II.10	Analysis
9.47	III.2.a,b/III.3	Analysis	N/A	N/A	II.1/II.5/II.10	Analysis
9.48	III.2.a,b/III.3	Analysis	N/A	N/A	II.1/II.4	Analysis
9.49	III.2.a,b/III.3	Analysis	N/A	N/A	II.1	Application
9.50	III.2.a,b	Analysis	N/A	N/A	II.1/III.2	Analysis
9.51	III.2.a/III.3	Analysis	N/A	N/A	II.1/II.4	Analysis
9.52	III.2.a,b/III.3	Analysis	N/A	N/A	II.1/II.4/II.9	Analysis
9.53	III.2.a,b/III.3	Analysis	N/A	N/A	II.1/II.5/II.10	Analysis
9.54	III.2.a,b/III.3	Analysis	N/A	N/A	II.1/II.3	Analysis
9.55	III.2.a,b/III.3	Analysis	N/A	N/A	II.1/II.5/II.10	Analysis
9.56	III.2.a,b/III.3	Analysis	N/A	N/A	II.1/II.4	Application
9.57	III.2.a,b/III.3	Analysis	N/A	N/A	II.1/II.5	Analysis
9.58	III.2.a,b/III.3	Application	N/A	N/A	II.4	Application
9.59	III.3	Application	N/A	N/A	II.1/II.3	Application
9.60	III.2.a,b/III.3	Analysis	N/A	N/A	II.5	Analysis
9.61	III.3	Analysis	N/A	N/A	II.1/II.5/II.9	Application
9.62	III.2.a,b/III.3/III.4	Analysis	N/A	N/A	II.1/II.4	Application
9.63	III.2.a,b/III.3	Analysis	N/A	N/A	II.5	Application
9.64	III.2.a/III.3	Analysis	N/A	N/A	II.1/II.4	Application
9.65	III.3	Analysis	N/A	N/A	II.1/II.4/II.5/II.9	Analysis
9.66	III.2.a,b/III.3	Analysis	N/A	N/A	II.1/II.4	Application
9.67	III.2.a,b/III.3/III.4	Analysis	N/A	N/A	II.1/II.10	Analysis
9.68	III.2.a,b/III.3	Analysis	N/A	N/A	II.1/II.4	Analysis
9.69	III.2.a,b/III.3	Analysis	N/A	N/A	II.1/II.3	Application
9.70	III.2.a,b/III.3	Analysis	N/A	N/A	II.1/II.4	Application
9.71	III.2.a/III.3	Analysis	N/A	N/A	II.1/II.4/II.10	Analysis
9.72	III.2.a,b/III.3	Analysis	N/A	N/A	II.1/II.3	Application
9.73	III.2.a/III.3	Analysis	N/A	N/A	II.1/II.3	Analysis
9.74	III.2.a/III.3	Application	N/A	N/A	II.1/II.3	Application
9.75	III.2.a,b/III.3	Application	N/A	N/A	II.3	Application
9.76	III.3	Analysis	N/A	N/A	II.1/II.4/II.10	Analysis
9.77	III.2.a,b/III.3	Analysis	N/A	N/A	II.1/II.3	Application
9.78	III.2.a,b/III.3	Analysis	N/A	N/A	II.1/II.5	Analysis
9.79	III.2.a,b/III.3	Analysis	N/A	N/A	II.5	Analysis
9.80	III.2.a,b/III.3	Analysis	N/A	N/A	II.3	Analysis
9.81	III.3	Application	N/A	N/A	II.1/II.4	Application
9.82	III.2.a/III.3	Application	N/A	N/A	II.1/II.4	Application

Chapter 10

Question	CCA Exam Competency	CCA Exam Level	CCS Exam Competency	CCS Exam Level	CCS-P Exam Competency	CCS-P Exam Level
10.1	III.2.a	Recall	N/A	Home Health	N/A	Home Health
10.2	III.2.a	Recall	N/A	Home Health	N/A	Home Health
10.3	III.2.a	Application	N/A	Home Health	N/A	Home Health
10.4	III.2.a	Application	N/A	Home Health	N/A	Home Health
10.5	III.2.a	Application	N/A	Home Health	N/A	Home Health
10.6	III.2.a	Application	N/A	Home Health	N/A	Home Health
10.7	III.2.a	Application	N/A	Home Health	N/A	Home Health
10.8	III.2.a	Application	N/A	Home Health	N/A	Home Health
10.9	III.2.a	Application	N/A	Home Health	N/A	Home Health
10.10	III.6	Recall	N/A	Home Health	N/A	Home Health
10.11	III.2.a	Application	N/A	Home Health	N/A	Home Health
10.12	III.2.a	Application	N/A	Home Health	N/A	Home Health
10.13	II.1.a	Application	N/A	Home Health	N/A	Home Health
10.14	N/A	ICD-10	N/A	ICD-10	N/A	ICD-10
10.15	N/A	ICD-10	N/A	ICD-10	N/A	ICD-10
10.16	N/A	ICD-10	N/A	ICD-10	N/A	ICD-10
10.17	N/A	ICD-10	N/A	ICD-10	N/A	ICD-10
10.18	N/A	ICD-10	N/A	ICD-10	N/A	ICD-10
10.19	N/A	ICD-10	N/A	ICD-10	N/A	ICD-10
10.20	N/A	ICD-10	N/A	ICD-10	N/A	ICD-10
10.21	N/A	ICD-10	N/A	ICD-10	N/A	ICD-10
10.22	N/A	ICD-10	N/A	ICD-10	N/A	ICD-10
10.23	N/A	ICD-10	N/A	ICD-10	N/A	ICD-10
10.24	N/A	ICD-10	N/A	ICD-10	N/A	ICD-10
10.25	N/A	ICD-10	N/A	ICD-10	N/A	ICD-10
10.26	N/A	ICD-10	N/A	ICD-10	N/A	ICD-10
10.27	III.3	Application	V.2.a	Application	II.1	Application
10.28	III.3	Application	V.2.a	Application	II.1	Application
10.29	III.3	Application	V.2.a	Application	II.1	Application
10.30	III.3	Application	V.2.a	Application	II.1	Application
10.31	III.3	Application	V.2.a	Application	II.1	Application
10.32	III.4	Application	V.2.a	Application	II.1	Application
10.33	III.4	Application	V.2.a	Application	II.1	Application
10.34	III.4	Application	V.2.a	Application	II.1	Application
10.35	III.4	Recall	V.2.a	Recall	II.1	Recall
10.36	III.4	Recall	V.2.a	Recall	II.1	Recall
10.37	III.4	Recall	V.2.a	Recall	II.1	Recall
10.38	III.2.a,b	Application	II.1	Application	N/A	N/A
10.39	III.2.a,b	Application	II.1	Application	N/A	N/A
10.40	III.2.a,b	Application	II.1	Application	N/A	N/A

Question	CCA Exam Competency	CCA Exam Level	CCS Exam Competency	CCS Exam Level	CCS-P Exam Competency	CCS-P Exam Level
10.41	III.2.a	Application	II.2	Application	II.1	Application
10.42	III.2.a,b	Application	II.2	Application	II.1	Application
10.43	III.2.a,b	Application	II.1	Application	N/A	N/A
10.44	III.2.a,b	Application	II.1	Application	N/A	N/A
10.45	III.2.a,b	Application	II.1	Application	N/A	N/A
10.46	III.2.a,b	Application	II.1	Application	N/A	N/A
10.47	III.2.a,b	Application	II.1	Application	N/A	N/A
10.48	III.2.a,b	Application	II.1	Application	N/A	N/A
10.49	III.2.a,b	Application	II.1	Application	N/A	N/A